About the Book ✍ W9-BZQ-042

There are **984 Aircraft Museums in the United States** and **127 Aircraft Museums in Canada** that contain Name, Address, Phone Number, Hours, Price of Admission, Gift Shop, Cafeteria, Theater, Restoration Facility, and All Aircraft on owned by that museum.

Second is **244 City Parks** that have an aircraft on display or as stated.

Third is **61 Restaurants** (2 more than 22nd edition) that have one or more aircraft inside or outside the building. Each has name, address, phone number, and some with meals and prices.

Fourth is **62 USS Naval Ship Museums** with address, phone number, hours, admission price and if there is any aircraft.

Fifth is **26 Armored & Artillery Museums** (New Category) with address, phone number, hours, admission price and if there is any aircraft.

Sixth is **17** Locations that served a purpose during **WWII** and still have an existing **Landmark**.

Seventh is **31** (5 more than the 22nd edition) Places offering **Rides in Aircraft**.

Eighth is **24 Credits** to people who have provided me information for this edition.

Last in **Alphabetical** order is a list of all **9660 Aircraft** (560 more than the 22nd edition) and what museums have that particular aircraft. Each aircraft has the following information: State - City - Museum of that aircraft, Manufacture, Aircraft Name, Personal Name, Serial (Buno) Number, N Number, Tail Letters, Side Numbers, Squadron Markings.

TABLE OF CONTENTS

To Order a Copy of This Book, Please Mail To:
Author / Publisher
MICHAEL A. BLAUGHER
124 EAST FOSTER PARKWAY
FORT WAYNE, IN 46806-1730
(260) 744-1020
E-mail: airmuseums@aol.com • www.aircraftmuseums.com
Quantity Discounts Available.

Museum Codes:

Adm	=	Admission
Appt	=	Appointment
Ave	=	Avenue
Blvd	=	Boulevard
CAF	=	Confederate Air Force
Dir	=	Director
Dr	=	Drive
Exec	=	Executive

Int'l	=	International
Jr	=	Junior
Mi	=	Miles
PA	=	Public Affairs
POB	=	Post Office Box
Pres	=	President
St	=	Street
Snrs	=	Senior Citizen
RoY	=	Rest of Year

ES	=	Easter
T	=	Thanksgiving
C	=	Christmas
N	=	New Years
D	=	Day
E	=	Eve
L	=	Labor
M	=	Memorial

Aircraft Status Codes:

Flyable	**(F)**
Static Indoor Display	**(D)**
Storage	**(S)**
Replica	**(Rep)**
Restoration Project	**(P)**
Static Outdoor Display	**(O)**
On Loan	**(L)**

Military Codes:

AFB = Air Force Base
ANG = Air National Guard
ARB = Air Reserve Base
NAS = Naval Air Station

23rd Edition Released May, 2005
ISBN: 0-9749772-1-7

1st Edition: April 1987
ISSN: 1074 9675

Front Cover, Top Photo by: Mandy Davis, Marketing Manager,
Museum of Flight, Seattle, WA

Front Cover, Bottom Left Photo by: Sarah Tittemore, Manager of Tourism
City of Portage la Prairie, Manitoba, Canada, T-33

Front Cover, Bottom Right and Back Cover Photo by: Dennis Repke,
Solo's Restaurant, Colorado Springs, CO (See Restaurants), KC-97
All information is based on letter responses I received from to 04/18/05.

Due to constant changes any information in this book may not be correct.
For current information call or Mail the museum. Some Military Bases
may not allow civilians on the base unless you get a pass.
Check ahead for the bases you plan to visit.

ALABAMA

Ardmore - Alabama Welcome Center, 26865 I-65, 35739, (256) 423-3891, Saturn I Apollo

Birmingham - Southern Museum of Flight, 4343 73rd St N, 35206-3642,
(205) 833-8226, Fax 836-2439, Tue-Sat 9:30-4:30, Sun 1-4:30, Adm Adult $3
Snrs & Child $2 Child Uner 5 Free, Library, Gift Shop,
Refurbishing Shop and Theater. www.southernmuseumofflight.org,
Halls A-D = HA-HD, Storage = S, On Loan = L, Antrium = A

A-4J(TA) Cockpit		F-105F	HB	Piel-Emeraude	SL
A-7E	SL	F-102A(TF)		Pitts Special	SL
A-12		F-106	SL	PL-4A	SL
AT-6G		F-111A	HC	PT-19 Project	S
Aero Commander 680	S	Foker D-7 Project		R4D-6Q	S
Aeronca 11AC	HB	Forney Ercoupe F-1		Rand KR-1	HB
Aeronca K	S	Great Lakes 2T-1A-2		RC-3	HC
Aeronca Sedan Floats	S	H-1(UH)		Rotorway Helicopter	SL
BD-4	S	H-6(OH)		Rotec Rally	SL
BD-5B	S	H-54B(CH)		Rutan Vari-Eze	SL
Beagle B.206	S	Harrison Mini-Mack		Sonerai II-T	HB
Bensen Gyrocopter	A	Huff-Daland Duster		Sport Fury	HC
BT-13B	SL	J-3 Project		Starduster	SL
Bushby Mustang II	HB	Link Trainer		Stinson SR-5	HB
Cumulus Glider	S	Longwing Eaglerock		Stinson 10-A	HB
Curtiss D.5 Rep	HC	MiG-15		T-33A	SL
F-4N		MiG-21	SL	T-37B	SL
F-84F 2ea		Mitchell B-10 Buzzard	SL	TG-4A	HB
F-86F		Monerai S Glider	SL	Vari-Viggen	HB
F-101		Mooney Mite M.18	SL		HB

Evergreen - Middleton Airport, (334) 578-1274, Stewart Flying Service
334-578-4905, 35747   FJ-3   T-28C

Huntsville - Alabama Space & Rocket Center, 1 Tranquility Base, Off I-565 Between
I-65 and US 231, 35805-3371, (800) 633-7280, (256) 837-3400, Daily 9-5 Except:
Memorial-Labor Day, Daily 8-7, Closed TD, CD, Adm Adult $12, Child (3-12) $8,
Under 3 Free, http://info.uah.edu/huntsville/tourist/space-center.html
Quick 1910,   A-12,   V-1 & V-2 Rockets Spacecraft

Aviation Challenge, 1 Tranquility Base, 35805-3371, (888) 364-3483
Aviation Camps for Grades 4-12 & Adult, One Week of: Land/Water Survival,
Principals and Simulator Flight Basics, From $399-899, Static Displays Include:

AH-1	F-14	MiG-17
F-4	F-111	YAV-8B Harrier II

U.S. Space Camp, 1 Tranquility Base, 35805-3371, (800) 637-7223
Space Camp for Grades 4-12 & Adult, One Week of: Space Training & Missions
From $399-899, Static Displays Include: SR-71, Apollo 16, Saturn V, Space Shuttle
www.spacecamp.com

Redstone Arsenal, Gate 9, Martin Rd and Mills Rd, Base Pass Needed

AH-1F	AH-64A	ACH-47A	UH-1M

Mobile - Battleship Memorial Park, POB 65, 2701 Battleship Parkway, 36601-0065,
Between Exit 27&30, (251) 433-2703, Daily 8-Sunset, Closes 4pm Oct-March,
6pm April-Sept, Closed CD, Adm Adult $10, Child 6-11 $5, Under 6 Free, Gift Shop,
Breakfast $14-18, Lunch $16-18, Dinner $24-27, www.ussalabama.com

A-12 Cygnus 938	F-16A(GF)	HU-16E	M-4 Tank
A-4L	F-86L	OS2U	M-26 Tank
F4U-7	F-8G(RF)	P-51D(F)	M-48AL Tank
B-25J	F4B-4 Rep	SBD-1	M-42A1 Tank
B-52D	F4U-7	UH-1B	M-60A1 Tank
C-47D(VC)	F9F-5P	YF-17(F/A-18)	T-55 Tank Iraqi
CH-21B	H-1B(UH)	USS ALABAMA	PBR Gun Boat
F-105B-IRE	H-19	USS DRUM Submarine	ICBM
F-4C	HH-52A	M-75 APC	

Montgomery - Gunter AFB, 36114, (334) 279-1110, Mon-Fri 8-4, Closed Holidays
C-47B,   GAM-72

Maxwell AFB, Chennault Circle, 36112-5000, (334) 293-2017, 3800
ABW/PA, Air University, Daily 7-6, Free Adm

B-25J"Poopsie"	F-4C	F-100C	F-105D	T-38A
B-52D	F-86L"Chris"	F-101C(RF)	T-38A	

2

ALABAMA (Continued)

Ozark - Alabama Aviation & Technical College, US Hwy 231S, 36361,
(334) 774-5113,   Lear Jet 25

US Army Aviation Museum, Fort Rucker, Bldg 617, POB 620610-0610,
36330, (334) 598-2508, Mon-Fri 9-4,Sat-Sun 12-4 Free Adm, Closed TD,
CE, CD, NE, ND, Gift Shop 598-9465, www.armyavnmuseum.org,

Bldg 600X		Bldg 600X		Bldg 600X		Bldg 600X	
AX-6	13	H-23B(OH)	0	L-6	7	T-28A	9
Bell 207	0	H-23C(OH)	7	L-13A	7	T-34A(YT)	S
C-7A(YC)	0	H-23F(OH)	9	L-15A(YL)	9	T-37A	
C-45H	C	H-25A	0	L-16A	0	T-39A	S
C-45J(UC)	C	H-26A(XH)	0	L-17A	7	T-41B	7
C-47A	0	H-30(YH)	8	L-17B		T-42	C
C-121A(VC)	C	H-32(YH)	7	L-18C	7	TG-3	13
C-126(LC)	0	H-34A(CH)	0	L-19A	7,S	U-1A	9
CL-475	8	H-34A(VCH)	8	L-19D(TL)		U-3A	S
DH 1A	0	H-37B(OH)	0	L-20A	0	U-4A	S
E-5A(YE)	7	H-39A(XH)	8	L-21A(TL)	8	U-6A(YU)	0
F-51D	9	H-40H(XH)	7	L-200A	9	U-8A	S
H-1	77	H-41A(YH)	7	MI-4	S	U-8G	S
H-1F (AH)		H-47A(ACH)		Nieuport 28C-1		U-9A	C
H-1G (AH)	0	H-51A(XH)		O-3G1(XAO)	13	U-9A(YU)	S
H-1J (AH)		H-55A(TH)	777	O-3A(YO)	0	U-9D(NRU)	C
H-1B (UH)	GG	H-56A(AH)	0	O-3BR(YHO)	0	U-10(YU)	8
H-1H (UH)	8	H-58A(OH)	GG	OV-1A(YO)	9	U-10A	S
H-1M (UH)	G	H-61 (UH)	13	OV-1B	C	U-21(YU)	9
H-1D(YUH)	0	H-61A(YUH)		OV-1C	C	V-1 (XV)	9
H-4A (OH)	8	H-63 (YAH)		P-2E (AP)	C	V-3A (XV)	
H-5A (OH)	7	H-64 (AH)		P-9 (AO)	9	V-5B (XV)	S
H-6A (OH)	78	H-64A(YAH)	0	P-51		V-6A (XV)	
H-6A(YOH)	0	H-347(CH)	S	PT-17		VZ-3RY	9
H-13B(OH)	77	J-3	0	QH-50C	13	VZ-ZAP	0
H-13E(OH)	0	JN-4D		QQ-50	13	X-14	7
H-13T(TH)	0	L-1A	9	R-4B	0	X-26B	9
H-18 (XH)	7	L-2A	9	R-5	9	XROE-1	0
H-19C	0	L-3A	7	R-9B (XR)	8		
H-19D(UH)	9	L-4B	0,7	RU-8D	0		
H-21C(CH)	0	L-5	0	S-60	13		
H-23A(OH)	0	L-5G	0	SE-5A			

DRONES: Fairchild Dragonfly   13 Philco-Ford Prairie II   0
         Lockheed Aquilla   0 Lockheed Test Bed   13
         N.V.   0 McDonnell Douglas Mark II

Tuskegee - General Daniel "Chappie" James Airman's & Industrial Museum,
Air Tuskegee, Flight Field, 1727 Airport Rd, 36083-2813, 3 Mi N of City,
(334) 724-0602,   F9F

Tuskegee Airmen National Historic Site, 1616 Chappie James Ave, 36803,
I-85 exit 38, Go 1 Mi S on Hwy 81, SE on Hwy 199 (Chappie James Ave)
Daily 9-4:30, Closed TD, CD, ND, Adm Free, Gift Shop, www.nps.gov/tuai,
Artifacts

ALASKA

Anchorage - Alaska Aviation Heritage Museum, 4721 Aircraft Dr, Lake Hood, 99502,
(800) 770-5325, (907) 248-5325, Fax 248-6391, May 1-Oct 1, Daily 10-6,
RoY 10-4 Closed Sun, Adm Adult $5, Theater, Gift Shop, www.alaskaairmuseum.com

American Pilgram 100B	Grumman G-44 Widgeon	Stearman C2B
AT-19	Hamilton Metalplane H47	Stinson 108
Bellanca Sr Pacemaker Fus	J2F-6	Stinson SR-9 CM
Bellanca Pacemaker CH-300	K1-84 Keystone Loening	Stinson SR
C-45H	L-5 Stinson Sentinel	Stinson A Trimotor
C-45F(UC)	Noordyn Norseman	T-50
Curtiss Robin	P-40E (P)=project	Travelair S6000B Floats (P)
DWC	PBY-5A	UH-1H
Fairchild FC2W Frame	S-43 (Nose Only)	Waco UIC
Fairchild 24G	Spartan Executive	Waco YKC Floats
Ford 5-AT Wreckage	Spencer Aircar	

Kulis ANG Base Museum, 6000 Air Guard Rd, 99502-1998, (907) 249-1176,
AT-6D   C-47A   F-86A   C-123J   F-80   T-33A

Elmendorf AFB, 3rd Wing Grp Info Mana, HQ 21ST TFW/PA 99506, (907) 552-5755,
CRC: Sgt, Matthew T Fast, F-4C   F-102A   T-33A

ALASKA (Continued)

Fairbanks - Alaskaland Pioneer Air Museum, 2300 Airport Way, 99701,
    (907) 451-0037, 452-2969, Mail: Interior & Arctic Alaska Aeronautical Museum,
    POB 70437, 99707-0437, Memorial-Labor Day, Daily 11-9, Open Holidays
    Adm $2 Family $5, www.fairbanks-alaska.com/air-museum.htm, www.akpub.com/akttt/aviat.html

B-10	MX Quicksilver	Rutan Vari-eze
Baking Duce II (F.M.1)	C-64A Mk.IV	Stinson SR-5 Jr
C-45F(UC)	Pereira S.P. 3	V-77/AT-19
Fairchild 24J	PT-22 (ST3KR)	UH-1H
Fokker Super Universal Frame	Raven S-50	
HO45	Rotorway 133	

Healy - Denali Wings, Box 254, 99743, (907) 683-2245,   Ford Tri-Motor

Wasilla - Museum of Alaska Transportation & Industry, 99687, POB 870646, 99687
    (907) 376-1211, Mem - Labor Day Sat 10-5, Sun 1-5, Adm Adult $3,
    Student $1.50, Family $7, Gift Shop, Train Museum, www.museumofalaska.org

Bowers Model A	JB-2			
C-47A	H-21B(CH)	F-102A	K-84	Stinson SR
C-123J	D.W.C.	HH-5	L-6A	Waco

Whitehorse - Yukon Transportation Museums, 30 Electra Cresent, Y1A-6E6,
    (867) 668-4792, Fax 633-5547, Mon-Sun, May 14-Sept 9, Mon-Sun 10-6, Sep 1-9, 12-4
    Adm Adult $4.25, Senior(55+)$3.25, Student $3.25, Child(6-12)$2, Family $9
    Gift Shop, www.yukontransportmuseum.homestead.com/files/ytmuseum1.html, DC-3

ARIZONA

Apache Jct - American Legion Post 27, 1880 Apache Trail, (480) 982-0220, T-33A

Coolidge - Coolidge Municipal Airport, E Kenilworth, 85228, (520) 723-9169,
    5 Mi SE of City,   MiG-15 (15ea)

Ft Huachuca - Huachuca Museum Society, Boyd & Grierson St, POB 766, 85613-6000,
    PA: (520) 458-4716, Mon-Fri 9-4, Sat-Sun 1-4,Free Adm, OV-1D, RC-121G

Gila Bend - Gila Bend AF AUX, (520) 683-6200,   F-105D   T-33A

Grand Canyon - Grand Canyon National Park Airport, (928) 638-2407,
    6 Miles S of city. AN-2 Russian Antonov, P-47

    Planes of Fame, Grand Canyon Valle Airport, 86023, (520) 635-1000,
    Hwy 64 & 180 Junction, Mail: HCR 34 Box B, Valle Williams, AZ, 86046,
    Daily 9-6, Closed TD, CD, Adm Adult $5.95, Child 5-12 $1.95,
    Under 5 Free, Constellation Tour $3.00, Gift Shop

D = Indoors,	O = Outdoors,	F = Flyable,	S = Storage
AT-6G	GAM-54		RP-5ARP-76B
Bede BD-5Vee (D,S)	HA-112		Rutan Long-EZ
Bf 109G-10/U4 (D)	KD6D-2		Schmitt Commuter (D,S)
Bristol F2.b (F)Rep	L-19A (F)		Siemens-Schuckert D.IV
C-121A(VC) (F)	MiG-15 (O,S)		(S)Rep
Curtiss Robin	MWM-74		Spitfire MK V
DH 100 Mk III	MXY-7 (D)		T-6G
F-84B (S)	P-51A (F)		T-33A (S)
F-86L Cockpit	PT-17Pitts S-2B (S)		TM-61
F11F-1 (O,S)	Q-5		US Navy Bat
Ford 5-AT (S)	RB-26C		

Green Valley - Titan Missile Museum, 85714, I-19 Exit 69, Take Duval Mine
    Rd West, Go 1/10 Mi past La Canada, Daily 9-5, Closed TD, CD, Last Tour 4pm
    (520) 625-7736,791-2929,Adm $6, Pima Air Museum & Titan Missile Museum from $13.50-24.00,
    www.pimaair.org, Titan II Missile Silo # 571-7,   UH-1F

    Williams AFB, 85240-5000, PA: (520) 635-8200, 82 FTW/DOOB

F-86E	P-80A	T-33A	T-38A(QT)

Mesa - CAF - Arizona Wing & Museum, 2017 N Greenfield Rd, Falcon Field, Sky Harbor Airport
    85215, Mail: POB 2969, 85214, (480) 924-1940, 981-1945, Daily 10-4, Adm Adult $5
    Child Under 14 $2.50, Child Under 5 Free, Gift Shop, www.arizonawingcaf.org

A-26C	B-25	C-54	O-2A	FM-2
AF-2S (Project)	C-45	Mig-15	SNJ	
B-17G	C-47	N2S-5	T-33	

    Goss Hawk Unlimited (Restoration Facility), 4636 Fighter Aces Dr, 85215, (480) 396-9644,
    Fax Same, Mail: POB 20455, 85277-0455, www.gosshawkunlimited.com,
    email: gosshawkunl@aol.com, Projects: Fw 190-D13   P-63C   P-63E

    Marsh Aviation Co, 5060 Falcon Dr, 85215, (480) 832-3770, Fax: 985-2840,
    Firefighting Fleet of S-2F1T & S2R Air Tankers

Phoenix - Deer Valley Airport, 702 W Deer Valley Rd, at 7th Ave, 85027, (623) 869-0975

AT-6(3ea)	C-123K	F-8K	MiG-15

Luke AFB(afres), 85309-5000, PA: (623) 856-6011, Daily 7:30-4, Tours Fri 9-1,

AT-6	F-84F	F-102A	HU-16E
F-4N	F-86F	F-104C	T-33A
F-15B	F-100C	HH-34J	

Global Aeronautical Museum, 12448 N 29th Ave, 85029

Phoenix ANG, Sky Harbor Int'l Airport, 97218-2797, (623) 288-5611,   F-104C

Prescott - Embry-Riddle Aeronautical University, 3200 Willow Creek Rd,
86301-3720, (928) 776-3728, North of Bookstore,   F-104

Scottsdale - Constellation Group, 15111 N Hayden Rd, #160-190, (602) 443-3967,
Fax: 443-0623,   C-121A(MATS L-749)

Tucson - Pima Air & Space Museum, 6000 E. Valencia Rd, 85706, (520) 574-0462, 574-9658,
Daily 9-5, No Adm After 4pm, Adm Adult Summer $9.75 (Winter $11.75),
Snrs/Military Summer $8.75 (Winter $9.75), Child 7-12 Summer $6 (Winter $8),
Under 7 Free, Closed CD, Snack Bar, Gift Shop 618-4815,
www.pimaair.org/, e-mail:pimaair@azstarnet.com

A-4C	BT-13A	F-101C(RF)	L-5B
A-6E	C-14(YC)	F-101H(RF)	L-23D (U-8)
A-7D (LTV)	C-45J(VC)	F-102A(TF)	Lark 95
A-7E	C-46D 2ea	F-102A	Learjet 23
A-10A	C-47	F-104D	LCM-25C
A-20G	C-47D	F-105D	Long EZ
A-26C	C-54D(DC-4)	F-105G	Martin 404
A3D-1(YEA-3A)	C-69 (L-049)	F-106A	MC-4C(J-2)
A4D-2N	C-78B(UC)	F-107A	MiG-15 bis
AD-5N1(EA-1F)	C-82A	F-111E	MiG-15 UTI
ADM-20C	C-97G(KC)	F11F-1A (F-11A)	MiG-17 F
Aerosport Quail	C-97G	F3D-2 (TF-10B)	MiG-17 PF
AEW Mk 3	C-117D (R4D-8)	F3H-2 (F-3B)	MiG-21 PF 2ea
AF-2S	C-118A(VC)	F4D-1(F-6A)	MM-2 Mustang II
AGM-12	C-119J	F4U-4	MQM-33
AGM-28A 2ea	C-119 Fire Fight	F7F-3N	MQM-57 Drone
AIM-4	C-121A	F8U-1 (F-8A)	MS-500
AIM-21A-1M	C-121T(RC)	F9F-4	N22B Nomad
AP-2H	C-123B	F9F-8	N3N
AQM-34L Drone	C-123K Fire Fight	Falcon II	NA-64(BT-14)
AT-6B	C-123K	FireFly 7 Balloon	O-2A
AT-7	C-124C	FJ-4B(AF-1E)	O-52
AT-9A	C-130A	Flagor SkyScooter	OA-10A
AT-11	C-130D	Fleet Model 2	OH-43D
AV-8C	C-131F 2ea	FM-2	OQ-3 Drone
B-10	C-133B	Fw 44-J	Osprey 2
B-17G(PB-1G)	C-135J(EC)	GNAT T-185	OV-1C
B-18B	C-135A(KC)	H-1S(AH)	OV-10D
B-23(UC-67)	C-141B	H-1F(UH)	P-39
B-24J	Cassutt Racer	H-1H(UH)	P-40K
B-25J	Cessna 120	H-1M(UH)	P-40N
B-26B(EDB)	Cessna 150L	H-3F(HH)	P-47
B-26K	Cessna 310C	H-5G(R-5)	P-47D
B-29A(TB)	CG-4A	H-13N(TH)	P-63E
B-377SG 201	CT-39A	H-19B(UH)	P-80B
B-45A	D-16	H-21C	P2V
B-47A	D-21	H-34C(VH)	P2V-7 (AP-2H)
B-47E(EB)	DC-7B	H-37B(CH)	P.Airwave 69 Kiss
B-50J(KB)	E-1B	H-43F(HH)	PBM-5A
B-52A	Ercoupe 415-C	H-52(HH) (S-62)	Pentecost Hoppicopter
B-52D	F-4C	H-52A(HH)	PGM-17(DSV-2C)
B-52G	F-4E(NF)	H-54A(CH)	Pitts Special S1
B-52A(NB)	F-4N(NF)	HO3S-1G	PQ-14 Drone
B-57E	F-4J(YF)	HTL-2(TH-13N)	PT-17
B-57F(WB)	F-5B	HU-16A (SA-16)	PT-19A
B-58A	F-9J(RF)	HUM-1	PT-22
B-66D(WB)	F-14A	HUP-2 2ea	PT-26
BC-12D	F-15A	HUP-3 (H-25A)	PV-2
Bede 4	F-84C	Icarus Hg	QH-50C/DSN-3
Bede 5	F-84F	II-2M3	Quickie
Bede 5J	F-84F(RF)	J-2	R-4B
Beech D-18S	F-86H	J-4A	R5O-5
Beechcraft 2000A	F-86L	J4F-2	RA-5C
Bellanca 14-13-2	F-89J	J-6A	RB-1
BGM 109G	F-84F	JRS-1/S-43	RNF
Bonanza N-35	F-94C	KD6G-2	S-1C
Bowers Fly Baby	F-100C	L-2M	S-43
Brewster Bermuda	F-101B	L-3B	(Continued Next Page)

```
(From Previous Page)T-2C        TH-55A              VT-29B
S2F-1 (2 ea)      T-28C         TV-2(T-33B)         Waco ZKS-6
SBD-5             T-33A         U-3A(L-27A)         Waco UPF-7
SE-210            T-37B         U-11A(UO-1)         Wright Flyer Rep
SHK-1             T-38          UC-36(L-10A)        X-15A-2
SNB-5(UC-45J)     T2V (T-1A)    UH-12C              XJL-1
Spad XIII Rep7/8  TBM-3E        VC-137B             YC-125A
SR-71A            TF-9J         VC-140B             YO-3A
Star Bumble Bee   TG-3A 2ea     Vickers 744         YQM-98A Drone
Swallow A         TG-6A         VP-1                Zuzvogel III-B
```

390th Memorial Museum, 6000 E Valencia Rd, Located at Pima Air & Space Museum, POB 15087,
85708-0087, (520) 574-0287, Fax 574-3030, 9-5 Daily, Closed CD, ND, www.390th.org/ B-17G

ARIZONA (Continued)

American Legion Post 109, 15921 S Houghton Rd, 84747, (520) 762-5652, F-4E

AMARC=Aerospace Maintenance and Regeneration Center (Boneyard)
Tours Only, Contact: Lynda McWilliams at Pima Air & Space Museum: (520) 574-0462
48 Hours Prior, Tickets & Departure at Pima Air Museum Gift Shop(9:30, 11, 12:30, 2, 3:30),

Closed Major Holidays, Adm Adult $5, Snrs/Mil $3.50, 17 & Under $3, Schools $2,
Photo ID Required, Containing of 4926 Aircraft in 2600 Acres of Outdoor Storage,
   139 Patrol Planes   570 Trainers
   426 Cargo Planes   1142 Ground Attack Jets
   562 Helicopters   2087 Jet Fighter

```
Davis-Monthan AFB, 85707-5000, 748-3900, Appt Thru Pima Air Museum
A-7D           B-52D          CH-3C          F-100F        OV-10A
A-10A          C-130A         F-4N           F-105D        U-2C
```

Hamilton Aviation, 6901 S Park Ave, 85706, (520) 294-3481,
Convair 580 (2 each) Outside Airport

Specialized Aircraft, HU-16 (4ea)

```
Tucson ANG, Tucson Int'l Airport, 85734, (520) 573-2210, HU-16 (2ea)
A-7D           F-84F          F-100D              F-102A
```

Western Int'l HU-16

Winslow - Meteor Crater, (928) 289-2362, 20 Miles W of Winslow Off I-40,
 Mail: Meteor Crater Enterprises, Inc, POB 0070,Flagstaff, 86002-0070,
 (May 15 -Sept 15) 7-7, Remaining 8-5, Adm Adult $7, Sr $6, Child 6-17 $2,
 5 & Under Free, 71 Space RV Park, 520-289-4002, 1 Mi Wide/570 Ft Deep Crater
 www.meteorcrater.com, e-mail: info@meteorcrater.com, Apollo Space Capsule

Yuma - Marine Corps Air Station, 85369-5001, (928) 341-2011,
 PA Chief: C.A.Demar Community Relations: Judy Yeadon, 2275,
 A-4   F-4(2ea)   AV/8A

ARKANSAS

Eureka Springs - Aviation Cadet Museum, 542 CR 2073, 72632, (479) 253-5008
 www.aviationcadet.com, F-100,   F-105 Cockpit

Fayetteville - Arkansas Air Museum, 4360 S School Ave, Drake Field, US 71, 72701,
 (479) 521-4947, Mon-Fri, Sun 11-4:30,Sat 10-4:30, Closed TD, CD, ND, Adm Adult $4,
 Child 6-18 $2, Under 6 Free, Restoration Viewing, Gift Shop Mon-Tue, Theater,
 www.arkairmuseum.org P = Project

```
A-4C                DC-3 Cockpit (P)    L-3 (P)         Stinson Junior S
A-7(P)              DGA 6               L-13 (P)        TravelAir Model 4000
American Aegle 230  DGA 11              L-16            T-2  (P)
AT-6G               DGA 18K             NE-1            T-33 (P)
BC-12D              Globe Swift         Neiuport 28C    T-34
Beech 3NM (P)       H-1S(AH)            PT-17
Curtiss CW-1        H-1H(UH)(P)         SE.5A
```

Fort Smith - Ebing ANG Base, 188TH TFG, Ft Smith Municipal Airport, 72906,
 (479) 648-5271, F-4   RF-84

Little Rock - Aerospace Education Center, 3301 E Roosevelt Rd, 72201, (501) 371-0331,
 376-4232 Gift Shop, Adm Adult $7, Snrs $6, Child 1-12 $5, IMAX, www.aerospaced.org,

```
Link                Wright Flyer        Headwind JD-HWL-7
Sopwith Camel F-1   Apollo CM           Bell Eagle Eye
Command Aire 5-C-3  Adventura
```

All Flags Heritage Park, Camp Robinson Army Reserve Base,
(501) 212-5020, F-104, USAF & Army Aircraft Displayed

ARKANSAS (Continued)

Little Rock - Little Rock AFB, 314 TAW/HO, 72099-5000, (501) 988-3131,

B-47E	C-119J	F-4C(RF)	H-1M(UH)
B-57C	C-130A	F-84(RF)	T-33A
C-47	C-131A(HC)	F-101C(RF)	M-60 Tank

Pine Bluff - CAF Razorback Wing, Grider Field, Sat-Sun,

A-26	BT-13	L-3	PT-19	SNJ
AT-6	C-45	PT-17	PT-26	

Pocahontas - Pocahontas Mncpl Airport, US Hwy 67, A-7, Sikorsky Heliocopter

Rogers - Rogers Municipal Airport, Carter Field, (479) 631-1626, F-101B

Springdale - CAF Blackhawk Squadron, 72764,

Ozark Military Museum, POB 1766, Springdale Mncpl Airport, 72765
(479) 422-0208, Several Military: Aircraft, Vehicles and Artillery

Walnut Ridge - Walnut Ridge Army Flying School Museum, 2 Sky Watch Dr,
Walnut Ridge, AR 72476, (870) 886-7357 or (870) 886-3859,
www.walnutridge-aaf.com/museum.htm, H-1(AH), Link Trainer, SNB/JNB Trainer

CALIFORNIA

Alameda - Alameda Naval Air Station, 1000 Cmdr Dr, Sn Brn, 94501, A-4, A-7

Atwater - Castle Air Museum, POB 5050 Santa Fe, 95301, (209) 723-2178, Adjacent
To Castle AF On Santa Fe Rd Off HWY 99, Gift Shop 723-2182, Restaurant 723-2177
Memorial-Labor Day 9-5, Remaining 10-4, Closed: ES, TD, CD, ND, Adm Adult $8,
Snrs (60+) & Child 8-17 $6, Active & Under 8 Free,
www.elite.net/castle-air/index.htm, email cam@elite.net, (S) = Storage

A-26B	C-45A	F-89J	KC-97L
AGM-28B	C-46D	F-100C	PT-17 (S)
AT-6	C-47A	F-101B	PT-22
B.2 Avro Vulcan	C-54E(R5D)(S)	F-102A	PT-23 (S)
B-17G	C-56	F-104D	O-2A
B-18A	C-60B(L-18C)(S)	F-105B	SA-16 (S)
B-23	C-78(VC) (S)	F-106	SR-71A
B-24M	C-119C	F-111A(FB)	T-33A
B-25J	C-123K	GAM-63	T-34(YT)
B-26B (S)	C-131A(HC)	HH-43B	TG-3
B-29A(B-50)	C-135A(KC)	HU-16B	U-3A
B-36H(RB)	CG-4 (S)	L-4 (S)	UC-78
B-45A	F-4	L-5E (S)	WB-50D
B-47E	F-80B	L-13 (S)	VH-13H (S)
B-52D	F-84F	L-21A (S)	U-6A(L-20A)(S)
B-57E(EB)	F-86H	KAQ-1	
BT-13			

Aviation Challenge, 3600 B St, 95301, 888-MACHONE, (209) 726-0156,
Located at Castle AFB, Aviation Camps for Grades 4-12 & Adult, One Week of:
Land/Water Survival, Principals and Simulator Flight Basics, From $399-899,

Bishop - Inyo National Forest, 798 N Main St, 93514, (760) 873-2529, TA-4B, Train

Burbank - Producers Air Force, 1 Orange Grove Terrace, 91501, Contact: Chuck Hood,
Replica's From Movies For Sale: F-5,   F-6,   F-15,   F-16

Calistoga - Calistoga Gliderport (Next to "Nance's Hot Springs"), 1546 Lincoln Ave
(707) 942-5000, Daily 9-5, Gift Shop, Glider & Bi-Plane Rides in
Schweizer 2-32, Schweizer 2-33, Schweizer SGS-126B,

Camarillo - WWII Aviation Museum, CAF Southern California Wing, Camarillo Airport
455 Aviation Dr, 93010, (805) 482-0064, Formerly Oxnard AFB, Daily 10-4, Adm Adult $5,
Child 7-16 $2, Under 7 Free, Gift Shop, www.orgsites.com/ca/caf-socal

A6M2	C-46F	F8F-2	SNJ-5
A6M-3 (P)	C-131D (T-29)	Fairchild 24	Spitfire
B-25J(PBJ) (P)	F6F-5	SNJ-4 (P)	YAK-3

Constellation Historical Society, Global Aeronautical Foundation,
POB 2617, Camarillo Airport, Contact: Wayne Jones, EC-121C

Corona - CAF Inland Empire Squadron, Riverside Municipal Airport, 6936 Flight Rd, 92504,
(909) 354-7954, Sat 9-2, L-4, PT-22, SNJ-5

El Cajon - CAF Air Grp 1 Museum, Gillespie Field, 1860 Joe Crosson Dr, Suite A, 92020,
(619) 448-4505, Wed-Sat 10-4, Free Adm, www.cafairgroup1.org

AT-6	FM-2	L-5	SNJ
AV-8A	J-2	P-82	UC-78B

7

El Cajon - San Diego Aerospace Museum, Gillespie Field, 335 Kenney St, 92020, (619) 234-8291
Mon, Wed, Fri 8-3, Free Adm, Restoration Facility, www.aerospacemuseum.org

A-4C	F-8J	H-1B(UH)	Pitts S-L-S
A-6E	F-14A	L-2B	Rearwin Cloudster
A-7B	F-16N	L-19	RV-4
AGM-129 Missile	F-86F	Mutual Blackbird	Ryan 147T Drone
AT-6	F-102A	NYP	SBD (3/4 Scale)
Atlas Missile	F4B-4	P-51D	Sopwith Pup
AV-8A	F8U	PCI-1A	Sundancer I
DH-60A	Great Lakes T2-1A	Pietenpol Air Camper	

El Centro - El Centro Naval Air Facility, 92243-5000, (760) 339-2524,
8 Miles W of City, N of I-8, A-4   A-7D,   F-18A

Chino - The Air Museum "Planes of Fame", WWII Cal-Aero Field, 7000 Merrill
Ave, Box 17, 91710, (909) 597-3722, Fax 597-4755, Daily 9-5, Closed TD, CD,
Adm Adult $8.95, Child 5-12 $1.95, Under 5 Free, Gift Shop, Plane Rides
"Fighter Rebuilders" Restoration Facility, www.planesoffame.org, Rep=Replica,
F=Flyable, S=Static, RF=Restore to Fly, RS=Restore to Static, ST=Storage,

S	A-4B		F6F-3	F	P-12E/F4B-3		
ST	A-37	F	F6F-5K	F	P-26A		
ST	A6M5	S	F7F-3N	F	P-38J-20-LO		
F	A6M5	R	F8F-1	S	P-39N-5-BE		
	AD-4N		F8F-2	F	P-40N		
RS	Aichi D3A2 Val Rep	S	F8U-1	F	P-47G		
F	AN-2	S	F9F-5P	F	P-51D		
S	Apollo Module Rep	S	FJ-3	RF	P-59A(YP)		
R	Apollo CM		Fokker DR.1		P-63		
F	AT-12A/2PA		Fokker D VII	S	P-80A		
S	B-17G		Formula 1 Racer		P-84F		
F	B-25J	S	FR-1 Ryan		PB4Y		
F	B-26C(RB)		G4M1		PQ-14/TDC-2		
S	B-50A Fuse	S	GAM-54	F	PT-17		
RS	Ba-349		H-1 Racer		PT-19		
	Bensen B-8M	S	H-23		PV-2		
	Blaty Orion	ST	H-34		R3C-2		
S	Bristol F2.b Rep	F	HA-1112	S	Ric Jet RJ-4		
RF	BT-15 Val		HD-1	S	Rider R-4 Rep		
ST	C-45/SNB		Hurricane Mk X	S	Rider R-5 8-Ball		
	Cessna 210	RS	He-100		RP-5A		
	Chanute Hang Glider	S	He 162A-1	S	RP-76B Drone		
F	Convair 240(C-131B)	S	Horten Ho.IV	S	RP-54D Drone		
	Cricket NC-12	RF	Howard 250	S	Rutan Long-Easy		
S	CSM/Escape Tower		J2F-6	S	Rutan Quickie 2		
ST	Curtiss Pusher	S	J2M3		S-S D.IV		
S	D-558-II	S	J8M1		S&N Flying Wing		
F	DH 100 Mk.VI	S	KD6D-2		Schmidt Helio		
ST	DC-3 Cockpit	S	L-5G	F	SBD-5		
S	Deperdussin Racer	F	L-13A	F	SNJ-5		
S	DGA-5		L-17	RF	Spitfire Mk.IXe		
S	Discoverer Capsule	S	L-18(C-60)	RS	T-2A Rockwell		
S	Easy Riser H.G.	S	LeBel VTO	S	T-33		
	F-14A		Lilenthal	F	TBM-3		
	F-26		LK-10	S	TM-61		
	F-80		Lockheed Q-5		TS-11		
S	F-84F		Luscombe Silvaire	F	TV-2		
S	F-84K(RF)		M-39		Ultralight		
	F-86F		Me 108	S	V-1(Fi-103)		
S	F-86LFuselage	S	Me 163B Rep		Williams W-7		
S	F-86H(QF)	R	Mercury Capsule		X-1		
RS	F-89J	S	MiG-15		X-2 Rep		
RT	F-89J	S	MiG-17		X-7		
S	F-100D	RF	Miles/Atwood Rep	S	Yak-18		
S	F-102A		MQM-74	ST	Yak-11		
	F-10	S	MXY-7	S	Yak-11		
ST	F-105B	F	N9M-B Flying Wing				
F	F3F-2		Nieuport 28C				
	F4U-1A		O-47				

CALIFORNIA (Continued)

Chino - Yanks Air Museum, Chino Airport West Side, 7000 Merrill Ave, Hangar A270, Box 35,
N Side of Airport, (909) 597-1734, Tue-Fri 8:30-3:30, Sat 8:30-2, Free Adm,
www.yanksair.com   R=Restoration; A=Awaiting Restoration

A-4B (A)	E-2 (A)	H-34 (A)	P-51A-1
A-4E (A)	EA-6B (A)	HU-1 (A)	P-51D-10
American Eagle A-1	Ercoupe 415-D (A)	JN-4D	P-63C
AQM-37A Drone	F-4C (2ea) (A)	KD6G-2 Drone	PT-26 (A)
B1 Mahoney Ryan	F-4J	KDB-1 Drone	SB2C-3 (A)
B-25J (R)	F-14A	L-5 (A)	SBD-4 (2 ea)
Bell 47D1	F-14A (A)	LP-3	SNJ-5
BQM-126A Drone	F-80C (A)	MC-1	Stearman 4D
BT-13B	F-86	Mig 27 Drone	Stearman Bull
Bruner-Winkle Bird	F-100C	M-S Salaman	T-33A (A)
Bruner-Winkle Sparrow	F-105	N3N-3(3 ea)	T-37 (A)
C-40 (R)	F4U-4B (R)	O-52	T-38A (A)
C-43(UC)	F6F-5	Ohka 11 (A)	T-50 (UC-78)
C-46 (A)	FJ-1 (A)	OS2U-3 (A)	TBF-1 (A)
Cessna AW	FM-2	P-38L	TDU-25B Drone
CG-4A (A)	G-1B(YG)	P-39N-0	Thomas Pidgeon (R)
Curtiss Robin C-1(R)	G-6 (A)	P-40E	YPT9B Clooudboy
Curtiss Robin	H-3(CH)	P-47D	
C-47 (R)	H-3E(CH) (A)	P-47M	
C-47A (A)			

Fairfield - Travis Air Force Museum, Bldg 80, Burgan Blvd, 4535-5000, I-80
to Airbase Parkway Exit, East to Main Gate, Right on Burgan Blvd, Mail:
POB 1565, Appt Only by Curator (707) 424-5598, Mon-Sat 9-4, Closed Federal Holidays,
Adm Free, Airpark Open Daily Dawn till Dusk, www.jimmydoolittlemuseumpromotions.com
Indoor Museum = *

A-26K	C-119	F-102A	Link Trainer *
AT-11 (P)*	C-123K	F-104A	O-2A
B-29 *	C-124C	F-105D	PT-19A *
B-52D	C-131D	Gonzales *	T-28 *
BT-13 *	C-140A	H-21B	T-39A
C-7A	CT-39A	H-34(VC)	U-3A
C-45H	F-4C	L-4 *	
C-54	F-84F	L-5 *	
C-56	F-86F	LC-126A	
C-118A(C-54Q)	F-101B		

Firebaugh - The Heritage Eagles Museum, Eagle Field, 11163 North Eagle Av
93622, Sat-Sun, www.b25.net/museum,   B-25

Fresno - Fresno ANG, Fresno Air Terminal, 93727-2199, (559) 454-5100,
26th NORAD Region & Air Div; 194th FIS, 144th FIW,

F-4	F-86L	F-106A	T-33A
F-86A	F-102A	P-51D	

Fountain Valley - Twin Beech Assoc, Mail: POB 8186, 92728-8186, Pres:
Enrico Bottieri (714) 964-4864, Historian Robert Parmerter (607) 638-9343

Fullerton - Air Combat USA, 230 N Dale Pl, Mail: POB 2726, 92833-2524,
(800) 522-7590, (714) 522-7590, Fly Laser Dog Fights in the SIAI Marchetti
SF260, $695 Phase I/II, $1295 Full Day Training & 2 Flight Missions &
G-1 Jacket, See Offerings for List of 18 Participating Cities.

Hawthorne - Western Museum of Flight, 12016 Prairie Ave, 90250,(310) 332-6228
Fax: 664-6778, Tue-Sat 10-3, Adm Adult $3, Child $2, Under 12 Free,
www.wmof.com/welcome.htm

A-4A	F-5A	Radioplane RP-5A	Engine
AT-6E(XA)	Gyrocopter	Radioplane RP-76	R-985-AN-1
DH 82	JB-1	Rogallo Wing	Engine
F-14A	Montgomery	A-1020 Engine	T-51R-5190
F-17(YF)	Glider	GR-1820-G205	Engine V-12
F-20 Fuse	Northrop KD2R-5 Engine		Engine
F-23(YF)	O-3A(YO)	J-79-GE-3A	

Hayward - Vintage Air Museum, Field Bud Aviation, 20301 Skywest Dr, 94544
(510) 782-9063

C-3 (2ea)	PA-12	Stearman 4CM-1
Cessna 180	PA-23-250	Stearman Stock
DH 89 Project	Ryan STA	Travel Air 4000

Hemet - Ryan School of Aeronautics Museum, 4280 Waldon Weaver Rd,
Mail: 5001 W Florida Ave # 176, 92545-3823, (909) 658-2716, Thur-Sun 10-3
Closed Major Holidays, Free Adm, Gift Shop, Theater, Artifacts

Imperial - Pioneer's Museum, 373 E Aten Rd, 92251, (760) 352-3211, F-14, M-60 Tank

Inyo - Inyo National Park, TA-4B, K30 N Gauge Train

9

Inyokern - US Aviation Museum, Pacific Coast Division, 1300 Airport Rd, 93527,
(760) 377-0012, Founder Tony Mazzolini

A-4	B-29 Project 2ea	F-35
A-7	F-4	F-86

Lancaster - Antelope Valley College, Aviation Dept, 3041 W Ave, 93536
(661) 722-0615, D-558-2 Skyrocket #3

Constellation Historical Society, 104 East Ave, K4 Suite G,
93535, (661) 945-2093, Fax 945-7055,   C-121C

Jethawks (Lancaster Municipal Stadium), 2400 W Ave I, 93536, (661) 726-5400
F/A-18

Milestone of Flight Museum, Mail: POB 2585, 93534, (661) 942-6555,

B-25C	C-97G	F-102A(TF)

Poncho Barnes Aviation, 4555 W Ave G, 93536, (661) 948-4048, Travel Air Mystery

Lemoore - Leemore Naval Air Station, 93245, (559) 998-4045,   A-1, A-4, A-7E

Los Alamitos - Naval Air Station, US 405 & 605, 90720, (562) 795-2533, UH-1, XFV-1

Los Angeles - California Science Center, 700 State Dr, 90037, Exposition Park,
(323) 724-3623, 7547, Mon-Fri 10-1, Sat-Sun 11-4, Free Adm, Parking $6
 Space Shuttle Cargo Bay, www.casciencectr.com

A-12	F-104D	Saturn V	X-1
Bell 47G-5	Gemini 11	Velie Monocoupe	
Comet Glider	Mercury MR-2	70	
DC-8-52	T-38	Wright Glider	
F-20			

The Cockpit, 7510 Melrose Ave, 90046, (323) 782-0617, Mon-Sat 10-6, Sun 12-5,
Aviation Clothing (WWI-Today Military & Civilian), P-51 Suspended From Ceiling

Marysville - Beale AFB, 9SRW/CCX, 95903-5000, (530) 634-2038, Mon-Fri 10-4,
Closed Holidays, Free Adm, BIG RED 1 Reenactment Grp.

A-26	B-25	C-97L(KC)	SR-71A	U-2R

Forgotten Warriors Museum, (530) 742-3090, Thur 7-10, 1st Sat Each Month,
Open Memorial / Veterans Day,   H-1H(UH)   H-6(OH)

Mather - Military Hospital, Mather AFB, 95655, (916) 364-2177,

F-105G	H-1H(UH)	H-58(OH)

Modesto - CAF Central California Valley Squadron, County Harry Sham
Airport, (209) 577-5318, L-5E

Mojave - Mojave Airport, 1 Mi East of City, 93501, (661) 824-2433

Convair 880	F-4

Mt View - Moffett Field, NASA Ames Visitor Center, Moffett Field, 94305,
Off Hwy 101, (650) 603-9827, Wed-Sat 10-2, 1st & 3rd Sun 12-2, Free Adm, Gift Shop,
www.moffettfieldmuseum.org/index.html

F-104	Mercury Space Capsule	U-2
HiMAT	P2V	Space Shuttle 1/3 Scale

U.S. Space Camp, Moffett Federal Airfield, P.O. Box 6, 94035, (800) 637-7223,
(650) 603-8902, Space Camp for Grades 4-12 & Adult,

Oakland - CAF Golden Gate Squadron, Oakland Int'l Airport, 94601, Mail: POB 6056, 94603
(510) 568-7708, www.ghostsquadron-ggw.org, MiG-17   SNJ   T-33A

Museum Department of History, 1000 Oak St, 94607, (510) 273-3842, Wed-Sat 10-5,
Sun 12-7, Free Adm,   1919 Meteor.

Oakland Western Aerospace Museum, Oakland Int'l Airport, Bldg 621, 8260 Boeing
St, North Field, Across From Hangar 6, Mail: POB 14264, 94614-4264
(510) 638-7100, Fax 6530, Wed-Sun 10-4, Adm Adult $7, Snrs $6, 6-12 $3, Under 6 Free
Gift Shop, Library, Short Solent Tour $3, www.westernaerospacemuseum.org

A-3B(KA)(A3D)	AV-8A(TAV)	Glasair	Monocoupe 110
A-4M	Bede BD-5B	Ikarus Aero 3A	PT-13
A-6D(KA)	F-86H	Link Trainer	Short Solent Mk.3
A-7E	Funk Model B	Lockheed 10-A	TBM-3
Arrow Sport F	GAM-72	MiG-15	Wright EX Vin Fiz

Old Sacramento - Challenger Learning Center, 101 "I" Street, 95814, (916) 264-7057,

CALIFORNIA (Continued)

Palm Springs - Palm Springs Air Museum, 745 N Gene Autry Trail, 109 S
Indian Canyon Dr, Palm Springs Regional Airport, 92262-6603, (760) 778-6262,
Daily 10-5, Closed TD, CD, Adm Adult $10, Snrs/Mil (65+)$8.50, Child 6-17 $5,
Child Under 6 Free, www.air-museum.org   E-Mail: info@air-museum.org

A-4J(TA)	F4F	JD-1	SBD-5
A-6	F6F-5K	N2S-3	Spitfire Mk.XIV
A-26C	F7F-3	N2S-5	T-28
AT-6G (SNJ)	F8F	P-40N	T-34B
B-17G	F-16N	P-47D	TBM-3E
B-25J	FG-1D	P-51D 2ea	Wright Flyer ½ Scale
C-1A(S-2)	FM-2	P-63A	
C-47B	G-21(OA-13)	PT-17	
F-14	J-3C	PT-22	

Palmdale - Palmdale Plant 42 Heritage Park, 2001 E Ave P, (661) 267-5115,
Fri-Sun 10-1, www.edwards.af.mil/museum/doc_html/blackbird_airpark.html

A-12	D-21	F-86H	F-105D	SR-71A

Paso Robles - Estrella Warbird Museum, CAF Estrella Squadron, 4251 Dry Creek Rd,
From Hwy 101 Go East on Hwy 46, North on Airport Rd, To Dry Creek Rd, 93446,
(805) 238-9317, Recording 227-0440, Sat 10-4, Sun 12-3, Free Adm, Gift Shop,
http://ewarbirds.org   * = Privately Owned,

A-4A	F-4D Parts	L-17A	T-28B
A-6E	F-4J	L-16A	T-33A (2ea)
A-7C	F-14	Morrissey	Titan II
AT-11 *	F-8G(RF)	2000C	M-60 Tank
Beech D45	F-86F(QF)	S-2D(US)	
BD-5B	H-1(UH)	SNV-1	
DH-100	JN-4D *	Stinson V-77	
F-104G(TF)	L-5E		

Point Mugu - Point Mugu Missile Park, SR 1 & Pacific Ave, (805) 989-1110

F-4	F6F	F-14	Missiles

Port Hueneme - Channel Island ANGB, 146th AW, Mail: POB 4001, 93041-4001, F-86

Ramona - Classic Rotors, 2898 Montecito Rd, Airport Hangar #G, Ramona Airport,
(619) 427-1330, (760)803-0244, 639-1221, Mon, Wed, Fri-Sun 10-5, www.rotors.org

Allied UAV	H-19D	Hiller Camel	Rotorway 133
Bell 47-B3	H-21B	Hobbycopter	Rotorway
Bolkow 102	H-23B(OH)	HUK	Javelin
Brantly 305	H-26(XH)	HUP-1	SA-341G
Cyclocxrane 2	H-30(YH)	H-25	SUD Djinn
GA-400	H-31(YH)	Ka-26	SO1221S
Gyrocopter	H-32 (3ea)	Monte Copter	TH-55 (2ea)
H-13	H-37	15	V-44B
H-18	H-46F	Roton Rocket	Westland WASP
H-19B(UH)	H-67(TH)		

Rialto - Klaers Aviation, 1462 N Fitzgerald Ave, 92376-8621, (909) 874-9108
Restores P-47's, Has two P-47D's from Brazil, B-25

Ridgecrest - US Naval Museum of Armament and Technology, China Lake Naval Weapons Center
Mon-Fri 10-4, (760) 939-3530, Gift Shop, www.chinalakemuseum.org,

A-4F(NT)	F-8L(DF)	H-1(UH)	Shrike
A-6E	F-11B	RA-5C	Sidewinder
A-7C	F-4B(RF)		Tomahawk
AV-8A	F-4D(XF)	Missiles:	
F/A-18	F-86(QF)	Polaris	

Riverside - March Field Air Museum, 22550 Van Buren, Off I-215, 92518-6463, (951) 697-6602
Fax 697-6605, Mail: POB 6463, Daily 9-4, Mem Day-Labor Day 10-5, Closed CD,TD,ND,ED
Gift Shop, 697-6603, Library 697-6604, Theater, Restoration Facility,
Donations Family $10, Adult $7, Child 5-11 & Military $3, Under 5 Free, www.marchfield.org,

A-7D	C-123K	F-105B	P-39Q
A-9A(YA)	C-131D	F-105D	P-6 Hawk
AN-2 Colt	C-135A(KC)	FB-111A	P-40 Replica
A-26C	C-141B	FO-141	P-59A
B-8M Bennson	CT-39A	H-1F(UH)	PT-6A
B-17G	F-4C	H-6A(OH)	PT-13
B-25J	F-4C(RF)	H-21B(UH)	PT-19B
B-29A	F-4E	HU-16E	R50-5
B-47E	F-14	L-5	SNJ-4
B-52D(GB)	F-84C	LGM-30 Minuteman II	SR-71A
B-57(EB)	F-84F	MiG-19	T-33A
BT-13A (2ea)	F-86H	MiG-21	T-37B
C-45F(JRB-4)	F-86L	MiG-23	T-38A
C-47A(VC)	F-89J	Nieuport II Rep	T-39A
C-54D	F-100C	O-2B	TG-2
C-97L(KC)	F-101B	OH-6A	U-9A
C-119F	F-102A	OH-58A	

CALIFORNIA (Continued)

Riverside - P-38 National Assoc, Tony LeVier Hangar Museum (At March AFB),
Mail: P-38 National Assoc, POB 6453, March ARB, 92518, www.p38assn.org; P-38, P-51

475th Fighter Group Historical Foundation, March AFB, Mail: POB 6463, 92518-0394,
Next to the P-38 National Assoc, www.475th.org, Artifacts

Rosamond - Edwards AFB, NASA Ames-Dryden Visitor Center, POB 273, 93523-0273, (661) 258-3954,
Gift Shop,   SR-71   X-1E   X-15   X-29

Edwards AFB, Air Force Flight Test Center Museum, 95ABW/MU, 405 S Rosamond Blvd,
Bldg 7211, 93524-1850, (661) 277-8050, Fax 277-8051, Tue-Sat 9-5, Closed Sun-Mon,
TD, CD, ND, Free Adm, Gift Shop 277-6500, e-mail: museum@po-box1.edwards.af.mil
www.edwards.af.mil/museum/index.html, INC = incomplete, OD = On Display,
OS = Off Station, R = Restoration, S = Storage, AT = Awaiting Transportation,
NS = Non Standard; Jet Engines: J35, J47, J57, J79, J85, YJ93, YF101, F-109;
Rocket Engines: XLR-8, XLR-11, XLR-99, LR-121

A-3D-1	S	C-123K	S	F-94A(YF)	R	NF-11(TT-20)	OD
A-7D(Y)	R	C-135A	S	F-100A	INC	P-59B(XP)	OD
A-7F(Y)	R	C-140A	S	F-100A	OS/AT	PA-48	R
A-9A(YF)	S	C-141A(NC)	R	F-100A(YF)	R	PGM-17A	OD
A-10B(Y)	R	CH-3E	OD	F-100A(YF)	S	Rutan 354	S
A-12	OD	CT-39A	OD	F-101B	OD	SR-71	OD
A-37B(NA)	OD	D-21	S	F-102A(TF)	S	T-28B	OD
AQM-34	OD	F-4C(NF)	OD	F-104A	OD	T-33A	OD
AT3	R	F-4C(RF)	R	F-104A	OD	T-33A	OD
B-26B(T)	R	F-4E(YF)	R	F-104A(NF)	OD	T-38A	OD
B-47B	INC	F-8G(RF)	S	F-105D	R	T-46A	S
B-52D	OD	F-10B	R	F-106B	R	Titan Missile	
B-57B	R	F-16B	R	F-111A(N)	R	U-2D	OD
B-58A(N)	INC	F-16B	OD	F-111A	OD	X-4	R
BQM-34A	S	F-20	S	H-21C	S	X-21A	INC
C-7B	S	F-80A(EF)	R/OS	H-34C(VH)	S	X-25B	OD
C-45J(U)	OD	F-84F	OD	H-34G(SH)	OD		
C-53	R	F-86F	OD	HUP-2	S		
C-119B	S	F-89D	S	MMC-845	S		

Sacramento - McClellan AFB, McClellan Aviation Museum, 3204 Palm Ave, North Highland
Palm Gate Entrance Off Watt Ave, 95660, (916) 643-3192, Mon-Sat 9-4, Sun 12-4.
Free Adm, Closed Holidays, Gift Shop, www.mcclellanaviationmuseum.org

A-1E	C-131D(VC)	F-100D	L-2M
A-7D	CH-3E	F-101B	MiG-17PF
A-10A	EC-121D	F-102A	MiG-21F
AT-6G	F-4C	F-104B	T-28B
C-45HJ(UC)	F-80B	F-105D	T-33A
C-53D	F-84F	FB-111A	T-39A
C-54D	F-86F	H-21C(CH)	
C-119G	F-86L	HU-16B	

San Bernardino - Norton AFB, 92409-5000, (909) 382-1110, CT-39A, F-105D

San Carlos - Hiller Northern California Aviation Museum, 601 Skyway Rd on Freeway 101,
94070, (650) 654-0200, Fax 654-0220, 10-5 Daily, Adm Adult $8, Snrs & Child 8-17 $5,
Under 8 Free, Gift Shop, Library, Theater, Restoration Viewing, www.hiller.org

Avitor Hermes, Jr	H-23A #234	PG-185
Boeing 747 Cockpit	H-23B(OH)	PT-22
Boeing Condor SST	H-23D(OH)	PT-24
Cole Flyer	H-23F(OH)	RC-3 Seabee
Culeopter	H-31(YH)(LZ-5)	Santa Clara Glider
Christen Eagle	H-32(HOE)	Sopwith Camel
Curtiss D	H-44(XH)	Stearman Hammond YS-1
Diamond	Hiller 360(HTE2)H-23A	Stinson Detroiter
Doman	HOE-1(HJ-1,YH-32) Hornet	T-13
FH-1099 CAMEL	J-10-Jet	Thaden Transporter
FH-1100	"Little Looper" Aerobatics	VZ1 Hiller 1031
Flying Crane	Montgomery "Gull Glider"	Waco 10
Gazda Helicospeeder	Montgomery "Evergreen"	Wright Brothers B
H-12(UH) 360	Montgomery "Santa Clara"	X-18(XC-142)
H-12B(UH)	Nasa Swing Wing	XROE (3ea)
H-12C(UH)-E4	NC5	YO3A
H-12E(UH)-NASA	Nelson Hummingbird	
H-12L(UH)	Pietenpol Aircamper	

CALIFORNIA (Continued)

San Diego - Miramar - Flying Leatherneck Aviation Museum, Bldg T2002 Anderson Ave,
MCAS Miramar, N Gate, Corfner of Miramar Rd & Rigel Ave, 92709, Mail: POB 45316,
92145-0316, (858) 693-1723, Tue-Sun 9-3:30, Free Adm, Gift Shop 693-1791,
Wed-Sun 10-4, Restoration Facility, www.usmcavhistory.org, S=Storage,
P=Project, PX=at PX, L=On Loan to Pensacola Wings of Gold TV Series,

A-4C	F/A-18A (L)	HOK-1(HH-34D)	R4D-8(C-117)2ea
A-6E	F2H-2 (P)	HRS-3(H-19)	R4Q-2(C-119)
A-4M	F3D-2(EF-10)	HUP-2(H-25)	R5D-2Z(C-54)
AH-1J	F4F-3(FM-2)	HUS(UH-34)(P)	RF-4B (P)
B-25(PBJ)	F4U-5NL	MiG-15	RF-8G(F8U-1P)
Bell 214	F9F-8P	OV-10D	SNJ-5 (S)
CH-53A	FJ-3	OY-1(L-5) (S)	TBM-3E(TBF)

San Diego Aerospace Museum, Inc, 2001 Pan American Plaza, Balboa Park,
92101, (619) 234-8291, Mem Day-Lab Day 10-5, RoY 10-4, Closed TD, CD, ND
Adm Adult $9, Snrs 65+ 7, Child 6-17 $4, Under 5 Free, Theater, Restoration Facility,
Gift Shop 234-8291 Ext 31, www.aerospacemuseum.org

See also El Cajon, CA Restoration Facility,
GF=Gildred Flight Rotunda, EC=East Concourse, SC=South Concourse,
WC=West Concourse, CY=Court Yard, FY=Front Yard, S=Storage,

A-12	FY	Fleet 2	SC	Nieuport 28	WC
A-4C	EC	Fokker Eindecker(R)		Ornithopter	WC
A6M7	EC	Fokker DR.I (R)	WC	P-40E	EC
Albatross D-Va (R)WC		Ford 5-AT-B P	S	P-51D	GF
Apollo Capsule	EC	Gemini	EC	PBY-5A	CY
B-5	SC	H-1(AH)	GF	PT-1	S
Bf-109G(Mock-Up)	EC	J-3	SC	PT-22	SC
Bleriot XI	WC	J-1	SC	Ryan STA	SC
Bowlus Albatross	EC	JN-4D	WC	S-4C	WC
C-3	WC	Lilienthal Glider	WC	SBD-4 (P)	EC
Cayley Glider	WC	Link Trainer		SPAD VII	WC
Curtiss B-1 Robin	SC	M-1	WC	Spitfire Mk 16	EC
Curtiss L. Looper	WC	Mercury Capsule	EC	Waco YKS-7	SC
Curtiss A-1 Traid	GF	Mercury Air Racer	EC	Wee Bee	EC
Deperdussin C	WC	MiG-15	EC	Wright EX Vin Fiz	WC
DH 2		MiG-17	CY	Wright Flyer	WC
F-4J	CY	Montgolfiere	WC	X-13	
F-86	EC	Montgomery	WC	YF2Y-1	FY
F4F-3A (P)	EC	N2S-3	SC		
F6F-3	EC	Nieuport 11 (R)	WC		

North Island NAS, C-2, S-3, SH36, SH60, SH2F

San Francisco - Crissy Field Aviation Museums Assoc, Pier One, Ft Mason
Mail: POB 210671, 94121, (415) 602-8625, Fax 425-977-9349, Appt Only, DH-4 Project

Pacific Heritage Museum, 608 Commercial, 94111
(415) 399-1124 Mon-Fri, 10-4, Artifacts of Pacific Flight

San Francisco Int'l Airport, North Terminal By United, Airlines Area,Arrow Sport

The Exploratorium, 3601 Lyon St, 94123, (415) 563-7337, Sun-Wed 1-5, Free Adm,
Glider   Spacecraft

San Luis Obispo - O'Sullivan AAF, Camp San Luis Obispo, Cal Rt 1,
Officers Club, (805) 541-6168,

H-13(OH)	H-23(OH)	H-47(CH)	U-6
H-19(CH)	H-34(CH)	O-1	

San Martin - Wings of History Air Museum, S County Airport, 12777, Murphy Ave, Off Hwy 101
Just North of Gilroy, POB 495, 95046-0495, Sat-Sun 11-4, (408) 683-2990, Fax 683-2291,
Airshow Memorial Day, Restoration Facility, Gift Shop, Restaurant, www.wingsofhistory.org

Alexander Primary Glider	Nieuport 11 Rep
American Eagle A-101	P-51
AT-11	Peel Glider Boat
Avro 595 (P)	Penguin Trainer
Beech 23	Pietenpohl Air Camper (P)
Bensen B.8M	Rutan Quickie
Bowlus Albatross	Security Airster (P)
Bowlus Baby Albatross	Sopwith Pup Rep
Bowlus Flybaby	Spad VII (P)
Bowlus Super Albatross	Stahltaube 3/4 Scale
Culver Cadet (P)	Stan Hall Cherokee II
DH 88 Rep	Stan Hall Safari
EAA Biplane	Stinson 10A
Link Trainer	Stolp 7/8 Scale
LNE-1	Taylor Titsch
Marske Pioneer II	VJ-21
Mitchell Wing	Waco 10
Nelson Glider	Wright Flyer Rep

CALIFORNIA (Continued)

Santa Barbara - CollectAir Aviation Art Gallery and Museum, 1324 De La Vina St
93101, (805) 560-1323, Tue-Fri 1-5, Sat 2-6, or Appt, Free Adm, www.collectair.com
Aircraft Recognition Training Aids Collection, Working Spitfire Gunsight

Santa Maria - Santa Maria Museum of Flight, 3015 Airpark Dr, 93455, (805) 922-8758
Fax 922-8958, Fri-Sun 10-4, Closed Holidays, Donations Requested, Pres: Dick Weber,
www.smmof.org, E-mail: smmof@thegrid.net

Bowers Fly Baby	F-86	Klemm 35	Stinson Reliant
DH 82a	Fleet II	KR-2	Volmer Jensen Glider
F-4S	Great Lakes 2T-1A	Parker Sailplane	

Santa Monica - **Closed until New Facility Complete in 2006,** Museum of Flying, Exit 405,
2772 Donald Douglas Loop North, 90405, (310) 392-8822, FAX 450-6956,
Summer Tue-Sun 10-5, Winter Wed-Sun 10-5, Adm Adult $8, Snr $6, Child 3-17 $4,
Under 3 Free, Gift Shop, www.museumofflying.com, email: webmaster@mof.com,

A-4D	F=Flyable	Curtiss Robin	Hurricane Mk.XII F
A6M3 F		DC-3(R4-D)	JN-4D	Stinson SA-10
AD-6		DWC-4	KI-61 (Project)	T-28B F
AT-19(V-77)		Fairey Swordfish	N2S-4 F	Voyager
Beachey		Fleet Finch 2	P-38 F	Waco Cabin
Beech D-17S		Fokker DR.I	P-39Q	Waco Model 10
BD-5J		G4M (Project)	P-51D F	YAK-3UA
Bf-109E F		Gee Bee Z Rep	Rutan Variviggen	

Santa Paula - Aviation Museum of Santa Paula, 824 E Santa Maria St, 93060, (805) 525-1109
Contact: Sally Phelps, Appt Only, www.amszp.org, Beech D17S, Fairchild F-24, Howard DGA

Santa Rosa - Pacific Coast Air Museum, Sonoma County Airport, 2330 Airport Blvd, 95403
(707) 575-7900, Fax 545-2813, Tue/Thur 10-2, Sat/Sun 10-4, $3 Donation, Pres: Don Doherty,
Gift Shop, Restoration Facility, Airshow 3rd Weekend Aug, www.Pacificcoastairmuseum.org,

A-4E	F-14A	HU-16A & (P)	T-28B
A-6E	F-16N(FC)	IL-14P	T-28C (P)
A-26 (P)	F-84F(P)	L-3 (P)	T-33
BD-5	F-86F(RF)	MiG-15 (P)	T-37
Broussard MH.1512	F-86H	Nanchang CJ-6 2ea	T-38
C-118(DC-6)	F-105F	P-51D	YAK 52
F-4C	F-106	PA-22	
F-8U	H-1H(UH)	PA-23(U-11A)	

Aero Crafters, 2232 Airport Blvd, 95403, (707) 527-8480, Contact Steve Penning,
WWII Aircraft Used as Fire Bombers

Shafter - Minter Field Air Museum, RTE 11, Shafter Airport, 401 Vultee St, Mail: POB 445
93263, (661) 393-0291, Fax 393-3296, Sat 10-2, Airshow in April,
www.minterfieldairmuseum.com, F-80 Cockpit, Link Trainer

AT-6 2ea	N2S-3	PT-22	T-50
BT-13	P-51	PT-26	
L-3	PT-17	T-33	

Simi Valley - Regan Library, 40 Presidental Dr, (800) 410-8354, Daily 10-5, Adult $5
Over 62 $3, Under 16 Free, Boeing 707 Air Force 1

Tulare - Tulare Mcpl Airport, Mefford Field, 93275, (559) 688-0660, B-17, BT-13, F-4

Twentynine - Twentynine Palms Marine Corps Air-Ground Combat Center, Box 788100
92278-8100, (760) 830-6000, A-4

Upland - CAF - 3rd Pursuit Squadron, Cable Airport, 1749 W 13th St, 91786, By Appt Only
(951) 751-1131, email: budsairplanes@msn.com, www.3rdpursuit.com, AN-2

CAF - Harvard6 Group, Cable Airport, AT-6

Van Nuys - Main Gate, F-104C

Victorville - George AFB, 92394-5000, (760) 269-1110, F-4C F-100D
F-86H	F-105D	F-104C		F-105G

Willows - Willows Airport, 95988, (530) 934-6489, AN-2

COLORADO

Aurora - Colorado ANG/PA, Buckley ANGB/STOP # 24, 140 TFG, 80011-9599
(303) 366-5363, PA Officer: Bruce Collins,

DHC-2	F-100A	F-86D	F-86F(RF)	T-6A

Weary Warriors Squadron, B-25H

Cannon - Cannon Airport, F-4

14

COLORADO (Continued)

Colorado Springs - Fort Carson, Butts Airfield, Free Adm, OH-6, OH-13, Many Tanks
US Air Force Academy/PA, 80840-5151, (719) 472-2025, 472-2555,

B-52D	F-16	F-105D	SV5-J	X-4
F-4C	F-104A	GF-16A	T-38A	Minuteman II

Peterson Air & Space Museum, Peterson AFB, 150 E Ent Ave, Bldg 981, 80914-5000,
PA: (719) 556-4615, Summer Tue-Sat 8:30-4:30, Closed Holidays, Free Adm, Gift Shop,
Curator 554-4915, www.petemuseum.org; (P = Project

CF-100	F-15A	F-102A	Air-2A Genie
CF-101B	F-86L	F-104C	CIM-10A BOMARC (P)
EB-57E	F-89J	F-106A (P)	Hawk
EC-121T (P)	F-94C	P-40E Replica	Nike Ajax
F-4C	F-101B	P-47N (P)	Nike Hercules
		T-33A	Vela Satellite

Denver - Centennial Airport - P-51D,

The 69th Battalion, POB 24286, 80224, (303) 782-3681, Fax 782-3694,
E-mail: robert@carik.com, Pyro/Special Effects Contractor, Flying:
A1-D, A-37, O1-A, O-2A, OV-1D, UV-18A,

Denver Int'l Airport, (303) 270-1500, JN-4D Hanging in Main Concourse
1930 Alexander Eaglerock Model A-14 Hanging at Opposite Concourse
Link Trainer at United Air Lines

J W Duff Aircraft Salvage, 8131 E. 40th Ave, 80207, (303) 399-6010,
Mon-Fri 8-4:30, Over 500 Aircraft Some Complete, Mostly Fuselage & Wings
www.jwduffaircraft.com/index.html

AT-6	L-4	PT-22	U-3A
AT-11	L-5	PT-26	U-6A
C-45	L-16	O-2	U-8
H-12(UH)	L-17	T-6	U-10
H-13(UH)	L-18	T-28	U-21
H-204	L-19	T-34B	UC-64
JR-3	N3N	TG-3A	UC-78

Wings Over the Rockies Air & Space Museum, Lowry AFB, 7711 E Academy Blvd,
80230-6929, (303) 360-5360, Fax: 360-5328, Mon-Sat 10-5, Sun 12-5,
Closed: ED, TD, CD, ND, Adm Adult $6, Snrs 65 $5, Child 6-12 $4, Under 5 Free,
Gift Shop, 360-5325, e-mail: worm@dimensional.com, www.wingsmuseum.org,

A-7D	F-4E	F-101B	Glider 1920
Alexander Eagle Rock	F-84K(RF)	F-104C	H-21C
B-1A	F-86H	F-105D(GF)	KR-1
B-18A	F-100D	F-106A	Space Module
B-52B(GB)	F-100D(GF)	F-111A	"Freedom"
B-57E	F-4E	FG-1D	T-33A
C-45	F-84K(RF)	Fokker D.VII	U-3A
DC-3	F-86H		

Fruita - Western Slop Vietnam War Memorial Park - I-70 Exit, Mail: PO Box 340, 81521,
(970) 242-0073, www.field-of-dreams.org, UH-1

Grand Junction - CAF - Rocky Mountain Wing, Walker Field (303) 244-9100, (970) 856-3412,
J-3, TBM-3   A-6 (F-11-F) Airport Pedestal

Pueblo - Int'l B-24 Memorial Museum, 31001 Magnuson Ave, 81001, (719) 543-3605,
Mon-Fri 10-4, Sat 10-2, Sun 1-4, Free Adm, Gift Shop, www.pwam.org

Pueblo Weisbord Aircraft Museum, 31001 Magnuson Ave, 81001, (719) 948-9219,
Fax 948-2437, Mon-Fri 10-4, Sat 10-2, Sun 1-4, Adm Adult $6, Under 10 Free,
Sit In A Cockpit, Last Sat Monthly, Different Aircraft Each Month, Gift Shop,
www.pwam.org

A4D-2	C-119G	F-100D	H-131A
A-26C	F-6A	F-101A	P2V-5
B-29A	F8Y(LTV)	F-104	PT-17
B-37(RB)	F9F-8	H-1(UH)	RA-5C
B-47E	F11F-1	H-21B(HC)	Stearman
C-47D	F-80	H-34J(SH)	T-28C
C-131A(HC)	F-84G	H-47B	T-33A

Westminster - CAF - Mile High Wing, Front Range Airport, Main Terminal, 80034-0528,
Mail: POB 4805, Parker, CO 80134-1462, (303) 851-1499, Info 303-841-3004,
3rd Sat ea Month 10am, www.milehighcaf.org, C-60A

CONNECTICUT

Hartford - Prop-Liners of America, www.propliners.com/index.html Convair 240 Restoration

Stratford - National Helicopter Museum, 490 Sherwood Place, Apt C 12, 06497, 203-375-5766, Old Train Station,May-Oct Wed-Sun 1-4, www.nationalhelicoptermuseum.org, H-1B(UH)

Sikorsky Memorial Airport, (203) 576-7498, FG-1D

Windsor Locks - Air National Guard, Bradley Airport, A-10, F-105, F-106

New England Air Museum, Bradley Int'l Airport, 06096, Exit 40(I-91) SR20W,SR75N, Suffield W, (860) 623-3305, Fax 627-2820, Daily 10-5, Closed TD, CD, NY Adm Adult $8, Snr 60 $7.00, Child 6-11 $4.50, Under 6 Free, Gift Shop, Theater, Restoration, www.neam.org,

A-3B	F-4A	HU-16E	Pratt-Read Line-1
A-4A	F-4B	HUP-1	PT-23A
A-10A	F-8K LTV	HUP-2(H-25)	R-3(M-B)
A-26C	F-104C	J-3	R-4B
A-24B	F-89J	JB-2	Rearwin Cloudster
AD-4N	F-94C	K-225	Republic Seabee
AEW3	F-100 Cockpit	K-16 V-STOL	Rutan Quickie
AT-6	F-100A	Laird Solution	Rutan Vari-eze
B-25H	F-105B	LH-34D	S-39
B-29A	F4D-1	Link ANT-18	S-60
B-57A(RB)	F4U-4(XF)	Lockheed 10A	S-51
Bell 47D-1	F6F-5K	Lockheed 12	SP-2E
Bensen B-8M	F9F-2	Lockheed 14	SR 71 Engine Only
Blanchard	FJ-1	Marcoux-Bromberg	Stinson Detroiter
Bleriot XI	FM-2	MC200	SUD VI-R
BT-13	Fokker DR.1	Mead Rhone Ranger	T-28C
C-7A	Gee Bee Model E	MiG-15	T-33A
C-50	Gee Bee R-1	Monerai S Sailplane	TV-2
CBY-3	Gee Bee Model A	Mosquito H. Glider	U-6A
CH-54B	Goodyear ZNP	NIK2-J	UH-1B
Chanute Glider	Great Lakes 2T-1A	Nixon Special	Viking Kittyhawk
Corben Jr Ace	H-5H	OH-23G	VS-44A Sikorski
Curtiss Pusher	Hanson-M. Quickie	OH-50C	XF15C-1
D-558-11	Heath Parasol	P-47D	Zephyr
DC-3	HH-43F	P-51D	
Dyndiuk Sport	HH-52A	Pioneer Flightstar	
E-1B	HRP-1		

Delaware

Dover - Air Mobility Command Museum, 1301 Heritage Rd, 19902-8001, (302) 677-5938 Fax 677-5940, Tue-Sat 9-4, Closed Fed Holidays Free Adm, Gift Shop, Restoration Facility, www.amcmuseum.org/ email: museum@dover.af.mil

AT-6	C-97(KC)	C-141A	H-1(UH)
B-17G	C-119G	C-141B	H-43(HH)
BT-13	C-121	CG-4A Project	Link Trainer
C-5	C-123K	F-16	P-51D
C-7A	C-124	F-101B	PT-17
C-45G	C-131D	F-106	T-33A
C-47A	C-133	F-106 Simulator	
C-54M			

New Castle - ANG, Greater Wilmington Airport, 19720, (302) 322-3361, F-86H

D.C.

Washington

Anacostia NAS, SE Wahsington D.C. Off Route 295 and Potomac River, T-28

Bolling AFB, 20332-5000, (202) 545-6700, 1100th ABG/CC, F-105D

US Postal Museum, 2 Massachusetts Ave, 20002, (202) 633-5555, Daily 10-5:30, Closed CD, www.postalmuseum.si.edu/, DH 4, SR-10F, Weisman Cook

US Soldiers and Airmens Home, 3700 N Capital St, (202) 722-3000, F-86, M60 Tank

D.C. (Continued)

Washington - National Air & Space Museum, Smithsonian Institution, Independence Ave at 4th St SW, 20560, (202) 633-1000, Daily 10-5:30, Free Adm, Gift Shop, Chairman - Dept of Aeronautics: Dr Thomas Crouch, www.nasm.si.edu

Gallery Number	Gallery Number	Gallery Number
203 A4D-2N(A-4C)	Fi-103	205 P-51D
205 A6M5	209 Fokker D.VII	9 P-59A(XP)
209 Albatross D.Va	2 Ford 5-AT	6 P-80(XP)
205 B-26B	2 G-21	2 PA-5
205 Bf 109G	4 G-22	206 Pfalz D.XII
7 Bleriot XI	7 Gallaudet Hydro-Kite	208 R3C-2
0 Boeing 247D	208 Gossamer Condor	213 Rockwell HiMAT
5 C-17L	5 H-1	LOB Rutan Voyager
7 Curtiss D	9 Hawker Siddeley Kestrel	203 SBD-6
2 DC-3	5 J-1	209 Spad XIII
2 DC-7 Fuse	7 Lilienthal	205 Spitfire Mk.VII
10 DH 4	208 Lockheed 5B Vega	206 Sopwith Snipe
ESC D-558-2	9 Lockheed 5C Vega	208 T-2(F.IV)
208 DWC-2	208 Lockheed 8 Sirius	10 U-2C
7 Ecker Flying Boat	2 M-2	206 Voisin Model 8
206 Explorer II	205 MC-202	5 Wittman
203 F4B-4	6 Me 262A	0 Wright Kitty Hawk
203 F4F-4(FM-1)	2 Northrop 4A Alpha	7 Wright Military Flyer
ESC F-104A	5 Northrop Gama	208 Wright EX Vin Fiz
2 FC-2	14 Northrop M2-F3	0 X-1
206 FE-8	0 NYP	0 X-15A-1
6 FH-1	4 P-26A	213 X-29

FLORIDA

Arcadia - Municipal Airport, (863) 494-7844, Fr 24, West Hanger

Starfighters, Inc, 15707 Fairchild Dr, 33762, www.starfighters.net
CF-104   CF-104D Both Flown at Airshows

Cocoa Beach - US Air Force Space Museum Cape Canaveral, AF Station, 32925, (321) 867-7110, Daily 9-3, Free Adm, 80 Spacecraft, Rockets & Missiles

Astronaut Memorial Planetarium and Observatory, Brevard Community College 1519 Clearlake Rd, 32922, (321) 634-3732, 631-7889

Daytona Beach - Embry-Riddle Aeronautical Univ, 32114, (386) 226-6175
Aircraft Here Are For Training Purpose Only,

Aerospatial Tampico	Beechcraft Dutchess	C-172Q	Mooney M.18
American General Tiger	C-303	C-303	PA-44
Beechcraft 35	C-172	C-182RG	Piper Cadet

Wright Flyer Replica In Front Of School For Public Viewing.

Miniature Golf, South Atlantic Ave, Beechcraft 18

DeLand - CAF - Florida Wing, PO Box 1944, 32721-1944
C-45, L-17B

Naval Air Station Museum, Mon-Sat 9-5, Wed & Thur 1-5, (386) 738-4149, A-6

Fernandina Beach - Amelia Island: Island Aerial Tours, 1600 Airport, 32034-0204, 35 Mi S of Jacksonville, (904) 261-7890, J-3, Waco Model 10

Ft. Lauderdale - The Discovery Center, 231 SW 2nd Ave, 33301-1892, Space Artifacts

Ft Lauderdale Executive, HU-16 (5 ea)

World Jet Aircraft Int'l Sales & Leasing, 1710 W Cypress Creek Rd, 33309-1806, (954) 776-6477, Planes May Be Sold, Check Ahead
B-25   Me-109   TBM
P-51   Nord

Ft. Myers - Ft. Myers Historical Museum, Jackson St, 1 Block S of Martin Luther King

Blvd (SR 82), 33901, (239) 332-5955, Tue-Sat 9-4, Adm Adult $6, Snr $5.50, Child 3-12 $3
Under 3 Free,   P-39   Railroad Caboose

Homestead - AFB, 33039-5000, 305-257-8011,   F-4D   F-100D

Indian Rocks Beach - Florida Aviation Historical Society, POB 127, 33535, Ford Flivver

FLORIDA (Continued)

Jacksonville - Commanding Officer Naval Reserve Officer Training Corps Jacksonville
University NROTC, 2800 University Blvd North, 32211-3394, (904) 745-7480,
Daily 8-4:30, A-7E (In Front of NROTC Building)

Jacksonville ANG, Int'l Airport, (904) 741-4902, F-106A   T-33A

MCAS New River, Heros Park, Off Hwy 17 S of City, AH-1W, CH-34, CH-53E, MV-22, UH-1

Museum of Science and History, 1025 Museum Circle, Southbank, 32207
(904) 396-7062, Mon-Fri 10-5, Sat 10-6, Sun 1-6, Adm Adult $5, Child $3, PT-17(N2S)

Naval Aviation Station Cecil Field, 14 Mi SW of Jacksonville, I-10 Then
Whitehouse Exit, S on Chaffe Rd to Normandy then R, Passes at Bldg 327 Main Gate,
Daily 7:30-2pm, 33821, PA: (904) 778-6055, HR: 778-5781, Info 778-5627,
        TR=Road To Tower, SS=Sea Strike Wing 1 HQ, CT=At Cecil Tower

A-4C (TR)	F8U-1 (TR)	S-2A (TR)	
A-7E (MR)	F/A-18A (TR)	S-3A (TR)	
A-7E (ST)	F9F-8 (TR)	TBM-3E (SS)	

Naval Air Station Jacksonville, Aircraft At Main Gate, (904) 270-6100

F/A-18	P-3A	P2V-5	PBY-5A	SH-3B

Key West - Naval Air Station Key West, (305) 293-3700, A-4E, A-5, F-4, EA-6A

Conch Republic Trading Company, 725 Duvall St, 33040, (305) 292-9002, Fax 292-0270
1946 Sea-Bee

HT Chittum & Co Sport Clothing Store, 725 Duvall St, (305) 292-9002, RC-3

Key West Int'l Airport, 33040, (305) 294-8687, Waco UPF-7   Pitts S-2A

Kissimmee - Flying Tigers Warbird Restoration Museum - Tom Reilly Vintage Aircraft, Inc,
231 N Hoagland Blvd, Off Hwy 192, 34746, (407) 933-1942, 847-7477, Fax 933-7843,
Mon-Sun 9-5, Closed CD, Adm Plus Tax Adult $9, Over 60 & Child 8-12 $8
Under 8 Free, Group Rate: (10 or more) Adult $7, Child $5, Restoration Facility with Tours
Gift Shop, Warbird Restoration Training Course $995 5 Days,
E-mail: programs@warbirdmuseum.com; www.warbirdmuseum.com

A-4 (P)(8ea)	F-100D (D)	HUP-1 (D)	PT-17 (F)
A-7 LTV(D)	F-101A (D)	J-3 (F)	PT-22 (F)
A-26 (F)(2ea)	F-101B Simulator	KR-21 (F)	S-2 (F)
AT-6G (F)	F-104A (D)	KR-34 (F)	SNJ-3 (F)
B-17 (P)	F4U-4 (P)	L-2 (F)	SNJ-4 (P)
B-25J (F)	F9F-7 (D)	MiG-21 MF (D)	SNJ-6 (2ea) (F)
C-1 (F)	FG1D (P)	OX-5 (F)	Taylor Young (F)
C-3 (F)	Fouga Magister (F)	P-38 (P)(2ea)	TB-25N (P)
C-47(F)	Fw-190 (P)	P-40E (P)	
DH-100 (F)	Funk (F)	P-1127 Kestrel	
F-4C (D)	H-34 (D)	PA-11 (F)	

Howard Johnson Lodge, Fountain Park Plaza Hotel & Conference Center
5150 W Space Coast Pkwy, (800) 432-0763, Titan I Missile

Mustang Operations & Preservation Soc, 3951 Merlin Dr, 34741, (407) 846-4051,

Warbird Adventures, Adjacent to Flying Tigers Warbird Air Museum, (800) 386-1593,
(407) 870-7366, Web: warbirdadventures.com, Warbird Flights

White 1 Foundation Inc, 822 N Hoagland Blvd, 34741, (407) 933-0277,
www.white1foundation.org, Restoring FW-190F-8

Lakeland - Florida Air Museum, 4175 Medulla Rd, Lakeland - Linder
Regional Airport, POB 6750, 33807, I-4 Exit 15, Go East on Medulla Rd,
(863) 644-0741 & 2431, Mon-Fri 9-5, Sat 10-4, Sun 12-4, Adm Adult $4,
Child Under 12 $2, Gift Shop, Theater, www.sun-n-fun.org

AT-11	Boeing A75N1	Ford Fliver
Aeronca LB	Bowers Fly Baby	FP-303
Aerosport Scamp	Brokaw Bullet	Glassair
American Eagle	Butler Blackhawk	GW-44A
Anderson Kingfisher	C-3	Hawker Tempst Mk II
Anglin Spacewalker II	Chief Oshkosh	Heath Super Parasol
Atkinson Eaglet	Cieslak Model 2	HU-16
Auster Mark 9	Command-Aire	Jurga-Tepete
B-17 Ball Turret	CP-65	Kit-Fox Model #1
B-17 Fuselage	CP-65 P	Laird Baby
B-29 Nose	Cricket MC-10	Lazair
Bakeng-Duce	CW-12W	Loving's Love
Barracuda	DGA 1-A	Lysander
Bede BD-4	EAA Acro-Sport	Mitchell P-38
Bede BD-5	Ercoupe 415-C	Monnet Moni
Beech D-17S	F-101F	Mooney M.18L Mite
Bensen B.8M	Flying Flea	(Continued Next Page)

N2S-4	Rans S-9	T-33A
Nesmith Cougar	Revolution Mini 500	Taylorcraft 1940
Nieuport 17-C1	Russ Ritter Special	Travelair D4000
OQ-19(KD2R-3)	Rutan Vari-eze	Travelair 2000
P-51D	Rutan Variviggen	UH-1H
P-63	SE5A	Vangrunsven RV-3
Pietenpol B-4	Smyth Sidewinder	V-22 Osprey
Pitts Special	Steen Skybolt	VJ-24
Q-1 Quickie	Stits Playmate	VP-1
Q-200 Quickie	Sunshine Clipper	Woody Pusher
Ranchero	Super Lancer Hang Glider	XFV-1 VTO
Rand KR-1	Swearingen SX-300	YF2Y-1

Exploration V, 125 Kentucky Ave, S, (863) 687-3869, Small Plane Cockpit

FLORIDA (Continued)

Mary Esther, Hurlburt Air Park, Hulburt Field, 131 Bartley St, Suite 315, 834 ABW/HO, 32544-5000, (850) 884-6402, Off Highway 98, www.hurlburt.af.mil/basewide/airpark

A-1E	C-46D	C-130A(AC)	O-2A
A-26A	C-47A(AC)	H-1P(UH)	OV-10
A-37B(OA)	C-119G(AC)	H-3E(HH)	T-28D(AT)
B-25N	C-123K(UC)	O-1E	U-10A

Merritt Island - NASA Kennedy Space Center, 32899, (321) 452-2121, Mon-Sun 9-6, Bus Tours 10-2:50,Closed CD, Adult $17-37, Child 3-11 $13-27, Gift Shop, Restaurant, www.kennedyspacecenter.com,

| Apollo II | Space Shuttle | Saturn V | Missiles | Launch Vehicles |

Miami - Wings Over Miami Museum, 14710 SW 128th St, Kendall-Tamiami Airport SW of Miami, 33196, (305) 233-5197, Thur-Sun 10-5:30, Adm Adult $9.95, Snrs 60 & Child Under 12 & Grps of 110 $5.95, Gift Shop, www.wingsovermiami.com

A-26C	F6F-3	P-38L Fuse
Abernathy Streaker	F7F-3	P-40N(TP)
Stephens Super Akro	F-86F	P-51D
B-17G	Fairey Swordfish Mk.IV	PBY-5A
B-23	Fairchild 24R	Pitts Special S-2-B
B-25	Fouga Magister	PT-17
B-29(P2B-1S) Nose	Hawker Tempest	PT-22
Boeing B-100	J-S	Sopwith Pup
Boeing 707 Simulator	J2F-6	Sopwith 1½ Strutter
Beech D17S	JN-4D	Sopwith Triplane
British Provost	KA-61	Spad VII
Cap 231	C-135(KC)	TBM-3
CJ6A Nanchang (2ea)	L-29	TU-2
Cessna 195RS	Me-108	Weeks Solution
Curtiss Falcon	MiG-15	Weeks Special
DeWoitine D.26	DH 98	YAK-11
DH-82	P2B-1S	YAK-52
F4U-4	P-35A	

George T Baker Aviation School, 3275 NW 42nd Ave, 33142, (305) 871-3143 Ext 300 www.universities.com/Schools/G/George_T_Baker_Aviation_School.asp

| A-4 | Boeing 707 | Martin 4-0-4 |
| Beech D18S | F-86 | T-33 |

Opa Locka - Opa Locka Airport, HU-16 (2ea)

Orlando - Church Street Station, 129 W. Church St, 32801, (407) 422-2434, Commander Ragtimes, Fokker D.VII   Fokker DR.1   SE-5A

Helicopter Inc, 240 N Crystal Lake Dr, 32803, (407) 894-7428,Owner: Fred Clark, Curtiss Robin B   Paramount Cabinaair

John Young Museum & Planetarium, 810 E Rollings St, 32803, (305) 896-7151, Daily 10-5, Free Adm, Spacecraft

Orlando Int'l Airport, Memorial Park (Near Air Freight Section) B-52D 1 Airport Blvd, 32827-4399, (407) 825-2001 Info, 825-2055 Commun.Relation

West Orlando Airport, (305) 656-7813, Byrid, Fr Kr 21, Taylorcraft A

Panama City - Vets Memorial Park, 1 Block E of Callaway Plaza, F-101B, F-15C

Gulf Coast Community College, Hwy 98 E, 12 Miles E of Gulf Coast Community College F-101B, ½ Mile East of Hathaway Bridge, F-15C

Tyndall AFB, 325 TTW/MAM, 32403, (850) 283-1113, Aircraft Along I-98 Thru Base, Inside Building At Flag Park.

B-57B(EB)	F-4C/D	F-100D	F-106A
BQM-34A	F-15D	F-102A	MQM-107
BQM-34F	F-86D	F-102A(TF)	T-33A
CGM-13	F-89J	F-104C	

FLORIDA (Continued)

Pensacola - National Museum of Naval Aviation, Bldg 3465, 1750 Radford Blvd, Exit 2 (I-10),
    Mail: Box 33104, 32508, (850) 452-3604, (800) 327-5002, Daily 9-5, Closed: TD, CD, ND
    Free Adm, Gift Shop, http://naval.aviation.museum/intro.html SW = South Wing,
    WW = West Wing, AD = Antrium Display, OD = Outside Display, IS = Inside Storage, OS = Outside

SW A-1 (TRIAD)	WW F2H-2P	CG HO3S-1G	SW NT-1
IS A-4A(A4D-1)	SW F2H-4	SW HO4S	OD NU-1B
IS A-4E (2ea)	OD F3D-2(F-10B)	SW HO5S-1	OE-1
AD A-4F (3ea)	SW F3F-2	SW HTE-1	WW OS2U-3
SW A-6E	SW F4D-1(F-6A)	IS HTK-1	SW OY-1
SW A-7E	SW F4F-3 (2ea)	SW HTL-4	OD P-3A
OD A3D-1(A3A-1)	WW F4U-4	OD HU-16E	WW P-40B
WW A6M-2B	SW F6C-1	WW HUP-1(UH-25C)	WW P-80A
OD AD-5Q(EA-1F)	WW F6F-3	OD HUS-1(UH-34D)	OD P2V-1(XP)
WW AD-6(A-1H)	SW F6F-5	IS Goodyear 195	OD P2V-7
WW AF-2S	SW F7C-1	WW J-3	OD P5M
SW AH-1J	WW F7F-3	WW J2F-6	WW PBY-5
OD AJ-2	SW F7U-3M	WW J4F-1	OD PB2Y-5R
WW AM-1	WW F8F-2	OD JD-1	OD PB4Y-2
AQM-37A	SW F8U-1(F-8A)	SW JN-4	PS-2
Arado AR 196A	OS F8U-1P(RF-8G)	IS JRC	OD RA-5C
SW AV-8C	WW F9C-2	WW JRF-3	OD R4D-5
SW BFC-2	WW F9F-2	WW K-47 CAR	SW RR-5
Bleroit XI	IS F9F-5P	KD-3G	SW S-3 & S-4C
OD C-1A	SW F9F-6	KD2G-2	OD S2F-3
OD C-46(R5C)	SW FF-1	KDB-1	WW SB2C-5
OD C-47H(R4D-5)	WW FG-1D(F4U)	L-4B	IS SB2U
OD C-117D(R4D-6)	WW FH-1	SW Le Rhone	WW SBD-2
OD C-118B(R6D-1)	WW FJ-1	IS LNE-1	WW SBD-3
OD C-121K(EC)(WV-2)	SW FJ-2	SW LNS-1	OD SH-3G
OD C-131F(R4Y-2)	IS FJ-3M	IS Meyers OTW	OD SNB-5P
Cessna 180F	SW FJ-4(F-1E)	SW MF-Boat	WW SNC-1
CH-19(HRS-2)	WW FM-2(F4F)2ea	SW N-9H	AD SNJ-5C
OS CH-19E(HRS-3)	SW Fokker D-VII	SW N2C-2	WW SNV-1
OD CH-37C(HR2S-1)	SW GB-2	SW N2S-3	SW Sopwith Camel
OD CH-53A	IS GK-1	N2S-5	SW T-28B
SM Command Module	SW H-1K(HH)	SW N2T-1	AD T-34B
IS D-558-1	IS H-2D(HH)	WW N2Y-1	WW TBM-3E
OD E-1B(WF-2)	OD H-3F(HH)	SW N3N-3	WW TD2C-1
OD E-2B	SW H-13M(TH)	SW NC-4	WW TDD-1
SW F-4N(F4H)	SW H-52A(HH)	WW NC-9-A	WW TDD-2
SW F-11A(F11F-1)	SW H-57C(TH)	N1K1	WW TDR-1
OD F-14A	SW HD-1	WW N1K2-J	SW TS-1
SW F-17(YF)	WW HNS-1	SW Nieuport 28	SW YRON-1
F/A-18(YF-18)	SW HO-49	WW NR-1	WW ZPG Rudder

    Pensacola Regional Airport, 3 Miles NE of City, GPI 904-43 5-1746, F11F-1 Blue Angels

    Visitors Center, 3 Miles West of City, F9-5 "Blue Angels #1"

    Belle Chasse NAS - NATTC, A-7,   A-10,   AH-1,   F-15,   F-18,   P-3

Pinellas Park - Freedom Lake Park, 9990 46ᵗʰ St N, US 19, F-16

Polk City - Fantasy of Flight, 1400 Broadway Blvd SE, I-4, Exit 21 N to SR 559 E,
    33868-1200, (863) 984-3500, Fax 984-9506, Daily 9-5, Closed TD, CD,
    Adm Adult 13-59 $24.95, 60+ $22.95, Child 5-12 $13.95, Under 5 Free,
    Year Pass $59.95, Limited Time Simulator $3.25, Compass Rose Restaurant 8-4,
    Gift Shop, www.fantasyofflight.com,

A-1	Curtiss Pusher D	Morane Saulnier 230
A-20	DH 98	Neuport 17
A-24	E-1 Standard	Norde Stampe
A.V. Roe 504J	F4U-4	NYP
A6M5	Fi-156	P-35A
AN-2	FG-1D	P-39
AT-6D	FM-2	P-51C
B-17G	Ford 5-AT-34-B	P-63
B-24J	FW-44J	SBD
B-25	Gee Bee Model Z	Short Sunderland Mk.V
B-26	HOE-1	Spitfire Mk.XVI
Ba 349	J-1 Standard	SV-4C
Beech D-17S	J2F	TBM
Bell 47G	JN-4D	Thomas-Morse T4M
Bristol Bolingbroke	JU-52	Travel Air B-4000
BT-15	Ki-61	Trautman Road Air #1
Bu 133	L-1 (2ea)	Valkyrie Replica
Bu 181	L-4	Week Solution
Curtiss Jr CW-1	Lockheed Vega 5A/5C	Wright Flyer Replica

    Pompano Air Center, (305) 943-6050, PT-13 Model 75

Sanford - Orlando-Sanford Airport, (407) 688-1198, Contact: Maurice A Roundy, starliner@gwi.net
www.starliner.net, L-1649A Project

Vertical Aviation Technology, Inc, Sanford Orlando Airport,
1642 Hanger Rd, (407) 322-9488, Fax 330-2647, Owner: Brad Clark
Restores Sikorsky S-55 Helicopters, Kits for "Humming Bird" Helicopter

Shalimar - Air Force Armament Museum, 100 Museum Dr, Building 3201, Eglin AFB,
32542-5000, N30, 28.017; W86, 33.745, (850) 882-4062, Gift Shop 651-5253, Daily 9:30-4:30,
Closed TD, CD, ND, Theater, Gift Shop, = Inside,

A-10A	C-47A(AC)	F-84F	P-47N *
Apollo Module	F-104D(TF)	F-89J	P-51D-11 *
B-52G	F-16	F-4C	SR-71A
B-47N(RB)	F-15A	F-86D	T-33A
B-17G	F-4C(RF)	GAM-77/AGM-28C-131B	TM-76
B-57B	F-80-1D *	IM-99 Bomarc	UH-1H
B-25J	F-100C	Link Trainer	V-1
BQM-34A	F-111E	MGM-13A	
BQM-34F	F-105D *	MIG-21	
C-130(AC)	F-101C	O-2A	

St Augustine - St John's County Airport, US Hwy 1 N, (904) 824-1995,
Ernie Moser's Aero Sport

St. Petersburg - St Petersburg Historical & Flight One Museum, 335 Second Ave, 33701
(727) 894-1052, Mon 12-7, Tue-Sat 10-5, Sun 1-5, Closed TD, CD, ND, Adm Adult $7, Snr 64 $5,
Child 7-17 $3, Under 6 Free, Gift Shop, www.stpetemuseumofhistory.org,
Benoist Airboat 1914 Replica, Ford Flivver Replica

Starke - Camp Blanding Museums and Memorial Park, Off SR16 Front Gate, Daily 12-4, Free Adm
Gift Shop, A-6A, A-7, Bell 206, C-47, OH-13, UH-1 (2ea), M4 Tank, M60 Tank, Cannons

Tampa - McDill AFB, 56 CSG/CC, 33608-5000, (813) 830-1110, B-50J(KB)   F-4E   F-15

Titusville - Astronaut Hall of Fame, 6225 Vectorspace Blvd, 32780, (321) 269-6100,
www.spacewalkoffame.org, Mercury Space Capsule Space Shuttle Simulator

U.S. Space Camp, 6225 Vectorspace Blvd, 32780, (800) 637-7223, (321) 267-3184,
Space Camp for Grades 4-12 & Adult, One Week of: Space Training & Missions, From $300-875

Valiant Air Command Museum, Space Center Executive Airport, 6600 Tico Rd
32780-8009, (321) 268-1941, Fax 268-5969, Daily 10-6, Closed TD, CD, ND, Adm Adult $9.00
Mil/Snr/Child $8, 12 & Under Free, Gift Shop, Restoration Facility, www.vacwarbirds.org
F = Flyable, O = Outside, R = Restoration, P = Partial Aircraft, X = Periodic Display

A-6E	F-14A	Link Trainer	Super Sport
A-7A	F-84F Project	Me-208 (R)	T-2 (P)
AN-2 (X)	F-86F (P)	MiG-17 (O)	T-28D (F)(X)
AT-6(SNJ)(X)	F-101B-115-MC(D)	OV-1D (O)	
C-45 (X)	F-105D (O)	OV-1 Simulator	T-33A
C-47A (R)	F-106 Simulator	P-51 3/4 Scale	TBM-3E (R)
C-123 (X)	F4U-1 1/2 ScalePT-17 (X)		TM-61A
Epps 1907	(X)	Rutan VariviggenUH-1A (O)	
F-4J (O)	FM-1	S2F	UTVA-66 (F)
F-8K	HA 200A (X)	SM8Z (X)	2B13 Mult Eng Sim
F9F-5 (R)	L-4J		

Wauchula - Wauchula Municipal Airport, 33873, (863) 773-9300
POB 891, 33873, Adm Adult $2, Child $1, Sat 10-3

Aero Commander	Beechcraft 35	Grand Commander	PA-23
AG-CAT	C-45	HH-3F	UH-1H
Beech D18S	F-86L	Lake Buccaneer	Missiles

West Melbourne - Air America Foundation, 1589 S Wickham Rd, 32904, (321) 725-4043,
www.airamfoundation.org C-123K

Whiting - Naval Air Station, (904) 623-7011, HU-57, SNJ-5C, SNJ-6, T-34C

Zellwood - Bob White Airport, 7011 W Jones Ave, NE Orange County,
From US 436 Turn W on Jones Ave, Go 1 Mi, (407) 886-3180, Appt Only
J-3 (3ea)   RV6 Homebuilt   Smith Mini Plane Stearman (8ea)

Jim Kimball Enterprises, POB 849, 32798, Restores Old Aircraft
Builds Replicas, Call (407) 889-3451 For Current Project, By Appt Only

GEORGIA

Atlanta - Delta Air Transport Heritage Museum, (Still in Planning Stages), 1050 Delta Blvd
  Bldg B, Hartsfield Atlanta, Int'l Airport, Dept 914, 30354, Mail: POB 20585,
  30320-2585, (404) 714-2371, Fax 715-2078, Mon-Fri 8-5, Gift Shop, www.deltamuseum.org
  DC-3   L-1011 Ground Trainer   Travel Air S-6000B

  Fernbank Science Center, 156 Heaton Park Dr NE, 30307,
  (404) 378-4311, Mon-Fri 9-5, Free Adm, Apollo Space Capsule

Augusta - ATZH-DPM, Bldg 36305, 37th St, 2 Mi Inside Gate 5, Ft Gordon, 30905-5020,
  (706) 791-2818, 780-2818, Mon-Fri 8-4, Sat-Sun 12-5, CLosed ES, TD, CD, ND,
  Independencs Day, Free Adm,   USD-4   USD-5

Calhoun - Mercer Air Museum, Mercer Airfield, 411 Belwood Rd, 30701, (706) 629-7371,
  I-75 exit 312, Daily 8-5, Free Adm, 17 Aircraft from 1944
  A-7   F8U-1   MGM-13   T-33A
  Bechcraft 35   F-84F   L-17   U-8D
  C-47   F-86C   L-21
  DC-3   H-34 2ea   T-29

Cordele - Exit 32 of I-75 At Hwy 300,   Titan I

  Georgia Veterans Memorial State Park & Gen Courtney Hodges Museum, Rte 3,
  9 Mi W of City on US 280, Mail: Box 382, 31015, (229) 276-2371
  Museum Daily 8-4:30, Park Daily 7am-10pm, Free Adm,
  B-29   FJ4B   German Tank   Stewart Tank
  F-84F   T-33A   Patton Tank   LTV

Douglas - Brooks Aviation, 402 S Peterson Ave, Mail: POB 2770, 31533,
  (912) 384-7818, DC-3 (Flights Available)

  Liberty Foundation, POB 1273, 31534, (912) 384-1068, www.libertyfoundation.org
  AT-6,   B-17 (2ea),   C-47,   P-40E

Ft. Benning - Army Ft Benning National Infantry Museum, Baltzell Ave, 31905,
  (706) 687-3297,   CG-4A (Storage)   C-119

Griffin - Alexander Aeroplane Co, Spalding County Airport, 118 Huff Daland Cir,
  30223, (770) 228-3901, 800-831-2949, DC-3 (2 Hour Flights), T-33

  Atlanta Air Salvage, 1146 Uniform Rd, 30224, (770) 227-4042, Parts

  Curtiss Hawk Factory,   P-36   P-40E (2ea)   P-40K

  Low Pass Inc, 127 Airport Rd, 30224, (770) 228-5875, F9F-5

Hampton - Army Aviation Heritage Foundation, Clayton County Airport, Tara Field,
  506 Speedway Blvd, 30228, (770) 897-0444, Fax 897-0066, Appt Only, Pres: Mike Brady
  Membership: Skip Powell, email: skippowell@aol.com, www.armyav.org
  DH CV-2   L-4B   H-1H(UH)   OV-1B
  H-1(UH) Project   L-19B   Off Site   H-1M(UH)   T-42A
  H-13   Project   H-1G(AH)   H-1P(TAH)   U-21G
  H-23   Off Site   H-1B(UH)   OH-6A   U-8F Project

Kennesaw - Atlanta FAA ARTC, McCollum Airport, 30144, (770) 422-2500,   F-100C

Macon - Macon ANG, Cocran Field, 912-788-3423, F-86L

  VFW Post 6605, 1011 Corder Rd, 31088, T-33

Marietta - Cobb County Youth Museum, POB 78, 30061, (770) 427-2563,
  Mon-Sat 9-2, Free Adm, F-84F

  Dobbins AFB ANG, 14th AF, 94th TAW, 30069-5000, PA: (770) 421-5055,
  B-29   F-84F   F-105G
  F-4C   F-100D   OV-1

  Lockheed Plant, Dobbins AFB, Building L 22, F-22 ½ Scale Model

  NAS Atlanta, Dobbins AFB, 1000 Halsey Ave, Marietta, GA 30060-5099
  (678) 655-5055, http://www.nasatlanta.navy.mil/ A-6, A-7E, AT-11, E-2C, T-33

Peachtree City - CAF - Dixie Wing, 1200 Echo Ct, 30269, Falcon Field Airport,
  (678) 354-1110, Mon-Sat 9-4, Gift Shop, www.dixiewing.org,
  A-24, F-16, P-63, Rides Available in: C-45, P-51D, PT-26, SBD

Pooler - Mighty Eighth Air Force Heritage Museum, 175 Bourne Ave, I-95 & US 80
Exit 18, 31322, Mail: POB 1992, Savannah 31402-1992, (800) 421-9428, (912) 748-8888,
Fax 748-0209; Daily 9-5, Closed ED, TD, CD, ND, Adm Adult $10, Snrs $9, Child 12-6 $6,
Under 6 Free, Gift Shop; Canteen, Mission Experience Theater, WWII Flight Simulation,
www.mighty8thmuseum.com; email marketing@mightyeighth,org; O=Outdoors / Rest Inside

B-24 Cockpit	Bf-109 Replica	Me-163	PT-17	1/6th B-24
B-47 (O)	F-4C (O)	P-51 Replica	MiG-17	

Warner Robins AFB, Museum of Aviation 78ABW/MU, 1942 Heritage Blvd,
31098-2442 Hwy 41/129 South, (478) 926-6870, 926-4242, Mail: POB 2469, 310,
Gift Shop, I-75, Exit 126 East to Hwy 247, South 2 Mi, Daily 9-5,
Closed TD, CD, ND, Free Adm, www.museumofaviation.org , *=Hangar 01,
C=Century of Flight Building, E=Eagle Building, P=Project,

A-37A [C]	C-54G	F-105G	RB-69A	
AC-47	C-60A	F-106A	RF-101C	
AC-130 [E]	C-119B	F-111E [C]	SR-71A [C]	
Aeronca Champ 7AC	C-124C	HH-3E [C]	T-28A [*]	
AGM-136A [S]	C-103A	HH-19D [*]	T-33A	
AIM 4D-G [S]	C-141B	HH-34J	T-37B	
AIM 9J [S]	CH-3E	HH-43A [*]	T-39A [C]	
AIM-26A [S]	CH-21B [*]	HH-43F [C]	TG-4A [E]	
AIR-2A [S]	Chanute Glider [E]	HU-16B [C]	(Continued)	
AQM-34V [C]	D-21 Drone	KC-97L	TH-13M [P]	
AT-6G [*]	EC-121K [E]	L-19A/O-2A [*]	TM-61A	
AT-11	Epp's Monoplane	MGM-13A	U-2D [C]	
B-25J [C]	F-4C	MGM-107B	U-3B [C]	
B-26C	F-15A [E]	MiG-17	U-4B [C]	
B-29B-55 [C]	F-80C [*]	O-1E [*]	U-6A [C]	
B-52D	F-84E [E]	O-2A [*]	U-10D [C]	
B-66D(WB)	F-84F(RF)	OH-23C	UC-78 [P]	
Bae Mk.53	F-84F [*]	OH-50C	UC-123K	
Bensen X-25A	F-86H	P-40N	UH-IF [*]	
BQM-34F	F-89J	P-51D	UH-1P	
BT-13A [*]	F-100C	PT-17D [E]	UH-13P	
C-7A [C]	F-101F	PT-19A [*]	VC-140B [C]	
C-45G	F-102A	PT-22 [C]	X-25	
C-46A	F-104A	RB-57A	YCGM-121B	
C-47A	F-105D	RB-57F	YMC-130H	

Savannah - Savannah ANG, 165 TAG/MA, Savannah Int'l Airport, 31402, (912) 964-1941,

165th TAG	F-84D	F-86L

Savannah State College, 31404, (912) 356-2186, PR Office, 356-2191, A-4L

Sparta - Georgia State Military Academy, National Guard Academy Off Hwy 16 South

H-54D(CH)	OV-1D

Woodstock - Air Acres Museum, 376 Air Acres Way, 30188.

J-5 (3ea),	J-35,	L-17,	PT-17,	Luscombe 8E

Warbirds of America Sq 17, 455 Air Acres Way, 30188,(770) 928-9042,
All are Projects in Process, except (X = Pending)

B-25	Cessna 182	L-2M (2ea) (X)	PT-17
BobCat Kit	Cessna 180	Loehle Mustang	PT-17 (X)
C-45J(RC) (X)	AgCat Custom (X)	Pietenpol Aerial	Stinson 108-3

HAWAII

Maui

Kahului - Paper Airplane Museum, 70 E Kaahumanu Ave, Maui Mall, 96732, (808) 244-4667
(800) 297-4928, Daily 10-6, Free Adm, www.bcair.com/pam/museum/museum.htm, 2500 models

OAHU

Barbers Point - Hawaii Museum of Flying, Bldg 1792 Midway Rd, NAS Barbers Point,(808) 682-4041,
Appt Only, www.barberspointaviationmuseum.com, A-4E (3ea), F-4C, H-3H(UH), P-3A(UP)

Honolulu - Hickam AFB, 15 ABW PA, (808) 449-2490, Tours only Wed 10-11, * = Location
B-25J * Scott Circle   F-86E * O'Malley Blvd
RB-26C *Scott Circle   F-102A (2ea)* Bas Op, Vickers & O'Malley

Located on O'Malley Blvd, F-4C, F-15A, F-86E, MiG-15

Hawaiian ANG, F-4C, F-86E, F-86L, F-106

Hickman AFB Firefighting Unit, F-4C (2ea)

Pacific Aerospace Museum, Honolulu Int'l Airport, Departure Level - Main Terminal
96819, Mail: Box 7, (808) 839-0777, Mon-Sun 9-6, Shuttle Cockpit

Kaneohe - Kaneohe Bay MCAS Marine Base (North Shore) 96744,
CH-53D,   F-4S,   F-8J,   P-3,   P2V-5,   S2

Waikiki - Fort DeRussy Army Museum, AH-1S

Wheeler AFB, 96854-5000, (808) 422-0531, Main Gate, P-40 Mock-Up
AH-1S, OH-23G, OH-58A, UH-1H

IDAHO

Boise - Boise ANG, Gowen Field, 83707, (208) 385-5011, 124th TRG,   F-102A

Driggs - Teton Aviation Center. 675 Airport Rd, Off Hwy 33, Mail: POB 869, 83422
(800) 472-6382, (208) 354-3100, Fax 354-3200, Daily 8-5, Closed TD, CD, Free Adm
www.tetonaviation.com, E-Mail: tetonav@pdt.net,
All Aircraft Flyable, Glider Rides Available & Aviat Husky A-1 Rides
A-1 Aviat   L-39   SNJ-5
Blanik Glider   MiG-15   T2-B
HU-16   N3N   T-28

Idaho Falls - Idaho Falls Airport Administration, 83402, (208) 529-1221,   F-86

Mountain Home - Mountain Home AFB, 83648-5000, (208) 828-2111, F-84F, F-100C, F-111A(RF)

Nampa - Warhawk Air Museum, 201 Municipal Dr, Nampa Municipal Airport, 83687,
(208) 465-6446, Fax 465-6232, April 2-Oct 14, Tue-Fri 10-5, Sun 11-5,
Oct 15-April 1 Tue-Fri 10-4, Sat 10-5, Adm Adult $5, Age 65 & 4-9 $4
3 & Under Free, Gift Shop, Library, Restoration Facility, All Flyable
www.warhawkairmuseum.org, DR-1   P-40E   P-40N
P-51C (Project)   P-51D   YAK-3

Twin Falls - N W Warbirds Inc, POB 1945, 83303-1945, (208) 734-1941,
Twin Falls Airport, Mon-Fri 8-5, Manager: Rob Werner, N3N   TBM

CAF - Idaho Squadron, Joslin Field (208) 733-5215, Jerome Airport, 83338, 208-324-3650

ILLINOIS

Belleville - Scott AFB, 62225-5000, (618) 256-1110, C-45J, T-39A(CT), C-140(VC)

Bloomington - McLean County Historical Society, 200 N Main, 61701, (309) 827-0428, Tilbury Flash Racer

Prairie Aviation Museum, Bloomington-Normal Airport, 2929 E Empire St, 61701, Mail POB 856, 61702, (309) 663-7632, Tue-Sat 11-4, Sun 12-4, Adm Adult $2, Child 6-11 $1, Under 6 Free, Charles Lindbergh's De Havilland Remains of Mail Run Crash in the Area, DC-3 Rides $80, www.prairieaviationmuseum.org

A-7A	B-25	DC-3	T-38
AH-1J	Cessna 310B	T-33 (Project)	

Cahokia - Saint Louis University Parks College, 62206, (618) 337-7500, Mon-Fri 8-4:30,

AT-6	Cessna 320	QU 22	T-33	T-39A(CT)
Cessna 310	H-1(AH)	Short Skyvan	T-39	

Greater St Louis Air & Space museum, St Louis Downtown Airport (CPS), 2300 Vector Dr, 62206, (618) 332-3664, Mon-Sat 10-4, www.airandspacemuseum.org Meyers OTW, AV-8B(YAV)

Cary - Phoenix Restoration Group, Inc, 209 Cleveland, Unit E, 60013-2978 (847) 516-0141, Mon-Fri 8-5, Sat Appt, Restoring Weeks Air Museum Aircraft

Chicago - Butch O'Hare Memorial, Terminal 2, O'Hare Int'l Airport, 60607 General info: (773) 686-2200, F4F-3

CAF Great Lakes Wing,Gary Regional Airport, (708) 430-1590, www.greatlakeswing.org
C-47,   Ju 52

Midway Airport, 5700 S Cicero Ave, 60638-3831, 9 Mi SW of Chicago, GPI: N41-47.16;W087-45.15, (773) 838-0600, SBD-4

Museum of Science & Industry, 57th St & S Lake Shore Dr, 60637-2093, (773) 684-1414, Summer Daily 9:30-5:30, Winter Weekdays 9:30-4, Sat-Sun 9:30-5:30, Closed CD, Adm Adult $9, Snrs 65 $7.50, Child $5, Gift Shop, www.msichicago.org

Apollo 8	HH-3 (S-61)	Morane-Saulnier
Boeing B 40B-2 Mail	HH-52A	Spitfire Mk.1A
Boeing 727	JN-4D	Travel Air Mystery S
Brown B-1 Racer	JU-87B-2/Throp	U-505 Sub
Curtiss Pusher	Mercury Aurora 7	Pioneer Zephyr Train
F-104C	New York Central 999 Train	

Danville - Midwest Aviation Museum, Vermillion Co Airport, 22563 N Bowman Ave, Suite 1, 61834, (217) 431-2924, Appt Only,

AT-6G,	BT-13,	P-47D,	P-51F-6(Photo Recon),	T-6G	T-33A

Edgewood - Keeler-Adams American Legion Post, Hwy 57, (618) 238-4193, 5" Naval Gun

Elliott - Commanche Flyer Foundation, Inc, Gibson City Municipal Airport, RR1, 574 N 1000 E Rd, Box 31, 60936, (217) 749-2371, 749-8295 Piper Commanche 1959 World Flying Record, Owner: Schertz Richard 749-2293

Glenview - Von Maur - 1960 Tower Dr, 60023, (847) 724-4199, PT-17(N3N-3)

Great Lakes - Great Lakes Naval Training Center, Main Entrance at Buckley & Sheridan Rd   A-4

Harvard - Blackstone Aeroplane, Richard C. Hill, 23903 Graf Rd, PO BOX 328 60033, (815) 943-7205, Appt Only, Bird Biplane Projects (4ea)

T-50	E-2	J-2	PA-20	PA-22

Joliet - Replica Fighters Assoc, 2409 Cosmic Dr, 60435, 5/8 & 3/4 Scale Aircraft Thru The US consisting of the Following Squadrons: 999th Sq

DH 98	F8F	Hawker FB.11	P-38	P-51
F4U	Fw 190	Ju 87 Stuka	P-40	Spitfire
F6F	Hawker Tempest	Me-109	P-47	F-86

Kirkland - Kirkland (Harold Bunger) Airport, 4 Mi S of City, (815) 522-3367,
Baby Ace   Fleet

Lincoln - Heritage in Flight Museum, Logan County Airport, 1351 Airport Rd, 62656, (217) 732-3333, Sat-Sun 8-5, Weekdays By Appt, Free Adm, Donations Accepted, Housed in WWII German P.O.W. Barracks,

A-7E	F-4B	H-13T(TH)	L-17
C-45	H-1H(UH)	L-16	T-33A

Marengo - B-17E Restoration Project, Contact Mike & Ken Kellner, 21010 Anthony Rd, 60152,(815) 568-9464, B-17E (XC-108) S/N 41-2595

Marengo - Mascoutah Community Unit Museum, 1313 W Main St, 62258, (815) 566-8523, 8-3:30, Free Adm, Military, Artifacts

  Milford - Lions Club Sign on Route 1, JB-2 Buzz Bomb

  Paris - Heartland Antique Auto Museum, 1208 N Main, 61944, (217) 463-1834
    Lincoln Page LP3A, PT-22, Engines, Artillery, Antique Autos

  Peoria - Peoria ANG, Greater Peoria Airport, 61607, (309) 697-6400, F-84F

    Wheels of Time Museum, 11923 N Knoxville Ave, 61601, (309) 243-9020, Red Baron Replica

  Poplar Grove - Vintage Wings & Wheels Museum, 11619 Route 76, Mail: POB 236
    61065, (815) 547-3115, April-Oct Sat 10-2, www.poplargroveairmotive.com/Museum,
    Corben Baby Ace,

  Rantoul - Octave Chanute Aerospace Museum, Rantoul National Aviation Center, Frank Elliott
    Field, 1011 Pacesetter Dr, 61866-0949, (217) 893-1613, Fax: 892-5774, Mon-Sat 10-5,
    Sun 12-5, Closed: ND,ED,TD,CD, Adm Adult $7, Snrs 62 & Mil $6, 4-12 $4, Under 4 Free,
    Gift Shop, Ntn'l Balloon Races, First Week-end in Aug, www.aeromuseum.org

A-4F	C-47D(VC)	F-86A	ICBM Silo(3Sections)
A-7D	C-97G	F-100C	JN-4D Rep
Aeronca 65LB	C-121K(EC)	F-100D	LGM-30A Minuteman I
AGM-28	C-130A	F-101B	Mong Sport
American Eagle	C-133A	F-104A	O-2A
AT-6A	Cessna 120	F-105B	P-51H
B-25J	Chanute Glider Rep	F-105F	Ryan NYP Rep
B-47E(XB)	F-4C(RF)	F-111A	T-33A
B-52D Cockpit	F-15A	Foker DRI	T-38A(F-5B)
B-58A	F-84F	H-1B(UH)	T-39A(CT)
B-66B	F-84G	HU-16B	Wright Flyer Rep

  Rockford - Greater Rockford Airport, Midway Village & Museum, 60 Airport Dr
    61109, (815) 965-8635, SM-8   T-28

    Courtesy Aircraft, Inc, 5233 Falcon Rd, 61109-2991, (815) 229-5112
    Sells Replica Aircraft, www.courtesyaircraft.com

  Springfield - Air Combat Museum, 835 S Airport Dr, 62707, (217) 522-2181,
    Tue-Sat 10-6, Closed Major Holidays, Donations,

Aero Commander	F-86F	L-2M	Soko Galeb
Aero Star	F-4	P-51D	T-34
AT-11	F-84F	PT-22	All Aircraft Fly
Extra 300L	F4U-5		

    Springfield ANG, Capitol Airport, 62707, (217) 753-8850, 183rd TFG, F-4, F-84

    Army Reserve Center, 62708, (217) 785-3600, F-86F, Tank, M9 3" Gun

    Springfiled Airport Terminal, 3 Mi NW of City, (217) 788-1060, Pietenpohl Air Camper

  St Charles - St Charles Airport, (630) 377-4500, DC-3

  Sugar Grove - Air Classics Museum of Aviation, 43W636 Veterans Memorial Parkway
    Aurora Mncpl Airport, 60554, US 30, (630) 466-7000, Tue-Sun 10-3, By Appt
    Adm Adult $5, Snr $4, Child $3, Under 6 Free, www.airclassicsmuseum.org

A-4J(TA)	F-4	H-1H(UH) 2ea
A-7E	F-86F(RF)	T-33
DHC-2(U6-A)	F-105	T-39A

  Urbana - Frasca Air Museum, Illinois Airport, Frasca Field, 1402 E Ellini,
    61801, (217) 367-8441, Appointment Only

F4F	Luscombers	P-40E	Travelair	Waco

INDIANA
  Auburn - Auburn-Cord-Duesenburg Museum, 1600 S Wayne St, Mail POB 271,
    46706-3509, (260) 925-1444, Daily 9-6, Adm Adult $5, Snr & Child $3.50,
    Under 6 Free,   Stinson 1911

    Hoosier Air Museum, 2822 CR 62, SW Side of Airport, Mail: POB 87, 46706
    (260) 927-0443, Mon-Sat 10-4, Sun 1-4, Adm Adult $5, Child $3, Pres Niles Walton,
    www.hoosierairmuseum.org

C-45(AT-11)	Nieuport 24	7/10Pitts Frame	T-50 (UC-78)
H-1(AH)	Scale	Smith Mini Plane	V-77 (Gullwing)
J-3	P-51 7/10 Scale	Speedbird	WR-3
LNE-1			

    WWII Victory Museum, 5634 CR 11A, Mail: POB One, 46706, (260) 927-9144
    Mon-Sat 9-5, Sun 12-5, Closed TD, CD, NYD, Adm Adult $10, Vet $4, Snrs 55 $8,
    Child 7-12 $6, Under 6 Free, www.wwiivictory.org, 150 WWII Vehicles (American & German)
    P-51 7/10 Scale on Loan From Hoosier Warbirds, Auburn, IN

Bippus - Penn Aviation Company, 46713, (260) 344-1168, Dave Van Liere, AT-6D

Columbus - Atterbury-Bakalar Air Museum, 4742 Ray Boll Blvd, Columbus Mncpl
  Airport, 47203, (812) 372-4356, Tue-Fri 10-2, Sat 10-4, Donations Requested,
  www.atterburybakalarairmuseum.org; F-4,   CG-4A Nose Project

  VFW Post 7964, 120 E Main Cross St, 46124, (812) 526-2777, F-80, M1 Tank

  CAF Columbus Squadron, Municipal (812) 376-2519, 47201-9114,

  Rhoades Aviation Inc, Columbus Mncpl Airport, 47203, (812) 372-1819, Fax 378-2708
  Operations Manger: Jim Davis,   DC-3 (4 ea)

Covington - VFW Post 2395, Liberty St & 12th, T-33A

Crown Point - Crown Point Village, Owner Bill Thornberry, Westfield, IN, 46074, L-17B

Edinburg - Camp Atterbury Museum and Memorial Complex, US 31 2 Mi N of Exit 76 (I-65)
  Jan-March Wed & Sun 1-4, Sat 12-4, RoY Wed & Sun 1-5, Sat 12-5, Gift Shop,
  www.IndianaMilitary.org, H-1M(UH), Tanks: M4A1 (2ea), M41, M42, M47, M50, M60,

Elkhart - Northern Indiana Aviation Museum, 12264 County Rd 148, Ligonier, In 46767
  Pres Steve Hay, (574) 642-4961, email: wawaseeaircraft@skyenet.com, www.niam.org
  A-4J(TA)   NA-50   T-33A Project

  AM Post 233, 500 Memorial Dr, 46124, (812) 526-9001, Historian Peter Long, T-38

Fairmount - American Legion Post 313, 522 E 8th St, IN 26, 46928, (765) 948-4431
  F-4C   UH-1A   M60 Al Tank

Fort Wayne - Mercury, 4021 Air St, 46809, (260) 747-1565, Appt Only,
  Owner of Aircraft: Dean Cutshall, F-5A,   F-100F-16,   GNAT

  Lt Paul Baer Terminal Bldg, 2nd Floor, Ft Wayne Int'l Airport, 3421 Air St, Mail:
  POB 9573, 46899, (260) 478-7146, Daily 7-7, Free Adm, Smith Aeroplane, Artifacts
  www.fwairport.com/museum.html

  Indiana ANG, 122nd TFW, Baer Field, Ft Wayne Municipal Airport,
  46809-5000, (260) 478-3210, F-4   F-86   F-100

  Kloffenstein Furniture, 6314 Lima Rd (Hwy 3), (260) 627-2115, 3/4 Scale P-51

  Memorial Coliseum, 4000 Parnell Ave, (260) 482-9502,   F-84F

Green Castle - Court House Downtown, Fi 103A-1 Buzz Bomb

Hagerstown - Wilbur Wright Birthplace Museum, 1651N CR 750E, 47346,
  (765) 332-2495, Apr-Oct Mon-Sat 10-5, Sun 1-5, F-84F, Wright Flyer Rep

Hobart - Richard A Boyd, 5253 S Liverpool Rd, 46342, (219) 942-8692,   T-33

Indianapolis - CAF Indiana Wing, Indianapolis Terry Airport (TYQ), (Executive Airport),
  Montgomery Aviation hangar, (317) 769-4487, www.indianawingcaf.org, PT-26

  American Military Heritage Foundation, 1215 S Franklin, Post Air Hangar, Mon-Sat 9-5
  (317) 335-2889, www.amhf.org
  BT-13A,   PV-2,   SNJ-5B

  Ropkey Armor Museum, 6424 W 79th St, 46278, (317) 632-5446, 8-5, (317) 875-0141 After 5,
  Fred N Ropkey III,
  A-4B   O-1   PT-17   T-11
  DH100 MK.IIc   P2V-7   T-2   T-33B

  Paul King Air Museum, 2750 E 62nd St, 46220, (317) 259-7979, Artifacts

La Porte - Door Prairie Auto Museum, 2405 Indiana Ave, Mail: POB 1771, 46350
  (574) 326-1337, Fax: 326-1437, Tue-Sat 10-4:30, Sun 12-4:30, Adm Adult $5, 60+ $4,
  Child 10-18 $3, Under 10 Free, www.dpautomuseum.com/index.htm,
  Pietenpol Air Camper   Sonerai II

Mentone - Mentone Airport, 2 Mi SW of City (574) 353-7330, BT-13, T-50

  Lawrence D Bell Aircraft Museum, S Oak St, Mail: Box 411, 46539, US31 Exit N on
  SR25, (574) 353-7296, June 1- Oct 1, Sun 1-5pm, Adult $1, www.bellaircraftmuseum.com,
  AH-1,   OH-13,   UH-1H,   UH-12,   Artifacts from Lawrence Bell

Mitchell - Spring Mill State Park, 812-849-4129, Grissom Gemini Capsule

Muncie - Academy of Model Aeronautics / National Model Aviation Museum,
5151 E Memorial Dr, 47302, (765) 289-4236, Mon-Fri 8-4:30, Sat-Sun 10-4,
Closed Sun TD thru ED, Adm Adult & Child 7-17 $2, Child Under 7 Free,
Gift Shop, www.modelaircraft.org   Displays Model Airplanes

Peru - Grissom Air Museum, 1000 W Hoosier Blvd, 46970-3647, US 31, (765) 689-8011,
Fax 688-2956, Indoor Displays Tue-Sun 10-4, Closed Mid Dec-Mid Feb;
Outdoors Daily 7-Dusk, Closed Holidays, Adm Adult $, Snrs & Child 7-18 $3,
Under 7 Free, Gift Shop, www.grissomairmuseum.com

A-10A	C-47D	F-89 Project	T-41
B-17G	C-97L(KC)	F-100C	T-33A Project
B-25J	C-119G	F-101B	U-3(A)
B-47D	C-135L(EC)	H-1(UH)	YS-11
B-58A(TB)	F-4C	F-105D	
C-1	F-11F	O-2A	

Portland - Museum of the Soldier, 510 East Arch St, Mail: PO Box 518, 47371, (260) 726-2967
April-Nov 1st & 3rd Sat & Sun each Month, Adm Adult $2, Student & Snrs $1, Under 10 Free
Jeep, M-37 Truck

Richmond - Wayne County Historical Museum, 1150 N, A St, 47374, (765) 962-5756, Davis Aircraft 1929

Sellersburg - Clark County Airport, (JVY), 7001 Airport Rd, Sellersburg, IN 47172,
N38-21.93; W085-44.29, (812) 246-7460, FG-1D, FJ-1, P-51, P-51D

Seymour - Freeman Army Air Field Museum, 1040 A Ave, Freeman Mncpl Airport,
Mail: POB 702, 47274, (812) 522-2031, US 50 go S on S Airport Rd(1st Ave).
www.indianamilitary.org   Parts from WWII Enemy Aircraft Stored There

South Bend - Jeep Acres - Contact: Charles R Dadlow 29430 SR2, 46624,
(574) 654-8649, HRP-3

Military Honor Park, South Bend Regional Airport, P-80(T-33), UH-1, M-60 Tank,
M-42 Tank, 155 Howitzer, Mk 14 Torpedo, 3" Guns, 2½ Ton Truck

Terre Haute - Terre Haute ANG, Hulman Regional Airport, 47803, (812) 877-5210,

F-4C	F-84F	F-100D

Valparaiso - Indiana Aviation Museum, Porter County Municipal, 4601 Murvihill Rd,
46383, (219) 548-3123, May-Oct Sat 10-4, Sun 1-4, Adm Adult $5, Snrs $4,
Child Under 12 Free, www.in-am.org

AT-6G	P-51D	T-28B
F4U-5N	T-28B	T-34B
L-2	PT-17	T-37A(AT)

Vincennes - Indiana Military Museum, 4305 Bruceville Rd, 2.8 Miles E of
Holiday Inn, 47591, (812) 882-8668, 882-4002, Mail: POB 977, Adm Adult $2,
Child 1-18 $1, Outdoors Daily 8-5, Indoors Daily 12-4,
Winter Sat-Sun 12-5, Weekdays by appointment,

C-47 Nose	1/2 Track	M3A1 Tank	M5A1 Tank
H-1(UH)	German PAK 40 Gun	M4A1E8 Tank	M-114

IOWA

Altoona - Sam Wise Youth Camp, Veterans Memorial, 8th St, A-7D

Ankeny - CAF - Hawkeye State Squadron, T-28A

Des Moines - Iowa State Historical Society, 600 E Locust, 50319, (515) 281-5111,
Tue-Sat 9-4:30, Sun 12-4:30, Free Adm,

Bleriot XI,	Curtiss Pusher	Quickie	Solbrig

Iowa National Guard, Beaver Dr, 50318, (515) 252-4236,

A-7	F-84	H-1(AH)	H-1(UH)	6 Tanks	7 Cannons

Ft. Dodge - Ft Dodge IA ANG, 133 TCF/CC, 50501, (515) 573-4311, 3611, F-84F

Greenfield - Iowa Aviation Museum, 2251 Airport Rd, Greenfield Mncpl Airport,
Mail: POB 31, 50849-0031, (641) 343-7184, Mon-Fri 10-5, Sun 1-5,
Oct 1-April 30 Sat 1-5, May 1-Sept 30 Sat 10-5, Closed E, TD, CE, CD, ND,
Adm Adult $3, Sr $2.50, Child 5-12 $1.50, Under 4 Free, www.flyingmuseum.com

A-7	DH 82C Canadian	Mead Primary Glider
AH-1	DH-87A	Northrup Primary Glider
Aetna-Timm #4	Easy Riser Glider	Schweitzer Secondary Glider
Curtiss Robin #6	J-2	Taylorcraft BC12
DH 82C Australian	J-3	

Grimes - Grimes ANG, Des Moines Municipal Airport, 50321, (515) 285-7182, F-84F

Grinnell - Grinnell Airport, (641) 236-8007, Artifacts

Ida Grove - Cobb Memorial Park, Hwy 59/175, AH-1, RF-84F

Indianola - US National Balloon Museum, 1601 N Jefferson St, Box 149, 50125,
(515) 961-3714, May-Dec Mon-Fri 9-4, Sat 10-4, Sun 1-4, Feb-April Mon-Sat 10-2,
Sun 1-4, Adm Adult $2, Gift Shop, Library, Theater, www.nationalballoonmuseum.com;
Helium/Hot Air Balloons: 1976 "Union Jack", 19770 "Fly On", "Serena's Song" Gondola

Johnston - Camp Dodge (HQ Iowa National Guard), NW Beaver Dr, Main Gate, A-7D, 2 Tanks

Marshalltown - Central IOWA All Veterans Memorial, American Legion
Post 46, 1301 S 6th St, (641) 752-0544, F-4C

Ottumwa - Airpower Museum, 22001 Bluegrass Rd, Antique Airfield, Route 2, Box 172,
52501-8569, (641) 938-2773, Mon-Fri 9-5, Sat 10-5, Sun 1-5, www.aaa-apm.org

Aeronca K	Culver LCA Cadet(LFA)	Nesmith Cougar
Aeronca C-2	Culver Cadet PQ-14B	Pietenpohl Sky Scout
Aeronca C-3	DSA-1 Smith Miniplane	PT-22 Ryan Recruit
Aeronca 65CA	Fairchild 22	Rearwind Cloudster
Aeronca LA65	Fairchild 71	Rearwind Skyranger 190F
Aeronca 65TC	Fleet 7	Rearwind Sportster
Aeronca 7AC	Funk Model B	Ritz Ultrlight
Aeronca 11AC	Great Lakes 2T-1A	Rose Parakeet A-1
AmEagle Eaglet	Kinner Sportster	Ryan STA
Anderson Z	L-4	Stinson S Junior
Arrow F Sport	LH-2	Stinson 10
Backstrom Plank	Luscombe 8F	Taylo-Young A
BD-5	Monocoupe 90	VJ-23
Bolkow Bo 208A-1 Jr	Monoprep	VP-1 Evans Volksplane
Brewster B-1	Mooney M-18 Mite	Welch QW-8
CP-40 Porterfield	Morrisey Bravo	

Indian Hills Community College, 60 Aviation Program Center, 52501, (641) 683-5111
www.ihcc.cc.ia.us

C-45	Cessna 421	Piper Aztec
Cessna 150	F-84	T-39
Cessna 172	H-1H(UH)	
Cessna 310	PA-22	

Sioux City - Mid America Air Museum, Sioux Gateway Airport, 6715 Harbor Dr,
Mail: POB 3525, 51102, (712) 252-5300, Tue-Sun 9-5, Closed TD, CD, ND, ED, Adm Adult $3,
Child 6-18 $1, Group Rates Available, Gift Shop, www.matamuseum.com

A-6A	Glider	T-18
A-7D	H-1B(UH)	T-33
Beech B80 Queen Air	Hawker-Siddeley Argosy	Ultralight Snoopy's BobCat
CallAir Spray Plane	KR-2	
F-84F	Ornithopter	

Sioux City ANG, Sioux City Mun Airport, 51110, (712) 255-3511,

A-7D	F-84F	F-100c
A-7K	F-84F Photo Recon	T-33

St Maries - David Freeman, Nicholas-Beazley Racer NR-1W

KANSAS

Ashland - Pioneer Krier Museum, 430 W 4th Hwy 160, N of Route 160, 67831,
(620) 635-2227, Summer Daily 1-5, Winter Daily 1-4, Free Adm,
Krier Kraft, DHC 1, Great Lakes Special

Hutchinson - Kansas Cosmosphere Museum, 1100 N Plum, 67501, 800-397-0330,
(620) 662-2305, Mon-Thur 9-6, Fri-Sat 9-9, Sun 12-6, Adm Adult $8, Age 60+
Child 5-12 $7.50, Child under 5 Free, For Museum/OMNIMAX/Planetarium
Adults $12.50, Snrs 60 $11.50, Child 5-12 $10, Under 5 Free, Gift Shop,
Cafe, Astronaut Training Programs, www.cosmo.org

Apollo 13	Lunar Lander	V-2 Flying Bomb	SR-71
Gemini	Lunar Rover	V-1 Rocket	T-38
Mercury 7	F-1 Saturn V Engine	F-104B	

Liberal - Mid-America Air Museum, 2000 W 2nd St, POB 2199, 67905-2199, (620) 624-5263,
Mon-Fri 8-5, Sat 10-5, Sun 1-5, Closed: TD, CD, ND, Adult $5, Snr(62+) $4, Child $2 (6-18)
Under 6 Free, Gift Shop, Restoration Facility, www.liberalairmuseum.com,

A-4L	B-25J	Cessna 140	Ercoupe 415C
A-7E	Baby Great Lakes	Cessna 145	F-4D
Aero Commander	Beech 35	Cessna 165	F-8U-2N
Aeronca 65C	Beech 150	Cessna 175	F-14A
Aeronca 65TC	Beech D17S	Cessna 195	F-80C
Aeronca K	Bellanca 190	Cessna 337	F-86H
Aeronca 7AC/L-16	BT-13A	Culver V	F-104C
Aeronaut	Bushby Mustang	CW-1 Jr	F-105
Avid Flyer	C-45	D-16	F4U-5
AT-19(V-77)	Cessna 120	Dragonfly	(Continued Next Page)

(From Previous Page)

L-2	OQ-19	Rearwin 8135T
Fairchild 24-C8F	L-3B	OV-10	Rearwin Skyranger
Fly Baby	L-5	PA-22	RLU-1 Breezy
Funk B-75	L-6	PA-23	Rutan Vari-Eze
Globe Swift GC-1B	L-9	PA-23-250	S2F-1
H-1S(AH)	L-17	PA-24	SA 102-5
H-1B(UH)	LB-5	Phoenix Glider	Shober Willie II
H-13	Luscombe 8	Pietenpol B4A	Skybolt
Hawker Siddley Gnat	Luscombe 8A	Pober Pixie P-9	T-18
HUP-3	Miller Fly Rod	PT-19A	T-28A
J-2	Moni Motor Glider	PT-22	T-37(XT)
J-3C	Mooney M.18C Mite	PT-23	T-38
J-4F	Nieuport 11	Rally 3	T-50D
KR-1	NW Porterfield	Quail 1969 Crop	TBM-3R
Koala II	OH-6	Rearwin 7000	X-28

KANSAS (Continued)

Newton - Blockbuster Video Store, 1411 N Main St, 67114, (620) 283-7086,
Tail of Aircraft Sticking Out of Front of Building.

Olathe - Old Olathe Naval Air Museum, 1 Navy Park Dr, (913) 768-1153
Mail: POB 1942, New Century Air Center, KS 66031,

A-4D	A-7D (2ea)	1930 Bi-Plane

New Century - CAF Heart of America Wing, #3 Aero Plaza, 66031, (913) 397-6376, Mail:
15011 West 147th St, Olathe, KS 66062, www.kcghostsquadron.org

AT-6	L-2 2ea	MiG-17	PT-19 2ea
BT-13 3ea	L-39	PT-17	T-28
F4F-3			

Topeka

Air Guard, 190th ARW, Forbes Field, 66619-5000, B-57, Helicopters, Tanks

American Flight Museum, Spooky Squadron, Hangar 603, Forbes Field, 66605,
Mail: 3624 SW 30th Terrace 66614, (785) 862-1234, www.squadron14.com, C-47(AC)   O-2

Combat Air Museum, Forbes Field, Hangar 602-604, J St, Mail POB
19142, 66619-0142, (785) 862-3303, Fax 862-3304, Mon-Sat 9-4:30, Sun 12-4:30,
Closed: ES, TD, CD, ND, Adm Adult $6, Snrs $5, Child 6-17 & Military $4
Under 6 Free, E-mail camtopeka@aol.com, www.combatairmuseum.org/
Hangar 602 = 2; Hangar 604 = 4; Outside Display = O,

A-4J(TA)	2	F-86H	4	H-1M(UH)	4	Nike Ajax	O
AT-6 Harvard Mk IV	2	F-105D	4	H-1B(UH)	O	O-47B	2
Bf-109 Rep Disa	4	F-101B	4	Honest John	O	RU-8D	4
BT-13 Disa	4	F11F-1	2	Little John	4	S-2A(US)	4
C-47D (2ea)	4	F3D	4	JN-4D	2	SNB-5	4
C-121T(EC)	O	F9F-5 Disa	4	Meyers OTW	2	T-28B	4
C-61K(UC)	4	H-53A(NCH)	4	MiG-15	2	Tartar Navy Missile	
Corporal M2 Missile	O	H-54(CH)	4	MiG-17	4		
F-84F (2 ea)	4,0	H-1H(UH)	2	Nike Tartar	2		

Kansas Museum of History, 6425 SW 6th St, 66615-1099, (785) 272-8681,
Mon-Sat 9-4:30, Sun 12:30-4:30, Free Adm,

Curtiss Pusher	Experimental Helicopter

Museum of Kansas Army National Guard, Forbes Field, 6700 S Topeka Blvd, 66619, (785) 862-1020,
Tue-Sat 10-4, Theater, F-16 Model ½ Scale

H-1(AH)	H-1(UH)	H-6(OH)	H-54(CH)	H-58(OH)

Wichita - Kansas Aviation Museum, 3350 George Washington Blvd, 67210, (316) 683-9242,
Fax: 683-0573, Tue-Fri 9-4, Sat 1-5, Closed ES, TD, CD, Adm Adult $5, Child 6-11 $1,
Under 6 Free, www.kansasaviationmuseum.org,

American Eagle	Funk	Prescott Pusher	T-33
B-52D	Jayhawk	O-2B	T-37
Beech 73 Mentor	Laird Swallow	Rans Ultralight	TV-2
BD-5	Lear 23	Sonerai	U-8
Cessna 206	Mooney Mite	Stearman Ariel	
Cessna 310	NS-1	Stearman 4D	
F-84F	Poude Ceil	Swallow	

Kansas & Historical Air, McConnell AFB, 184th TFG, 2801 S Rock Rd, 672221-6225,
(316) 652-3141, Historic Property Custodian: Jerry L Ferguson, MSTG

F-4D	F-84C	F-100C	F-105F
F-80C	F-86L-LO	F-105D	T-33A-5-LO

Aviation Education Center, 2021 S Eisenhower, (316) 833-3595, F-86

CAF Jayhawk Wing, 2558B S Kessler, Westport Airport, 67217, (316) 943-5510,
2nd Mon ea Month 7:30pm, www.cafjayhawks.org, Member Aircraft = *, Rides = R

C-45 (*),	PT-22 (*),	C-78(UC)(R),	PT-23 (R)

KENTUCKY

Fort Campbell - Don F Pratt Memorial Museum, Bldg 5702 Tennessee Ave, 42223-5335,
(720) 798-4986 or 3215, Mail: Att: AFZB-IT-M, Mon-Sat 9:30-4:30, Free Adm,
www.campbell.army.mil/pratt/index.htm

A-10	C-47	C-119	CG-4A	H-1(UH)	H-56(AH)

Fort Knox - Patton Museum of Calvary & Armor, POB 208, 40121,
(502) 624-3812, Daily 9-5, Free Adm, Registrar: C Lemon,

H-1B(UH)(2ea)	H-1G(AH)	H-13E(OH)	H-23B(OH)	L-19A

Frankfort - Boone National Guard Center, 40601, (502) 564-8464,

F-84F	F-101C(RF)

Lexington - Aviation Museum of Kentucky, Blue Grass Airport, Hangar Dr, Off
US 60 Right off Airport Rd, Mail: POB 4118, 40544, (859) 231-1219, Gift Shop
Library, Tue-Sat 10-5, Sun 1-5, Adm Adult $5, Seniors $4, Students 6-16 $3, Under 6 Free
www.aviationky.org/

A-4L	H-58A(OH)	LNE-1	Travel Air D4D
Aeronca Model K	Heath Center Wing	Nimbus II Glider	Youngsters Sim
Cessna 150	L-4B	Pulsar Ultralight	
Crosley Moonbeam	L-10 Electra	Sellers Quadraplane	
F-4S	Link Trainer	T-38B(AT)	

Louisville - Bowman Field, 5 Mi SE of City, (502) 368-6524, AT-6, DC-3/C-47 Flights

Louisville ANG, Standford Field, 40213, (502) 364-9400, F-4C(RF), F-101H(RF)

Museum of History & Science, 727 W Main St, 40202, (502) 561-6100,
Daily 10-5, Adm Adult $5.00, Child 2-12 $4.00,

Apollo XIII,	Gemini Trainer
Bushbee Mustang I,	Sellers Quadraplane Rep,

Middlesboro - Lost Squadron, Bell County Airport, 1420 Dorchester, 40965, (606) 248-1149,
Daily 8-5, Gift Shop, Restoration Facility, www.thelostsquadron.com,
E-mail: mrp38@eastky.net, P-38, F-86 M-60 Tank

LOUISIANA

Alexandria - England AFB, Flying Tiger Heritage Park, 23TFW/PA, 71311-5004,
(318) 448-2401, 1406 Van Gossen Ave 448-1083 Or 3908 Coliseum Blvd 448-0701,
A Sponsor or Escort & Public Affairs Office Is Required To Visit Museum,

A-7D	A-10	F-84F	F-86E	F-105G

Baton Rouge - USS Kidd & Nautical Center, 305 S River Rd, 70802-6220, (225) 342-1942
Daily 9-5, Closed TD, CD, Adm Adult $4, Sr $3, 6-12 $2.50,

A-7E	P-40E Rep	USS KIDD (Camping aboard available groups of 20)

Bossier City - Barksdale AFB, 8th AF Museum, 71110, (318) 456-3065, North
Entrance, POB 10, Daily 9:30-4, Closed TD, CD, ND, Gift Shop

B-17G	Sled	BeechF-84F	SR-71
B-24J	18	F-111(FB)	T-33
B-29	C-47A	MiG-21	Vulcan B Mk.2
B-47E	C-97L(KC)	P-51D	
B-58A	Rocket		

Many - VFW Post 4858, 1738 San Antonio Ave, 71449, (318) 256-2143, M4 Sherman Tank

Monroe - Aviation Historical Museum of Louisiana, 701 Kansas Lane, Monroe Regional Airport
Mail: POB 13113, 71213, (318) 361-9020, Sat 9-5, Sun 1-5,www.airhistory.org, Artifacts

New Orleans - D Day Museum, 945 Magazine St, 70130, (504) 527-6012, Daily 9-5,
Adm Adult $14, Snrs 65 & Student $8, Military & Child 5-12 $6, Under 5 Free,
www.ddaymuseum.org, L-5, Spitfire Mk.VI, TBM, Higgins LCVP Boat, M4A3 Tank, M3 Half Track

New Orleans Naval Air Station, Alvin Callender Field, 70143,
(504) 394-2818, 159th TFG, F-86D F-100D F-102A(YF)

New Orleans - Friends of Jackson Barracks Military Museum, Jackson Barracks, Bldg 53,
70146-0330, (504) 278-8241, Mon-Fri 7:30-4:00, Free Adm,
www.122nd.com, e-mail jbmuseum@cmq.com, R-2800 Engine

A-4C	F-4C	F-102(YF)	OH-58A
A-26	F-15A	H-1(AH)	T-33A
AT-11	F-86D	H-1(UH)	
Cessna 172	F-100D	H-23	

Patterson - Wedell-Williams Memorial Aviation Museum, 394 Airport Circle, Off
IA 182 Hwy, Mail: POB 655, 70392, (985) 395-7067, Tue-Sat 10-4, Adm Adult $3
Snrs & Mil $2, Child Under 12 Free, http://lsm.crt.state.la.us/site/visitor.htm

Aero Commander 680	Farley Vincennt-Starflight	Stearman	
Beech D17S Replica	P-47 (½ Scale)		Wedell-Williams Racer 44
Bf 109 (½ Scale)	PT-17		

LOUISIANA (Continued)

Reserve - American Military Heritage Foundation Museum, St John Baptist
Airport, 355 Airport Rd, 70084, (985) 536-1999

A-4	AT-6G (2ea)	H-6(OH)
A-7E	C-45	T-28 (2ea)

Ruston - LA Tech Univ ROTC, Det 305, (318) 257-4937, Col: Stamm,

T-33A	ICBM	Minuteman 1

MAINE

Auburn - US Airline Industry Museum, Starliner Base, Lewiston-Auburn Airport,
1649 Constellation Dr, 04210, (207) 770-7077, By Appt Only,
Contact: Maurice A Roundy, www.starliner.net, L-1649A (2ea)

Bangor - Bangor ANG, 04401-4393, (207) 947-0571, 101st ARW, F-101B(CF)

Maine Air Museum (Maine Aviation Historical Society), Waterville Airport, Next To The
Civil Air Patrol Headquarters, 04901, Mail: POB 2641, 04402, (207) 941-6757,
800-280-MAHS In State, Closed Winter, www.maineairmuseum.org, email: townsend@acadia.net

EAA Balloon	P2V-3	F-89J	Bo-Mark Silo
Luscuming 8A	Stinson 10A	P-3 Possibly	

Brunswick - Naval Air Station Brunswick, 010 Bath Rd, 04011-0010,
(207) 921-1110, P-3A P2V-5

Owls Head - Owls Head Transportation Museum, Box 277, Knox County Airport
Route 73, 04854, (207) 594-4418, Fax 594-4410, April-Oct Daily 10-5, Nov-March
Daily 10-4, Closed CD, ND, Adm Adult $7, Snrs 65 $6, Child 12-17 $7, 5-11 $7,
Child Under 5 Free, Family $18, www.ohtm.org,

Antoinette	Etrich Taube	Nieuport 28
Bellanca	FE8	Penaud Planaphore
Bleriot XI	Fokker C.IVa	S.E.5a
Burgess-Wright F	Fokker DR.I	Sopwith Pup
Cayley Glider	Henri Farman III	Spad XIIIc.1
Chanute Glider	J-1	Stearman A75N/1
Clark Bi Wing	J-3C	Waco UBF-2
Curtiss Pusher D	JN-4D	Wright B Flyer
Damenjoz	Lilienthal Glider	
Deperdussin	Milliken Special	

Presque Isle - Presque Isle Air Museum, 650 Airport Dr, Suite 10, 04769-2088, (207) 764-2542
http://welcome.to/piairmuseum, email: piairmuseum@femail.com Artifacts

MARYLAND

Aberdeen - Aberdeen Proving Ground, 21005-5201, (410) 278-3602, 2396, 7472,
End of State Route 22, Mon 12-4, Tue-Sun 10-4, Closed Holidays, Free Adm,
Gift Shop , www.ordmusfound.org, 225 Items of a 25 Acre Tank & Artillery Park,
Some Examples: FZG-76, Rheintocher, V-2, Mk IV Tank

Andrews AFB, 89th Airlift Wing/PA (MAC), 20331-5000, (301) 981-9111,
Open House May 22-23, F6F, F-4, F-105D, F-106, H-1B(UH)

Annapolis - US Naval Academy Museum, 118 Maryland Ave, 21402-5034,
(410) 293-2108, Mon-Sat 9-5, Sun 11-5, Closed TD, CD, ND, Free Adm,
www.nadn.navy.mil/Museum A-4A F4F

Baltimore - Baltimore ANG, GL Martin Airfield, 212220-2899, (410) 687-6270,
F-86H HU-16B XF2Y-1

Baltimore Museum of Industry, 1415 Key Hwy, 21202, (410) 727-4808,
Martin 162A PBM-1 2/3 Scale

Beltsville - Naval Reserve Center, 2600 Powdermill Rd, (301) 394-3966, Missle

Cambridge - Cambridge Airport, (410) 228-4571, UC-78CE

College Park - College Park Aviation Museum, 1985 Corporal Frank Scott Dr, 20740,
(301) 864-6029, Fax 927-6472, Daily 10-5, Closed Holidays, Adm Adult $4, Snrs $3,
Child $2, Annual AirFair Sept, www.avialantic.com/collpark.html

Berliner 1924 Helio	J-2	PT-17
Bleriot XI	JN-4D	Taylorcraft
Ercoupe 1946	Monocoupe 110	Wright B Aeroplane

Ft Meade - National Vigilance Park, East Off of I-95 on Route 32, Left on Colony 7
Rd After Passing Baltimore-Washington Parkway (Rt295), C-130A RU-8D(L-23D)

Quest Masters, Box 131, 20755, http://www.geocities.com/quest_masters,
email: questmasters@bigfoot.com, All Projects in Storage, By Appt Only

B-24J Nose LNE-1 Cockpit	P-61B Nose	UC-45F Cockpit
B-24L Fuse SNJ-5B	TBM-1C (Firewall to Radio compartment)	

MARYLAND (Continued)

Frederick - CAF - Stars & Stripes Wing, 140 W Patrick St, 21702, (301) 631-5357, TBM-3E

Ellicott City - VFW 7472, 86-J Falls Run Rd, 21043, F-86H

Glenburnie - VFW 160, Glen Burnie Col Harry L Cooper Post, Jet

Hagerstown - Washington County Regional Airport, Rt 12, Box 62, Off Rt 11 & I-81, Dave Rider (301) 791-6231, AT-6   DC-3   J-2

Lexington Park - Patuxent River Naval Air Museum, Pegg Rd & Route 235 Mail: POB 407, 20670-0407, (301) 863-7418, Tue-Sat 10-5, Sun 10-4, Closed ED, TD, CD, Free Adm, Gift Shop, www.paxmuseum.com

A-4M	F4J	H-1J(AH)2ea	T-39D
A-6E	F4 Cockpit	H-53A(CH)	TH-1L
A-7A	F-6A(F4D-1)	RA-5C	
AV-8B	F-14A 2ea	S-2	
E-2B	F/A-18A	SH-2G	

Massey - Massey Air Museum, 33541 Maryland Line Rd, 21650, (410) 928-5270
Tue-Sat 10-4, Adm Adult $5, Restoration Facility, www.masseyaero.org,

Aeronca Champ	J-3C	Sea Rey
Bailey-Moyes Dragonfly	Kolb Fire Star	Slip Stream Genesis
Bailey-Moyes Tempest	Kolbfull Lotus	Slip Stream Revelation
Bell 47G	PA-15	Smith Miniplane
Bu 133	PA-22/20	Super Drifter
Buccanner II	PT-17	V-77
Cessna C150	Quicksilver	

Middle River - Glenn L Martin Aviation Museum, 701 Wilson Point Rd, 21220, Martin State Airport, Mail: POB 5024, 21220, (410) 682-6122, Wed-Sat 11-3, Closed Holidays, Free Adm, Gift Shop, www.marylandaviationmuseum.org, * = Storage

A7D	* F9F	* F-101F	* P6M Fuse/Tail	TA-4J
B-57A(RB) 2ea	F-84F(RF)	* F-105G	T-33	
F-4	F-100F 2ea	Martin 4-0-4	P&W R2800	

Suitland - Paul E Garber Facility, (Closed to Public), 3904 Old Silver Hill Rd, 20746, (202) 357-1552, www.nasm.si.edu/museum/garber, All Aircraft to Be Sent to Udvar-Hazy Center in Next 7 Years. Building Number (2, 3, 6, 7, 9, 22) = Storage

Building Number		Building Number		Building Number	
23	A-26(VB)	23	Cessna 180	24	Hiller 1031
22	A-1H	22	Convair 240	07	HJD-1(XHJD)
21	Abrams Explorer	22	Crowley Hydro-Air	?	HMM 163
23	Akerman Tailess	22	Curtiss E Boat Fuse	22	HRP-1(XHRP)
20	AN-2	22	CW 1 Junior	23	HV-2A
22	Ar 196A	23	CW X-100	03	Icarus I
20	Arlington Sisu 1A	23	DH 98 Mk.35	23	Ilyushin IL-2m3
22	B-43 (XB)	24	Daedalus 88	21	J-1
22	B-42A(XB)	23	de Bothezat	22	J-2A
22	B-17D	20	DO 335	23	J-29
0D	B-17G	23	DQ-2A/TDD-1	21	J1N1-S
0D	B-25J(TB-25M)	24	DQ-14	07	J7W1
0D	B-57B(EB)	22	DSI/NASA RPRV	?	JB-2 Loon
24	B-58 Escape Capsule	09	Eberhart Target	21	JC-1
22	B6N2	20	Erco 415	20	JN-4D
22	B7A1	23	Extra 260	23	JRS-1(S-43)
20	Bachem Ba 349	22	F-4A	20	Ju-388L
24	BB-1	23	F-101C(RF)	21	Kasperwing 180B
22	Beechcraft D18S	24	F-100	20	Ki-46
23	Beechcraft 35	22	F-100D	07	Ki-115
20	Bell 206	23	F-5L	20	Laird LCDW 500Fus
07	Bell Rocket Belt	D	F-8G(RF)	07	Lippisch DM-1
23	Bell ATV VTOL	22	F-105D	21	M.18C
23	Bellanca 14-13	23	F9F-6	24	Martin, JV, K-III
24	Bellanca C.F.	22	FA-3-101	07	Maupin-Lanteri
23	Bensen B-6	21	Farman Sport	22	Me 410A-3
24	Bensen B-8M	10	FE-8	22	Moni Motor Glider
22	Berliner Helicopter	20	Fi 156	02	MX7Y-K2
23	Bertelsen Aeromobile	24	Fowler-Gage	22	N1K2-J
21	Bu 181	07	Fw Ta-152H	22	Nakajima Kikka
07	Burgess-Curtis	20	G4M3 Nose	23	NASA Parasev
22	BV-155B	22	Go 229	10	Nieuport 28C-1
07	C-8	0D	Goodyear K-Car	23	O-2
07	C-64(YC)	22	Goodyear Gondola	22	O-47A(RO)
0D	C-121	23	H-34D(UH)	23	O-1A(L-19)
23	C-35(XC)	23	H-1H(UH)	06	Olmstead Pusher
20	C-2	22	HA-200B	23	P-39Q
0D	C-130	07	He 219A	23	P-55(XP)
24	C-97L(KC) Cockpit	20	He 162A	22	P-61C
07	C6N1-S	20	Helio No. 1	20	P-63A
20	CCW-1	20	Henschel 293B	23	P-84(XP)Fuse
23	Cessna 150L	20	Henschel 117		(Continued Next Page)

07	P1Y1-C	24	RT-14	22	VZ-9V
23	PA-12	21	Rutan Quickie	24	VZ-1
0D	PA-23	23	SG. 38	23	VZ-2A
07	PCA-1A	23	SNJ-4A(AT-6)	09	Waco Primary Glider
23	Pentecost E III	07	Stanley Nomad	24	Waco UIC Cabin
23	PG-185B	21	Stearman-Hammond Y	24	Waco 9
21	Phoenix Streak	21	Stout Skycar	22	Waterman Whatsit
21	Phoenix Vipper	21	T-33	21	Waterman Aeromobile
21	Phoenix 6	20	TBF-1	23	Windecker Eagle I
24	Pitts S-1-S	20	TD2C-1	22	XF2Y-1
20	Princeton Air Scooter	23	TG-1A	22	XFY-1
20	PS-2	24	TTD-2 Radioplane Drone	07	XR-1
23	PT-19A	24	Turner Meteor	23	Yak-18
07	R-8(XR)	23	U-2	23	Yokosuka P1Y1c
23	R-5(XR)(VS-317)	07	V-173	23	Zimmerman
21	RC-3	23	V-1(XV)		
		20	Valkyrie Glider		

MARYLAND (Continued)

Suitland - Airmen Memorial Museum, 5211 Auth Rd, 20746, Take I-95 Exit 7B, Then North on Branch Ave, Right on Auth Rd 3 Blocks, (800) 638-0594, Mon-Fri 8-5, www.afsahq.org/AMM/amm-htm/mwelcome.htm, Artifacts

Wallops Island - NASA/Goddard Visitor Center, Rte 175, 20771, (301) 286-8981 March-Nov Thru-Mon 10-4, Free Adm, Tours on Thur at 2pm, 1.5 Hrs long, Gift Shop, Special Events every Sun, www.wff.nasa.gov/vc; Rockets only

West River (Baltimore)- Due to Open in Spring 1999, USS Forrestal Naval Museum, P.O. Box 59, 20778, Inner Harbor Area and Ft McHenry, CSX Pier A/B www.forrestal.org, USS Forrestal Aircraft Carrier

MASSACHUSETTS

Bedford - Hanscom AFB, 01731, 781-861-4441, F-86H ?   P-40N ? May not be there

Boston - Museum of Science Park, 02114-1099, (617) 589-0100, Daily 10-5, Adm Adult $2, Child $.50   Five Spacecraft

Cape Cod - Coast Guard Air Station, Race Point Beach, End of Rte, HH-60, HU-16E, HU-25

Hq Massachusetts Military Reservation, 02542, (508) 968-1000, 7:30-4, T-33

Otis ANG, MASS ANG Museum, 02542-5001, (508) 968-4090, 102nd FIW,

F-84F	F-86	F-100D	T-33A

Chambridge - New England Escadrille, 26 Cambridge St, 01803-4604, Mail: POB 605, Kendal Square Station, (617) 273-1916, 02142, By Appt Only

Needham - New England Warbird Assoc, 140 Gould St, POB 849, 02194

Stow - Bob Collings Foundation, POB 248, (978) 568-8924, www.collingsfoundation.org, R=Restoration, All Flyable except (NF)

A-4J (R)	Bleriot	H-1E(UH) (R)	T-33
A-26 (R)	C-78(UC)	PT-17	TBM
A-36 (R)	F-4D	S-2F	W r i g h t E x V i n
B-25J	F4U-5 (R)	T-6	Fizz (NF)
B-17G	Foker DR-1 Rep		Yak 3UA (R)
B-24J	Fi-156	T-33 (R)	

Westfield - MA ANG, 104 TFG/CC, 01085, (413) 568-9151   F-100D

Pioneer Valley Military & Transportation Museum, Inc.

MICHIGAN

Battle Creek - ANGB, 49015-1291, (269) 963-1596, A-10(Active),

A-37	F-100F	T-37B	UH-1B	Tank

Belleville - Yankee Air Museum, **(Fire Damaged)** Temporary Located at Hangar 2 Willow Run Airport 48112-0590, Mail: POB 590, 48112, (734) 483-4030, Fax 483-5076, Daily 10-4, Airpark Adm Adult $3, Child 6-12 $2, Under 5 Free, Gift Shop, www.yankeeairmuseum.org; Privately Owned = (P) Loan from USAF Museum =(L), Flyable = (F), Static = (S)

A-4 Cockpit		B-8M Bensen	(D)	F-84F	(L)
A-6A(EA)		B-17G	(F)	F-84F(RF)(3ea)	(L)
A-7D Project	(L)	B-25D	(F)(P)	F-86D	
A-10 Cocpit		B-52D	(L)	F-101B(NF)	(L)
A-W 650-101		B-57A(RB)	(L)	F-102A(TF)	(L)
Argosy		C-47B(TC)	(F)	F-102 Cockpit	
AT-6D :Yankee Flyers	(F)	C-60A-5-LO	(P)	H-1D(UH)	
AT-6D :Max Holman	(F)	CG-4A	(P)	HM-293	
AT-6D :Jack Rouch	(F)	DC-6B(C-118)		L-39C :Bob Lutz	(F)
AT-11	(S)	F-4C	(L)	Link Trainer	
AT-19(V-77)	(F)	F-4 Cockpit		(Continued Next Page)	

(Continued From Previous) SA-300 Starduster Too   T-33A :Connie Katitta
P-38J   T-28A :Yankee Flyers   (F) TS-11   :Yankee   Spark
PB4Y-2G   T-28C :Stu Dingman   (F) Flyers(F)
PT-19A :Leslie Day (F)   T-33A (2ea)   Wallis Model 3 1976

Divisions of the Yankee Air Force are at the following locations:
NE = North-East Division, Sussex Airport, POB 1729, Fairfield, NJ, 07007-1729
SAG = Saginaw Valley, Michigan - Harry Browne Airport, Saginaw, MI
WUR = Wurtsmith, Michigan - Oscoda County Airport, Division - Oscoda, MI

MICHIGAN (Continued)

Blissfield - American Legion Hall, High St & US 223, (517) 486-3312, F-105D

Calumet - Calumet AFS, 49913, (906) 337-4200, T-33A

Dearborn - Henry Ford Museum, 20900 Oakwood Blvd, POB 1970, 48121-4088,
   (313) 982-6100, Daily 9:30-5, Closed TD, CD, Adm Adult $14, Snr $13, Child 5-12 $10
   Under 5 Free, Gift Shop, www.thehenryford.org/museum/heroes/home.asp

Bleriot XI	Ford 4-AT-15	NYP
Boeing 40B-2	Ford Flivver	PA-18
Curtiss Canuck	Laird LC-D W500	RB-1 Racer
DC-3	Lockheed Autogyro	Stinson SM-1
Fokker F.VIIa	Lockheed Vega	VS-3000A

Detroit - The National Museum of Tuskegee Airmen, 6325 W. Jefferson Ave, 48209
   (313) 297-9360, Wed-Sun 9-5, Artifacts Only,

Farmington - Marvin's Marvelous Mechanical Museum, 3100 Orchard Lake Rd, (248) 626-5020
   100 Model Airplanes suspended on Conveyor Line,

Frankenmuth - Michigan's Own, Inc, Military & Space Museum, 1220 Weiss St, 48734,
   (989) 652-8005, Mar-Dec Mon-Sat 10-5, Sun 12-5, F-86 Rep

Grand Haven - Grand Haven Memorial Airpark, Gate Entrance, 49417, (616) 842-4430, F-100

Grand Rapids - CAF West Michigan Wing, 49315, AT-11

   Gerald R. Ford Museum, 303 Pearl St, NW, 49504-5353, (616) 254-0400, Fax 254-0386
   Daily 9-5, Closed ND, TD, CD, Adm Adult $5, Snr 62 & Child $4, Under 16 Free,
   www.fordlibrarymuseum.gov,   UH-1

Greenville - Fighting Falcon Military Museum of the Flat River Historical Museum,
   PO Box 188, 48838, (616) 754-3686 or 5296, CG-4A Project

Jackson - EAA Chapter 304, Jackson County Airport, 49202, www.eaa304.org, T-33

   Michigan Space Center, Jackson Community College, 2111 Emmons Rd, 49203
   (517) 787-4425,   Rockets

KI Sawyer AFB - Sawyer Heritage Air Museum, KI Sawyer AFB,49843,(906) 346-6511,
   41 BMW/MAT, www.sawyersixproject.com

B-52,	F-106A,	F-101,	FB-111,	T-33

Kalamazoo - Kalamazoo Air Zoo, 3101 E. Milham Rd, 49002-1700, (269) 382-6555, Fax:
   382-1813, April-Dec Mon-Sat 10-6, Sun 12-6, Jan-March Mon-Sat 10-5, Sun 12-5,
   Closed Holidays, Adm Adult $19.50, Snrs 60 $17.50, Child 6-15 $15.50, Under 6 Free,
   Order online Save 20%, Gift Shop, Theater, www.airzoo.org

A4D-2(A-4B)Project	F-84F-35RE	HUP-3	PT-22
AD-4NA	F-86A	J-3C-65	PT-23HO
Aeronca 65 CA	F-80 Cockpit	Lear-23	Renegade Spirit
Aeronca O-58B	F-104	Link Trainer	SBD-3 Project
AT-6G	F-106 Cockpit	L-4H	SNJ-5 2ea
Avid Flyer	F4U-4B 1/2 Scale	L-19	Sopwith Camel
B-25J	F6F-5K	LNS-1	SPad VII
B-57B	F7F-3P	MiG-15	SR-71B
Boeing 727-25C	F8F-1D	MiG-21PF Project	SRC-B7
BT-13	F9F-2 Project	Morane-Saulnier 733	Sun Hang Glider
C-4A (5-AT)	F11A-1	N2T-1	T-28 Cockpit
C-47	FG-1D	N3N	T-28B
C-135(KC)	FM-2	OQ-20A	T-33B(TV-2)
CG-4A	Ford Tri-Motor 5-AT	OV-1D	T-34B
Doran Simulator	GH-2	P-38J Rep	Taylor Monoplane
Ercoupe 415C Project	Guff R/C	P-39Q-20BE(RP)	TG-2(LNS-1)
F-4E	H-1J(AH)	P-40N	TG-4A
F-8J	H-23(UH-12)	P-47D	Waco INF
F-9J(TF)	H-25(UH)	P-51 (Winter Only)	Wright Flyer Rep
F-14A	H-53(CH) Cockpit	P-55-CS(XP)	X-28
F-16 Cockpit	HA-1112-M1L	P-80	
F/A-18	Heath Parasol	PT-13D-BW/N2S	

MICHIGAN (Continued)

Lake Orion - Canterbury Village Toy Shop, 2369 Joslyn Ct, 48361, SE-5A Replica

Lansing - Michigan Historical Museum, 717 West Alliegan St, (517) 373-3559, 48918
Mon-Fri 9-4, Sat 10-4, Sun 1-5, Free Adm, Gift Shop, Daily Except Mondays.
B-24 Nose Section

Lapeer - Yankee Air Force Mid-Michigan 3rd Division, Lapeer Airport, 1232 Roods
Lake Rd, 48446-8366, (810) 664-6966, These Aircraft Are In Storage:
| A-6 | F-84K | F-84F(RF) | Stinson Model 10A | UH-1D |

Ludington - Mason Cnty Airport, E Ave, 49431, (231) 843-2049, T-38

Mt Clemens - American Legion Post 4, 401 Groesbeck, F-101

Selfridge Military Air Museum, 127WG/MU, 27333 C St, Bldg 1011, Mail: Box 43,
48045, (586) 307-5035, Fax 307-6646, April-Oct, Sat-Sun 12-4:30,
Closed ED, Mem & Indep Day, $3 Donation, Gift Shop, www.selfridgeairmuseum.org

A-4B	F-4C	F-101C(RF)	O-2A
A-7D	F-16A	F-102A(TF)	P-3B
B-26C(GB)	F-84F	F-106A(NF)	S-2F
B-57A(RB)	F-84F(RF)	FG-1D	SNB-5
C-45B	F-86A	H-1F(AH)	T-33A
C-130A	F-100D	H-1H(UH)	U-3A
C-131D	F-100F	HH-52A	Nike-Ajax & Hercules

Muskegon - Hidden Cove Park, Norton Shores, Mona Lake, BS 96, UH-1

Oscoda - Yankee Air Force Wurtsmith Division, Oscoda-Wurtsmith Airport,
Mail: POB 664, 48750, (989) 739-7555, Fax 739-1974, Mid May-Mid Oct Fri-Sun 11-3
Adm Adult 3, Uchild Under 12 $2, Gift Shop, Restoration Facility Viewable,Library
www.wurtsmith-yaf-museum.org, (See Aircraft Status Codes Page 1)
Barracuda Homebuilt (D)	L-9B	(S)	T-33A-1-LA (S)
CG-4A	(P)	L-19A-CE	(P)	T-33A-5-LO (P)
DC-8-55JT	(O)	Link Trainer	(P)	Stinson 10A
H-1D(UH)-BF	(D)	Sperry Messenger	(P)

Plainwell - Plainwell Municipal Airport, 630 10th St, 49080-1005, (269) 685-5343, T-38

Saginaw - Yankee Air Force Saginaw Valley Division, Harry Browne Airport,
Airport Number (989) 754-2459, 4821 Jones St 48601, Not Available to Public
DC-65 (L-2B) Flyable   L-4 Replica Project

Sterling Heights - Freedom Hill McComb County Park, Metropolitan Parkway Between Schoenherr &
Utica Rds, F-4,   HU-1,   M60A1 Tank   US Navy Torpedo Mk.14

MINNESOTA

Alexandria - Alexandria Airport, Chandler Field, 2 Mi SW of City, 210 Nokomis St
56308, (320) 762-1544, 762-2111,   T-33

Blaine - American Wings Air Museum, NW Corner of Anoka County Airport, 8891 Airport Rd NE,
55449, (763) 786-4146, Tue & Wed 6-9, Fri 12-5, Sat 8-5, Mail: POB 49322, 1260 Colorado Ave
St Paul, MN 55112-0901, Adm Adult $4, Snrs 55/Mil/Child $3, Under 6 Free, www.americanwings.org

Anoka County-Blaine Airport, Privately Owned Aircraft: Mike Rawson (A-25), Patrick Harker
(Grumman Albatross, L-13, L-15, P-82, Waco UPF-7); Doug Weske (L-29, L-39, MiG 17, Piper Seneca
Super Cub); Unkown (Ryan Navion B, SE Asia Cammo, C-123(2ea)).

An-2	H-34D(CH)	O-2	OV-1D
AO-1A	L-2M	OV-1 Cockpit	S2F-1
JOV-1A	L-3B	OV-1B	T-34A
JOV-1C	O-1E	OV-1C	

Golden Wings Flying Museum,8891 Airport Rd, Anoka County Airport, C-6, 55449, (763) 786-5004
Greg Herrick's Collection, www.goldenwingsmuseum.com, All Flying Except (R)=Restoration

Aero Car	Ford 4-AT (R)	PT-19	Stinson SM-7A (R)
Aeronca C-3	Hawker Hurricane	PT-23A	Stinson SM-6000-B
Alliance Argo	Interstate S-1-A	PT-26 (2ea)	Stinson SM-1B
Arrow Sport M (R)	Keystone K-84 (R)	Sikorsky S-39-C (R)	Taylor Aerocar
Avro Avian	Kreutzer K-5	SM-6000-B	TG-1A
Buhl Sport Airsedan	KR-34C (R)	Spartan C2-60	Travel Air A-6000-A
Call-Air A-4 (R)	Kreutzer K-5	Stearman	Waco CUC-1
Fairchild F-45 (R)	N2S-4(A75L3)	Stinson A Tri-Motor (R)	Waco UKC
FC-2-W2	Paramount Cabinair (R)	Stinson C2-60 (R)	YPT-9
Fleetwings Seabird	PT-6F	Stinson Detroiter (R)	

Brainerd - Crow Wing County Regional Airport, 3 Mi NE of City, (218) 829-6873, F9F-6

Chisholm - Minnesota Museum of Mining, 218-254-5543, F-94C

  Duluth - Duluth Int'l Airport, 6 Mi NW of City, (218) 727-2968, F-4

    Lake Superior Squadron 101, 4931 Airport Rd, Hangar S101, Duluth International Airport Duluth, 55811, (218) 733-0639, www.cafduluth.org, B-25 Simulator, Link Trainer, PBY-6A, PBY-6ACF

  Eden Prairie - Planes of Fame East, Flying Cloud Field, 14771 Pioneer Trail, County Rd 1
    (952) 941-2633, Restoration Only of: P-47   P-51D   T-28

    Wings of the North, 9960 Flying Cloud Dr, Suite 204, 55347, (952) 746-6100
    http://www.wingsofthenorth.org, email: info@wotn.org, AT-6, BT-15, SB2C

  Fountain - Fillmore County Museum, 55935, (507) 268-4449, Limited Hours, Pietenpohl

  Minneapolis - Jim Johns, (612) 881-1797, 9108 Logan Ave, 55400
    AT-6 Harvard   BT-13   L-13   TBM-3

    Minnesota Air Guard Museum, Temporarily Closed for F-16 Crews, All Aircraft in Airpark
    POB 11598, ANG, Minneapolis-St Paul, International Airport, 1 Scanlan Plaza, 55111-0592,
    (612) 713-2523, Mon-Sat by Appt, April 15-Oct 15, Winter 2nd & 3rd Sat 11-4, Gift Shop,
    www.mnangmuseum.org

A-12(SR-71)	C-131E	F-94C	L-4
BC-1A(AT-6)	Curtiss Oriole	F-101(Black)	MiG-15
C-45	F-4C(RF)	F-101B	O-47
C-47B	F-4D	F-102A	P-51D
C-97	F-4E(RF)	H-1H(UH)	T-33A
C-130A	F-89H	JN-6H	A-7

    Minneapolis/St.Paul Int'l Airport, Wold Chamberlin Field, 6 Mi SW of
    City, Gate 12 West side of Main Lobby, (612) 726-5032,
    Spirit of St Louis Replica,   Waco 125 Gate 15
    Link Trainer at North West Air Lines   Curtiss Pusher Gate 12

  St Paul - CAF Minnesota Wing, 310 Airport Rd, Fleming Field, Hangar 3,
    (651) 455-6942, 55075-3551, Wed 10-6, Sat 10-5, Adm Donation, www.cafmn.org,
    B-25J,   BT-13A,   Harvard Mk IV,   L-5A,   P-51C,   PBY,   PBY-6A

    Minnesota Air & Space Museum, Holman Field Airport, POB 75654, 55175
    (651) 291-7925, DC-7   Steco Aerohydro-Plane

  Stewartville - Carr Care Center, 211 S Main St, 55976, (320) 533-8175, Culver Dart

  Winoma - Max Conrad Airfield, Winoma Mncpl Airport, F9F-5, O-1, T-33

    Winoma Technical Institute,

C-45	Erocoupe	Luscombe 8	Taylorcraft
Cessna 2ea	Hiller	PA-31	Unident Aztec
Colt	L-19	S-61	

MISSISSIPPI
  Bay St Louis - NASA's National Space Technology Laboratories, Visitor Center Bldg,
    1200, NSTL, 39529, (228) 688-2211

  Biloxi - Keesler AFB, 39534-5000, (228) 377-1110
    F-104C   F-101C(RF)   T-33A
    F-105D   T-28   F-100(YF)

  Columbus - Columbus AFB, 39701-5000, (662) 434-7322   T-37B   T-38A

  Jackson - Jackson ANG, Jackson Municipal Airport, Allen C Thompson Field,
    39208-0810, (601) 968-8321, 173rd TAG, A-26B   F-84F(RF)   F-101C(RF)

    Jackson AFB Museum, Hawkins Field, 39201, (601) 373-1574, 965-5790

    National Agricultural Aviation Museum / Jim Buch Ross Mississippi Ag &
    Forestry Museum, 1150 Lakeland Dr, (601) 354-6113,

    CAF - Mississippi Wing, C-45, Lockheed 10A

  Meridian - NAS, T-2A

  Petal - M W Hamilton Machine Museum, 39465, (601) 583-9117 / 583-8836
    Aircraft Restorations - All Aircraft Semi-Restored
    B-25J   C-47   F9F   PT-17
    BT-13   DC-3   HUB-1

  McLaurin - Armed Forces Museum at Camp Shelby, 12 Mi S of Hattiesburg on Hwy 49
    (601) 558-2757, Mon-Fri 9-4, Sat-Sun 1-5, Free Adm, CH-54

MISSOURI

Branson - Veterans Memorial Museum, 1250 W 76 Country Music Blvd, 65616, Mail: POB 2010,
(417) 336-2300, Fax: 336-2301, Daily 8-9pm, Adm Adult $12.50, Child 6-12 $5
www.veteransmemorialbranson.com, P-51

Chillicothe - Chillicothe Municipal Airport, 64601, (660) 646-5270, F-105

Kansas City - Airline History Museum Inc, 201 NW Lou Holland Dr, Hangar 9
64116-4223, (816) 421-3401, 513-9484, Mon-Sat 10-4, Sun 12-4, Closed Holidays
Adm Adult $7, Snrs 65 $6, Child 6-13 $3, Under 6 Free, Gift Shop,
Restoration Facility, www.airlinehistorymuseum.com
L-1049H,   Martin 404   DC-3

Knob Noster - Whiteman AFB, 351 CSG/DEER, 65305, (660) 687-1110,
B-29   B-52D   B-47B   C-97G(KC)   H-1F(UH)

Malden - Malden Army Airfield Preservation Society, Malden Industrial Park Office,
167 Mitchell Dr, 63863, (573) 276-2279, Mon-Fri 8-12 & 1-5, www.maaps.net Artifacts

Maryland Heights - Historic Aircraft Restoration Museum, Dauster Flying Field,
Creve Coeur Airport, 3127 Creve Coeur Mill Rd, 63146, (314) 434-3368, Fax 878-6453
Sat-Sun 10-4, By Appt, Adm Adult $10, Child 5-12 $3, Under 5 Free, Gift Shop
Rides: SNJ $75, Stearman $50, www.historicaircraftrestorationmuseum.org

Aeronca C-3	KR-31	Stearman
AN-2	(Continued Next Page)	Stinson SM.8A
AT-6(SNJ)	(Continued)	Timm Collegiate
C-2	KR-21	Travel Air 4000 (R)
Curtiss Air Sedan	Monocoupe Clipwing	Waco ARE
Culver Dart	Monocoupe 90	Waco ATO
Curtiss Robin (R)	Mooney Mite	Waco JWM
DH-89	N3N-3	Waco QCF-2
Driggs Dart	NB-8G	Waco UBA
Fairchild CBA	Pietenpohl Air Camper	Waco VKS-6
Flagg	Piper Vegabond	Zenith Biplane (R)
Hisso Standard	PT-22	
JN-4D		

St Charles - CAF Missouri Wing, St Charles County Smart Field, Mail: POB 637
(636) 250-4515, B-25   L-3B   TBM-3E

St Joseph - St Joseph ANG, 139 TAG/CC, Rosecrans Memorial Airport 64503,
(816) 271-1300,   C-97L(KC)

St Louis - McDonnell Douglas Prologue Room, McDonnell Blvd, & Airport Rd,
Lambert St Louis Airport, Box 516, 63166, (314) 232-5421, 10 Mi NW, June-August,
Mon-Sat 9-4, Replica Gemini,   Mercury Capsules

McDonnell Planetarium, 5100 Clayton Rd, 63110, (314) 535-5810, Daily 9-5,
Adm Adult $1.25, Child $0.75,   PGM-17   Spacecraft

National Personnel Records Center, 9700 Page Ave, (314) 538-4261
H-1B(UH)   Bradley Fighting Vehicle   WWII 8" Howitzer

Missouri History Museum, Forest Park, (314) 746-4599, Ryan NYP Replica

MO ANG St Louis, Lambert Field, 63145, (314) 263-6356, F-4E, F-15A, F-100D

Museum of Transportation, 3015 Barrett Station Rd, Lambert St Louis
Int'l Airport, 63122-3398, (314) 965-7998, Daily 9-5,Sept-April Tue-Sat 9-4,
Sun 11-4, Closed TD, CD, ND, Adm Adult $4, Child 5-12 & Snr 65 $2, Under 5 Free,
Gift Shop 965-5709, Restoration Facility, www.museumoftransport.org,
C-47A(VC)   T-33 Project

St Louis Lambert Int'l Airport, Terminal Entrance C Concourse,
17 Mi W of City, (314) 532-2222, Monocoupe

St Louis Aviation Museum, Spirit of St Louis Airport, POB 5867, 63134, 17 Miles
West of City, JS McDonnell Personnel Cart
AT-6   F-101   Meyers
F-2H-2N   Fairchild   Stearman

Sikeston, Sikeston Veterans Park, One Industrial Dr, 63801, (573) 471-2498, F-4J, M-60 Tank

Springfield - Air & Military Museum of the Ozarks, CAF Ozark Mountain Squadron,
Springfield Regional, 2305 E Kearney St, 65803, (417) 864-7997, Fax 882-0188,
May 1-Oct 31, Thur-Sat 1-5; Nov 1-Feb 28, Thur-Sat 1-4, Adm Adult $3, Child 7-12 $1,
Under 6 Free Artifacts, www.ammomuseum.org, AH-1

MONTANA

Dutton - American Legion Freeborn Post 64, 201 Main East, 59433, (406) 476-3304, F-104

Great Falls - Great Falls ANG, Great Falls Int'l Airport, 59401-5000, (406) 727-4650,
F-86A   F-89J   F-106A   T-33

Lion's Park, 10th Ave, F-102A

Malmstrom AFB & Airpark, 314 Space Wing/MU 2177ᵗʰ St North, 59402-5000, (406) 731-2705
June-Aug Mon-Sat 12-3, Apr-May & Sept-Oct Mon-Fri 12-3, RoY Mon, Wed & Fri 12-3,
B-25M   C-97L(KC)   F-101F   T-33A
B-57B(EB)   F-84F   H-1F(UH)

Helena - Montana Historical Society's Museum, Helena Municipal Airport,
South Side Corner, 59620, Summer Mon-Sat 9-5, DH 60 #179, UH-1

College of Technology, 2300 Poplar(Airport)Rd, 59601, (800) 241-4882, www.hct.umontana.edu/
EC-121   F-89   F-102A   H-19(S-65)   T-39

Firefighting Training Center, Helena Municipal Airport, A-7D

Missoula - Museum of Mountain Flying, Missoula Int'l Airport, 713 S 3ʳᵈ St West, 59801,
(406) 549-8488, May-Oct Daily 10-5, Thur-Mon Rest of Year, Adm Adult $4, Snr/Mil $2,
Student $1, C-45, C-47(DC-3), J-3, Homebuilts, PT-17, Smokejumper & Parachutes Artifacts

Smokejumper Center,US Dept of Agriculture, US 10W, Aerial Fire Depot
Airport Terminal, Box 6, 59801, (406) 329-4900, Memorial Day - July 4th Mon-Fri
8:30-5, July 4th-Labor Day 8:30-5 Daily, Hourly Tours,
Beech 58P   Cessna 206   DHC 6
Beech 99   DC-3   Sherpa C203A

NEBRASKA

Ashland - Strategic Air and Space Museum, 28210 West Park Hwy, 68003,
Exit 426, Off I-80, Mail: POB 8343, Omaha, NE, 68108-0343, (402) 944-3100,
Fax (402) 944-3160, Daily 9-5, Closed TD, CD, ND, Adm Adult $7, Sr $6, 5-12 $3,
Under 5 Free, Gift Shop, Snack Bar, www.strategicairandspace.com

A6M3	B-58A	F-101B	Ki-43
Atlas D	C-47A	F-102A	MiG-21
A-26B	C-54D	F-105	P-40C
B-17G	C-97G(KC)	F-111A(FB)	SR-71A
B-25J (2ea)	C-119G	F6F	T-29A
B-29(BA)	C-124A	H-19B(UH)	T-33A
B-36J	C-133B	H-21B(CH)	T-39A
B-45C(RB)	C-135C(EC)	He-111	U-2C
B-47E	F-84F	HU-16B	Vulcan B-2 Mk.II
B-52B(RB)	F-86F	ICBM,Minuteman I	XF-85
B-57E	F-86H	JN-4	

Fairbury - Engels J T Airport, 68352, (402) 729-3248, F-100

Lincoln - Lincoln ANG, Lincoln Municipal Airport, 68524-1897, (402) 473-1326, 155th TRG
F-4C(RF)   F-84F(RF)   F-86L   T-33A

Minden - Harold Warp Pioneer Village Foundation, POB 68, 68959-0068, 138 E Hwy 6, 68959
(800) 445-4447, (308) 832-2750, Daily 8-5, Closed CD, Adm Adult $9, Child (6-12) $4,
Under 6 Free, Gift Shop, Cafe 832-1550, All Indoor Exhibit,
Motel and Campground in Village, Airport .5 Mi North; www.pioneervillage.org

Bensen B-6	Ercoupe 67	P-59	Swallow
Bensen B-7	Hartman	PA-23	Weed Hopper
Cessna	Heath Parasol 5	PCA-2	Wright Flyer
Curtiss	J-2	Sikorsky	
Curtiss JN9	JN-4D	Stinson Detroiter 30	

Omaha - Freedom Park, 2497 Freedom Park Rd, 68110, (402) 345-1959, From I-29 Go W
on I-480 Then N on Freedom Park Rd, Apr 15-Oct 31, Daily, 10-5, Adm Adult $5,
Snr 65 $4, Child 5-12 $3,Under 5 Free, Group Rates, www.freedomparknavy.org

USS Hazard AM-240 Mine Sweeper
A-4D   H-1(UH)   USS Marlin SST-2 (Submarine)
A-7   SH-3   USS Towers DDG-9 Captains Gig

Offutt AFB, 68113-5000, Hangar 20 E, (402) 294-1110, 8 Mi S of Omaha,
B-17G   B-52   C-135(KC)

S Sioux City - Martin Flying Service, W. Hwy 20, 68776, (402) 494-3667,   A-7D

NEVADA

Carson City - Yesterday's Flyers Ltd, Carson City Airport, 3 Mi NE of City, (775) 882-1551

Bellanca	Curtiss Robin	N3N	Stinson SR-4E
BT-13	Depordussin	Starduster II	T-28
Curtiss Junior	Pfalz D.XIII	Steen Skybolt	

Fallon - Naval Air Station Fallon, 4755 Pasture Rd, 2 Mi NE of City, 89496-5000
(775) 426-5161, AP = Air Park; CU = Credit Union; MG = Main Gate

A-4	MG	AD-4B	AP	F-16	AP	MiG-23	AP
A-4	AP	E-2C	AP	F-86	AP	RA-5C	CU
A-7	MG	F-4	AP	FA-18	AP	UH-1	MG
A-7E	AP	F-8	AP	MiG-15	AP		
A-6	AP	F-14	AP	MiG-17	AP		

Indian Springs - City Park, West 1 Block Off I-95, Between the 2 exits, F-84F

Jean - Casino, South Side of the Highway, WWI Replica Fighters From Ceiling

Las Vegas - CAF Nevada Wing, AT-19

Lost Birds, 3172 N Rainbow Blvd, Mail: Box 266, 89108, (775) 646-6524,
Contact Doug Scroggins, www.LostBirds.com,

B-720B Boeing(Cockpit)	CV-880-22 Convair	KC-97G (Cockpit)
Boeing 737-222 (Cockpit)	DC-3 (Cockpit)	L-1011 (Cockpit)
C-402 Cessna (Fuse)	F-27A Fairchild (Cockpit)	

McCarran Int'l Airport, 5757 Wayne Newton Blvd, 2nd Level Above Baggage Claim,
Near Scenic Airlines, 89119, (775) 261-5192, POB 11005, 89111, Open 24 Hrs,
Free Adm, Ford 5AT, Cessna 172,   C-124 next to Comfort Inn South

Military Heritage Command, POB 12543, 89112-0543, (800) 347-4385, P2V-7(SP2H)

Nellis AFB, 157 NFWW, 89191-5000, (775) 643-1800,

F-4C	F-86	F-105G
F-5E	F-100D	F-117A

Reno - May ANG Base, Cannon Int'l Airport, 89502, (775) 788-4500, RF-101B

Reno-Stead Airport, 4895 Texas Ave, 89506-1237, (775) 328-6570,

MiG-15	MiG-17	MiG-19

Nevada Aviation Historical Society, 3035 Slatter Court, 89503, (775) 747-3888, F-86D

NEW HAMPSHIRE

Danville - Atlantic Warbirds, 23 Pleasant St, 03819-3221, Mail: POB 715, 01845,
North Andover, MA, (603) 382-3493, DC-4 (C-54)

Mason - Dakota Aviation Museum, 492 Old Ashbury Rd, 03048, (603) 878-1622

Nashua - FAA Air Traffic Control Center, A-4

Wolfeboro - Wright Museum of American Enterprise, 77 Center St, 03894, (603) 569-1212
Army Spotter Plane, 2 Tanks

NEW JERSEY

Fairfield - Yankee Air Force NE Division, Caldwell-Wright (Essex County) Airport
171 Passaic Ave, 07004-3502, Mail: POB 1729, 07007-1729, Not Open to Public

C.51 Pembroke (Storage)	DC-62 (L-2C)(Flyable)	L-13A (Storage)

Farmingdale - Berlin Airlift Historical Society, Mail To: POB 782, 07727
(732) 818-0034, www.spiritoffreedom.org,   C-54   C-97G

Ft Monmouth, US Army Communications-Electronics Museum, Kaplan Hall Bldg 275,
07703-5103, (732) 532-4390, 542-7267, Mon-Fri 12-4, Free Adm, ANTSC-54 Satellite

Lakehurst - Navy Lakehurst Historical Society, POB 328, 08733, (732) 244-8861
www.nlhs.com, Crash Site Tour & Artifacts from Hindenburg

Naval Air E Center,   A-7B   E-2B

Lumberton - Air Victory Museum, 68 Stacy Haines Rd, South Jersey Regional Airport,
08048, (609) 267-4488, Fax: 702-1852, Wed-Sun 10-4, Closed ED, TD, CD, ND
Adm Adult $4, Snrs $3, Child 4-13 $2, Gift Shop, www.airvictorymuseum.org/

A-4B	F-4B	F-104G	H-53D(RH)
A-7A	F-14A	FP-404	
E-2B	F-86L	H-1A(AH)	

Millville - Millville Army Air Field Museum, Municipal Airport, 1 Leddon St,
08332, (856) 327-2347, Tue-Sun 10-4, Closed Holidays, Free Adm
Gift Shop, www.p47millville.org, Link Trainer,   A-4

NEW JERSEY (Continued)

Pomona - Air National Guard - Atlantic City Int'l Airport, F-16, F-100F, F-106B

Rio Grande - Cape May, Naval Air Station Wildwood Foundation, Cape May Airport,
500 Forrestal Rd, (609) 886-8787, Spring-Summer: Mont-Sun 9-5, Fall-Winter:
Mon-Fri 8-4, Sat-Sun 9-3, Adm Adult $5, Child 3-12 $3, Under 3 Free, www.usnasw.org

A-4	H-13 (Bell47)	PT-17	TBM
H-1(AH)	H-52A(HH)	T-28C	V-2
H-1(UH)	L-19	T-33	
H-6(OH)	MiG-15	T-33 2Seater	

Rockaway - Picatinny Arsenal Museum, 07801, Rt 15, Pitcatinny Base, Phipps Rd,
(973) 724-2797, Tue, Wed & Thur 9-3, Outdoor Displays Open Daily, Free Adm,

AGM-22 M3	M31	M51

Sea Girt - National Guard Militia Museum, P.O. Box 277, 08750, (732) 974-5966
Gift Shop, Library, Artifacts

Teterboro - Aviation Hall Of Fame & Museum of New Jersey, 400 Fred Wehran Dr,
Teterboro Airport, 07608, (201) 288-6344, Fax 288-5666, Tue-Sun 10-4, Adm Adult $6
Snrs/Mil/Child 2-17$ 4, Gift Shop, www.njahof.org

H-1 (UH)H-13	Lockheed Bushmaster	Cobra
H-52A(HH)	Martin 202 Airliner	Stinson Voyager

NAPC Trenton,   A-4B

Wrightstown - McGuire AFB Museum, 08562, (609) 724-1100, 724-1110, 438 MAW/SEN,

C-118A	F-4	F-84F	P-38L	F-105B

NEW MEXICO

Alamogordo - Holloman AFB, 833 CSG/CD 88330-5000, (505) 479-6511,

F-4C	F-84F	F-100D	F-105D
F-80C	F-86E	F-104C	

New Mexico Museum of Space History, (877) 333-6589, Mail: POB 5430, 88311,
Gift Shop, Daily 9-5, Closed TD, CE, CD, Adm Adult $2.50, Snrs $2.25, Child 4-12 $2,
Under 4 Free, IMAX Theater, Shuttle Camp $85-450, www.spacefame.org
Little Joe Rocket   Satellites,   Sonic Wind I Rocket Sled,

Albuquerque - New Mexico ANG Complex, Bldg 1055, 87100, (505) 678-3114, A-7D, F-100A
At Falcon Rd & Air Guard Rd, F-80, P-51

At 551st Op Sq, Bldg 4279, Frances St & Hercules Way SE, CH-3

Albuquerque Int'l Airport, 4 Mi SE of City, (505) 768-3830, Coordinator:
Jane Sprague,   Ingram/Foster Biplane

Anderson/Abruzzo Int'l Balloon Museum, Opens Fall 2005, 6121 Indian School Rd NE,
87110, South End of Fiesta Park, POB 16314, 87191, (505) 271-12119, Fax: 271-2358,
Cafe 880-0500, Theater, Gift Shop, www.balloonmuseum.org

CAF Lobo Wing, PO Box 20576, 87154-0576, AT-11,   PT-26

Kirtland AFB, 58th Special Ops, 87117-5000, Doris St & Aberdeen Ave,
Sgt Ronald Carrillo: (505) 853-5856

CH-21B(2ea)	H-1F(UH)	H-13E(OH)	H-43(HH)
	H-5G	H-19F(UH)	HU-16A

At Eileen St & Aberdeen Ave : HH-34(S-58), PBY-5(OA-10), SC-47

National Atomic Museum, 1905 Mountain Rd NW, Mail: POB 5800, MS 1490, 87104,
(505) 245-2137, Daily 9-5, Closed ED, TD, CD, ND, Adm Adult $5, 60+ &
Child 6-17 $4, Under 6 Free, Gift Shop, www.atomicmuseum.com

A-7C(TA)	B-52B	F-105D	ICBM	SM-2
B-29	CIM-10A	MGM-13A	TM-61C	

Angel Fire - Vietnam Veterans National Memorial, NW of Angel Fire on US64,
28 Miles E of Taos on US64, Contact: David Westphall, POB 608, 87710,
(505) 377-6900, Fax: 377-3223, UH-1H

Carlsbad - Carlsbad Museum & Art Center, 418 West Fox, 88220, (505) 887-0276,
Mon-Sat 10-5, Free Adm, Artifacts

Cavern City Mncpl Airport, 1505 Terminal Dr, 88220, (505) 887-9001, AT-11

Clovis - Cannon AFB, Public Affairs, 27 FW/PA, Cannon Airpark, 88103-5000,
(505) 784-4131, PA: Michael Pierson, 1Lt, Historian: 784-2460,
www.cannon.af.mil/default.stm,

F-80B	F-86H	F-101A	
F-84C	F-100D	F-111A *	T-33A

NEW MEXICO

Clovis - City Display, 7th & West Hwy 60 & Hwy 84,   F-111F

Gallup - Gallup Municipal Airport, Old Hwy 66,   T-38

Hobbs - CAF New Mexico Wing, Flying Museum, POB 1260, Lea County Airport,
(505) 395-2377, Daily 8-Sunset,

BT-14	C-45	Me-108	SNJ-4

National Soaring Foundation, POB 684, 88241, (505) 392-6032, http://207.149.139.31/nsf/

Blanik L-13	Grob 103	Schweizer 1-26	Schweizer 2-33

Las Cruces - Las Cruces Int'l Airport, 8960 Zia Blvd, 88000, (505) 525-2762,

C-46	F-100F

Southwest Aviation, Las Cruces Int'l A, 88000, (505) 524-8047, 7 Mi West of City,

A-26B	C-46	PV-2

White Sands Missile Range Museum & Park, Las Cruces or El Paso Gate, 88002-5047,
(505) 678-2250, Mon-Fri 8-4, Sat-Sun 10-3, Free Adm, Gift Shop 678-8824,
www.wsmr-history.org

C-6A(VC)	H-1M(UH)	V-2 Rocket

Melrose - Melrose Bombing Range, N of Hwy 84, In Town, (505) 784-6644, F-100

Moriarty - Southwest Soaring Museum, POB 3626, 87035, (505) 832-0755, www.swsoaringmuseum.org

B-10	KA-6	SG-1A	TG-4A
KA-4	MSK	TG-1	Zoegling Rep

Portales - Hwy 70 & Ave K, 181 Airport Rd, 80130, (505) 478-2863, F-111F

Roswell - Int'l UFO Museum & Research Center, 114 N Main, 88202, (505) 625-9495,
Fax 625-1907, Daily 9-5, Free Adm, Gift Shop, Library, www.iufomrc.com

Roswell Goddard Rocket Museum, 100 W Eleventh St, (505) 624-6744,
Mon-Sat 9-5, Sun & Holidays 1-5, Free Adm,

UFO Enigma Museum, 6108 S Main, (505) 347-2275, Mon-Sat 9:30-5, Sun 12-5, Adult $1,
Child $0.50

Santa Teresa - War Eagles Air Museum, 8012 Airport Rd, 88008, Dona Ana County Airport,
(505) 589-2000, Tue-Sun 10-4, Adm Adult $5, Sr $4, Child Under 12 Free, Gift Shop,
www.war-eagles-air-museum.com

A7-E	F4U-4	J-3	TF-51D
A-26C	F-84F	L-13A	T-28
AT-6F	F-86 Mk VI	Link Trainer	T-33
AT-19	FJ-2	MiG-15 2 Seater	T-38A
BT-13	Fi-156	MiG-21PFM	TBM-3E
Cessna 140A	Great Lakes Sport	P-38	TU-2
CW Simulator	Trainer	P-40E	Waco EGC-8
DC-3		P-51D	
DH 82	Hawker Sea Fury	PT-17	

NEW YORK

Albion - Vintage Aircraft Group, 4906 Pine Hill Rd, 14411, www.vintageaircraftgroup.org

PT-26 Project	T-33 Project

Amherst - Amherst Museum, 3755 Tonawanda Creek Rd, 14228-1599, (716) 889-1440, GA-36

Bayport - Bayport Aerodome, Hangar 23, POB 728, 11705, Rte 97 Go West on Church St to Vitamin Dr,
June-Sept Sat-Sun 10-4, Adm Free, www.bayportaerodrome.org

Aeronca 7AC	DH 82C 2ea	PT-17 2ea
Aeronca 11AC	Fleet 16B	PT-19
Bleriot (Queen Monoplane)	J-3	PT-26
Brunner-Winkle Bird 2ea	N2S-3(V)	Stearman
Cessna C-140 2ea	N3N-3	Austin 2ea
Cessna 310	PA-20 Pacer	

Binghamton - Link Flight Simulation Corp, Colesville Rd, 13904, (607) 721-5465, Link Trainer

Binghamton Regional Airport, 13901, (607) 763-4471, 763-4456, Link Trainer

Brooklyn - Northeast Aircraft Restoration Facility & Museum, Floyd Bennett Field
(718) 338-3799, Mon, Thur & Sat 9-1,

A-4	DC-3	SH-3A Coast Guard Helio
C-45 Twin Beech	P2V	HU-16 Albatross Coast Guard
C-54	PBY	Fantasy Island Sea Plane

Buffalo - Amherst Museum, 3755 Towanda Rd, 14228, Aircraft

Buffalo & Erie County Historical Museum, 25 Nottingham Court, 14216,
(716) 873-9644, Tue-Sat 10-5, Sun 12-5, Adm Adult $6, Snrs 60 & Child 13-21 $4,
Child 7-12 $2.50,   J-1

Buffalo & Erie County Naval & Military Park, 1 Naval Park Cove, 14202,
(716) 847-1773, April 1-Oct 31 Daily 10-5, Nov Sat-Sun, 10-4, Dec-March Closed,
Adm Adult $8.00, Snrs 60+ & Child 6-16 $5.00, Under 6 Free, www.buffalonavalpark.org

F-101F	P-39Q "Snooks 2nd"	USS Little Rock (CLG-4)
FJ-4B	PTF-17 Boat	USS Croaker SSK-246
M-84 A.P.C.	UH-1H	USS Sullivans (DD-537)
M-41 Tank	X-RON 1	

Buffalo Intl Airport, New Terminal, Bell 47

Calverton - Grumman Memorial Park, I-495 Go W on Rte 25(Edwards Ave)to Rte 25A,
Daily 9-5, Mail: POB 147, 11933, (631) 369-9449, Fax 9489, www.grummanpark.org,
A-6,   F-14A

Cheecktowaga - Cal Span Cheecktowaga Airport, 42 Stone Church Rd, (716) 632-7500,
A-26   X-22

Coronia - New York Hall Of Science 47-01 111th St, 11368, (718) 699-0005,
Atlas-Mercury   Saturn V Boat Tail   Titan II-Gemini

Elmira - National Soaring Museum, 51 Soaring Hill Dr, 14903-9204, (607) 734-3128,
Fax 732-6745, Daily 10-5, Adm Adult $6.50, Snrs 60 $5.50, Child 5-17 $4, Under 5 Free
Gift Shop, Sailpane Rides $65-75, www.soaringmuseum.org

ASW-12	Group Genesis I	Prue IIA
Backstrom EPB-1C	H-17	R-6
Backstrom EPB-1A	Hall Cherokee II	RJ-5
Baker McMillen Cadet	Hall Ibex	Rogallo Hang Glider
BB-1	Herring-Arnot	SGP-1-1
Berkshire Concept 70	HP-10	SGS 2-12
BG-12BD	HP-11A	SGS 2-32 (2EA)
Bowlus Sneior Albatross	HP-16	SGS 1-19 (4EA)
Bowlus Super Albatross	HP-18	SGS 1-23D
Bowlus Baby Albatross (2ea)	HP-8	SGS 1-23HM
CG-4A	Johnson Adastra	SGS 1-24
Chanute-Herring	Ka-6E	SGS 1-26
Coward Pacific D8	L-Spatz 55	SGS 1-26E
Croff Batwing	LK-10A	SGS 1-29
Culver Ridgid Midget	LP-15	SGS 1-35
Dagling Primary	Miller Trn	SGU 1-7
Dawydoff UT-1	Mitchell Nimbus III	Sisu 1-A
Franklin PS-2 (5ea)	Nelson Hummingbird (2ea)	Slingsby Kirby Gull
Glasflugel BS-1	Nelson Dragonfly	T-3
Glasflugel H-301	Peel Flying Boat	U-2
Goppingen I	PG-130	Wright 1911
Goppingen III	PR-G1	Wright 1902
Gross Sky Ghost	Prue 215	

Farmingdale - American Airpower Museum, New Highway South of Conklin Ave,
(212) 843-8010, Thur-Sun 10:30-4, Adm Adult $9, Snr $6, Child $4,
www.americanairpowermuseum.com

A-1	F-48(RF)	L-39	TBM
AT-6	F-105	P-40	
B-25	F-111	P-47	
F-84	FG-1D	T-33	

Garden City - Cradle of Aviation Museum, Charles Lindbergh Blvd, Mail: One Davis Ave,
11530, (516) 572-4111, Fax 572-4079, Tue 10-2, Wed-Sun 10-5, Adm Adult $9,
Child 2-12 $8, Gift Shop, IMAX Theater Adult 8.50, Child 2-14 $6.50,
Museum & Theater Adult $16.50, Child $13, www.cradleofaviation.org

A-6F	F-14A & Cockpit	Lilienthal
A-10A	F-84B	Merlin Glider
Aircraft Eng Co Ace	F-84F	NGT(T-46)
Bleriot-Queen XI	F-105B	OV-1B
Boeing 707 Cockpit	F-105D Simulator	P-47N
Breese Penquin	F3F	Paramotor FX-1
Brunner-Winkle Bird	F4F-3	Peel Z-1 Glider
C-47 Simulator	F6F-5	QH-50C
Cassutt B	F9F-7	RC-3
CG-4	Fleet 2	Ryan B-1
Commonwealth	G-21	Ryan NYP
Convertawings A	G-63	S-56
Convair 340 Cockpit	Gyrodyne 2C	S2F & Cockpit
Curtiss Robin 50C	(Continued Next Page)	S4C
E-2C	(Continued Previous Page)	SE-5 (4/5 scale)
F-11A	JN-4	(Continued Next Page)

(From Previous Page)	Douglas M-6 Nike Hercules	Grumman TBM
Sperry AT	Fairchild Petrel	Maxson AQM-37A Drone
Sperry M1	Goddard A-Series Rocket	Maxson A6M-12C Bullpup
TBM-3E	Grumman Missile Rigel	Republic JB-2 Loon
Veligdans Monerai	Grumman Echo Cannister 7	Republic Rocket Terrapin
Wright EX VinFiz	Grumman AWS	Rockwell Command Module
XRON-1	Grumman LM Simulator	Sperry SAM-N-7 Terrier
Spacecraft, Missiles	Grumman LM L-13, LTA-1	Sputnik Satilite
Convair/Sperry SAM-N-7	Grumman LRV Molab	

Geneseo - 1941 Historical Aircraft Group Museum, Geneseo Airport, 3489 Big Tree Lane,
14454, Mail: POB 185, 14454,(585) 243-2100, April 14-Nov 1 Mon, Wed, Fri, 10:30-4,
Summer Daily 10-4, Closed TD, CD, ND, Adm Adult $4, Child 12 & Under $1,
Restoration Facility, www.1941hag.org

AD-4W	C-119G	L-16A	Lancair Simulator
AN-2 (2ea)	Ercoupe 415C	L-17	YO-55 2ea
C-47	L-2	L-21B	

Ghent - Parker-O' Malley Air Museum, 435 Old Rte 20, SW Side of Columbia County Airport,
POB 216, 12075, (518) 392-7200, Adm Adult $5, Child 5-12 $3, Under 5 Free,
www.parkeromalley.org   Rides available

Fleet 2	Me-108	Star Cavalier
Harvard IV	NE-1	Travel Air 4000
Link Trainer	PT-17	

Glenville - Empire State Aerosciences Museum, Schenectady County Airport,
250 Rudy Chase Dr, (Route 50), 12302-4114, (518) 377-2191, Thur-Sat 10-4,
Sun 12-4, Adm Adult $6, Snrs $5, Child 6-16 $2, Under 6 Free, Gift Shop,
Restoration Facility, Research Library, www.esam.org,

A-4F (O)	Curtiss Pusher Rep (D)	H-1F(UH) (O)	RAND Kr-2	(S)
A-6E (O)	F-4D II (O)	H-6A(LOH)	RP-1	(D)
A-7E (P)	F-14A (O)	Huntington Chum (D)	Sky Scooter Rep (D)	
A-10 (O)	F-84F (O)	J4 Javelin (S)	Sonerai II	(S)
AKAGI Rep	F-86D	L-3	Starlite	(S)
B-26 (P)	F-101F (O)	Lockheed 10 (D)	Stits Skycoupe	(D)
C-47 (P)(O)	F-105G (O)	MiG-17F (O)	STRAT M-21	(O)
C-123K (O)	Fisher 303 (S)	MiG-21MF (O)	T-38	
Chanute Hang Glider(D)	GNAT (O)	Mooney Mite (S)		

Hammondsport - Curtiss Museum, 8419 Route 54, 14840, ½ Mile South of Hammondsport,
(607) 569-2160, Fax 569-2040, May 1-Oct 31, Mon-Sat 9-5, Sun 10-5, Nov 1-April 30,
Mon-Sat 10-4, Sun 11-5, Closed Mon-Wed Jan-Mar,TD,CE,CD,ND, Adm Adult $7, Snr 65+ $5,
Child 7-18 $4, 6 & Under Free, Family $20, Gift Shop, Theater, Restoration Facility,
www.linkny.com/~curtiss/

C-46 (Project)	Curtiss June Bug	Link Trainer (Proj)	Silver Dart
Curtiss A-1 Triad	Curtiss Oriole	Mercury S-1 Racer	Target Drone
Curtiss D Pusher	Curtiss Robin	Mercury Chick	OX-5 Engine
Curtiss E Boat	Curtiss Wright Jr	OHM Special Racer	Curtiss Motorcycles
Chanute Glider	JN-4D	P-40 3/4 Scale	

Horseheads - Corning Regional Airport, 6 Mi NW of City, (607) 739-5621,
Stuka Ju-87-B 7/8 Scale, By Richard H. Kurzenberger, Horseheads, NY

Wings of Eagles Discovery Center, 17 Aviation Dr, Elmira-Corning Regional Airport, 14845,
Off Route 17, Exit 51, (607) 739-8200, Fax: 739-8374, Mon-Fri 10-4, Sat 9-5, Sun 11-5, Closed TD,
CD, ND, Adm Adult $7, 65+ $5.50, Child 6-17 $4, Under 6 Free, Family $18, Gift Shop, Snack Bar,
Art Gallery, Theater, Restoration Facility, Wings of Eagles Airshow Third Weekend of September,
Rides: AT-6 $225, PT-17 $150, PT-19 $99, www.wingsofeagles.com, (R) = Restoration, (S) = Storage

A-7D	C-45H(SNB)	H-1C(UH)	MiG 21
A-10A	F-14A	H-1H(UH)	LNS-1(TG-2)
A-37B	F-15B	H-1H(UH) (2ea) (S)	OV-1C
AIM(RIM-7) Missile	F2H-2P	H-6A(OH)	PBY-6A
AT-6D	F4-B	HAR-10 Missile	PT-17(N2S-3)
B-26B	F9F-7	J-3B	PT-19B
B-57A(RB)	F9F-8P	J-3C	R4D-5(C-47)
B-17G(VB)	FH-1	LNE-1(X)(HH-2)	TBM-3E
BTD-1	GAM77(AGM28) Missile	MiG 17	

Jamestown - Lucille M Wright Air Museum, Chautaqua Cnty Airport, 20 Meadow Lane, 14701,
(716) 487-0838

Johnstown - Fulton County Airport, 160 Cnty Hwy 153, 12095, (518) 762-0220, A-3D

Long Island City - The Cockpit, 595 Broadway, (718) 925-5455,   AT-6

Manhattan - The Cockpit, 652 Broadway, 10012, (212) 254-4000

Mayville - Dart Airport, POB 211, Route 430, 14757, (716) 753-2160,
Mon-Fri 8-5 Appt Only, Summer Weekends, Free Adm, Owner Bob Dart

Curtiss Wright Jr	Heath Parasol	Mead Primary
Ercoupe 415	J-2	Melberg
Fleet 16B	J-3	Schweizer I-19

Moria - American Legion Post 939, Hwy 11 East of Town, T-38

Newburgh - Red Star Aviation Museum, Stewart Intl Airport, (980) 813-1398, Contact: David R Sutton,
http://aeroweb.lucia.it/~agretch/RedStarAviation/, email: Sutton@classicjets.org
Antonov, CASA Saeta, Fouga Magister, L-29, L-39, MiG-15UTI, MiG-21, YAK

New York City - Intrepid Sea-Air-Space Museum, 1 Intrepid Plaza, Pier 86, 12th &
46th, 10036, (212) 245-0072, 2533, April-Sept Mon-Fri 10-5, Sat-Sun 10-6,
Oct-March Tue-Sun 10-5, Closed TD, CD, ND, Adm Adult $16.50, Snr & Vets $12.50,
Child 6-17 $11.50, Child 2-5 $4.50, Under 2 Free, www.intrepidmuseum.org

A-4B	F3D (TF-10B)	H-21C	RA-5C
A-4D	F3F-2	H-23(OH) (2 ea)	S-58D
A-6A	F-3H	H-34(UH)	SB2C-4 Replica
AH-1J	F-4N	H-3S(OH)	SE5A
Apollo Capsule Rep	F6F-5 Rep	H-52A(HH)	Sea Hawk F.1
AV-8C	F-80F	HU-16E	SR-71A(A-12 Actually)
Boeing 707 Cockpit		LEM Grumman	Supermarine Scimitar F1
Curtiss Pusher Rep	F-84F		T-33A
Demoiselle Rep	F9F	Lunar Lander Rep	TS-2
E-1B	FJ-3	M-42 Duster Tank	TV-2
Gmini Capsule Rep	H-13S(OH)	M-60 Patton Tank	UH-340
F-14	H-1A(UH)	Mercury Aurora 7 Capsule	USS Growler
F-16	H-1M(UH)	Neptune Submersible	USS Intrepid
F-3B			Voisin Rep

Westchester County Airport Museum (HPN), (914) 997-1612, Artifacts Only

Niagara Falls - Niagara Aerospace Museum, 345 Third St, POB 1181, 14304-8021,
(716) 278-0060, Tue-Sat 10-3, Closed ND, TD, CD, ED, Adm Adult $7, Snrs/Students $6,
Child 5-18 $4, Under 5 Free, Gift Shop, Theater, Restoration Facility,
www.niagaramuseum.org/, e-mail: niagaeromus@juno.com

Bell 47B-3	F-94G	J-2	Schweitser Glider
Bell 47H-1	GA-36	JN-4D	X-22A
Curtiss Pusher	H-1F(AH)	P-39Q	
F-94A	I-23	Pietenpol Air Camper	

Niagara Falls ANG, Int'l Airport, 914 TAG/RMX, 14304-5000, (716) 236-2000

F-100D	F-101F	F-101C(RF)	F-4C

Oriskany - Village of Oriskany, 13424, (315) 736-3512, A-4E

Plattsburg - Plattsburg AFB Military Museum, Route 22, 12901, (518) 565-5000,
565-5165, B-47E F-111

Rhinebeck - Old Rhinebeck Aerodrome (See Top of Next Page)

Riverhead - Raceway Equipment, RD #2, BOX 92K, Horton Ave, 11901, (631) 727-6191,
Mon-Fri 8:30-4:30, Sat By Appt, President: Joe Gertler

Aeronca C-3	C-78(UC)	L-19	Taylorcraft BC-12D
Birdwing Imperial	Emigh Trojan	Luscombe 8E	
Bleriot Original	J-3	Nieuport 27	

Talmage Field Aircraft Collection, Friars Head Farm, 36 Sound Ave, (631) 727-0124, John Talmage

Aeronca Champ	Curtiss OX5 Engine	Hovercraft
Burrner CK Bird	Curtiss OXX6 Engine	Quick Kit Seaplane
Continental R670	Fokker D VII Project	Rearwin Cloudster
Curtiss J6-7	Hispano-Suiza	Travel Air 4000

Rome - Griffiss AFB Museum, Mohawk Valley B-52 memorial, 13441-5000,
Contact: Henry P Smith Post 24, 325 Erie Vlvd W, 13440, (315) 336-2680,
www.borg.com/~post24/monument.html, B-52G

Rhinebeck - Old Rhinebeck Aerodrome, 44 Stone Church Rd, Mail: BOX 229, 12572
(845) 752-3200, Fax: 758-6481, May 15-Oct31, Daily 10-5, Adm Adult $6, Snrs $5
Child 6-10 $2, Under 6 Free, Airshows June 15-Oct 15 Sat-Sun 2pm, Adult $15,
Snrs $10, Child 6-10 $5, Gift Shop, Cafe, Restoration Viewing,
1929 New Standard Biplane Rides 15 Min $40 Per Person, www.oldrhinebeck.org/,
(1)=Pioneer Bldg, (2)=WWI Bldg,(3)=Lindberg Era Bldg, (4)=New Bldg,
(F)=On Field, (EF)=EastSide of Field.

(Aircraft)	(Building)	(Aircraft)	(Building)
Aeromarine 39B	(Pieces)	J-1	(Pieces)
Aeromarine Klemm	(3)	J-2	(F)
Aeronca C-3	(F)	J-3	(EF)
Albatross D-Va	(2)	J-5A	(EF)
Albree Pigeon Fras.	(2)	JN-4D	(F)
American Eagle	(4)	Morane Saulnier A-1	(4)
Ansaldo Ballila SVA-5	(2)	Morane Saulnier MS130	(3)
Avro 504-K	(F)	Morane Saulnier N	(2)
Bleriot XI (3ea)	(1,4,F)	New Standard D-25(4ea)	(F)
Boeing-Stearman	(F)	New Standard D-29(2ea)	(4F)
Breguet 1911	(Pieces)	Nicholas Beasley	(3)
Brunner Bird CK	(3)	Nieuport 2N	(1)
Bucker Jungmann		Nieuport 10/83	(2)
Caudron G.III	(F)	Nieuport 11	(F)
Chanute Glider	(1)	Passett Ornithopter	(1)
Curtiss Fledgling	(F)	Pietenpol Air Camper	(F)
Curtiss Pusher D (2ea)	(F)	Piper Vagabond	(EF)
Curtiss Wright CW-1	(F)	Pitcairn Mailwing	(3)
Davis DIW	(F)	PHSC Scout	
DH-80A		RAF BE.2C (2ea)	(EF)
DH-82 (3ea)	(EF)	RAF FE.8	(2)
Demoiselle (2ea)	(4F)	Rabkaatsentein Glider	(2)
Deperdussin (2ea)	(1)	Ryan NYP	(1)
Dickerson Glider	(3)	Short S-29	(1)
Ercoupe	(EF)	Siemens-Schucker DIII	(2)
Fairchild 24-C8F	(4)	Sopwith Camel	(2)
Fleet Finch 16B	(F)	Sopwith Dolphin	(2)
Fokker Dr.I (3ea)	(2,F)	Spad XIII C1	(4)
Fokker D.VII (2ea)	(F)	Spartan C-3	(3)
Fokker D.VIII	(F)	Stampe SV-4B	(F)
FOkker E.III	(Stored)	Taylor E-2	(Shop)
Great Lakes T21MS	(F)	Thomas-Morse S4.B	(2)
Gyrodyne 2B Chopper	(4)	Thomas Pusher E	(1)
Handriot HD1	(F)	Voisin 8 Bomber	(4)
Heath-Parasol LNA	(3)	Waco 9	
Howard DGA-15P	(EF)	Waco 10	(3)
Luscombe 8A	(EF)	Wright Flyer	(1)
Monocoupe 90	(3)	Wright Glider	(1)
Monocoupe 113	(3)		

Shirley - Brookhaven L.I. Airport, Dwn Dr, 11967, (631) 281-5100

Convair 240	Me-109	SNJ-4
Erocoupe F-1 (Fornaire)	Swift GC-1 Globe	

National Aviation & Transportation Center, Dowling College Annex, Brookhaven
Airport, Pitts Special   PT-17   PT-26

Syracuse - Syracuse ANGB, Hancock Field, 13211-7099, (315) 458-5500, F-86H, F-94B, F-102A

Airport Exhibit, I-81, Hancock Int'l Airport, Center Lobby Main Floor, Artifacts, Cafe

Westhampton Beach - Francis Gabreski Airport, 11978-1294, (631) 288-4200,   F-102A

Williamsville - Niagara Frontier Aviation & Space Museum, 5583 Main St,
Municipal Bldg, 14221, (716) 631-3276, Vice Chairman: Jack Prior

NORTH CAROLINA

Asheboro - North Carolina Aviation Museum, 2109 Pilots View Rd, 27203, Mail: POB 1814,
27204-1814, (336) 625-0170, Fax 629-1520, Mon-Sat 10-5, Sun 1-5, Adm Adult $5,
Students $3, Child Under 6 Free, Grp Rates, Gift Shop, Restoration Facility,
Airshow 1st Weekend in June, www.ncairmuseum.org

AT-6G	F-84F	O-2A 2ea	T-34A
B-25J Project	J-3 Flitfire	P-3 Pilatus	TBM-3E
BT-13A	L-4	PT-13D	
C-45H	L-19A	T-28B	

Candler - Enka Junior High School, 475 Enka Lake Rd, 28715, (828) 667-5421, F-84F(RF)

Charlotte - Carolinas Aviation Museum, 4108 Airport Dr, Hangar 4108, Charlotte/Douglas Int'l
Airport, 28208-5709, Mail: POB 555, Richfield, 28137, (704) 359-8442, Fax 359-8442,
Tue-Fri 10-4,Sat 10-5, Sun 1-5, Adm Adult $3, Snrs $2, Gift Shop, Restoration Facility
www.chacweb.com

A-4	F-84G	HOK-1	T2A
A-7	F-80C	L-5	T-28 Cockpit
An-2	F-101F	Link Trainer	T-28B
Bellanca 14-9L	F-102A(YF)	Mercury Capsule rep	T-33 Cockpit
Bushby Mustang	H-1HA(UH)	OV-1D	T-33A
C-97 Cockpit	H-1HB(UH)	OV-10	T-33B
CG-15A	H-1J(AH)	P-80	Wright Glider
DC-3	H-34C(CH)	Regulasa Missile	M551A Sheridan Tank
F-4	H-50C(QH)	Skycat	
F-86L	HO3S-1	SNJ-5C	

Charlotte ANG, Charlotte/Douglas Municipal Airport, 28208, 145 TAG/CC
(704) 399-6363, 145th TAG,   F-86L

Cherry Point - Cherry Point Marine Base, Pres Edward Ellis, (252) 447-2346, F-4U, PBY

Durham - North Carolina Museum of Life & Science, 433 Murray Ave, POB 15190, 27704-
3101, (919) 220-5429, Mon-Sat 10-5, Sun 1-5, Adm Adult $3.75, Child 4-12 $2.75, DC-3, F-11A

Fayetteville - Fort Bragg, 82nd Airborne Division War Memorial Museum, POB 70119,
Ardennes & Gela St, Bldg C-684128307-0119, (910) 432-3343, Tue-Sun 10-4:30, Free Adm,
Gift Shop 436-1735, www.bragg.army.mil/18abn/museums.htm

C-7	C-47B	C-123K
C-46F	C-119L	H-1(UH)

Airborne & Special Operations Museum, 100 Bragg Blvd, From I-95, 28301, (910) 483-3003,
Fax 485-2024, Tue-Sat 10-5, Sun 12-5, Free Adm, www.asomf.org,

C-47,	CG-4A	H-6(AH)	H-1(UH)	M551 Tank

John F Kennedy Special Warfare Museum, Ardennes & Marion St, Bldg D-2502, (910) 432-1533
Tue-Sun 11:30-4

Pope AFB, Main (Reilly Gate), 28308, (910) 394-0001, * Located Off Hwy 23 FW Ramp

A-7D *	A-10A(OA) *	C-119	F-105D *
A-10A *	C-47B	C-123K	P-40

Goldsboro - Seymour Johnson AFB, 4th Wing HQ Wright Brothers Ave, 27531-5000, (919) 736-5400,

F-4C	F-15B/E	F-86E	F-105D
F-4E	F-15E	F-86H	

Havelock - Cherry Point Marine Corps Air Station, Hwy 70 & Cuningham Blvd, 28533-5001,
2 Hour Tour 1st & 3rd Thur ea Month at 8:45am, Adm Free, (252) 466-5895,   AV-8

Havelock Tourist Center, 202 Tourist Cntr Dr, 28532, (252) 444-6402, Mail: POB 368

A-4M	F4B-3	F9F-6P	RF-4B

Hendersonville - Western North Carolina Air Museum, 1340 Gilbert St, (828) 698-2482, Mail To:
POB 2343, 28793, (Mar-Oct) Sat 10-5, Sun & Wed 12-5; (Nov-Feb) Sat-Sun & Wed 12-5, Free Adm,
Gift Shop, www.wncairmuseum.com (P)=Project

Aeronca C-3	Curtiss Robin 4C-1A	J-3C	SE-5
Aeronca Champ	E-2	J-5	SNJ-5
BC-12D Taylorcraft(P)	Ercoupe 415CD	L-2	Stearman N2S
Cessna 120	Heath Parasol (P)	Nieuport Bebe 11	Stearman N4S
Corbin Junior Ace	J-2	PA-12	Wittman Tailwind W-8

Hickory - Hickory Municipal Airport, (828) 328-4078,

A-7B	F-4B	F-105B	FJ3	T-33	LTV

Kill Devil Hills - Wright Brothers National Memorial, US 158(Croaton Hwy)
& E Ocean Bay Blvd, (252) 441-7430, Mail: POB 1903, 27948, Mon-Sat 10-4, Sun 1-4
www.nps.gov/wrbr/index.htm, Dec 17, 2003 100th Anniv Flight

Manteo - Wright Brothers National Memorial, POB 457, 27954, Virginia Dare
Trail-By Pass, (252) 441-4481, Daily 8-8, Free Adm, Wright Flyer, Glider

Maxton - Gulledge Aviation, Laurin-Maxton Airport, (910) 844-3601, Jetliner Salvage

Raleigh - North Carolina Museum of History, 5 E Edenton St, 27601-1011,
(919) 715-0200, B-8M Bensen Gyrocopter, Rogallo Wing, Wright Flyer Replica

Newbern - Clarendon Blvd, Hwy 17 South, City Park,   F-11A

Southern Pines - CAF - Carolinas Wing, Moore County Airport, http://30seconds.org/caf/, AT-19

NORTH CAROLINA (Continued)

Topsail Beach - Topsail Island Museum, The Assembly Bldg, 720 Channel Blvd,
Mail: POB 2645, 28445, Mid April-Oct Mon, Tue, Thur-Sat, 2-4, Nov-March Appt Only
(800) 626-2780, (910) 328-4722, Gift Shop, www.topsailmissilesmuseum.org
Talos Rocket from Operation Bumblebee 1959

Waynesville - VFW Post 5202,2116 Miller St, 28786, (828) 452-3127, UH-1, Tank

Wilmington - Wilmington Aviation Foundation, 1740 Airport Blvd, 28405, (910) 254-9989
www.ilmfoundation.org

NORTH DAKOTA

Bismarck - State Historical Society Museum, Liberty Memorial Blvd, 58501,
(701) 224-2666, Daily 8-5, Sat 9-4, Sun 1-5, Free Adm,

Casselton - Aero Replicas, Casselton Regional Airport, 58012, (701) 347-4680, 2½ Mi S
of City, Mail: POB 64, email: RJM1003@acol.com, Daily 8-5,

Bf-109 Replica	F-4C	Pitts S-1-C

Fargo - CAF - Red River Valley Wing, Hector Int'l, (701) 241-1501, Elden C Herrmann,
Curtiss Golden Flyer

Fargo Air Museum, 1609 19th Ave N, 58102, Mail: POB 8190, 58109-8190, (701) 293-8043,
Fax 293-8103, Tue-Sat 9-5, Sun 12-4, Closed E, TD, CD, ND, Adm Adult $6, Snrs/Mil $5,
Child 5-12 $4, Under 5 Free, Group Rate Adult $4, Child $2, Gift Shop, Restoration Facility,
www.fargoairmuseum.org

A6M2 Model 21 Beech D17	F4U-4	P-51D	
AT-6	DC-3	LNE-1	PT-19
B-25	F2G-1D	P-40	TBF

Fargo ANG, Hector Field, 58105-5536, (701) 237-6030,

C-45J	F-16A	F-101B	
C-47B	F-89J	F-101F	F-104C
F-4D	F-94C	F-102A	P-51D

North Dakota State University, 1301 12 Ave N 58102, (701) 237-7130, F-104

Grand Forks - Center For Aerospace Sciences, Box 8216, Univ Station, 58202
(701) 777-2791, Project Officer: Lt Col Terry Young

Grand Forks AFB Heritage Center, Building 125, 58205, (701) 747-6924, 319BW

A-26C	B-52G	F-102A	H-19D	Minuteman III
B-25J	F-101B	H-1F(U)	Transporter Erector	

Minot - Dakota Territory Air Museum, Minot Int'l Airport, Mail: POB 195, 58702-0195
(701) 852-8500, May-Oct Mon, Wed, Fri-Sat 10-5, Sun 1-5, Adm Adult $2, Child 6-17 $1
www.dakotaterritoryairmuseum.com

A-7	Ercoupe	T-33
Arrow Sport	J-2	Taylorcraft
Arrow Monoplane	J-3	Travel-Aire 3000
Breezy Open Air	L-29	Veri-ezee
Breezy RL-1	Monocoupe 110	Volks Plane
C-47 Cockpit	Pietenpol	Waco
C-47	AR-5A Stinson	Waco GXE
Cessna 195	Starduster Two	Waco UPF-7

Minot AFB, 919 MW/CVS58705, (701) 727-4761, F-102A, F-106A, H-1F(UH), T-33A

Wahpeton - Tri State Aviation, Wahpeton Airport, (701) 642-5777,
Mon-Fri 8-5, Manager: Jerry Beck

B-25	Howard DGA,	P-51	TBM
F4U-4	L-4	PT-17	

West Fargo - Bonanzaville USA Historical Museum, Civil and Military Aircraft
W Fargo Fairgrounds I-94 & Hwy 10, (701) 282-2822, Oct-May Tue-Fri 9:30-4,

Sat-Sun 1-5, Bowers Fly Baby	J-1	VC-47

OHIO

Akron - Goodyear World of Rubber, 1144 E. Market St, 4nd Floor, 44316, (330)796-2121
Daily 8:30-4:30, Free Adm, FG-1D Fuse

Alliance - Alliance High School, 400 Glamorgan St, 44601, (330) 821-2100, A-7

Forest Barber, Airport, 3 Mi N of City, (216) 823-1168, Taylorcraft Model A Series 45

Batavia - Tri State Warbird Museum, 4021 Borman Dr, 45103, Clermont Cnty Airport,
(513) 735-4500, AT-6D,   B-25,   FG-1D,   P-51D,   TBM-3

Bryan - Military Heritage Museum, American Legion Post 284, 519 E. Butler St
43506, (419) 636-7354, By Appt, Artifacts all Wars

OHIO (Continued)

Carroll - Historical Aircraft Squadron, 3266 Old Columbus Dr, 43112, (641) 653-4778
  Wed, Sat 9-5, Gift Shop, Restoration Facility, www.historicalaircraftsquadron.com,
  A-26 Project   BT-13 Project

Chardon - Curtiss Robert, 15215 Chardon Airport, 44086, (440) 298-1417, D-31 New Standard

Cincinaatti - Blue Ash Airport, B-17E "My Gal Sal" Restoration from Greenland
  Contact: Bob Ready, Exec Aviation, 4393 Glendale Milford Rd, 45242, (513) 984-3881,
  www.ultimatesacrifice.com,   E-mail: bob_ready@hotmail.com

  Cinncinnati Municipal Airport Lunken Field, 3 Mi SE of City, (513) 321-4132,
  Fax 871-6801, E-mail: dan.dickten@cingen.rec.org, F-86

Cleveland - Burke Lakefront Airport, Marjorie Rosenaum Plaza, 1501 Marginal Rd, 44100,
  (216) 781-6411, F-4J   F-4E

  Frederick Crawford Auto-Aviation Museum, 10825 E Blvd, (216) 721-5722,
  Mon-Sat 10-5, Sun 12-5, Adm Adult $7.50, Snrs $6.50, Child $5.50, Under 3 Free
  www.wrhs.org/crawford

Cessna 182P	DGA-3	Gee Bee R-1 Rep
Chester Special	DH-4	Great lakes 2T-1A
Curtiss Bumblebee	F2G-2D	P-51K
Curtiss MF	Fulton Airphibian	Weddell-Williams Special

  International Women's Air & Space Museum, Inc, Burke Lakefront Airport
  Room 165, 1501 N Marginal Rd, 44114, (216) 623-1111, Fax: 623-1113,
  Mon-Fri 10-4, Free Adm, www.iwasm.org, Artifacts

  NASA-Lewis Research Center/Visitor Information, 21000 Brookpark Rd,
  MS 8-1, 44135, (216) 433-2000, Mon-Fri 9-4, Sat 10-3, Sun 1-5, Free Adm,
  Apollo Skylab III Command Module

Columbus - CAF - Ohio Valley Wing, 2000 Norton Rd, Bolton Field, 43228,
  www.cafohio.org, L-5(OY-2)

  Center of Science & Industry, 333 W Broad St, 43215, (614) 221-2674,
  Mon-Sat 10-5, Sun 1-5:30, Adm Adult $3.50, Child $2,PT-12, Mercury Capsule

  Columbus DCSC, 3990 E Broad St, 43213, (614) 238-3131, F-100D,   F-105D

Dayton - Carillon Park, 2001 S Patterson Blvd, 45409, (937) 293-3412,
  Tue-Sat 10-8, Sun 1-8, Free Adm, Wright Flyer, Six Trains

  National Aviation Hall of Fame, 1100 Spaatz St, WPAFB, 45433,Mail: POB 31096,
  45437, (937) 256-0944, Daily 9-5, Closed: TD, CD, ND, ED, Adm Free, Artifacts

  US Air Force Museum, 1100 Spaatz St, Wright-Patterson AFB, From I-75S Exit 61A
  To I-70E to Exit 44A to I675S to Exit 15; From I-75 Exit 43 to I-675S to Exit 15
  45433-7102, (937) 255-3284, Daily 9-5, Closed TD, CD, ND, Free Adm, Annex Hours:
  Daily 9:30-3, IMAX Theater (937) 253-IMAX, Media Relations: Diana Bachert 255-4704 ext 332,
  www.wpafb.af.mil/museum, **Location Codes:** OP = Outdoor Airpark S = Storage
  Gallery Codes:

Cold War	= CW	Missiles	= M	Space Flight = SF
Early Years	= EY	Modern Flight	= MF	Vietnam War = VW
Inter War Years	= IWY	Presidential	= P	World War I = WWI
Korean War	= KW	Research & Development = RD	World War II = WWII

A-1E Skyraider	KW	AT-6D	MF
A-7D	MF	AT-6G	S
A-10A Thunderbolt II	MF	AT-6G	EY
A-10(YA)	OP	AT-9 Jeep	WWII
A-17A	IWY	AT-10 Wichita	WWII
A-20G Havoc	WWII	AT-11 Kansan	WWII
A-24	WWII	AT-38B	CW
A-25A	WWII	Avro 504K	WWI
A-26C Invader	KW	B-1B	MF
A-36A Apache	WWII	B-2 Spirit	MF
A-37A(YA) Dragonfly	KW	B-3	RD
A6M2 Zero	WWII	B-10	IWY
AC-130A	MF	B-17G Flying Fortress	WWII
ADM-20 Quail	CW	B-18A Bolo	WWII
Aerojet Aerobee Rocket	SP	B-23	OP
Agena Space Vehicle	SP	B-24D	EY
AGM-28B Hound Dog	CW	B-25B Mitchell	WWII
AGM-86B (ALCM)	CW	B-26G Marauder	WWII
AGM-129A	CW	B-26K Counter Invader	KW
AGM-136A Tacit Rainbow	RD	B-29 Fuselage	KW
Apollo Capsule	SP	B-29 Superfortress	WWII
AQM-34L Firebee	KW	B-36J	CW
AQM-34N	CW	B-45C Tornado	KW
AQM-91A Compass Arrow	RD	B-47E	MF
ASV-3 ASSET Lifting Body	SP	(Continued Next Page)	

(Continued From Previous Page)

B-47H(RB)	CW	F-84E Thunderjet	KW
B-50D(WB) Superfortress	CW, OP	F-84F Thunderstreak	CW
B-52D Stratofortress	KW	F-84F(YRF)FICON	RD
B-57B(EB) Canberra	KW	F-84K(RF)	CW
B-57D	CW	F-84H(XF)	RD
B-58 Hustler	CW	F-85(XF) Goblin	RD
B-66B Destroyer	KW	F-86A Sabre	KW
B-70(XB) Valkyrie	RD	F-86D Sabre	CW
Bf 109G-10	WWII	F-86H Sabre	CW
BGM-109A Griffon	M	F-89J Scorpion	CW
Bleriot Monoplane	EY	F-90(XF)	CW
Block IV Satellite	SP	F-91(XF) Thunderceptor	RD
Boeing Bird of Prey	MF	F-92A(XF)	RD
Boost Glide Reentry Vehicle	SP	F-94A Starfire	KW
Boeing 707, (Air Force One)		F-94C Starfire	CW
BQM-34	CW	F-100(CF) Mk IV	CW
BQM-34F	CW	F-100D Super Sabre	MF
Bristol Beaufighter	WWII	F-100F Super Sabre	KW
BT-9B	IWY	F-101B Voodoo	CW
BT-13B Valiant	WWII	F-101C(RF) Voodoo	CW
BT-14	EY	F-102A Delta Dagger	CW
C-6A(VC)	P	F-104A	
C-7A Caribou	KW	F-104C Starfighter	CW
C-39A		F-105D Thunderchief	KW
C-43(UC) Beech Staggerwing 17	EY	F-105F Thunderchief	KW
C-45H Expeditor	CW	F-106A Delta Dart	CW
C-46D Commando	WWII	F-107A	RD
C-47D Skytrain	WWII	F-111A	KW
C-54C(VC) Sacred Cow	P	F-111F Aardvark	MF
C-60A	OP	F-117A Nighthawk	MF
C-82A	OP	Fa-330 Sandpiper	WWII
C-97L(KC) Stratofreighter	CW, OP	Fairchild Model 24-C8F	WWII
C-118(VC) Independence	P	Fi 156C-1 Storch	WWII
C-119J Flying Boxcar	SP, OP	Fokker D.VII	WWI
C-121D(EC) Constellation	KW, OP	Fokker Dr.I	WWI
C-121E(VC) Columbine III	P	Fw 190D-9	WWII
C-123K Provider	KW	Gemini Capsule	SP
C-124C Globemaster	KW	H-3E(CH)	KW
C-125B(YC) Raider	OP	H-5A(YH)	KW
C-126A(LC)	CW	H-1P(UH) Iroquois	KW
C-130A(AC)	OP	H-13J(UH) Sioux	P
C-130A(JC)	OP	H-19B(UH) Chickasaw	KW
C-131D	OP	H-20(XH) Little Henry	RD
C-133A Cargomaster	CW	H-21B(CH) Workhorse	CW
C-135E(EC)ARIA	OP	H-26(XH)	RD
C-135A(NKC)	OP	Halberstadt CL IV	WWI
C-137C(VC)	P	Hawker Hurricane MkIIa	IWY
C-140B(VC) Jetstar	P	HE-111	S
C-142A(XC) LTV	RD	HGM-25A Titan I	M, OP
Caproni Ca.36	WWI	HH-43B Huskie	KW
Caquot Type R Obser Balloon	WWI	HU-16B Albatross	CW
CG-4A Hadrian	WWII	ICBM Hard Mobile Launcher	SP
CGM-13B Mace	CW, OP	J-1	WWI
CIM-10A Bomarc	CW, OP	J-1 (Fabric removed)	WWI
Convair Atlas Missile	CW	J-3 Cub	WWII
Curtiss 1911 Model D	EY	JN-4D Jenny	WWI
D-21B	CW	JU-52	OP
Dart Aerial Target	CW	Ju-88D-1	WWII
DH-4B	IWY	Kettering Bug Torpedo	WWI
DH 82A Tiger Moth	IWY	L-1A Vigilant	WWII
DH 89B Dominie	WWII	L-2M Grasshopper	WWII
DH 98 Mosquito	WWII	L-3B Grasshopper	WWII
DSP Satellite	SP	L-4 (O-59A)	EY
EF-111A Raven	MF	L-4A Grasshopper	WWII
Ercoupe 415	S	L-5 Sentinel	WWII
Excelsior Gondola	SP	L-6 Grasshopper	WWII
F-4 Phantom cockpit Rep	KW	L-17A Navion	CW
F-4C Phantom II	KW	LGM-30 Minuteman II	M
F-4C(RF)Phantom II	MF	LGM-30A Minuteman I	M, OP
F-4E(YF) Phantom II	RD, OP	LGM-30G Minuteman III	M, OP
F-4G Wild Weasel	MF	LNE-1 (TG-3A)	S
F-5A Skoshi Tiger	KW	Lockheed Satellite	SP
F-12A(YF)	RD	LTV A-7D Corsair II	KW
F-15 Streak Eagle	OP	LTV ASAT Missile	SP
F-15A Eagle	CW	Lusac-11	EY
F-16 Cockpit Mock-up	CW	M-1 Messenger	TWY
F-16A	MF	Manhigh II Gondola	SP
F-22(YF) Raptor	MF	Martin Peacekeeper	M
F-80C Shooting Star	KW	MB-2	IWY
F-80R(XF)	AP	MC-200 Saetta	WWII
F-82B Twin Mustang		McCook Field Wind Tunnel	WWI
		(Continued Next Page)	

50

(Continued From Previous Page)

Aircraft	Code		Aircraft	Code
Me 163B	WWII		RQ-3A Global Hawk	MF
Me 262A Schwalbe	WWII		S4C Scout	WWI
Mercury Capsule	SP		SA-2 Surface-to-Air Missile	KW
MiG-15bis Fagot	KW		SE-5E	IWY
MiG-17 Fresco	KW		SICM	M
MiG-19S Farmer	CW		SM-62 Snark	RD, OP
MiG-21PF Fishbed	KW		SM-65 Atlas	M
MiG-23	OP		SM-68 Titan II	M
MiG-29 Fulcrum	CW		Sopwith F-1 Camel	WWI
Minuteman II Trainer	M		SPAD VII	WWI
MQM-107	CW		SPAD XIII	WWI
MXY7-KI	AP		SPAD XVI	WWI
N1K2-J George-21	WWII		SR-71A	CW
Nieuport N.28C-1	WWI		Stargazer Gondola	SP
NT-33A	RD		Supermarine Spitfire Mk XI	WWII
O-1G	KW		Supermarine Spitfire MkVc	WWII
O-2A Skymaster	KW		SV-5D PRIME Lifting Body	SP
O-38F	IWY		T-28A	MF
O-46A	IWY		T-28B Trojan	KW, OP
O-47B	IWY		T-33A(NY)	AP
O-52 Owl	IWY		T-33A Shooting Star	CW
OA-1A	IWY		T-34A Mentor	CW
OA-10 Catalina	WWII		T-37B Tweety Bird	CW
OA-12 Duck	CW		T-38A Talon	CW
OQ-14	WWII		T-39A Sabre Liner	P
OQ-2A Aerial Target	WWII		T-41A Mescalero	CW
OV-10A Bronco	KW		T-6	KW
OV2-5	SP		Tacit Blue (Whale)	RD
P-6E	IWY		Teal Ruby Satellite	SP
P-12E	IWY		TM-61A Matador	CW, OP
P-26A	IWY		U-2A	CW
P-35A	WWII		U-3A	CW
P-36A Hawk	WWII		U-4B	P
P-38L Ligntning	WWII		U-6A Beaver	CW
P-39Q Airacobra	WWII		U-10D Super Courier	KW
P-40E Warhawk	WWII		UC-43 Traveler	WWII
P-47D Razorback	WWII		UC-64A Norseman	WWII
P-47D-30	WWII		UC-78B Bobcat	WWII
P-51D Mustang	WWII		V-1 Buzz Bomb	WWII
P-59B Airacomet	RD		V-2 with Meilerwagen	WWII
P-61C Black Widow	WWII		V-6A(XV) Kestrel	RD
P-63E Kingcobra	WWII		Wright 1909 Military Flyer	EY
P-75A	RD		Wright Brothers 1901 Wind Tunnel	EY
P-80R(XP)	RD		Wright Brothers 1911 Wind Tunnel	EY
P-81(XP)	RD		X-1B	RD
PA-48 Enforcer	RD		X-3 Stiletto	RD
Packard LePere LUSAC	IWY		X-4	RD
Panavia Tornado	MF		X-5	RD
Peacekeeper RV Bus	M		X-7A	RD
PGM-17 Thor	M, OP		X-10	RD
PGM-19 Jupiter	M, OP		X-13 Vertijet	RD
PQ-14B	WWII		X-15A-2	SP
PT-1 Trusty	IWY		X-17	SP
PT-13D Kaydet	IWY		X-21	RD
PT-16(YPT)	RD		X-24A	SP
PT-19A Cornell	IWY		X-24B	SP
PT-22 Recruit	WWII		X-25A Gyrocopter	RD
PT-26			X-29A	RD
QU-2B	KW		X-32 Joint Strike Competitor	MF
R-4B Hoverfly	WWII		XC-142A	
R-6A Hoverfly II	WWII		XGAM-63 Rascal	RD
Redstone Booster	SP		YCGM-121B Robotic Vehicle	RD
RK-86F	CW		Yokosuka Ohka Trainer	WWII
RQ-1A Predator	MF		YQM-94A Compass Cope B	RD
RQ-3A Dark Star	RD			

Dayton - Museum of Pioneer Aviation and Wright Brother's Aeroplane Company, PO Box 204 45383, 4th & Ludlow St (Wilkies Bookstore), www.first-to-fly.com
Replica Wright Flyer 1 & 3

Eaton - CAF-Wright Stuff Squadron, 223 E Somers St, 45320, Dahio Trotwood Airport (I44), Mail: 1334 N Lutheran Church Rd, 45427, (937) 456-4722, 248-4777
www.wrightstuffsquadron.com, T-50

Elyria - CAF - Cleveland Wing, Lorain Co Reginal Airport, 44050 Russia Rd, 44035 (440) 323-8335, Sat 9:30, www.clevelandwing.org, SNJ

S Euclid - United States Aviation Museum Assoc, Mail: PO Box 21846 Cleveland, 44121, Contact: Tony Mazzolini, 4477 Mackall Rd, 44121, (216) 381-5270, Fax 318-8801
A-1   B-25   C-45

Fairborn - Wright-Patterson Material Command Headquarters, Route 44, Bldg 262, F-4 2ea

Fremont - Fremont Airport, St Rd 53, 43420, (419) 332-8037, Howard DGA-5 In Storage

Groveport - Motts Military Museum, Inc, 5075 S Hamilton Rd, 43125, (614) 836-1500
Fax 836-5110, Tue-Sat 9-5, Sun 1-5, Adm Adult $5, Seniors $4, Student $3
www.mottsmilitarymuseum.org, M47 Tank - Arnold Schwarzenegger Drove in the Austrian Army
M42A1 Tank, M151 Jeep, PA 36-7 Higgins Boat, M110A2 Howitzer, 105mm Iraq Cannon

Leroy - Pheasant Run Airport, 081-07-29.354W / 41-42-35.178N, By Appt Only, (216) 298-1314,
Mail: Chuck F Reed, 5782 Trask Rd, Madison, OH 44057,

Beechcraft JRB	Junkers Fighter/Bomber	Meyers OTW	SE-5
Fokker DR.I	L-6	Miles & Atwood Racer	Plus 13 More
J-3	L-16	Ryan ST3-W	

Lockbourne - Rickenbacker ANGB, 43217, Off Rte 317, (614) 492-8211, 121st TFW

A-7D 2ea	F-15A	F-100D	T-33A
C-131E(TC)	F-84B	O-2A	
F-4C(RF)	F-84F	P-80C	

Madison - Charles F Reed, 5782 Trask Rd, 44057, (440) 298-1314, Appt Only

Aeronca Champ (2 ea)	Luscombe	Smith Miniplane
Bowers Flybaby Biplane	OTK Myers	Stinson 108
Fleet Model 2	Piper J-5	
Fokker Dr.I	PT-22	

Miamisburg - Wright B Flyer Museum, 10550 Springboro Pike, Off Rte 741, Wright Brothers Airport
(Dayton General Airport), 45342, (937) 885-2327, Tue,Thur,Sat 9-2:30,
Closed Holidays, www.wright-b-flyer.org, Wright B Flyer Flyable Rides for $150

Mansfield - Mansfield ANG, Mansfield Lahm Airport, 44901-5000, (419) 522-9355, F-84F

Newark - Newark AF Museum, 2803 ABG, 43057-5000, PA: (740) 522-7779, F-4C, T-33A

Newbury - **(Closing)** Walter A Soplata Aviation Collection, 11721 Hickory Dale Rd,
(440) 564-5326, Private Collection. Appt Only

A-1E	C-45	F-861	P-80A
AT-6G	C-82	FG-1D	P-82(XP)
AT-11	DC-7	H-34(SH)	PT-19
B-25J	F2G-1	KC-97	T-2
B-26(VB)	F7U-3	O-52	T-28A
B-36A(YB)	F11F-1	P2V-7	T-33A
B-57	F-84E	P-39	T-50
BT-12(YBT)	F-84F	P-47L	TBM
BT-13A	F-84F(RF)	P-51K	
BT-15	F-86E	P-63	

North Canton - Maps Air Museum, 2260 Int'l Prkwy, 44720, (330)896-6332,
W Side of Akron-Canton Airport Off Rte 241,(Spring-Fall)Mon-Tue & Thur-Sat 9-4,
Wed 9pm-9, Adm Adult $4, Seniors $3.50, Child Under 12 $2, Gift Shop, www.mapsairmuseum.org,
(UR) = Under Restoration   (S) = Storage

A-24B(SBD-5) (S)	F-11F	L-2D	P-51
A-7E	F-100	L-17B	PT-19
B-25	F-101	Link Trainer 2ea	S-2F
B-26(UR)	F-102	MiG-17F (UR)	T-28S (S)
C-47B(UR)	H-1B(UH) (S)	O-2A	
DHC-6	H-1S(AH)	P-39Q (2ea)(UR)(S)	
F-4	H-58(OH)		

Norwalk - Firelands Museum of Military History, 4755 SR601, (419) 668-8161,
Mail: c/o Richard Rench, 202 Citizens Bank Bldg, 448547,
UH-1H,(Rides Available), AH-1A, Tanks: M-42, M-60; APC Fort T-16, Mark VII Ferrett
(UH-1H 2ea in Storage 961, 20 East Norwalk Airport)

Oberlin - Oberlin FAA, ARTCC, 58357, (440) 774-0100,   F-101B

Springfield - OH ANG, Springfield ANG, 183rd TFG,Springfield-Beckley Mncpl, 45502-8783
5 Mi S of Town Off Hwy 68 on Rd 794, (937) 327-2100, F-84C   F-84F   F-100D

Swanton - Toledo ANG, Toledo Express Airport, 43558, (419) 866-2078, F-84F   F-100D

Toledo - Toledo Suburban Airport, D Keller, 4720 S Arvilla Dr 43623,
(419) 885-3907,   BT-14

Troy - Waco Aircraft Museum & Aviation Learning Center, 105 S. Market St, 45373, Mail: POB 62
(937) 335-9226, May-Oct Sat-Sun 1-5, Gift Shop, www.wacoairmuseum.org, Junkin Brukner
Waco: CG-4A,   ATO,   CTO,   Glider,   UPF-7W,   YMF,

OHIO (Continued)

Wapakoneta - Neil Armstrong Air & Space Museum, I-75 Exit 111 (Bellefontain St), POB 1978, 45895-0978,(419) 738-8811, (800) 860-0142, Tue-Sat 9:30-5, Sun 12-5, Adult $7, Child 6-12 $3, Under 6 Free, Groups $3, www.ohiohistory.org/places/armstron/
Wright Model G Aerobaot, Aeronca 7AC, F5D-1, Gemini VIII

OKLAHOMA

Altus - Altus AFB, 73523-5000, (580) 482-8100, 443rd MAW, 47th FTW, C-118B, T-34B

Bartlesville - Woolaroc Museum, Frank Phillips Foundation Inc, POB 1647, 74005, (918) 336-0308, Tue-Sun 10-5, Adm Adult $2, 16 Under Free, Woolaroc Airplane

Vance AFB, 73705-5000, (580) 237-2121, 71st FTW, F-105D   T-28A   T-33A

Fort Sill - US Army Field Artillery & Fort Sill Museum, 437 Quanah Rd, 73503-5100, (580) 422-5123, Sat 8:30-4:30, Sun 12:30-4:30, Closed CD, ND, Free Adm, http://sill-www.army.mil/Museum/

H-1B(OH)	H-23F(OH)	L-4	L-19	T-41B	Missile Park

Guymon - CAF Cimmaron Strip Wing, C-45

Lexington - Citizen Potawatomee Territory, Hwy 59 West, H-12

Oklahoma City - CAF Oklahoma Wing,7100 NW63, Wiley Post Airport, Hangar 201, Mail: POB 42532, 73123-3521,   PT-19

CAF Sierra Hotel A-26 Sponsor Group, 7100 NW63, Wiley Post Airport, Hangar 301,

FAA Aeronautical Center, Academy Building, Room 101, 6500 S. Mac Arthur Blvd, 73169, (405) 954-4709, POB 25082, AMG-400D, Librarian: Virginia C. Huges, Aviation: Reference, Electronics, Mathematics, Education, Management.

45th Infantry Division Museum, 2145 NE 36th St, 73111, (405) 424-5313, Tue-Fri 9-4:15, Sat 10-4:15, Sun 1-4:15, Free Adm, www.45thdivisionmuseum.com,

A-7	H-1B(UH)	H-13E(OH)	H-58(OH)	L-17A	L-20
F-86L	H-6A (OH)	H-23C(OH)	L-4B	L-19	T-33A
F-80C					

Aerospace Museum, 6000 N Martin King Blvd, (405) 685-9546, Curtiss Pusher

Kirkpatrick Center - Air & Space Museum, 2100 NE 52nd, 73111, (800) 532-7652, Main 405-427-5461, Hours & Information (405) 427-7529, Adm Adult 13-64 $7.50 Snrs & Child 3-12 $6, Under 3 Free, Winter Mon-Fri 9-5, Sat 9-6, Sun 11-6, Gift Shop, Cafe 425-7529, Omni Dome, Planetarium, Prices start at Adult $12.50, Snrs $10.50, Child $10.50 www.omniplex.org

American Eaglet	Curtiss Pusher D	Lunar Module	Stinson Voyager
Apollo Capsule	F-104	Mercury Capsule	T-33A
Apollo Module	Fokker DR.1 (2 ea)	Nieuport 11	V-2
Bu.133	Gemini Capsule	Parker Pusher	Wiley Post
Bunker 154	Gulfsteam Peregrine	Star Cavalier	

State Fair Grounds, B-47   B-52D   C-47   Gulfstream SC

Tinker AFB, 73145, (405) 734-7321, B-29   B-47(RB)   B-52D
C-47(EB)   C-121K(EC)   C-135(KC)

Tinker ANG, 3000 S, 73125, (405) 734-2778, F-105D,   F-86D,   T-33A

Tulsa - CAF - Spirit of Tulsa Squadron, PT-19

Tulsa ANG, Tulsa Int'l Airport, 74115, (918) 832-5208, F-100D, F-86D

Tulsa Air & Space Center, Tulsa Int'l Airport, 7130 E Apache, 74115-3708, Hangar 5 (918) 834-9900, Fax 834-6723, Tue-Fri 10-4, Sat 10-5, Sun 1-5, Adm Adult $4.50, Snrs & Students $3.50, Child 6-12 $2.50, Under 6 Free, Gift Shop, Library, Closed ES, MD, July 4, LD, TD, CD, Space Artifacts, www.tulsaairandspacemuseum.com
C-2,   C-3,   F-14A   HK-47   Ranger 2000   T-37

Richard Lioyd Jones Jr Airport, (918) 299-5886, Hanging From Main Lobby, JN-4D

Riverside Airport, Contact David Wheaton, B-25 "Martha Jean"

Weatherford - General Thomas P Stafford Museum, Jim Cobb Rd, Stafford Airport, 73096, (580) 772-6143, Mon-Sat 9-5, Sun 1-5, Adm Adult $5, Child Free, www.staffordairandspacemuseum.com

Curtiss D	F-86	Ryan NYP Rep	Wright Flyer Rep
F-16	MiG 21	T-38	

OREGON

Clackmas - Clackmas ANG, 6950 SW Hampton, 97015, (503) 557-5368, F-86F(QF), F-86F

Eugene - Oregon Air and Space Museum, 90377 Boeing Dr, 97402-9536, (541) 461-1101,
Thur-Sun 12-5, Adm Adult $3, Child 6-11 $1, Under 6 Free, Gift Shop,

A-6	Fokker DR 1	RLU-1	
A6M2 Rep	L-19	Smith Termite	Yak 50
F-4C	MiG-17	Taylor 21 Buller	
F-86	Nieuport 17		

Klamath Falls - Kinsley Field Oregon ANG, Klamath Falls In't Airport,

F-4	F-15A	F-16A

Hubbard - Lenair Corp, 29502 S Meridian Rd, 97032-9405, (503) 651-2187,
www.LenhardtAirpark.com, Restores CG-4A's

McMinnville - Evergreen Aviation Museum, 3850 SE Three Mile Lane, Hwy 18 E of City,
97128, (503) 768-5083, 472-0011, 472-9361 Ext 4635, 434-4180, Daily 9-5,Closed TD,
CD, ND, Adm Adult $11, Vet & 65+ $10, Child 6-18 $7, Under 6 Free, Gift Shop
www.sprucegoose.org, All Flayable except marked S=Static, R=Restoration

A-4E	DC-3A (C-47)	HK-1 Spruce Goose	S-64
A-26C Storage	DH-4M-1 (S)	J-3C-65	SNJ-4(AT-6)
A6M3 (R)	DH-100	JN-4 (S)	Spitfire Mk.14
B-17G	F-89J (R)	MiG 15 UTI 2ea (S&R)	SR-71
BD-5B (S)	F-15AF-89J (S)	OV-1D1	T-28B
Bf 109G-10	F-102A (S)	P-38L	T-33A-15-LO (S)
Bonanza 35	FG-1D	P-40N	T-38A (S)
C-130 (F)	Ford 5-AT-B	P-51D	TBM-3E
CW-15-D (R)	Great Lakes Baby	PT-13	TH-55 (S)
CW-A-22	H-1H(UH)	RODA Homebuilt (S)	Wright Flyer (S)
D-17A Staggerwing(S)	H-12E(UH) 2ea (S&R)	S-2B	YAK 50 (S)

Milwaukie - Wings of Freedom, 13515 SE McLoughlin Blvd, 97222, (503) 654-6491, B-17

Pendleton - Pendleton Air Museum, POB 639, 97801, (541) 566-3906,
www.pendletonairmuseum.org, B-25

Portland - OR ANG Portland, 142 FIG/MAW, Portland Int'l Airport, 97218-2797
(503) 288-5611   F-101B

UFO Museum, 1637 Sw Alder St, 97205, (503) 227-2975

Medford - Rogue Valley Int'l Airport, 3650 Biddle Rd, (541) 776-7222, F-16, KC-97

Tillamook - Tillamook Air Museum, 6030 Hangar Rd, 97141, (503) 842-1130, Fax 842-3054,
Sept 3-June 3 Daily 10-5, RoY 9-6, Closed TD, CD, ND, Adm Adult $10.50, Snrs $9.50
Child 6-17 $6, Under 6 Free, Cafe, Gift Shop, Restoration Center, Theater,
www.tillamookair.com, e-mail: info@tillamookair.com,

A-4B	Bf-109	H-43B(HH)	P-51
A-7E	Boeing 377	H-58(OH)	P2V-7
A-24	C-47	HUK-1	PBY-5A
A-26	Cessna 180	J2F-6	PT-17
AD-4W	Chris-Teena Coupe	Ki-43	PV-2
Alien Blimp	F-14A	L-17A	Quickie
AM-1	F4F (Project)	L-29 (2each)	Sopwith Spad XIII
AT-6	F4U-7	ME-109(HA-1112)	Spitfire Mk.VIII
B-25	F8U Cockpit	Nord 1101	T-28 (2each)
Beechcraft V35B	FM-2	P-38	TBM-3E
Bell Helicopter	GK-1	P-39	
Bellanca 66-75	H-1H(UH) Project	P-47	

Tillamook County Pioneer Museum, 2106 Second St, 97141, (503) 842-4553, Artifacts

PENNSYLVANIA

Annville - Annville ANG, 17003, (717) 948-2200, F-102A(TF)

Beaver Falls - Air Heritage Museum, Inc, Beaver County Airport, 15010, (724) 843-2820
Mon-Sat 10-5, Sun 11-6, Free Adm, Restorations in Progress, Gift Shop,

A-20H	Cessna 401	Nanchang CJ6A	T-28
AT-19	H-1H(UH)	OV-1D	
C-123K	L-21B	P-39N	

Bethel - Golden Age Air Museum, 371 Airport Rd, 19507, (717) 933-9566, May-Oct Fri-Sat 10-5
Sun 11-5, RoY by Appt, Adm Adult $5, Child 6-12 $3, Under 6 Free, Gift Shop,
Restoration Facility, (UR)=Under Restoration, (AR)=Awaiting Restoration, (F)=Flyable,
www.GoldenAgeAir.org

Allison Sport (AR)	DR.I (UR)	Pietenpol Air Camper (F)
Bird CK (F)	E-2 (F)	Star Cavalier Model B(AR
C-3 (UR)	Great Lakes (F)	Star Cavalier Model E
Cessna AW (AR)	J-1 (UR)	(AR)
Cessna 195 (F)	JN4D (UR)	Windstead Special (F)
Dormoy Bathtub (AR)	Monocoupe Model 90A (AR)	

Eldred - Eldred WWII Museum, 201 Main St, Mail: POB 273, 16731, (814) 225-2220, Fax: 225-4407
Tue, Thur, Sat 10-4, Sun 1-4, www.eldredwiimuseum.org, Artifacts

Greencastle - AR Johns Exper Aircraft, Johns Alvin R, 346 Frank Rd, 17225, (717) 597-2256
Homebuilts: Green Demon, Rason Warrior X-3 (5 Seater), Aero Sport, Tornado JV,

Harrisburg - Pennsylvania Historical State Museum, 17108-1026, (717) 787-4980
Tue-Sat 9-5, Sun 12-5, Free Adm, J-3C   Jacobs   OX-5

Latrobe - Westmoreland County Museum, 2 Miles SW of City, 15650, (412) 539-8100,
AT-19   Stinson Gull-Wing

Lock Haven - Piper Aviation Museum. One Piper Way, 19301, Mail: PO Box J-3,
17745-0052, (570) 748-8283, Mon-Fri 9-4, Sat 10-4, Sun 12-4, Adm Adult $5, Snr $4,
Child 12-18 $1, Under 12 Free, www.pipermuseum.com,
Aztec   J-2 J-3   PA-11   PT-1   Link Trainer   Tomahawk Simulator

Philadelphia - Franklin Institute, 20th & Benjaman Franklin Parkway, 19103-1194,
(215) 448-1200, 9:30-5 Mon, 9:30-9 Tue-Thur, Sun, 9:30-10 Fri, Sat, Adult $8.50,
Child 4-11 $7.50, Omniverse $7 & $6, Planetarium $6 & $5, www.fi.edu/wright
Quickie   PA-38-2   RB-1   T-33   Wright Brothers B

CAF - Delaware Valley Wing, Northeast Philadelphia Airport, Fi 156, L-6

Pittsburg - Pittsburgh ANG, Greater Pittsburgh Int'l Airport, 15231, (412) 269-8350,
F-84F   F-86L   F-102A

Reading - Mid Atlantic Air Museum, Reading Regional Airport, 11 Museum Dr, Bldg #401, RD #9,
Rte 183 North Side of Airport, POB 9381, 19605, (610) 372-7333, Daily 9:30-4:00
Closed Major Holidays, Adm Adult $6, Child 6-12 $3, Pres: Russ Strine, www.maam.org/

Aeronca Model K	Heath CNA-40	Pietenpol Aircamper
Am Aerolites Eagle 2ea	HH-52A	PT-13D
Auster MKV J/1	J-2	PT-19
B-25J	KD-1A Kellet	PT-19B
Bede 5B (2 ea)	L-20A	PT-23
Beech G-18S	L-21B	PT-26
Bf-108	Martin 4-0-4	RC-3
BT-13A	N2S3	Reid Flying Submarine
C-3	N3N-3	ROTEC
C-119F	NE-1	Rotorway Exec 152
Cessna 150M	Nord 1002 (2 ea)	Rutan Vari-Eze
Commonwealth 185	Nord 1101 (3 ea)	SNJ-4B
Custer CCW-5	P-61B-1	SP-2H (2 ea)
CV-580 Prop Jet	P-84	T-28D
Elias EC1 Aircoupe	P2V	Taylor Young Model A
Erco 415G	PA-22-125	Troyer VX
F-84B-35-RE	PA-22-150	UC-78
F-86F-25	PA-23-250	UH-34D
H-21B	PA-34-200	Vickers 745D Viscount
Hawker Mk 58A	PA-38-112	

Smethport - Allegheny Arms & Armor Museum, Rte 46, 2 mi N of City, (814) 362-2642,
Daily 10-6, Gift Shop, A-6, UH-1 (2ea), Coast Guard Boat, M-42, M-48A1, M-115,

Toughkenamon - Colonial Flying Corps Museum, New Garden Airport, Newark Rd
POB 171, 19374, (610) 268-2048, Airshow 2nd Sunday In June, Sat-Sun 12-5, Adm Adult $1
Child Under 12 50¢,

Barlett M-8	FM-2	PT-19B
Bergfalke 11	L-2A	PT-26
C-3	Latter	Ryan ST-3KR
Cessna 185	Liverpuffin 11	SNJ
DH 82A	MPA	
DHC	PT-19A	

Waterford - Thermal Gliderport Air Museum, 9001 Hamot Rd, 16441, (814) 866-1131,
Appointment Only,   Six Gliders

PENNSYLVANIA (Continued)

West Chester - American Helicopter Museum, Brandywine Airport, 1220 Americaqn Blvd,
1420 Phoenixville Pike, 19380, (610) 644-4430, Wed-Sat 10-5, Sun 12-5, Adm Adult $6, Snrs $5
Child 2-18 $4, Under 2 Free, Gift Shop, www.helicoptermuseum.org

Air Command 447 Autogyro	H-2D(HH)	PV-2
Bell 30-1A	H-12D(UH)(H-23)	QH-50C
Bell 47B	H-21	S-51(R-5)
Bell 47D-1(H-13)	HUP-2	S-52(HO-55)
Bell 47H-1	MH-6J(MD 530)	S-61(HH-3A)
Bell 47J Cockpit	OH-6A	S-62(HH-52)
Bell 206 Jet Ranger	Parsons Autogyro	TH-55
Benson Autogyro	PCA-1A Autogyro	V-22
Brantley B-2	Princeton GEM X-2	VS-300 Cocpit
Enstrom F 28 A	Robinson R22	VZ-8P
Sud-Quest SO-1221 Djinn	Rotorway Scorpion	XR-4 Cocpit
H-1(AH) Cockpit	Rotorway Scorpion II	XRG-65
H-1L(TH)	RPV Rep	

West Miffin - CAF - Keystone Wing, Allegheny County Airport, Hangar # 20, 15122,
(724) 887-4816 Eve Only, 2nd Fri Monthly, www.c4ever.com/keystone/, L-5, L-9B

Willow Grove - Willow Grove Naval Air Station, DVHAA Wings of Freedom,
19090-5010, (215) 443-6039, Fax 675-4005, Wed10:30-3, 5-8, Sat-Sun 10:30-5, Free Adm,
e-mail: jbenton@voicenet.com, www.dvhaa.org/

A-4M	F8U-1	UH-1V	Rotarcraft
A-10A	F9F-2	UH-34D	Helio
A-37	FJ-4B	UH-53D	
C-1A	HUP-2P-3B	YF-2Y	
F-14	Me-262B1-B	Z9 Eastman	
F7U-3	P-80C		

RHODE ISLAND

N Kingstown - Quonset Air Museum, Quonset State Airport, 488 Eccleston Ave, I-95N
Exit 8, Rte 4S & Quonset Point, Davisville Exit, Mail: POB 1571, 02852,
401-294-9540, Daily 10-5, Closed ED, TD, CD, ND, Appt Available, Adm Adult $3,
Child Under 12 $1, Gift Shop, Restoration Facility,
http://users.ids.net/~qam/qam, email: qam@ids.net, (P) = Project

A4D-2N(A-4C)(P)	C-1A	H-6A(OH)	B-4
A-4F	CW XF15C-1	H-58A(OH)	Rutan Solitair
A-4M	F3D-2 Project	H-21 Project	Glider
A-6E	F-4A	L-9B	Stinson 10A
A-7D	F-14A	Me 208 (Nord 1101)	Stolp Starduster 2
Aero Commander 680	F6F-5 Project	MiG-17f	T-28S
AH-1S	H-1S(AH)	Mr D Robert Myer's	TBM-3E
American Eaglet	H-1H(UH)	Racer O-2A	
Antonov AN-2TD	H-1M(UH)H-3H(SH)	Pietenpol Aircamper	

SOUTH CAROLINA

Anderson - Anderson County Airport, 100 S Main St, 29624, Daily 8:30-5,
(864) 260-4163, F-105B

Beaufort - Marine Air Station, (843) 522-7100,

A-4L	F-4N	FJ-3	F8U-2

Charleston - Charleston AFB, 29404-5000, (843) 554-0230,

C-47D(VC)	C-124C	F-106A
C-121C	F-4C	T-33A

The Citadel, 171 Moultrie St, 29409, (843) 953-5000, www.citadel.edu/ginfo/tour/jet.html
AH-1, F-4C, M4A3 Sherman Tank, LVT-H-6, Redsotne Missile

Columbia - Ft Jackson Museum, UH-1B

South Carolina State Museum, 301 Gervais St, 29202-3107, (803) 737-4978,
POB 100107, Daily 10-5, Adm Adult $4, Child, Snr & Military & Student $2,
Science Adm: Nat Pemdelton,1929 Clemson Plane, B-25C

McEntire - McEntire ANGB, Memorial Park, 29044-9690, (803) 776-5121,

A-7D	F-80H	F-102A	T-33A
F-4	F-86H & L	F-104C	

SOUTH CAROLINA (Continued)

Mt Pleasant - Patriots Point Museum, 40 Patriots Point Rd, 29465, 29464, 800-248-3508, 843-884-2727, Daily 9-5, Closed CD, Adm Adult $14, Snr & Mil $12, Child 6-11 $7, Under 6 Free, Gift Shop, Snack Bar, www.patriotspoint.org

A-4 2ea	F-4J	J-2	USS Laffey
A-6	F-14	H-3	USS Yorktown
A-6B(EA)	F-18	N2S	USS Clamagore
A-7E	F11F-1	S-2E	MARK I Patrol
AD-4N	F4F-3A	SBD-5	Boat
AH-1	F6F	TBM-3E	Mercury Capsule
B-25D-NC	F8U	UH-34	Rep
E-1B	F9F	UH-1H	
E-2C	FG-1D	USCG Ingham	

Myrtle Beach - Myrtle Beach AFB, Air Base Redevelopment A, 1181 Shine Ave, 354 TFW/PA, 29577, (843) 238-7211, 238-0681,   F-100D

North Myrtle Beach - Mayday Miniature Golf, 715 Hwy 17N, 29582, (843) 280-3535, Daily 9am-10pm, Adm Adult $7.50, Child $6.50, www.maydaygolf.com, PV-2, UH-1

Sumter - Shaw AFB, 29152-5000, (803) 668-3621, Open House May, PA: Fran Hutchison

B-66C(RB)	F-16A	F-105	O-2A
F-4C(RF)	F-101C(RF)	P-47D Replica	

SOUTH DAKOTA

Great Plains - Great Plains Airport, 57064, (605) 368-2841,   A-7D

Huron - Huron Regional Airport, 57350, (605) 352-4577,   A-7D

Mitchell - Soukup & Thomas Int'l Balloon & Airship Museum, 700 N Main St, 57301, (605) 996-2311, Memorial Day - Labor Day Daily 8-8, May, Sept-Nov Mon-Sat 9-5, Sun 1-5, Closed January, Feb-April Fri, Sat, Mon 9-5, Sun 1-5, Adm Adult $3, Sr $2.50, 13-19 $1.50, 6-16 $1, Under 6 Free, Gift Shop, 1890's Charles Dolfus Balloon Baskets Shennandoa Gerders/Control Room Doors, Hindenburg (LZ-129) Dishes
HOT AIR BALLOONS:

Chesty (US Marine Bulldog)	US Aero Star Int'l
Chic-I-Boom (Carmen Miranda)	WWI Observation Balloon Basket
Hilda (13-Story Witch On A Broom)	WWI Paris Basket
Matrioshka Russian Nesting Doll	WWI US Army Gas Balloon
Super Chicken Gondola 1st Non-Stop	"Zanussi" Trans-Atlantic Capsule
Uncle Sam (100 Foot Tall)	

Pierre - SD ANG Pierre, SDNG Museum, Dakota & Chapelle, POB 938, 57501-0938, (605) 224-9991,   A-7D

Rapid City - Ellsworth AFB, South Dakota Air & Space Museum, Bldg. 5208, 57706, (605) 385-5188, POB 871, Box Elder, 57719-0871, Exit 66 Off I-90, Hours 8:30-6 Daily Mid May-Mid Sept, 8:30-4:30 Winter, Gift Shop: Beverly LeCates, Free Adm, Minuteman Missile Silo Tours,

A-26K	BT-13A	F-102	T-33A
A-7D	C-45	F-105B	T-38
B-1	C-47A	FB-111A	Titan I
B-2 Rep	C-54	H-13-H(OH)	U-3A
B-25J(VB)	C-131	L-5	U-8D
B-29	C-135(EC)	Minuteman II	UH-1F
B-47	F-84F	Nike-Ajax	
B-52D	F-86H	O-2A	
B-57B(EB)	F-101B	Quail	

Sioux Falls - SD ANG Sioux Falls, Industrial & Algonquin, Box 5044, 57117-5044, (605) 333-5700,   A-7D   F-102A   T-33A

TENNESSEE

Arnold - Arnold AFS, 37389, (931) 454-3000, AEDC/DOPO, F-4C   F-105D

Athens - Swift Museum Foundation, Inc, McMinn County Airport, Hwy 30, Mail: POB 644, 37303, (423) 744-9696, Swift Aircraft Displays

Caryville - Campbell County Military Display, I-75 Exit 134 & US 25W on Hwy 116(Old SR 9) UH-1   M-60A3 Tank

Chattanooga - Chattanooga ANG, 37412, (423) 892-1366, F-101B   F-104C

Crossville - Cumberland High School, 660 Stanley St, 38555, (931) 484-6194 A-4   T-33A

Johnson City - Radio Controlled Flying Field, Contact: Vic Koening, 502 Steeple Chase Dr, 37601, T-33

Knoxville - Knoxville ANG, McGhee Tyson Airport, 37901, (865) 970-3077, 134th ARG,
   F-104C

Memphis - Memphis Belle Memorial Association, 125 N Front St, Mud Island, 38103,
   Mail:POB 1942, 38101, (901) 767-1026, 412-8071, MD-LD Daily 10-5, RoY Tie-Sun 10-5
   Adm Charge, 1990 Movie "Memphis Belle" Shown Twice Daily, www.memphisbelle.com
   A-7E   B-17 (At Millington Municipal Airport)

Millington - NSA Memphis (NATTC), 38053, (901) 873-3033, A-4M   A-5 Outside Officers Club

Nashville - Nashville ANG, Nashville Metropolitan Airport, 37217-0267,
   (615) 361-4600,   F-84F(RF)

   Bristol Heritage Collection, 210 Club Parkway, 37221-1900, Mail: POB 210876, (615) 646-2473,
   383-9090, Mon-Fri 9-5, Wetland Lysander MK111A, Fairey Swordfish, Bristol Beaufort, Bollingbroke

Pigeon Forge - Professor Hacker's Lost Treasure Golf, 3010 Parkway, 37863, (865) 453-0307, Beech D18S

Rossville - CAF - Tennessee Volunteer Squadron, 38134,

Sevierville - Tennessee Museum of Aviation, Hanger One, 135 Air Museum Way
   Gatlinburg-Pigeon Forge Airport, 37862, Mail POB 37864-5587, (866) 286-8738, (865) 908-0171
   Fax 908-8421, Mon-Sat 10-6, Sun 1-6, Closed TD, CD, Adm 12.95, 65+ 9.95, Child 6-12 6.95
   Vets & Military & Child 5 & under Free, Gift Shop, www.tnairmuseum.com Flyable=(F)

AT-6D (F)	MiG 21	T-33-A-N (F)
F-86	P-47D-40 (2ea F)(1 Display)	T-33A
H-34(UH)	PBY	TBM-3E (F)
MiG 17(2ea)	T-28B (F)	

Tullahoma - Staggerwing Museum Foundation, Inc, POB 550, Tullahoma Airport, 37388,
   (931) 455-1974, Mail: POB 550, 37388, March 1-Nov 31 Mon-Fri 10-2, Sat-Sun 1-4
   March-Nov, Closed All Holidays, Adm Adult $4, www.staggerwing.com

Beech A17R	Beech E18S	C-45H
Beech B17L 2ea	Beech F17D	Travel Air 1000D
Beech C17B	Beech G17S	Travel Air 4000
Beech D17S 2ea	Beech S18D	Travel Air 6000A
Beech D18S	Beechcraft 35	Travel Air R
Beech E17B		

TEXAS
Abilene - CAF - Big Country Squadron, 4886 Newman Rd, Abilene Mun. Airport, Elmdale Airpark,
   Hangar #2, 76601-6720, Mail:POB 6511, 79608, (915) 676-1944, Daily 9-5, Squadron Meetings
   6:30 PM First Tue Monthly, http://bigcountrysquadron.org, C-94(UC)

   Dyess Linear Air Park, Arnold Blvd, Dyess AFB, Mail: 7 WG/CVM 650, 2nd
   St 9607-1960, (915) 793-2199, Need Free Pass at Visitor's Center, 696-2432, Daily
   5:30-10pm, www.dyess.af.mil/airpark/index.htm

A-26C	C-47A	F-86L	T-28A
AGM-28A	C-97L(KL)	F-89H	T-29C
AT-6F	C-123K	F-100C	T-33A
B-17G(DB)	C-130A	F-101B	T-34B
B-47E(EB)	C-135A(KC)	F-104A	T-37B
B-52D	F-4D	F-105D	T-38A
B-57B(EB)	F-84F	HU-16E	
B-66A(RB)	F-84F(RF)	O-2A	T-39A
C-7A(YC)			

Addison - Cavanaugh Flight Museum, 4572 Claire Chennault, Addison Airport, 75001,
   (972) 380-8800, Mon-Sat 9-5, Sun 11-5, Adm Adult $8.00, Child 6-12 $4.00,
   Under 6 Free, All Aircraft Flown Regularly, Canteen Area, Gift Shop,
   Founder: Jim Cavanaugh, www.cavanaughflightmuseum.com

AT-6D	FG-1D	Me-109G	PT-19A
B-25(TB)	F9F-2B	MiG-15UTI	PT-22
BT-13(SNV-2)	FM-2	MiG-17	S-2F
Christine Eagle Project	Fokker D.VIIa	MiG-21	Sopwith Camel
DH 82	He-111	N2S	Spitfire Mk.VIII
F-86E	Hawker Hurricane	P-40N	TBM-3E
F-4C	J-3	P-47N	TS-11
F-104A	L-3B	P-51D	
F-105F	L-4J	Pitts S-1-S	

Amarillo - CAF - Dew Line Squadron, 903 S Carolina, Perry Lefors Field, 79103,
   (806) 665-1881, L-5

   English Field Air & Space Museum, 2014 English Rd, Mail: POB 31535,
   79120-1535, (806) 372-6999, Sun-Fri 12-5, Sat 10-5, Winter Sat-Sun 12-5, Free Adm,
   Gift Shop, Restoration Facility, Annual Air Show, www.texasaviationmuseum.org
   C-71,   F-84F,   OV-1B,   Viking Mars Lander

Arlington - Air Combat, 921 Six Flags Dr #117, 76011-5123, (817) 640-1886, Daily
1½ Hour Simulators $39.95: A-4   F-8   F-16   F-111

Austin - Adjutant General's Dept, TAG, Camp Mabry, POB 5218, 78763-5218, F-4C, F-86D

Texas Military Forces Museum, Texas ANG, West 35th St & MoPac Freeway (Loop 1),
Camp Mabry, (512) 465-5167, 409-6967, Wed 2-6, Sun 10-4, Closed Holidays,
F-4   F-86   H-1H(UH)   H-1M(UH)   L-4

Bastrop - VFW Post 2527, Rockne Hwy, 78602, (512) 321-2610,   F-4

Beaumont - Babe Didrikson Zaharious Memorial Park, Interstate Hwy 10,   RF-101

Beeville - Chase Field Naval Air Station, PA, (512) 354-5464,   A-4J(TA)

Courthouse, 105 W Corpus Christi,   A-4

Big Spring - Hangar 25 1911 Apron Dr, Webb AFB, 79720, Mail: POB 2925, 79721
Bldg 1106, 2000 Air Park W, 79720, (432) 264-1999, Fax 466-0316, Mon-Fri 9-5,
Sat 10-2, Sun 1:30-4, Closed Holidays, Adm Donation, Gift Shop,
www.hangar25airmuseum.com/main/history.asp, email hangar25@crcom.net

A-10 Cockpit	B-52 Nose	T-28	T-37
AT-11	Harrier	T-33	T-38

Vietnam Memorial, 7th & Sword St, 7 Blocks E of Hangar 25, F-4E,   UH-1H

Brownsville - CAF - Rio Grande Valley Wing, Brownsville/South Padre Is. Int'l Airport,
955 Minnesota, 78523, (956) 541-8585, Oct-March Mon-Sat 9:30-4:30, April-Sept Mon, Wed,
Fri-Sat 9:30-3:30Adm Adult $6, Snrs 55 $5, Child 12-18 $3, Under 12 Free, www.rgvwingcaf.com

BT-13(2ea)	FW-44	L-6	PT-26(2ea)
C-47 Project	J3C-65	DH 94 Moth Minor	SNJ
C-54	L-2	PBY-5A Project	Swith Bi-Plane
CM-170R	L-3	PT-17	Train 2-4-2
P.H. 94 S	L-4	PT-19(2ea)	
Fleet Finch 16B	L-5	PT-22(2ea)	

Burnet - Highland Lakes Sq CAF (Hill County Squadron), Burnet City Airport
2402 S Water St, 78611, (512) 765-2226, Mail: POB 866, Mon-Sat 9-5, Sun 12-5,
Adm Adult $3, Snr $2, Child $1, Gift Shop, www.highlandlakessquadron.com

A-7D	L-5	PT-17	T-38
C-47	L-17B	PT-19	
F-100F	PT-13	T-37	

College Station - George Bush Library Museum, 1000 George Bush Dr, 77845,
(979) 691-4000, Mon-Sat 9:30-5, Sun 12-5, Closed TD, CD, ND, Adm Adult $7,
Snr 62+ $5, Child 6-17 $2, Under 6 Free, Gift Shop 888-388-2874, (979) 862-2874
http://csdl.tamu.edu/bushlib, TBM-3

Conroe - CAF -Big Thicket Squadron, Montgomery County Airport, BT-13A,

Corpus Christi - Corpus Christi Museum of Science and History, 1900 N Chaparral,
(Bayfront Arts & Science Park), 78401, (361) 883-2862, Tue-Sat 10-5,
Sun 1-5, Closed Holidays, Adm Adult $2, 6-12 $0.50, Sat 10-12 Free Adm
F-4 Cockpit   SNJ (Can Sit In)   N3N

Int'l Kite Museum, Best Western Sandy Shores Beach Hotel, Quarium
Village, 3200 Surfside, Mail: POB 839, 78403, (361) 883-7456, Daily 10-5, Free Adm.

Naval Air Station, PA, 78419, (361) 961-2568, PBY-5A, T-28, TBM-3E

CAF - Third Coast Wing, 1309 S Airport Rd, 78332, (361) 661-0321, Gift Shop,
Sat-Sun 9-4, www.thirdcoast.org, L-6

USS Lexington Museum, 2914 Shoreline Dr, Mail: POB 23076, 78403-3076,
(361) 888-4873, Daily 9-5, Adm Adult $11.95, Snrs & Mil $9.95, Child 4-12 $6.95,
Under 4 Free, Closed CD, Gift Shop, Food Court, www.usslexington.com

A-4B (2ea)	F-14A	L-4 Storage	T-28B
A-4J(TA) Trainer	F2H-2	N3N-3	T-34B
A-6E	F9F-8T(TF-9J)	PINTA and MARIA	T-6 Storage
A-7B	GH-3	PV-2D	T2C
DGA Storage	H-1S(AH)	SBD-3	TBF-3E
F-4A	KA-3B(A3D)	SNJ-5	USS Lexington

Dallas - CAF Dallas/Fort Worth Wing, Lancaster Mncpl Airport, E Beltline Rd,
(972) 227-9119, Sat 9-4, www.dfwwing.org, BT-15, L-5, R4D,

Frontiers of Flight Museum, 8008 Cedar Springs Rd, Mail: Love Field Terminal LB-18,
2nd Floor, 75235-2852, (214) 350-3600, Fax 351-0101, Mon-Sat 10-5, Sun 1-5, Closed TD, CD, ND,
Adm Adult $2, Child Under 12 $1, Gift Shop 350-1651,Airshow 2nd wknd In Sept,

BS-1	F-105F	Sopwith Pup	Temple Sportsman
F-4C	Quicksilver MXL-II	T-33	TH-1L

History of Aviation Collection, Univ of Texas at Dallas, Eugene McDermont Library
2901 N Floyd Rd, 75221, Mon-Thur 9-6, 9-5 Fri, Free Adm,
James Doolittle Library, Artifacts, Glasflugel BS-1 Sailplane

Del Valle - Del Valle High School 2454 Cardinal Loop, 78614, (512) 385-1921, F-4C(RF)

Del Rio - Laughlin AFB, 78843-5000, (830) 298-5675, 47OSS/CC

B-57B(EB)	F-84F	T-33A	T-38
C-45J(UC)	T-6	T-34B	U-2C
C-123K	T-28A	T-37A	

Denison - Perrin AFB Museum, 4575 Airport Dr, Perrin Airport, 75020, Mon-Fri 10-4,
(903) 893-6400, www.perrinfield.org

Denton - Hangar 10 Antique Airplane Museum, Denton Mncpl Airport, 1945 Matt Wright Ln
76207, (940) 565-1945, I-35E, West Oak Exit, R on Airport Rd, Mon-Sat 8:30-3,
Adm Donations, www.hangar10.org/

LC-126	OH-58	C-60A
Howard DGA	Interstate Cadet	L-17A

Texas Women's Univ Library Blagg H, 76201, (940) 898-2665, WASP's Artifacts

World Aeronautical Museum, Jim Holder, (940) 464-0080, Tue-Wed

Bear	B-25	L-39

Ellington - Ellington ANGB,TX 77034-5586, (821) 929-2892, 147 FIG/MA,

F-101F	F-102A	T-33A

El Paso - Air Defense & Artillery Museum, Building 5000, Pleasant Rd,
Near Robert E Lee Rd, Daily 9-4, Artifacts

Fort Bliss - Third Cavalry Regiment Museum, ATZC-DPT-MM, Forrest & Chaffee Rds,
Bldg 2407, 79916-5300, (915) 568-1922, Mon-Fri 9-4:30, Free Adm,
S-55,   M-2 Half Track,   M-4AS Sherman Tank,   M-8 Armored Car

US Army Air-Defense Artillery Museum, Blvd 5000, Pleasonton Rd & Robert
E Lee Blvd, 79916-5300, (915) 568-5412, Daily 9-4:30, Closed ES, TD, CD, ND,
Free Adm, Bofors 40mm Gun from "Movie 1941", 88mm German Anti-Aircraft Gun, V-2
Missiles: Firebee   Hawk   Nike Ajax   Nike Hercules

Fort Davis - McDonald Observatory, Atop Mt Locke, 16 Miles from Ft Davis on Hwy 118
Mail: WL Moody, Jr Visitors Information Center, POB 1337, 79734-1337,
(915) 426-3640, Gift Shop, Theater, Daily 9-5, Closed TD, CD, ND, Daily 2pm
Tour (March-Aug 9:30am)Adm Adult $4, Child 6-12 $31, Under 5 Free, Free Solar
Viewing: 11am, 3:30pm, Wed Eve,

Fort Worth - American Airlines C.R. Smith Museum, 4601 Hwy 360 & FAA Rd, Next To
American Airlines Flight Academy, Just South of the Dallas/Ft Worth Airport,
76155, (817) 967-1560, Wed-Sat 10-6, Sun 12-5, Adm Adult $4, Snrs 55 $2, Child 2-12 $2,
Under 2 Free, Gift Shop 967-5922, Theater, www.crsmithmuseum.org,
DC-3, Airline Cockpits: 757, 767, F-100

Aviation Heritage Museum, Mail: 306 West 7th St, Suite 311, 76102, (817) 551-1967,
www.aviationheritagemuseum.com, B-36 Peacemaker Museum, POB 150943, 76108,
www.b-36peacemakermuseum.org, Restored B-36J Awaiting Building of the New Facility

A-12	B-36J	BT-13	L-450	T-33(Project)

Fort Worth Science and History, 1501 Montgomery St, 76107, (817) 255-9300
Sept-Feb Mon-Wed 9-5, Thur-Sat 9-9, Sun 12-9, March-Aug Mon-Sat 9-9, Sun 12-9
Adm Adult $7, Snrs & Child 3-12 $6, Under 3 Free, Omni/Planetarium/Museum $13/$11,

www.fwmuseum.org	Bell 47	Boeing 727 Cockpit	PT-17

NAS Ft Worth Joint Reserve Base, Carswell Field, 76127, (817) 782-7815,

A-4J(TA)	F-4E	F-86L	H-34(UH)
A-4M 2ea	F-14A	F-105D	H-58(OH)
C-97L(KC)	F-16N	FA-18	
F-4D	F-80L	H-1(UH)	

Fort Worth - Pate Museum of Transportation, 18501 Highway 377 S, 76035, (817) 396-4305,
Tue-Sun 9-5 Except Holidays, Free Adm, www.pmot.org

A-4	F-8A(F8U-1)	F-100	H-43B(HH)
BQM-34	F9F-6P	F-101B(CF)	T-28
C-119	F-80	F-105	T-33A
C-47	F-84F(RF)	F-86H	UH-34
CH-21B	F-14	H-16B(HU)	
F-4D	F-16	H-23B(OH)(2ea)	

Texas Airplane Factory, Meacham Field, 76106, (817) 626-9834, Contact:
George Tischler, Fax (817) 626-7354, Fax 609-702-1852, Me-262B-1a (2ea)
Ki-43 (4ea)(Project for Champlin Fighter Museum), 2 are for sale $850,000 ea

Vintage Flying Museum & Texas Air Museum & OV 10 Bronco Assoc, 505 NW 38th St
Hangar 33 S, 76106, S On Main Off US 820, W On 38th St, S Runway of Meacham Airport
Mail: Box 820099, 76182, (817) 624-1935, (800) 575-0535, Fax 485-4454, Sat 10-5, Sun 12-5
Weekdays by Appt, Adm Adult $6, Child 13-17 $5, 6-12 $3, Under 6 Free, Gift Shop,
www.vintageflyingmuseum.org, www.ov-10bronco.net

American Flea	Convair	Hawker Hunter	OV-10 Replica
AT-6	F-86	Knight Falcon	Piaggio
B-17G	Fouga Magister	L-3	Amphibian
Beech D18S 3ea	H-1(UH)	L-5	Stearman
C-140	H-58(OH) 3ea	L-450	

Fredericksburg - National Museum of the Pacific War, 340 E Main St, POB 777,
78624, (830) 997-4379, 7269, Daily 10-5, Adm Adult $5, Child $3, Under 12 Free
Groups $3 ea, Closed CD, www.nationalmuseumofthepacificwar.org

B-25J	LVT4	M7 Priest Tank	N1K-1
D3A-1	MK3 Tank	Japanese Tank Chi-ha	
FM-2	M3 Tank	USS Pinato Conning Tower	
TBM-3E	PT Boat	Japanese Midget Sub Type A	

Fulshear - Covey Trails Airport, (281) 531-6540, WF Russel, Houston, Owns: Beech 18R

Galveston - Lone Star Flight Museum, 2002 Terminal Dr, 71554, (409) 740-7722, Fax 740-7612
Mail: POB 3099, 77552-0099, Daily 9-5, Closed ED, TD, CD, ND, Adm Adult $8, Snrs &
Child 5-17 $5, under 5 free, Gift Shop, Theater, Restoration Viewing,
All Aircraft Flyable, Project = P, Non Flayable = N, www.lsfm.org

A-20G	F-100 (N)	L-5	Spitfire (P)
AT-6A	F3F-2	N3N-3	T-34A
AT-11	F4U-5N	P-38-L5	T-50
B-17G	F6F-5K	P-47	T-28C
B-25	F8F-2	PB4Y-2 (P)	TBM-3E
B-58A(TB) (N)	FM-2	PBY-5A (P)	
Beech D18H4	Harvard Mk.IV	PV-2D (N)	
C-1A Project	Hawker Hurricane	A-24B(SBD-5) (P)	

Gilmer - Flight of the Phoenix - Hangar One, Fox Stephens Field, Texas Mncpl Airport
(903) 843-3811, Mon-Fri 10-5, Sun 2-Dark, Sat appt, Free Adm, www.flightofthephoenix.org,
AT-6G,   Aero Commander 520,   Beech D-18S,   Great Lakes 2T-1A-2,   DH-82

Graham - CAF - Cactus Squadron, Grahm Mncpl Airport, POB 861, 76450,
Robert E Richeson Memorial Museum, SB2C

Grand Prairie - Texas Air Command Museum, 4531 Crane Court, 75052-3516, Mail: P.O. Box
542071, 75054, (972) 642-8282,
AT-6   F-86F(2ea)   Hawker Hunter   T-33A   UH-1H

Hawkins - RRS Aviation (Restoration Facility), POB 233, 380 N Beaulah,
75765, (903) 769-2904, Pres Bob Schneider,

Bristol Beaufort	Hawker Hurricane (5ea)	PBM	TBM-3
F9-5	P-40		

Houston - CAF - Gulf Coast Wing, 11503 Brantly, Ellington Field, 77089, (281) 484-0098
Meetings 3rd Sat Monthly 8:30, www.gulfcoastwing.org, A6M Rep, B5N Rep, B-17, BT-13, D3A Rep

CAF - West Houston Squadron, West Houston Airport, Hangar B-5, 18000 Groeschke Rd
77084, 281-578-1711, Appt Only, www.westhoustonsqdn.org, M = Member Owned

AT-6D	Champion 7FC (M)	N2S (M)	S-108
BT-13A	Fly-Baby 1A (M)	N3N	SNJ-5 (M)
C-60A	Mooney (2ea)(M)	P-63	

West Houston Airport Entrance, H-1H(UH) on Groeschke Rd.

Houston Museum of Natural Science, 5800 Carolina St, 77004, (281) 526-4273, Sun-Mon 12-5,
Tue-Fri 9-5, Sat 9-9, Free Adm, Mercury 6 Spacecraft

Houston Space Academy, 403 NASA Rd 1, Ste 360, 77598, (218) 486-4446,
Summer Space Camps Ages 6-20, Astronaut Training, Rockets, Simulators

TEXAS (Continued)

Houston -
  NASA Lyndon B Johnson Space Center, 2101 NASA Rd 1, 77058,
  (218) 483-4321, Daily 9-4, Free Adm,   PGM-11A   Spacecraft

  Space Center Houston at LBJ Space Center, 1601 NASA Rd 1, Off I-45, 77058
  (218) 244-2100, 800-972-0369, Mon-Fri 10-5, Sat-Sun 10-7, Adm Adult $17.95,
  Snrs $16.95, Child $13.95, Closed CD, Gift Shop, www.spacecenter.org, Shuttle

Kerrville - Mooney Aircraft Factory, West Side of Louis Schreiner Field On Hwy 27,
  (830) 996-6000, Mon-Fri, 1 Hour Tours at 10am.

Kingbury - Pioneer Flight Museums part of Vintage Aviation Historical Foundation,
  190 Pershing Ln, 78638, (830) 639-4550, On Farm Road 1104 Off of IH10,
  www.vintageaviation.org, Flyable(F)
  Bleriot XI (F)   Fokker Dr.I (P)   Rearwin 2000C (P)
  Bristol Fighter (P)Rep Luscombe 8A (F)   SE-5a (P) Rep
  Bristol Fighter (P)   Meyers OTW (F)   Thomas-Morse Scout (F)
  Curtiss Canuck(P)   Pietenpol Sky Scout (F)
  Fokker D.VII (P)   Piper J-3 (P)

Kingsville - Naval Air Station, Hwy 77 South of City, 1201 E Caesar Ave, 78363,
  (361) 516-6200, A4D-2N

Lago Vista - Lago Vista Airpower Museum, Rusty Allen Airport, Flight Line Rd,
  Hangar 9, Lago Vista Airport, 78645, (512) 267-7403, Sat-Sun 1-5, From I-35
  Take F.M. 1431, R on Bar-K Ranch Rd, F-4C(RF),   F-100C,   L-4,   PT-13

Lancaster - CAF - Dallas / Ft. Worth Wing, Lancaster Airport, Belt Line Rd, 75146
  (972) 236-1319, 6 Mi East of I-35E in SE Dallas County, Sat 9-4, Adm $2,
  BT-15   FG-1D   L-5   R4D   V-77

Laredo - Airport, 3 Mi NE of City, (956) 795-2000,
  Aero Commander   C-46   J-3   YS-11
  Beech 35   Convair 340   Rotoway Exec 162F
  Bell 47   Convair 440 (2ea) T-28
  C-45   DC-3 (3ea)   T-39 Parts

Lubbock - Lubbock State School, 3401 N Univ & Loop 289, 79417, (806) 763-7041, T-33A
  Science Center, 2579 S Loop 289, 79423, (806) 745-2525,   T-28A

  Silent Wings Museum,6202 N I-27, (806) 775-3126, Tue-Sat 10-6, Sun 1-5, Adm Adult $4,
  Snrs $3, Child $2, Under 12 Free, www.silentwingsmuseum.com
  CG-4A   Culver Cadet   Lyster 1943
  Coffman Glider   L-4   PT-22A

McAllen - McAllen Miller Int'l Airport, Ceiling of Main Lobby, 2 Mi S of City,
  (956) 682-9101, White Monoplane Rep.

Manchaca - VFW Post 3377, 12921 Lowden Ln, 78652, (512) 282-5664, F-4

Marshall - CAF - Lone Star Wing, Gregg County, PT-17

Midland - American Airpower Museum, Part of above, www.airpowermuseum.org,
  AT-6   B-25   P-47N
  AT-19   DC-3 Cocpit Sim 3ea TBM
  B-17G   P-40N

  CAF - B-29/B-24 Squadron, Mail POB 61945, 79711-1945, www.cafb29b24.org, B-24, B-29

  CAF - Commando Squadron, C-46

  CAF - High Sky Wing, 9603 Wright Dr, Midland Int'l Airport, Mail: POB 61064,
  79711-1064, (432) 563-5112, C-61(UC)   Fairchild 24   PT-19   SNJ-4

  CAF - West Texas Wing, Municipal Airport, (915) 549-6150,
  http://mywebpage.netscape.com/westtexaswing/Home+Page.htm,   SB2C

  Commemorative Air Force Museum, 9600 Wright Dr, Midland Int'l Airport, POB 62000
  79711-2000, (915) 567-3009, 563-1000 Recording, 567-3047 Fax, Mon-Sat 9-5, Sun &
  Holidays 12-5, Closed TD, CD, Adm Adult $10, Child 13-18, 65+ $9, 6-12 $7, Under 6 Free
  Airshow Dates: 800-CAF-SHOW, www.commemorativeairforce.org,

A-1E	B-25J	C-46	DC-3C
A-20J	B-29A	C-47D(VC)	F-4D
A-57A(RA)	B-47E(RB)	C-54D	F-89J
A6M2	B5N Rep	C-60	F-84F(RF)
AH-G	BT-14	C-97G(KC)	F-100
AM-1	BT-15	C-119C	F-102A
AT-6B	BT-13A	C-124C	F-105D
AT-11	C-45J	CG-4A	F8F-2
B-23		Cornell II	HA-112-MIL
B-24(LB-30)		D-18S	(Continued Next Page

62

(Previous Page)	Lockheed 18-50	PBY-6A	SB2C-5
Harvard Mk.II	Me-108B24	PBY-5A	SNJ-5
Harvard Mk.IV	Me-109B	Pliska	TBM-3
HU-16B	Mosquito	PT-22	TG-3A
JRB-4	P-38	PT-19	UC-78
Kittyhawk IV	P-39Q	PT-17	YO-55
I-16	P-47N	PT-26	
L-3E	P-63A	R-4	
L-5	PB-1W		

TEXAS (Continued)

Odessa - CAF - Desert Squadron, Odessa-Schlemeyer Airport, (915) 335-3021, PT-13, PT-19, T-33A

Pampa - Freedom Museum USA, 600 N. Hobart, VFW Post 1657, 79065, Mail: POB 66,
(806) 669-6066, Tue-Sat 12-4, Library, Gift Shop, www.freedommuseumusa.org
UH-1F	B-25(PBJ)	M110A2 Howitzer

Paris - Flying Tiger Airport, Hwy 82, 75461, (903) 784-3613,
Daily 8-6, Free Adm, A-4D	AT-6	F-86D	SAM

Plainview - Hale County Airport, 79073, T-33A

Pyote - Pyote Museum and Rattlesnake Bomber Base, 79777, 15 Mi W of Monahans,
On I-20, In Ward County Park (N Hwy 18, 79756, (915) 943-5044), Sat 9-6, Sun 2-6,
Artifacts of Former 19th B-17 Base.

Richardson - History of Aviation Collection, 2901 N Floyd Rd, Eugene McDermott Library,
Special Collections, University of Dallas, 75083, POB 830643, 75083-0643, (972) 883-2570,
Fax: 883-4590, Mon-Thur 9-6, Fri 9-5, Free Adm, www.utdallas.edu/library/special/cataa.html,
(Jimmy Doolittle and China Air Transport) Artifacts

San Angelo - Mathis Field Airport, 8618 Terminal Circle, Suite 101, 76903,
(915) 659-6409,   UH-1H   CAF Ft Concho Squadron Also There

Goodfellow AFB, 76908-5000, (915) 657-3231, 3480 ABG, B-25N(TB), F-100A, T-28A

San Antonio - City Park Between San Antonio and the Coast Off I37, A-4

Museum of Aerospace Medicine(Hangar 9)Museum, (Edward H White II Memorial), Brooks AFB
70th ABG/MU, Inner Circle Rd, 78235-5329, (210) 536-2203, Mon-Fri 8-4, Free Adm,
www.brooks.af.mil/ABG/MU/master.html,   F-100D   JN-4

Lackland Static Airplane Display/Lackland AFB,78236-5000, (210) 671-3444, 3055,
Mon-Fri 8-4:45, Closed Holidays, Free Adm, Closed ED, TD, CD, ND,
A-10A	C-47D	F-84B	P-38L Rep
AT-6D	C-45J(UC)	F-86A	P-47N
B-17G(TB)	C-118	F-100A	P-51H
B-24M Replica	C-119C	F-101B	P-63G(RP)
B-25H	C-121S(EC)	F-101F	SR-71A
B-26C	C-123K	F-104C	T-28A(GT)
B-29A	F-4B	F-104D(TF)	T-29B(VT)
B-52D	F-5B	F-105B(GF)	T-34A
B-587(RB)	F-16	F-105D	T-38A
B-66(WB)	F-82E(EF)	JN-4D	

Int'l Liaison Pilot & Aircraft Assn Museum, 16518 Ledgestone, 78232,
(210) 490-4572, Pres: Bill Stratton,
AE-1	L-2	L-4	L-6
L-1	L-3	L-5	L-8

Randolph AFB, 78150-5001, (210) 652-1110
AT-6D	T-33A	T-37B
T-28A	T-34B	T-38A

San Antonio Museum of Transportation, Hemisfair Plaza, 78209,
(210) 226-1201, Daily 10-6, Free Adm,   JN-4D

Texas Air Museum, Stinson Chapter, 8406 Cadmus, Stinson Mncpl Airport, 78214
(210) 977-9855, Fax 927-4447, Mon-Sat 11-5, Adm Adult $4, Snrs 55/Mil $3,
Child 12-16 $2, Under 12 $1, Gift Shop, www.texasairmuseum.org,
Aerobat 1-A	Ercoupe (Project)	Funk B (Project)
Avro 652	F-4C	FW-190A-8 (Loan)
Bleriot Monoplane	F-89	H-34C
Bu 133	F-101	J-3C65
Chistofferson	F-103	Waco
Curtiss Model D	F-105	

San Marcos - CAF - Centex Wing, 1841 Airport Dr, 78666, (512) 396-1943,
Mon, Wed, Fri-Sat 10-4, Adm Adult $3, Child Under 6 Free, Gift Shop, Library
www.realtime.net/centex/index.html
B5N2 Replica	L-5	P-39Q	PT-17	T-34
C-78(UC)	L-8	P-40N	T-33	Yak 18

TEXAS (Continued)
  San Marcos - CAF - Yellow Rose Squadron, B-25

  Schulenburg - Stanzel Model Aircraft Museum, 311 Baumgarten St, 78956,
    (979) 743-6559, Fax 743-2525, Mon, Wed, Fri-Sat 10:30-4:20, Sun 1:30-4:30,
    Adm Adult $2, Senior $1, Under 12 Free, www.stanzelmuseum.org,
    30 Static Model Displays

  Slaton - Texas Air Museum, Caprock Chapter, Slaton Airport, Mail: POB 667,
    79364, (806) 828-4664, Sat 9-4, Adm Adult & Child $2, Gift Shop, Restoration Facility
    Contact: Mike De Lano 828-4334, Malcolm Laing 794-0190,

A-7B	Fokker D-7	L-17	PT-19
AD-5	Fokker DR-1	M- 2 Halftrack	Quick Silver MX
AT-19	Funk F-23	M- 4 HSTractor	Rumpler CV 1704
BC-12D	Fw-190A-6	M-16 Halftrack	T-2
CG-15 Waco	Greenwood Witch	M-59	T-33A
F-4	H-1H(UH)	Me-109f4	TG-5
F-105D	HOS4	Mystery Ship	

  Sweetwater - City Park, Mail: Chamber of Commerce, POB 1148, 79556, (915) 235-5488
    Fax 235-1026,   T-33A   UH-1

    National WASPS WWII Museum, Avenger Field, Mail: POB 456, 79556, (254) 710-7202
    www.waspwwii.org,

  Terrell - British Flying Training School Museum, 119 Silent Wings Dr,
    Terrell Mncpl Airport, (972) 524-1714, Fri-Sat 10-5, Sun 1-5,
    www.terrelltexas.com/attract.htm#britishflying

    Terrell Heritage Museum, 207 N Frances St, (972) 653-6082, Wed-Thur,
    Sat-Sun, Artifacts

  Tulia - VFW Post 1798, 300 SE 2nd St, 79088, (806) 995-2513, F-86

  Waco - CAF - Ranger Wing, Waco Regional Airport, Mail: POB 8060, 76714-8060
    A-26   T-37

  Wichita Falls - Sheppard AFB Heritage Center, 76311-5000, (940) 851-2511,
    Mon-Fri 9-3:30, Sat 10-2, www.sheppard.af.mil/82trwpa/public_heritage_center.htm

B-52D & G	F-15A	F-105D	T-29A
C-130A & E	F-100D(GF)	F-111A	T-33A
C-135	F-101C	GT-29A	T-38A
F-4C & D & E	F-102A	GYA-37A	
F-5E	F-104C	QT-33A	

UTAH
  Heber - Herber Valley Aero Museum, 2002 Airport Rd, Russ McDonald Field, 84032
    Mail: POB 680405, Park City, UT, 84068, (435) 657-1826, Thur-Sun 10-5, Gift Shop
    Free Adm, www.hebervalleyaeromuseum.org , Boeing Stearman, J-3, MiG-15, P-51, T-28

  Ogden - Hill Aerospace Museum, 75th ABW/MU, 7961 Wardleigh Rd, 84056-5842
    (801) 777-6868, Exit #341 & I-15, Mail: POB 612, 84067, Daily 9-4:30,
    Closed TD, CD, Adm Free, Gift Shop, Theater, www.hill.af.mil/museum/

A-1E	BT-13B	F-18A	Mark 7
A-10A	BU-15	F-80A Mock-Up	MiG-17
ADM-20C	Burgess-Wright	F-84F	MiG-21F
AGM-65A	C-130 Sim	F-84G	O-2A
AGM-84L	C-7A	F-86L	OH-6
AGM-86	C-45H	F-89H	OQ-2A
AGM-109	C-47D(VC)	F-100A	P-38J
AIM-4D	C-54G	F-101B	P-40N-5-CU
AIM-7	C-119G	F-102A	P-47D
AIM-9B	C-123K	F-105D	P-51DT-38A
AIR-2A	C-124C	F-105G	PT-17
AN-T-18	C-130B	F-106A	RB-57A
AQM-34L	C-131D	F-111E	SR-71C
A-26B	(Continued)	GBU-8	T-28B
AT-6	(From Previous) GBU-12		T-29C
B-1B	C-140	GBU-24A/B	T-33A
B-17G	CBU Mk20	H-1(HH)	T-37B
B-24D Project	CIM-10A	H-3E(CH)	T-38A
B-25J	CIM-10B	H-13T(TH)	T-39
B-26	F-4C	H-21C(CH)	Trinity A Bomb
B-29	F-4D	H-34J(HH)	U-3A
B-47E(WB)	F-4E	H-43B(HH)	V-1
B-52G	F-4C(RF)2ea	JN-4D	Wright Flyer
B-57A(RB)	F-5E	L-4	XSM-62a
BGM-109G	F-15A	LGM-30A	YA-7F
BOLT-117	F-16A	Mark 6	

Missiles:

AGM-65	Bomarc A Snark	LGM-30A	SM-2
AGM-86B	Bomarc B Snark	Mark-5	V-1
AIM-04	CIM-10	Mark-6	
AIR-2A	CIM-10B	Mark-7	

UTAH (Continued)

Salt Lake - CAF - Utah Wing, www.cafutahwing.org   PT-17

Salt Lake City ANG, Salt Lake City Int'l Airport, 84116, 151st ARG,

F-86A	F-105B

Washington - Southern Utah Air Museum, 400 W Telegraph Rd, 84780
(435) 656-8292, Restoration of Nose Sections

Wendover - Historic Wendover Airfield, Inside Operations Bldg, 345 S Airport Apron
84083, Daily 8-6, www.wendoverairbase.com, Artifacts

VERMONT

Burlington - Burlington ANG, Burlington Int'l Airport, 05401, (802) 658-0770, 158 TFG

B-57B(EB)	C-131	F-89J	F-102A	T-33A
C-45	F-4D	F-94C	T-29	

Post Mills - Experimental Balloon & Airship Museum, Post Mills Airport, Robinson
Hill Rd, Mail: POB 51, 05058, (802) 333-9254, Apt Only,
www.myairship.com/ebaa/, Over 60 Balloons and Airships, 24 Other Vehicles.

VIRGINIA

Bealeton - Flying Circus Aerodrome, 15S. Route 17, BOX 99, 22712, (540) 439-8661,
Daily 11-Sunset, Adm Adult $9, Child $3, Open Cockpit Rides $25,
Acrobatic Rides $50, Cub Rides $17.50, Airshow Every Sun at 2:30, May Thru Oct,
President: Bex Goppert

Corbin Jr Ace	Fleet Biplane	PT-17	Waco UPF-7
Cub (2 each)	Fokker D.VIII	Stearman A-75 (8 ea)	

Chantilly - NASM, Udvar-Hazy Center, 14390 Air and Space Parkway, Washington Dulles Int'l Airport
SE Corner, 20151, (202) 357-2700, Mail: National Air & Space Museum, Independence Ave at 6th St SW
Suite 3700, Washington, DC, 20560-0321, 202-357-4487, Daily 10-5:30, Free Adm, 135 Spacecraft,
www.nasm.si.edu/museum/udvarhazy/ E-Mail: dullescenter@nasm.si.edu, (D) = Displayed,
Rest of Collection in Storage

"Double Eagle II" (balloon gondola only)	Bü-181B
A-1H (AD-6)	C-2 Collegian
A-6E (D)	C-35(AC)
American Aerolights Double Eagle	C-121C
Applebay Zuni II (D)	C-150L
Arado Ar 234B-2 Blitz (Lightning) (D)	Caudron G.4 (D)
Arlington 1A Sisu	Cessna 180
Arrow Sport A2-60 (D)	Cessna Citation
Avro VZ-9AV Avrocar	Concorde (D)
B-17D	Curtiss E Boat
B-25J (TB-25J-20)	Curtiss-Wright X-100
B-26B	CW-1 Junior
B-29-35-MO (D)	Dassault Cargo Fanjet Falcon 20C (D)
Bachem Ba 349B-1 Natter (Snake)	DH-98 B/TT Mk.35
Baldwin Red Devil	DHC.1 (D)
BB-1	Do-335A-1
BD-5A/B (D)	Double Eagle II
Beech D18S	Eipper-Formance Cumulus 10 (D)
Beech 35 Bonanza	Erco 415 Ercoupe
Bell 30	Extra 260XP
Bell 47J (VH-13J)	F-100D
Bell ATV (Air Test Vehicle)	F-105D
Bellanca CF	F-4S-44 (D)
Bennett Phoenix Viper 175 Delta Wing (D)	F-86A (D)
Bennett Phoenix Streak Delta Wing (D)	F4U-1D (D)
Bennett Phoenix 6B Delta Wing (D)	F6C-4 (D)
Bennett Mariah M-9 Delta Wing (D)	F6F-3 (D)
Bennett Phoenix 6 Delta Wing (D)	F8F-2
Bennett Model 162 Delta Wing (D)	F9C-2
Benoist-Korn (D)	F9F-6
Bensen B-8M Gyrocopter	Fa 330
Bensen B-6 Gyroglider	Fa 330A-1 Bachstelze (D)
Berliner 1924 Helicopter No.5	FA-3-101
Boeing 727-100	Farman Sport
Boeing 307 Stratoliner (D)	FB-5 Hawk (D)
Boeing 367-80 (D)	Felixstowe (NAF) F5L
Bowlus BA-100 Baby Albatross (D)	Fowler-Gage Tractor
Bowlus-Du Pont Albatross (D)	Fw 190F-8/R1 (D)
BT-13A	G-21 (D)
Bü-133C (D)	(Continued Next Page)

(Continued From Previous Page)
G-22(D)
G4M3 (nose section only)
Gates Learjet 23 (D)
Goodyear K-Car (airship gondola)
Goodyear (airship gondola)
Gossamer Albatross
Grob 102 Standard Astir III
Grunau Baby Iib (D)
H-1H(UH) (D)
H-13J(VH)
H-34D(UH) Choctaw (D)
H-44 (XH)
Halberstadt CL.IV
Hawker Hurricane Mk.IIC (D)
He 162A-2
He 219A-2
Helio No. 1
HM.14 Pou du Ciel (D)
HOE-1
Horten IIIf
Horten IIIh
Horten VI-V2
HV-2A
Ikenga 530Z
Ilyushin IL-2 Sturmovik
J-1
J-3 Cub (D)
J1N1-S
JC-24C Windecker Eagle I (D)
JN-4D
Ju 52/3m (CASA 352L)(D)
Junkers 388L-1
K-225
Ki-43-Iib
Ki-45 (D)
KR-34C (D)
L-5 (D)
Langley Aerodrome A (D)
Lazair SS EC
Lockheed 5C Vega (D)
Loudenslager Laser 200 (D)
M-18C Mite
M6A1 (D)
Mahoney Sorceress
Manta Pterodactyl Fledgling (D)
Martin, J.V., K-III Kitten
Me 410A-3/U1
Me 163B-1a
MIG-15bis (D)
MIG-21F-13 (D)
Monnett Moni (D)
Monocoupe 110 Special(D)
Monocoupe 70
N-1M (D)
N-9H
N1K2-Ja (D)
N2S-5 Kaydet (D)
NAF N3N-3 (D)
Nagler-Rolz NR 54 V2
Nieuport 28 (D)
O-1A (L-19A)

O-2A
O-47A
O-60(XO)
Ohka 22 (D)
OS2U-3 (D)
P-26A Peashooter (D)
P-38J-10-LO (D)
P-39Q
P-40E Warhawk (D)
P-47D-30-RA (D)
P-51C (D)
PA-12Super Cruiser
PA-18 Super Cub (D)
PA-23 Apache
Pitcairn AC-35
Pitts Special S-1S
Pitts Special S-1C(D)
PV-2
R-4(XR)(VS-316)
RC-3
RF-8G
Rockwell Shrike Commander 500S (D)
Rotorway Scorpion Too
RP-63A
RT-14
Rutan Quickie
Rutan VariEze (D)
(Continued Next Page)
(Continued From Previous Page)
SB2C-5 Helldiver
SGU 2-22 EK (D)
Sharp DR 90 (D)
SNJ-4 (AT-6)
SPAD XVI (D)
Sportwings Valkyrie (D)
SR-71 (D)
Stanley Nomad
Stearman-Hammond Y
Stout Skycar
Su-26M (D)
T-33A
Ta 152H-1
TBF-1C
TG-1A(D)
Travel Air D4D Pepsi Skywriter (D)
Ultraflight Lazair SS EC
Verville Sport Trainer
VZ-1
VZ-2A
Waco 9
Waco UIC
Waterman Arrowbile
Westland Lysander IIIa
X-35 (D)
XH-44
XP-84 (forward fuselage only)
XR-5 (VS-317)
XR-8
XV-1
XV-15 (D)
Yak-18 "Max"

VIRGINIA (Continued)

Chesapeake - CAF - Old Dominion Wing, Hampton Roads Executive Airport, Rte 58,
   (757) 421-7161, www.olddominionsquadron.org

C-60A	N2S-3	T-28
L-5	SNJ	US-2B

Danville - American Armoured Foundation Tank Museum, 3401 US Hwy 29, 24540,
   (434) 836-5323, Fax: 836-532, Mon-Sat 10-5, Closed TD, CD, Adm Adult $10,
   Snr 60 & Child Under 12 $9.50, Gift Shop, www.aaftankmuseum.com
   AH-1, Nike-Hercules, Tanks: M4A3E8, M5A1, M42A1, M551A1, T54-55, M110A1, M-20,

VIRGINIA (Continued)

Ft Eustis - US Army Transportation Museum, 300 Washington Blvd, Besson Hall,
23604-5260, (757) 878-1115, Daily 9-4:40, Free Adm, Closed Winter, Holidays
www.transchool.eustis.army.mil/Museum/museum.html

Bell Rocket Belt	H-13B(OH)	H-37B(CH)	U-1A
CV-7	H-13E	H-54(CH)	U-6A
DeLacker Aerocycle	H-13E(OH)	H-56A(AH)	U-8D
DH 4	H-15A(UH)	H-64(YAH)	VZ-4-DA
GEM	H-19	L-4	VZ-8P1
GEM-2X	H-19C(UH)	L-21	VZ-8P2
GEM X-2	H-21C(CH)	O-1(L-19)	VZ-4DA
H-1B(UH)	H-23C(OH)	OV-1	X-2
H-6A(OH)	H-25(UH)	RU-8D	
H-13B	H-34C(CH)	TH-55A	

Hampton - Air Power Park, 413 W Mercury Blvd Off Hwy 64 West, 23666,
(757) 727-1163, Daily 9-4:30, Free Adm,

A-7E	F-101B	(Missiles & Rockets)	
F-4C(RF)	F-105D	Argo-D-4	NIM-14
F-86L	Hawker P.1127	AIM 4	NIM
F-89J50	P-1127	Copral M2	SM-78
F-100D	T-33A-1	MA14/LJ-5B	Polaris A-2

Langley AFB, 23665-5548, (757) 764-2018, 1st FW/PA

B-52D	F-15A(YF)	F-16A	F-86H	F-105D

Virginia Air and Space Center, 600 Settlers Landing Rd, 23669-4033,
(757) 727-0900, 800-296-0800, Mon-Wed 10-5, Sun 12-5, Closed CD, Gift Shop,
Adult $8.50, Snrs $7.50, Child 3-11 $6.50, www.vasc.org

American AA-1	F4U-1D	F-104C	P-39Q
Apollo 12	F-16A(YF)	F-106B(NF)	Pitts S-1-C
B-24 Nose	F-16 Cockpit	H-1M(UH)	Rutan Vari-eze
F-4E	F-84F	Langley Aerodrome	Schleiche ASW-12

Manassas - CAF - National Capital Squadron, Mail: POB 185, Falls Church, 22040
www.natlcapsq.org, Funeral Flyovers & Ash Dispersals Available, Rides Available (R)

AT-6G,   BT-13A (R),   DHC-1,   L-4,   L-5(R),   Yak-3

Newport News - Virginia War Museum, 9285 Warwick Blvd (US 60), Huntington Park,
23607, (757) 247-8523, Mon-Sat 9-5, Sun 1-5, Closed TD, CD, Adm Adult $6, Snrs 62 $5
Child 7-18 $4, Under 7 Free, www.warmuseum.org   HH-52A

Norfolk - Naval Air Station,   Eugene Ely Air Park

A-6	F-14	HSL-30	SH-2F
E-2C	H-53	HT-033	

Nauticus Maritime Museum, A-4

Oceana - Naval Air Station, (804) 433-3131

A-4E	F-4B	F-14B F4D-1
A-6E	F-8A	F/A-18
A-7	F-11	F2H-3
AD-1	F-14A(009)	F9F-2

Quantico - Marine Corps Air-Ground Museum, Closed Until 2006 at New Facility,
Brown Field, 2014 Anderson Ave, I-95 & US 1, 22134-5002, (703) 784-2606 & 5856,
Apr 1-Nov 15, Tue-Sat 10-5, Sun 12-5, Closed ED, Free Adm,
http://users.erols.com/hyattg/usmcguns/usmcvols.htm, (S) = Storage

A-2	F6F-3	HRS-1	PV-1 (S)
B-25D Nose	F9F-2	HTL-4	R4D-6
Balloon Basket	FB-5	JN-4D	SBD-5
DH 4(S)	FG-1A	Link Trainer	SNJ-5
EF-10 (S)	FJ-3 (S)	MiG-12 (S)	T-28C (S)
F-4A (S)	H-1(UH) (S)	MiG-15	Tanks
F4D-1 (S)	H-1J(AH)(S)	N2S-3	TBM-3
F4F-4	H-53A(CH)(S)	OE-2 (S)	Thomas-Morse S.4
F4U-4	HO3S-1	Oka Mod II	YRON-1
F6F-4	HO5S-1 (S)	OY-1	

Richmond - Defense General Supply Center, 8100 Jefferson Davis Hwy, (804) 279-3861,
F-84F

Science Museum of Virginia, 2500 West Broad St, (804) 257-1013,
Barbara & William B Thalhimer Jr Hall of Science,

A-4	J-3	Solar Challenger
F-4	Lear Jet	Wright Glider

VIRGINIA (Continued)

Richmond - Virginia Aviation Museum, Richmond Int'l Airport, 5701 Huntsman Rd, 23250-2416, Take Exit 197 South off I-64, (804) 236-3622, Mon-Sat 9:30-5, Sun 11:30-5, Closed TD, CD, Adm Adult 13-59 $8.50, Snrs & Child 4-12 $8, Under 4 Free, Gift Shop, Theater, Viewable Restoration Facility, www.smv.org

A-7D	Fleet Model	Taylorcraft E-2
Aeronca C-2N	Heath Super Parasol	Travel Air B-2000
Aeronca C-3	J-3 Piper Cub	Vultee V-1
Bellanca Skyrocket	N2S-3	Waco YOK
Bruner Winkle Bird	PietenpohlAir Camper	Wright Brothers 1900
Bucker Jungmeister	Pershing II Missile	Wright Brothers 1901
Curtiss Robin J-1D	Pitcairn PA-5	Wright Brothers 1902
Curtiss A-14	SPAD VII	Wright Brothers 1903
Ercoupe 415-D	SR-71	WB Kite 1899
Fairchild 24G	Standard E-1	XV-6A
Fairchild FC-2W2	Stinson SR-10G	

Sandston ANG, 192 TFG/CC, Byrd Int'l Airport, 23150, (804) 272-8884,

A-7D	F-84F	F-105D

The Wright Experience, 10301 Jefferson Davis Highway, 23237, (804) 796-4733, Artifacts Photos, Documentation, Contact: Rick Young, e-mail: ryoung3@richmond.infi.net

Suffolk - Fighter Factory, Tidewater Tech, 240 Municipal Airport Rd, Suffolk Mncpl Airport 23434, (757) 539-8440, Fax 539-5331, Mail: Suite 500, 4455 S Blvd, Virginia Beach, VA 23452, www.fighterfactory.net, email dsa@integrityonline18.com
(R) = Restoration   (S) = Storage Virginia Beach Facility

A-26 (R)	Hurricane II (R) 2ea	P-39 (S)	Stearman
AD-4	I-16 (R)	P-40E (R)(2ea)	T-28D
B-25J (R)	I-16	P-51D (R)	T-34TBM
Bf-109E-7 (R)	I-153	P-63 (S)	V-1
DH 82	L-5	PBY 5-A	Wright Model B
Fi-156 (R)	OS2U	Po-2	Yak-52 (R)
Fleet 2 (S)	Me-108	Polikarpov I-15bis	
FG-1D	Me-208	Spitfire Mk IXe	

Virginia Air National Guard, Camp Pendleton, 23458, (757) 437-4600, F-84F

Wallops Island - NASA Visitor Center, Bldg J-17, 23337, (757) 824-298, Fax 824-1776 Thur-Mon 10-4, Adm Free, Gift Shop, Rockets, www.wff.nasa.gov/vc/
Beech C23   Rockets: Little John, Nike-Cajun,

WEST VIRGINIA

Charleston - Charles ANG, 25311-5000, (304) 357-5100,   P-51D

Clarksburg - Benedum Airport, (304) 842-3400, Dave Reese,   AT-6

WASHINGTON

Arlington - Flying Heritage Collection, Bldg 17622 51st St, (360) 435-2172, By Appt Thur 9-4 Fri-Sat 10-12 & 2-4, Adm Adult $20, Snrs $16, www.flyingheritage.com

A6M3-22	F-105G	Me 163B
A6M5-52 (2ea)	FG-1D	Me 262A-1a
AD-4N	Fi-103/V-1	MiG-21
B-17E	Fi-103R	P-38F
B-25D	Fi-156-C2	P-38L
B-25J	FM-2	P-40C
BAE/GR-3	FW 190A-5	P-47D
Bf 109E-3	Hurricane Mk XIIb	P-51D
DH.98	He-111H (2ea)	Spitfire Mk.Vc
F6F-5	IL-2M-3	U-2/PO-2
F-8	Il-16	V-2
F-84G	JN-4D	Yak-3U
F-86A	Ki-43-1b	

Bellingham - Heritage Flight Museum, Bellington Int'l Airport, 2000 W Bakerview, Suite B, 98226, Mail: 4152 Meridian St, # 105-135, 98226, (360) 733-4422, www.heritageflight.org,

A-1	F8F	LLTV	T-28
A-10	F-15E	P-51D	T-38
AT-6	F-89	PT-13	YMF-5
Apollo 8	F-101	PT-19	Widgeon
Beaver	L-13	SNJ-4	
Broussard	L-39	T-6F	

Chimacum - Port Townsend Aero Museum, Jefferson County Int'l Aiport, Hangar G, SR 19 Mail: POB 101, 98325, (360) 531-0252, Wed-Sun 9-4, Gift Shop, www.ptaeromuseum.com

Corben Baby Ace	Travel Air 4000	SM-8A (2ea)
Benny Howard Racer Rep	Funk Model B-75	Stinson (2ea)
J-3	C-3 Aeronca Master	Irwin Meteor
L-3	CW-1 Jr Rep	
Aeronca 7AC (3ea)	DH-82B	

Everett - CAF/Evergreen Wing, Snohomish County (Paine Field), 98003, L-2

Everett Tour Center, I-5 exit 189, West on Hwy 526 3½ Mi, Gift Shop across from center
at 3003 W Casino Rd, M-F 9-5, Adm Adult $5, Snrs & Child 15 & Under $3, 800-464-1476
Reservations (425) 342-8500 Mon-Fri 8:30-2; http://boeing.com/companyoffices/aboutus/tours/

The ME 262 Project, Paine Field (Snohomish County Airport, Bldg 221, (Next to Fire Station)
10727 36ᵗʰ Pl SW, 98204, (425) 290-7878, Mon-Fri 9-5, Contact: Jim Byron,
email: me262project@juno.com, www.stormbirds.com, Me-262 (5ea) Reproduction (3 for sale)

Ft. Lewis - Fort Lewis, 98433, (253) 967-0015, Exit 120, H-1B(UH), Nike Missile
Ajax Missile   Iraq Vehicle   Tanks Issaquah

Olympia - Olympic Flight Museum, 7637 A Old Highway 99SE, 98501, (360) 705-3925,
Tue-Sun 11-5, Adm Adult $5, Child 7-12 $3, Under 6 Free, Gift Shop, www.olympicflightmuseum.com

A1-E	F4F-3	Hawker Sea Fury P-63	
A6M2	FB-11	L-2	S-E2
AT-6 (2ea)	FG-1D	L-39	Stearman
BAC-167	FM-2	P-51D	TBM-3

Seattle - Boeing Tour Center, POB 3707, m/s OE-44, 98124-2207, (206) 342-9330, Fax 342-7787
www.boeing.com/companyoffices/aboutus/tours/; Tours of the Boeing Plant

King County Municipal Airport, Boeing Field,
4 Mi S of City, (206) 296-7380,   Boeing 707   P-51D

Pacific Science Center, 200 Second Ave N, 98109, (206) 443-2001, Mon-Fri 10-5,
Sat-Sun 10-6, Adm Adult $10, Snrs 65 $8.50, Child 3-12 $7, www.pacsci.org
Gemini XI,   Lunar Orbiter,   Bell 206 Ranger

Seattle Historical Society Museum of History & Industry, 98112, (206) 324-1125,
2700 24th Ave, Adm Adult $1.50, Child $0.50, B-1 Flying Boat

Museum of Flight, 9404 E Marginal Way S, King County Int'l Airport, 98108-4097,
(206) 764-5700, Daily 10-5, First Thur of ea Month Free Adm from 5-9pm, Closed TD, CD,
Adult $14, 65+ $13, Child 5-17 $7.50, Under 5 Free, Group Discounts, Gift Shop, Cafe,
Theater, S=Storage, P=Paine Field, R=Restoration Facility, www.museumofflight.org

A-4F	D-21B Drone	Lear Fan 2100
A-6E	R da Vinci Uccello	R LF-107
A-12 Blackbird	S DC-2	Lilienthal Glider
A-26	DC-3	R LNE-1 (PR-G1)
AT-6D	R DGA-15P	M-1
Aerocar III	R DH 4C Comet	M-21
Aeronca C-2	DH 4M	McAllister Yakima Clipper
Aero Sport Scamp 3	R DH 100	MiG-17
Albatross D Va	LNE-1	MiG-21 PFM
Alexander Eaglerock	R Durand Mk.V	S Monnett Monerai
S An-2	R Eipper Cumulus	MQM-105
R AV-8C	R Ercoupe 415-C	P N-62 Sather RPV (DEX-1)
Aviatik D-I	F-4C	S Nieuport 24
Beech Starship	F-5A(YF)	Nieuport 27
Bede BD-5B	F9F-8	Nieuport 28
R Bensen B-8M	F-14A	P OMAC-1
R Bf 108	F-18L Mockup	P-12
Boeing 80-A	F-86	P-47D-2 (5/8 Scale)
R Boeing 247-D	F-104C	R P-80C/TV-1
Boeing 707-100	Fairchild F-24W	P P-86A (P)
R Boeing 727-022	Fiat G.91 PAN	Pfalz D-XII
Boeing 737-130	FG-1D	PT-13A
Boeing 747-121	Fokker D VII	Quickie Q.200
R B-17F (P)	Fokker D VIII	QH-50C
B-29	Fokker E III	RQ-3A
B-29 Nose	Fokker DR I	Resurs 500 Capsule
(Continued Next Page)	R FM-2	R RF-4D
(From Previous Page)	Gossamer Albatross II	S Rotec Rally IIIB
B-47E (P) Boeing Field	R H-1H(UH)	Rotorway Scorpion Two
R B-52G	H-12(UH)	R Rutan Quickie
R BC-12	R H-21B	R Rutan Vari Viggen
Bf-109E-3	H-32(YH)	Rumpler Taube
Boeing B&W Replica	R H-52(HH)	SE-5A
R Bowers Flybaby BA-100	R Heath Parasol	Sopwith F.1
P Bowlus BA-100	R Huber 101-1 Aero	Sopwith Pup
C-1 Curtiss Robin	Insitu Aerosonde	Sopwith 7F.1 Snipe
C-3B Stearman	R J-2	Sopwith Triplane
C-45	J-3C-65	Spad XIII
C-137B(VC) #970	JN-4D	Spitfire Mk IX
S C-140	Ki-43-IIB	P Sorrell Bathtub Parasol
CA-20	S Kolb Ultralight	P SR-71A Cockpit
S Cascade Kasperwing 180-B	L-3B	P Stephens Akro
Chanute-Herring	P L-13B (CL-13B)	Stinson SR Float
P CG-2	P L-106 Alcor Glider	(Continued Next Page)

```
(Continued From Previous Page)    Williams X-Jet          KD6C-2 Drone
  Swallow CAM 3                    Yak-9                   Apollo Module
  T-33 (Project)                 R XF8U-1                  Boeing Upper Stage
  T-33 Cockpit                   S XF2Y-1                  Hibex Nose Section
S Task Silhouette                  Wright Glider           Mercury Capsule Replica
R Taylorcraft A                    Missiles:             R Pterodactyl Ascender
P T-18                             AGM-86A               R Pterodactyl Ascender II
  Wickham B                        IM-99 Bomarc            Sputnik
```

WASHINGTON (Continued)

Restoration Facility 2909 100th SW, Hangar C72, Everett, Wa 98204, Tue-Fri 8-5, Sat 9-5,
(206) 745-5150, Adm Free, I-5 Exit 189, W on Rte 526, Left on Airport Rd to Snohomish County Airport

Spokane - Fairchild AFB Heritage Museum, 92-CSG Bldg 3511, 99011, (509) 247-2100,
POB 50, Mon, Wed, Sat 10-2, Fri 6-6,

```
B-52D               F-101           F-105               NIKE
C-47D               F-101           T-33A               AJAX
F-86E               F-102           GAM 72
```

Stevenson - Columbia George interpretive Center, POB 396, 990 SW Rock Creek Dr
98648, (800) 991-2338, Daily 10-5, www.columbiagorge.org   JN-4

Tacoma - McChord Air Museum, McChord AFB, Bldg 517, 98438-0205, Ext 125 Off I-5,
E on Bridgeport Way, Main Gate to Visitors Center, Mail: POB 4205, (253) 982-2485/2419,
Wed-Sat 12-4, Closed: TD, CD, ND, Free Adm, Gift Shop, www.mcchordairmuseum.org

```
A-10A               C-47C(TC)       F-4C                F-102A
B-18A               C-82A           F-15A               F-106A
B-23A               C-124C          F-86D               SA-10A(PBY)
B-25 Nose           C-141B          F-101F(CF           T-33A Last Built
```

Glen E Spieth Museum Antiques, 5928 Steilacoom Blvd, 98499, (253) 584-3930,
Sat 11-5, By Appt, T-33A   T-33 Fuse   B-17 Parts

Mr Benhouser, AT-11 in Front Yard, 121th Ave

Tillicum - Camp Murray Air National Guard Park, Exit 122, (253) 512-8524
F-101B   M-5 Stuart   M-47 Walker Bulldog Tank

Vancouver - Pearson Air Museum, 1115 E 5th St, 98661, (360) 694-7026,I-5 Mill Plain Blvd Exit
Go East, Wed-Sat 10-5, Closed TD, CD, ND, Adm Adult $6, Snr $5, Child 13-18 $3, 6-12 $2,
Gift Shop, Theater, Restoration Facility, www.pearsonairmuseum.org, e-mail: pearson@pacifier.com

```
ADOCK               Formula 1 Racer 3ea Nieuport Rep        Starduster II
Aeronca C-3B        GAT-1 Link Trainer Polan Special        Stearman 1942
AN-2                H-1(AH)         PT-17               Student Prince
AT-6(SNJ)           J-3             PT-19B              Taylor Craft
Curtiss Pusher      JN-4D           PT-21/22            Travel Air B-4000
DH 82               L-4             Rearwin Sportster   Waco UPF-7
DC-3                Meyers OTW      Rutan Quickie       Wasol Racer
Fairchild 24        Mini-Cab        Ryan STA            Wright Flyer Rep
Foker Dr.I          Mooney Mite M-18C Seahawker Biplane WSA-1
```

Whidbey Island Naval Air Station, (360) 257-2211, KA-6D

Yakima - McAllister Museum of Aviation, 2008 S 16th Ave, McAllister Field,
Yakima Air Terminal, (509) 457-4933, Sat 9-5, Free Adm, www.mcallistermuseum.org,
J-3,   Sceptre Twin Tail Pusher

WISCONSIN

Amery - Amery Municipal Airport, 2 Mi S of City, (715) 268-8932,
Owner: Bill Geipel, L-29 Czech Delfin (3ea)

Beloit - Beloit Airport, 4046 E County Tk P, 53512, (608) 365-1971, T-28

Boscobel - Airport, 5178 Hwy 133 E, 53805, (608) 375-5223, AT-6, T-28

Camp Douglas - Wisconsin National Guard Memorial Library & Museum, Camp Williams,
Volks Field, 54618-5001, 800-752-6659, (608) 427-1280, Wed-Sat 9-4, Sun 12-4, Free Adm,

```
A-7D                F-4C            F-100C              O-2A
A-10                F-84F           F-102A (2ea)        P-51D
C-97L(KC)           F-86H           F-105B              UH-1
```

Fond Du Lac - Wisconsin Aviation Museum, N6308 Rolling Meadows Dr, Fond du lac County Airport
54935, (920) 924-9998, Fax 921-3186, www.fdl.net/wami,

```
Ercoupe                 RV-6                Taylor Monoplane
Pietenpol AirCamper      Steen Skybolt      Woodstock Glider
```

Hardwood Range Target Range, Public Viewing Area, A-4 on Display
Target Planes: A-6   F-4   T-33   Vigilante
Remnants: C-135(KC)   USCG Cutter

Janesville - Black Hawk Airways, Hwy 51 S, 53542, (608) 756-1000, Beech D18S(C-45)

Black Hawk Technical School, Aviation Center, P.O. Box 5009
53547, (608) 757-7743,   HH-3   T-33

Yankee Air Force Stateline 4th Division, Rock County Airport, POB 10, 53547-0010,
AT-11   F4F   P-40

Kenosha - Gateway Technical Aviation Center, 4940 88th Ave, 53144, (262) 656-6976, F-84F

Madison - Truax Field Museum, Dane County Regional Airport, 4000 Int'l
Lane, In the New Pax Terminal, 53704, (608) 246-3380,
Corben Super Ace   Cobra   F-16   H-1(UH)

Wisconsin Veterans Museum, 30 W. Mifflin St, Capitol Square, 53703-2558
(608) 264-6086, Mon-Sat 9-4:30, Sun 12-4, Free Adm, http://museum.dva.state.wi.us,
Sopwith Pup Rep,   P-51 Rep

Milwaukee - Milwaukee Aera Tech, 422 E College Ave, 53200, (414) 571-4799,
L-19   H-3 (HH)   T-34

Milwaukee's General Mitchell Int'l Airport, Gen Billy Mitchell Field, 53207-6156
(414) 747-5300, www.mitchellairport.com, B-25J(TB)

Milwaukee ANG, De Havilland Heron   T-33A

Mitchell Gallery of Flight, 5300 S Howell Ave, Main Terminal Gen Mitchell
Int'l Airport, 53207-6156, (414) 747-4503, Fax 747-4525, Daily 24 Hours,
www.mitchellgallery.org/, Curtiss Pusher

Monroe - Gen Twining Park, Park Dr, 53566, F-86D

Oshkosh - EAA Air Adventure Museum, Wittman Airfield, 3000 Poberezny Rd,
POB 3065, 54903-3065, US 41 Exit 44, (920) 426-4818, Mon-Sat 8:30-5, Sun 10-5,
Closed TD, CD, ND, Adm Adult $8.50, Snrs 62 $7.50, Child 6-17 $6.50,
Under 6 Free, Family $21.00, Group Rates, Gift Shop, Library,
www.airventuremuseum.org

A-4B(A4D-2)	Curtiss-Wright B-2	GA-22
A-1E/AD-5	Curtiss/Abbott	GA-400-R-2J
A-1E/AD-3	Curtiss/Thompson	Glastar 3
Acroduster SA-700 H.G.G.	Cvjetkovic CA-61	Globe OQ-2A
Aero Sea Hawk	DH 98B Mk.35	Globe K2DG-2
Aeronca C-2N	DH DHC-1B2	Great Lakes 2-T-1AE
Aeronca LC	DH 100 Mk.35	Grouod Trainer
Aeronca C-3	DH 82A	Gunderson Trainer
Aeronca K	DH 89A MK.IV	H-1S(AH)
Anderson Greenwood 14	DC-3	H-21B
B-17G	Double Eagle V	H-10
B-25J	Driggers A 891H	HA-1112-M1L
Baby Ace D Lambert	DSA-1	Hamilton Glasair
Baker 001 Special	E-2	Hardly Abelson
Barlow Acapella	EAA Super Acro Sport	Harlow PJC-2
Barrage Kite	EAA A-1	Haufe Dale Hawk 2
Bates Tractor	EAA P-8	Hawker Hunter Mk 51
Bede XBD-2	Eipper MX-1 Quicksilver	Heath Parasol
Bede BD-5 Micro	Ercoupe 415-C	Heath LNA-40 Super
Bede BD-4 Stricker	F-14	Heath Feather
Bee Honey Bee	F-51D	Heath Super Parasol
Bensen B-11 Gyrocopter	F-80C(GF)	Hegy R.C.H.I.
Boeing E75N1	F-84C	Henderschott Monoplane
Brock Kem 8M Gyroplane	F-84F(GF)	Henderson Highwing
Brown-Bushby-Robinson	F-86 Mk V	Hill Hummer
Brown Star Lite	F-86 Mk V/VI	HM-360
Brown B-1 Racer	F-86H	HP-10
Brugioni Mario Cuby	F-89J	HP-18-LK-G Sailplane
Bu 133	F-100A	Hugo VPS HU-GO Craft
Bu 133L	F4U-4	J-1
Bugatti 100	F8F-2	J-2
Burgess Twister Imperial	Fairchild 24W-46	J-3
Cessna 150H	Fairchild 24 C8	J2F-6
CG-2 186V	Fairchild 24 C8A	JC-1
Chanute Hang Glider	Falck Racer	JC24-B
Chester Racer	FC-2W2	JN-2D-1
Christen Eagle I 2ea	Fi 156C-2	JN4-D (2ea)
Christen Eagle II	Fike Model C	JP-001
Christen Eagle IF	Fokker DR-1	Kaminskas RK3
Collins Aerofoil Boat	Fokker DR-1	Karp Pusher 107
Corbin D Baby Ace	Folkerts Gullwing	Ki-43B
Corbin C-1	Ford 4-AT-E	Kiceniuk Icarus V
Co-Z	Ford Flivver 268	Knight Twister
CR-4	Funk B	(Continued Next Page)

(From Previous Page)	P-38L	Spartan 7W Executive
Kotula-Lundy Graflite	PA-22-150	Spinks Akromaster
L-5E-1VW	PA-28-140	Spitfire Mk.IXE
LC-DW500	PA-39	Starduster SA-300
Learfan LF-2100	Pedal Plane	Stinson SR-9C
Lincoln PT-K	Pereira Osprey II	Stits SA-2A
Lincoln Biplane	PG-1	Stits SA-3A
Loving Racer	Pientenpol B4A Pientenpol	Stits SA-8
Luscombe Phantom 1	Pientenpol P-9	Stits DS-1
M-1 Special	Piper PT	Stits SA-11A
Mace Model III	Pitts P-6	Stolp SA300
Marinac Flying Mercury	Pitts 1	Stolp V Star
MC-12	Pitts Racer	Stolp SA500L
McHolland Acro-Sport	Pitts S-1	Swallow Model 1924
Meyer Little Toot	Pitts S-1 Special	Swenson S1
MiG-15	Pitts S-1S Special 2ea	T-18
MiG-21	Pitts S-2	T-33 Mk 3
Midgnet Pou du Ciel	Pitts SC-1	T-33A
Miles M.2.W.	Player Sportplane	T-40
Mitchell Wing A-10	Pober Super Ace	Taylor Aerocar
MJ-5	Pober Jr Ace	Taylorcraft BC
Mong Sport	PQ-14B	Tessier Biplane
Monnett Moni Van WYK	PT-3	Travel Air E-4000
Monnett Sonerai II	PT-19B/M-62A	Travel Air 2000
Monnett Monex	Quickie Herron	UFM Solar Riser
Monnett Moni	Questair 200 Venture	UHM Easy Riser]
Monocoupe 110 Special	Rand KR-1	V-260/USD
Monocoupe 110	Rasor 21	Vector 27
Monocoupe 90A	Riderf A-1	Waco CTO
Monocoupe 90AW	RLU-1 (2ea)	Waco RNF
Monocoupe 113	Rotorway Scorpion I	Waco YKS-7
MS 181	Rutan 72 Grizzly	Wag-Aero Cuby
N2S-2	Rutan Solitaire	Warwick W-4
Neibauer Lancair 200	Rutan Vari-eze	WD-A
Neiuport 24	Rutan 50-160 Variviggen	WE-1
Nitz Executive	RV-3 VanGrusven	Welsh Rabbit Model A
Oldfield Special BGL	RV-4 VanGrunsven	Whitaker Centerwing
OQ-2A	Ryan NX-211	Wings Avid Flyer
OQ-19D	Ryan SCW-145y	Wisman Pusher
OTW-145	Schemp-Hirth Nimbus II	Wittman Midwing
P-5	Scorpion II 754RW	Wittman DFA
P-51(XP)	Shafor Ganagobie	Wittman Tailwind WO
P-51D	SM-8A	Wittman W
P-64	Smith Miniplane	Wittman WV
P-6E	Smyth Sidewinder	Wright Flyer
P-9	Sorrell DR-1	
P-10	Spad VII Swanson	

WISCONSIN (Continued)

Oshkosh - Basler's Flight Service, Whittman Field, 54901, Restores DC-3's

Pleasant Prairie - Kenosha Military Museum, 11114 120th Ave, 53159, (262) 857-3418
Across State Line on I-94 Exit 347 Hwy 165, May-Sept Wed-Sun 9-5, Oct-April
Sat-Sun 10-5, Adm Adult $5, Child 3-17 $3, Under 3 Free, www.kenoshamilitarymuseum.com

A-7C(TA)	M-60 Tank	M-38
F-4 Cockpit	OV-1D (5ea)	M-38A1
H-58(OH)	T-33A-5-LO	M-41 Walker Bulldog Tank
H-1(UH) 3ea	M-2 Half Track	M-42 Duster (2ea) Tank
H-54(CH) (2ea)	M-3 Stuart Tank	M-47 Patton (2ea) Tank
H-6(OH)	M-4 Sherman Tank	M-151
HH-3 (3ea)	M-5A Stuart Tank	PBR River Boat Nam
Hiller Helicopter	M-7 Stuart Tank	U-9
Hughes Helicopter		

Stoughton - VFW, W Veterans Rd, 53589, (608) 873-9042, T-33

Superior - Richard IRA Bong Heritage Center, 2231 Catlin Ave, 54880, 15 Miles W
of Poplar, The Bong P-38 Fund, Inc, POB 326, 54864, (715) 364-2623, 392-7151,
May 30-Oct 31 Daily 9-5, Nov-May Tue-Sat 9-4, www.bongheritagecenter.org, P-38

Waukesha - CAF/Wisconsin Wing, N9 W24151 Blu M, 53186, Mail: PO Box 1998,
53110-1998, (262) 547-1775, PV-2D

WYOMING

Afton - Cal Air Museum, 1042 S Washington, 83110, (307) 886-9881,
  Callair Airplanes (3ea)

Cheyenne - Francis E Warren AFB Museum, 90 SMW/CV, Bldg 210, 82005-5000,
  (307) 775-2980, Mon-Fri 8-4, Free Adm, www.pawnee.com/fewmuseum/, H-1F(UH)

  WY ANG Cheyenne, BOX 2268, Mncpl Airport, 82003-2268, (307) 772-6201, CMS: MD Duncan,
  F-84F   F-86L   F-86E   T-33A

Greybull - Hawkins & Powers Museum of Flight and Aerial Firefighting,
  Greybull Airport, 82426, (307) 765-4482, On Hwy 14, Firefighter Facility,
  Mon-Fri 8-5, Sat-Sun 10-7 (Summer), Adm Adult $2.50, Child 6-18 $1,
  Under 6 Free, Gift Shop, PA: Sue C Anderson

A-26	C-118 2 ea	H-54B(CH)	PB4Y-2
C-45	C-119 2 ea	Hiller 12E	SL-4
C-54	C-130A 2 ea	L-18	
C-82	Fairchild F-27	Monocoupe 1928	
C-97(KC) 2 ea	H-34A	P-2V 2 ea	

Jackson - Golden Wings Flying Museum, Yellowstone Aviation, Inc, POB 6291,
  83002-6291, (800) 550-4008, (307) 739-8175,

Alliance Argo	K-84	PT-6F	Stinson SM-1B
Call-Air A-2	KR-34C	PT-23A	Taylor Aerocar
Fairchild F-45	Kreutzer K-5	PT-26 (2ea)	TG-1A
FC-2-W2	N2S-4(A75L3)	SM-6000-B	Travel Air A-6000-A
Fleetwings Seabird	Paramount Cabinair	Spartan C2-60	Waco CUC-1
Ford 4-AT	PT-19	Stinson 7M-7A	

CANADA

ALBERTA

Airdrie - Arcot Aviation, Airdrie Airport, RR #2, T4B 2A4, (403) 948-2399, Harvard Mk IV

Claresholm - SNJ

Calgary - Aero Space Museum of Calgary, 4629 McCall Way NE, T2E 8A5, (403) 250-3752,
  Fax 250-8399, Daily 10-5, Closed ND, CD, Adm Adult $7, 60 & Child 12-17
  $4.50, Child 6-12 $3.50, Under 6 Free, Family $18, Gift Shop, Restoration Facility,
  www.asmac.ab.ca/ e-mail: aerospace@lexicom.ab.ca
  (C) = Courtyard; (NM) = Naval Museum; (R) = Restoration Project; (S)=Storage

Avro Anson Mk II(S)	DC-3 (C)	Quickie II
Avro Lancaster Mk.X (C)	F-86	S-51 (C)
Bagjo BG12 Glider	F-100(CF) Mk.III	S-55 (S)
Barkley Grow T8P-1	F-101B(CF)(C)	Silver Dart
Beech D-18S Mk.III (C)	Link Trainer	Sopwith Triplane
Bell 47G	Harvard Mk IV	T-50 (R)
Cessna 188 AG	Hawker Hurricane XIIb	Taylorcraft Auster Mk.VII
DH 82	JN-4 (Project)	Waco 10
DH 98 (R)	Michell U2	Waco EQC-6
DH 100	Noorduyn Norseman Mk V (NM)	
DHC 6	PD-18(HUP-3)	

Cold Lake - F-5(CF)F-101(CF), F-104(CF), T-33(CT)

Edmonton - Alberta Aviation Museum Assoc, 1140 Kingsway Ave, T5G 0X4, Bldg 11, (403) 453-1078,
  Fax: 453-1885, Mon-Fri 10-6, Sat-Sun 10-4, Adm Adult $5, Snrs 60 $4, Child 13-17 $3, 6-12 $2,
  Under 6 Free, Gift Shop, www.ualbertaaviationmuseum.com

Argus	F-101B(CF) 3ea	Stinson 108 (R)
Avro Anson Mk.II (R)	Fairchild 24W	T-33
B-37(RB)	Harvard	Tocan Ultrlight
Beech D18S	Hawker Hurricane 5/8 Scale	Vickers Viking Mk.IV 7/8 Scale
Cranwell CLA4 (R)	Link Trainer Mk.IV (R)	Waco UIC
DH98 Mk B35	Noorduyn Norseman (R)	Westland Lysander 2/3 Scale
F-86	PT-26	
F-100(CF)	Stinson SR-9FM	

  Venture Memorial Flight Assoc, 14210-24A St, T5Y 1L7, (403) 478-8992,

Grand Center - City Diplayed CF-5, CF-104

Harbor Grace - City Displayed DC-3

Leduc - T-33(CT)

Lethbridge - T-33(CT)

Nanton - St Paul (See Next Page)

ALBERTA (Continued)

Nanton - Nanton Lancaster Society, POB 1051, T0L 1R0, (403) 646-2270, Fax 646-2214, May-Oct Daily 9-5, Nov-April 10-4, Free Adm, www.lancastermuseum.ca,

Avro 683 Lancaster 2ea	CF-100	Link Trainer
Avro Anson MkII (P)	DH 82	PT-18
Beech D18	Fleet Fawn Mk II	PT-26
Bristol Blenheim (P)	Fleet 7C	T-20 Crane
BT-14 Yale	Harvard Mk.II	T-33

Stephanville - Harmon Field, F-102

St Albert - T-33(CT)

St Paul - UFO Landing Pad, Hwy 28, NW of City, Mail: Box 887, T0A 3A0, (888) 733-8367 (780) 645-6800, June 22-Aug 31 Mon-Fri 9-6, Sat-Sun 9-5, RoY Mon-Fri 9-5, Artifacts

Wetaskiwin - Reynolds Museum, East of Airport, 4118 57st, T9A 2B6 (403) 361-1351, Mail: POB 6360, T9A 2G1, Sept 24-May 9 Tue-Sun 10-5, Adm Adult $6.50, Snrs 65 $5.50, Child 7-17 $3, Under 7 Free, Family $15, RoY Adult $9, Snrs $7, Child $5 Family $20, www.cahf.ca/

Aeronca O-58	DH 60	Lincoln Sport
Aeronca C-3	DH 60GM	Link Trainer
Aeronca Chief	DH 60M	Meade Glider
Auster AOP-6	DH 60X	Meyers MAC 145
AT-6 Harvard Mk.4	DH 82C	Miles M11A
Avro Avian CF-CDV	DH 100	N-75
Avro Anson MK II	DHC. 1	Pietenpohl Air Camper
B-25	DC-3	PT-19
BC-12	Fairchild 24-C8E	PT-26
Bellanca Skyrocket	Fairchild 71	RC-3
Beech 18 Expeditor	Fleet 16	Reynolds Sport
Beech D17S	Fleet Fawn II	Reynolds Star
Boeing Stearman	Focke Wulf Weihi	Stinson HW75
Bristol Bolingbroke MK.IV	Funk B.85C	T8P-1
BT-14	H-34	T-33
C-1(EC)	Hawker Hurricane MK.XIII	T-50
C-37	J-2	TBM
C-64	J-5A	Waco UPF-7
C-64 Mk.4	Jacobs Jaycopter	Waco 10 GXE
Curtiss Robin	JN-4	Waco YKS-7
DGA-15P	L-5	Waco YPT-14
	F-101(CF)	Waco ZQC-6
	F-104(CF)	T-134(CT)

BRITISH COLUMBIA

Abbotsford - Abbotsford Int'l Airport, F-101(CF)

Langley - Canadian Museum of Flight & Transportation, Hangar #3 - 5333, 216th St, Langley Airport, V2Y 2N3, (604) 532-0035, Fax 532-0056, Daily 10-4, Closed CD, Adm Family $12, Adult $5, Sr/Youth $4, Under 6 Free, Gift Shop, www.canadianflight.org, Flying = F, On Display = D, Restore to Fly = R, Restore to Static Display = S, Storage = C

Aeronca Chief 11AC		F-11-2 (2ea)	Piasecki Model 44B (S)
Auster AOP.6		F-100(CF) Mk.38	PT-26A
Avro Anson Mk.II	C	F-104D(CF)	PT-27 (P)RC-3
Avro Anson Mk.V	C	Fairchild 71	Rutan Quickie
Beechcraft 3 NMT		Fairchild 82A (P)	S-55D(H-19) (S)
Bell 47J2		Fairchild Cornell	S-58D (P)
Bensen B7	C	Fleet Finch Mk II Rep	Scheibe Bergfalke II (P)
Bensen B8	C	Flight Simulator (S)	SE-5A (P)
Bensen B8M	D	Grunau Baby IIB (S)	Sopwith Camel Replica
Bowers Fly-Baby	C	H-21BPH	Struchen Helicopter
Bowlus BB-1 (S)		Handley-Page 52	Supermarine Stranraer (P)
Brantley 305		Harvard Mk IIB	SV-4C (S)
Bristol Bolingbroke IVT		Hawker Hurricane IIB (P)	T-18 (P)
C-64 Mk.V (S)		HM-290	T-33AN
C-64 Mk.IVW (S)		HO3S-1(S-51/H5) (S)	Taylor Monoplane (P)
C-45-3NM		HUP-3(PD-18)	TG-1AFR (2ea)(S)
Cyclo Crane		L-1(O-49)(S)	TG-3ASW (P)
DH 60GM		Lockheed 18-08	Vertol 44
DH 82C		Mignet Pou du Ciel	Waco AQC-6
DH 100 Mk3		Mooney M18C Mite	Waco INF (S)
Dagling Primary 1 (S)		Muller Arrow Hang Glider	Westland Lysander MkIII(S)
DC-3		OQ-RP	
DGA-15P (P)			

Lazo - Comox Air Force Museum, Canadian Forces Base, 19 Wing, V0R 2K0
(250) 339-8162, Daily 10-4, Adm Donations, www.comoxairforcemuseum.ca

C-47	F-100(CF)	MiG 21	T-33
CT-114	F-101B(CF)2ea	P-107(CP)	
DC-3	F-104(CF)	S2F(SC)	
DH U-6A	H-21	Spitfire Mk IX	

Kamloops - Kamloops Airport, F-5(CF)

Port Alberum - Sproat Lake, Vancouver Island West of City, Martin Mars Flying Boat 2ea.

Sidney - British Columbia Aviation Museum, 1910 Norseman Rd, V8L 4R1, On Vancouver Island
Next To Victoria Int'l Airport, (250) 655-3300, Summer Daily 10-4, Winter Daily 11-3,
Adm Adult $7 Child $3, Gift Shop, www.bcam.net

A-26	Eastman E-2	Pac Aero Tradewind
Avro Anson Mk II	Gibson Twin Plane	Pietenpol
Bell 47D-1	Luscombe 8A Silvaire	RC-3
Bristol Bolingbroke Mk IV	Nieuport 17 7/8	SE.5A
Chanute Glider	Nooruyn Norseman	
DH82C		

Army, Navy and Air Force Assoc, 4th St, F-86 Mk. 6

MANITOBA

Brandon - Commonwealth Air Training Plan Museum, Inc, Brandon Mncpl Airport, R7A 6N3,
BOX 3, Group 520, RR5, (204) 727-2444, Fax 725-2334, N of Trans Canada Hgwy on #10,
Oct-Apr Mon-Fri 9-4:30, May-Sept, Daily 9-4:30, Closed Sat-Sun, Adm Adult $3.50, Child $2

Anson	Cornell	F-104(CF)	Stinson
AT-6 Harvard	DC-3 (CC-129)	Fleet Fort Project	T-33(CT)
B-25	DH 82	H-136(CH)	T-134A(CT)
Beech 18	F-5(CF)	Hurricane Mk I	T-50
Bristol Bollingbroke	F-86 Mk VI	Link Trainer	X-44(CX)
C-45 (CT-128)	F-100(CF)	P-121(CP)	
Casara Prayer	F-101B(CF)	PT-26	

Comfort Inn, Route 10 & Trans Canada, Bollingbroke

Brandon Airport, Route 10, T-33

Gimili - 1st Ave Off Center St, T-33

Moncton - F-5(CT)

Moose Jaw - SNJ

Portage la Prairie - 260 Royal Road South, Island Park, Mail: City of Portage la Prairie,
97 Saskatchewan Ave East, R1N 0L8, (204) 239-8334, email: info@city-plap.com, T-33

Southport Aerospace Centre, Portage La Prarie Manitoba Airport (CFB),
Cresent Rd & Royal Rd, C-45,   CT-114,   CT-134A,

Fort La Reine Museum, Hwy 26 & Hwy 1A, (204) 857-3259, May-MidSept 9-6, July-Aug
Wed-Fri Extended 9-8, Adm Adult $5, Snr $4, Child 6-12 $2, Under 6 Free, CT-134A
http://www.rm.portage-la-prairie.mb.ca/museum.htm

Shilo - The Royal Canadian Artillery Museum, CFB, R0K 2A0, (204) 765-3000 Ext 3534,
Victoria Day - Thanksgiving Day, Mon-Fri 8-4, Sat-Sun 1-4, Winter Tue-Fri 8-4,
Free Adm, www.artillery.net, E-mail: rcamuseum@artillery.net, Cannons, Rocket

Winnipeg - Ness Ave & Conway, F-5

Western Canada Aviation Museum, Inc, Hangar T2, 958 Ferry Rd, R3H-0Y8,
(204) 786-5503, Fax 775-4761, Mon-Fri 10-4, Sat 10-5, Sun 12-5, Adult $7.50,
Snrs $5, Child 3-12 $3, Under 3 Free, Family $18, Closed Boxing Day, Good Fri,
CD, ND, www.wcam.mb.ca/ e-mail: info@wcam.mb.ca

AT-6 Harvard	DH 100	H-136(CH)
Avro Anson Mk.II	DHC.3	HA-1112
Beech D18S	F-5(CF)	Hiller Helicopter
Beechcraft 23 Musketeer	F-101B(CF)	JU 52/1M
Bellanca 66-75	F-100(CF)	Link Trainers
Bensen B-7	F-11A	Lockheed 10A
Bristol Freighter	F-101B(CF) Cockpits	Norseman Mk IV
BT-14	F-104(CF)	NA-64
C-37	F-86 Mk.3	Saunders ST-27
C-45	Fairchild 24W46	Schweizer 2-22
CL-84	Fairchild 71C	Stinson SR-8
CP-121	FC-2	U-6
CT-134	Froebe Hellicopter	Vickers Vedette V
CX-144	Froebe Ornithopter	
DH 82C	Gruneau 2 Glider	

MANITOBA (Continued)

Winnipeg - Air Force Heritage Museum, 500 Wing, Memorial Park,
Sharpe Blvd, Off Ness, (204) 833-2500 ext 5993, Weekly 9-4, Free Adm

B-25	F-5(CF)	Harvard(AT-6)
Beech 23 Musketeer	F-100(CF)	H-136(CH)Kiowa
C-4/6 Canadair	F-101(CF)	S2F(CP-121)
C-45(CT-128)	F-104(CF)	T-33
C-47(DC-3)	F-86	

Woodland Park, Portage Ave & Woodhaven, F-86,   T-33

NEW BRUNSWICK

Chatham - Canadian Forces Base, CF-101

Cornwallis - F-101(CF)

Edmunston Airport, Lancaster 10AB

Hillsborough - Preservation Park, Main Rd S of Town, CF-101

Moneton - Centenial Park - CF-100 Mk 5

Moose Bay, Labrador - T-33(CT)

St. John - New Brunswick Museum, 277 Douglas Ave, Market Square, E2K 1E5,
(506) 643-2300, Mon-Fri 9-9, Sat 10-6, Sun 12-5, Adm Adult $6, Snr $4.75,
Child 4-18 $3.25, 3 & Under Free, Family $13, Wed 6-9 Free,
Dr Wallace Rupert Turnbull Exhibit, TBM

NEWFOUNDLAND

Botwood - In Town, PBY-5A

Gander - North Atlantic Aviation Museum, POB 234, A1V 1W6, May 15- Sept 6
Daily 9-9, Sept 7 - May 14 Mon-Fri 8:30-4:30, (709) 256-2923, Faz 256-4777
Adm Adult $3, Senior/Child 6-15 $2, 5 & Under Free, E-mail: cjtaylor@avalon.nf.ca,

Beech D18S	DC-3 Cockpit	Lockheed Hudson	Quickie 1
CF-101B	Link Trainer	Lockhee Hudson	PBY-5A

Goose Bay - Happy Valley, Labrador Heritage Society Museum, (709) 896-5445, F-101(CF) XL361

Town Hall, Hamilton River Rd, T-33

5 Wing Goose Bay Hq, Forbes Rd, Bldg 512, CF-100

Harbour Grace - DC-3

NORTHWEST TERRITORIES

Hay River - Buffalo Airways, Box 4998, NWT, X0E 0R0, (403) 874-3333, C-47(3ea) Rides

NOVA SCOTIA

Baddeck - Alexander Grahm Bell National Historic Park, PO BOX 159,
B0E 1B0, HD-4 Hydrofoil Remains, Silver Dart 1909

Bedford - F-101(CF)

Clementsport - HMCS/CFB Cornwallis Military Museum, Bldg 41-3 Cornwallis Park,
Mail: POB 31, B0S 1E0, (902) 638-8602, CF-101,   T-33

Greenwood - Greenwood Military Aviation Museum, Canex Bldg, Ward Rd, Mail: POB 786,
B0P 1N0, (902) 765-1494, June-Aug Daily 9-5, Sept-May Tue-Sat 10-4, Free Adm, Gift Shop

CP-140 Arora	C-61	CT-114	T-33
Avro Anson (P)	C-130	KR-34C	
Avro Lancaster Mk X	Ch-113 Labrador	P2V-7	
Bollingbrooke (P)	CP-107 Argus	PBY-5A Canso	

Halifax - Atlantic Canada Aviation Museum Society, 1747 Summer St, B3H 3H6
Exit 6 from Hwy 102, Mail: POB 44006, 1658 Bedford Hwy, Bedford, NS, B4A 3X5
Mid-May to Mid-Sept 9-5, (902) 873-3773, $4 Donation, Gift Shop, Picnic Area,
http:/acam.ednet.ns.ca, (R=Being Restored), (P=Project) (S=Storage)

Aeronca C-3 (P)	CP-140	Lockheed 1329-8
Bell 47-J-2	Erco 415C Ercoupe	Lockheed Hudson Mk.6 (S)
Bell 206B	F-86 Mk.5	PBY-5A (R)
CL-13	Fi-103(V1)FZG-76 (R)	Pitts Special S1-C
CF-5	Hang Glider Eletroflyer	Scamp 1 Homebuilt
CF-100	Harvard Mk.II	Silver Dart Rep
CF-101B (S)	L-19	T-33(CT) Cockpit
CF-104 (S)	L-Spatz-55	TBM
CP-107 Simulator(S)	Lincoln Sports	
CP-121	Link Trainer	

NOVA SCOTIA (Continued)

Halifax - Halifax Aviation Museum - CF-5,   CF-100 Mk 5,   F-86,   TBM **2ea**

Shearwater - Shearwater Aviation Museum, Canadian Forces Base Shearwater, 12 Wing,
  Mail: POB 5000 Stn Main, B0J 3A0, (902) 460-1083 & 1011 ext 2139 Chris Noon
  May&Sept Tue-Thur 10-5, Sat 12-4, June-Aug Tue-Fri 10-5, Sat-Sun 12-4, Dec-March Closed
  Free Adm, Gift Shop, Library & Restoration Facility 460-1011 ext 2165,
  www.shearwateraviationmuseum.ns.ca, email: awmuseum@ns.sympatico.ca

AT-6 Mk.II	F2H-3	HO4S-3	TBM-3
CP-121	Fairey Swordfish	S2F-3	
F-116B(CF)(F5B)	Firefly Mk.I	T-133	
F-101(CF)	Harvard 277	T-114(CT)	

ONTARIO

Barrie - RCAF Assoc, 441 Wing, Hwy 90, East of City, T-33A

Borden - CFB Borden Military Museum, L0M 1C0, Dieppe Rd & Waterloo Rd,
  (705) 424-1200, Tue-Fri 9-12 & 1:15-3, Sat-Sun 1:30-4, Closed Day After Holiday Weekend.
  AFA = Air Force Annex, Hangar 11, Hangar Rd, Sat & Sun 1-4, Closed Day After Holiday
  AP = Air Park

Avro 504	AFA F-100(CF)	AP L-13(CL)		Panzer Tank
DH 82	AFA F-101(CF)	AP S2F(CS)	AP	Renault Tank
F-5(CF)	AP F-104(CF)	AP T-33	AFA	Sherman Tank
F-86	AP JN-1	T-114(CT)	AFA	Stuart M5AI

Belleville - Zwicks Centennial Park, Hwy 2 at Bridge, In Town, F-86 RCAF

Bradford - Guild of Automotive Restores Inc, 44 Bridge St, (705) 775-0499, A-6 Project

Brockville - Brockville Marina, Blockhouse Island, Hwy 2 West, F-86
  Hwy 2 West of Town, T-134(CT)

Campbellford - Memorial Military Museum, 230 Albert St, K0L 1L0, (705) 653-4848,653-1398

Beech 18 Parts	F-100(CF)	PBY Parts	T-50 Project
F-5(CF)	F-105 Replica	T-33(CT)	T-134(CT)

Cheltenham - The Great War Flying Museum, 13691 McLaughlin Rd, Brampton Airport,
  May-Sept Daily 2-4, or By Appt, www.bramfly.com/museum
  Flyable: Fokker D.VII Rep, Fokker DR.I, SE-5A, SE-5A 7/8

Collingwood - Collingwood Classic Aircraft Foundation, Collingwood Mncpl Airport,
  Mail: Box 143, L9Y 3Z4, (705) 445-7545, Thur 9-4, Adm Free,
  www.classicaircraft.ca/homepage.htm, Smith Miniplane, Stinson 105
  Rides in: Aeronca Champ 7AC, DH 82A, Fleet Canuck

Cornwall - RCAFA 424 Wing, Water St, T-33(CT) 2ea

Dunnville - City Library, Chestnut Ave, Off Hwy 3, Harvard
  No 6 RCAF Dunnville Assoc, Dunnville Airport, Hangar 1, Regional Rd 11, (905) 701-RCAF
  DH-82,   Harvard

Dundas - T-33(CT)

Ear Falls - Ear Falls Museum, Waterfront off Hwy 105, Beech 18, Mike

Fort Erie - Niagara Parks, Garrison Rd & Central Ave, Royal Canadian Airforce Assoc
  484 Wing, T-33

Goderich - Sky Harbour Gallery, 110 N St, N7A 2T8, (519) 524-2686, Fax 524-1922
  www.huroncountymuseum.on.ca/skyh-gen.htm, Artifacts

Grand Bend - Pinery Antique Flea Market, Hwy 21 6 Km S of Town, T-33

Hamilton - Canadian Warplane Heritage, Hamilton Civic (Mt Hope)Airport,
  9280 Airport Rd, L0R 1W0, (905) 679-4183, Fax 679-4186, (800) 365-5888
  Daily 9-5, Closed CD, ND, Adm Adult $10, Snrs & Child $8, Family $30, Gift Shop,
  Library, Theater, www.warplane.com, e-mail: museum@warplane.com

AN-2	F-5(CF)	Link Trainer
AT-6G Harvard 3 ea	F-86	N.A. 64 Yale
Auster	F-100(CF) Mk.5	PT-26B Cornell
Avro Lancaster BX683	F-104D(CF)	PT-27 Stearman
Avro 652 Anson V(2ea)	Fairchild F-24R	S-51
B-25J	Fairey Firefly Mk.5	Sopwith Pup Replica
Bollingbroke Nose	Fleet Finch 16B	T-28
C-45D(UC)	Fleet 21K	T-33A
CF-104D	Fleet Fort 60K	Westlander Lysander 3
DH 100	Fleet 7C Fawn II	Widgeon
DH 82C	Hawker Hurricane	
DHC. 1	Hawker Hunter Mk.IIB	
DC-3	Hurricane Replica	

Hamilton - Hamilton Airforce Assoc, T-33(CT)

Hamilton Military Museum, York Blvd (Dundurn Park), L8R 3H1, (905) 546-4974
June 15-Labor Day Daily 11-5, Labour Day-June 14 Tue-Sun & Holiday Mondays 1-5
Closed CD, ND, Military Artifacts

RCAF Assoc 447 Wing, Unit 350, Mount Hope Airport, 9300 Airport Rd, L0R 1W0, F-100(CF)

Ignace - City Display, Beechcraft D18 on Floats

Kapuskasing - The Kap Air Collection 17 Lang Ave, P5N 1E5, Airport (705) 331-2611

Kingston - CFB Kingston, Hwy 2 East, F-5(CF)   H-136(CH)

Kingston Airport, RCAFA 416 Wing, Regional Rd 1, (613) 389-6404, AT-6 Harvard,   CT-134

Royal Military College, Point Frederick,Hwy 2, East Of Town, (613) 541-6000, F-86, CF-100

Kitchener - Spitfire Emporium, 666 Victoria St South, Spitfire Replica

Kitchener Waterloo Regional Airport, Fountain St (Regional Rd 17), Diamond Katana

Lambeth - Lambeth Legion Hall, Box 701 Lambeth Station, N6P 1R2, (519) 652-3412

Lindsay - Lindsay Airport, Hwy 35, West of City, (705) 324-8921, F-101B(CF)

London - Airport Hotel, Dundas St East at Airport, Diamond Katana

London Airport, Crumlin Rd, Diamond Katana

Royal Canadian Regiment Museum, Carriageway Wolseley Hall, N5Y 4T7,
Oxford/Elizabeth Streets, (519) 660-5102, 5136

Malton - F-100(CF)

Mount Hope - See Hamilton, AB

North Bay - CFB North Bay, North Bay Airport, F-100(CF)   F-101(CF)

Lee Park, Memorial Dr by North Bay Marina, Bomarc   F-101(CF)

North Kitchener - Spitfire Emporium, 666 Victoria St, N2H 5G1, (519) 745-2661
Fax 744-1563, Mon-Sat 10-5, www.spitcrazy.com, email: Ray@spitcrazy.com
Aviation Store with Spitfire MKIX AHV Replica

Oshawa - Oshawa Aeronautical, Military, & Industrial Museum, 1000 Stevenson Rd N, L1J 5P5,
(416) 728-6199, Easter-Nov Tue-Sat 12-5, Sun 1-5
A-26   Armored Ambulance   M 24 Tank   Ferret Scout Car
Chevrolet Staff Car 1942   Jeep 1942   Sherman Tank

Oshawa Flying Club, Oshawa Airport, Robert Stuart Aero Collection,
End of Stephenson Rd North,   F-86 Mk.5

Ottawa - Canadian Aviation Museum, Rockcliffe Airport N, K1A 0M8, (800) 463-2038,
(613) 993-2010, Mail: POB 9724, Station T, Winter Wed-Sun 10-5, Summer Daily 10-5, Adm $6 Adult,
Senior & Student $5, Child 4-15 $3, Under 4 Free, Family $14, Group Rates
www.aviation.nmstc.ca/

AEA Silver Dart	DH 98	HTL-6 Bell 47G
AEG G.IV	DHC. 1B2	HUP-3
AT-6 Harvard Mk.II	DHC. 2	JN-4
AT-6 Harvard Mk.IV	DHC. 3	Junkers W-34f/fi
AV-8A Harrier	DHC. 6	Lockheed 10A
Avro 504 (3ea)	DHC. 7	Lockheed 12A
Avro Anson V	E-2	Lockheed Jetstar
Avro Lancaster Mk.X	F2H-3	Maurice Farman S.11
B-24L	F-18(CF)	McDowall Monoplane
B-25	F-100(CF) Mk.5D(2ea)	Me 163B (2ea)
Bellanca Pacemaker	F-101(CF)	Mig 15
Boeing 247D	F-104(CF)	Northrop Delta Fuse
Boeing M1M-10B	F-105(CF)	P-40
Bristol Beaufighter	F-116A(CF)	P-51D
Bristol Bolingbroke IVT	Fairchild FC-2W-2	PBY-5A
C-47-IV	Fairey Swordfish	RAF B.E.2c
C-64 Mk.VI	Fleet Model 16B	Sopwith Camel 2F.1
CL-13B Mk.6 2ea	G-2 Goose	Sopwith Snipe 7F.1
CL-28 Mk.2	H-135(CH)	Sopwith Triplane
CL-84	Hawker Hind	SPAD SVII
Curtiss Seagull	Hawker Hurricane XII	Stearman 4EM
DC-3	Hawker Sea Fury F.B.11	Stinson SR
DC-4M	HO4S-3	Stits SA-3A
DH 80A	HS-2L	(Continued Next Page)

```
    (From Previous Page)      Taylorcraft BC-65        Vickers Viscount
    Spitfire Mk.IX-LF         Travel Air 2000          Westland Lysander III
    T-114(CT)                 V-1                      Wills Wing XC
```

ONTARIO (Continued)

Ottawa –
Canadian War Museum, Museum, 330 Sussex Dr, (613) 922 2774, Daily 1-5pm, Closed Monday
Mid-Sept-Apr, Closes 9pm Tuesdays in summer, H-136(CH), Nieuport 17, Spitfire Mk VII

Ottawa Int'l Airport, Breadner Blvd & Royal Route (Formerly CFB Uplands), F-101(CF)

Petawawa – CFB Pettawawa Military Museum, (613) 687-5511 ext 6238, C-47, L-19A

Peterborough – Riverview Park, Water St, North of Town, F-86 Mk.6

Picton – Along Union St, East of City, T-33, T-134(CT)

Red Lake – Howie Bay Waterfront, Howie St, Norseman

Sarnia – Germaine Park, East St, F-86

Sault Ste Marie – Ontario Bushplane Heritage, 50 Pim St, Station Mall Postal Outlet,
P6A 3G4, Mail: POB 23050, P6A 6W6, (705) 945-6242, Fax 942-8947, Toll-Free (800) 287-4752
June 1-Sept 30 Daily 9-9, Oct1-April30 Daily 9-6, Adm Adult $10.50, Senior $9.50, Student $5
Child $2, www.bushplane.com, email: bushplane@soonet.ca,

Aeronca 11AC	DH 83C Fox Moth	Great Lakes 2T-1A	S-2A
Beech D18S (3 ea)	DH 89 Dragon Rapide	Link Trainer	Silver Dart Rep
Bell 47D-1	DHC 2-Mk.I	KR-34	ST-27
Buhl C6 Airsedan	DHC 2-Mk.III (2 ea)	Noorduyn Norseman Mk.I	Stinson SR-9 Reliant
C-3	DHC 3	Noorduyn Norseman Mk.IV	Taylor Model 20
C-64 (CY-AYO)	F-11 Husky	OPAS Buhl	U-6A
C-64 (CF-BFT)	Frasca IFR Simulator	RC-3 Seabee	U-6A Turbo
CL-215			

Smith Falls – Victoria Park, Lombard South, AT-6 Harvard IV

Tillsonburg – Canadian Harvard Aircraft Assoc, Tillsonburg Airport, Mail: POB 774
Woodstock, N4S 8A2, (519) 842-9922, By Appt,

BT-14 Yale Project	Private Flying Club with:
DH-82 Tigermoth	Harvard MKA
Harvard (4 EA) HWX, MTX, RWN, WPK	Harvard NDB

Toronto – Ontario Science Centre, 770 Don Mills Rd, Sopwith Pup Rep

Toronto Aerospace Museum, Parc Downsview Park, 65 Carl Hall Rd, M3K 2B6, (416) 638-6078,
Fax 638-5509, Thur-Sat 10-4, 416-638-6078, Fax: 638-5509, Adult $8, Senior $6,
Child 18-6 $5, Under 6 Free Family $20, www.torontoaerospacemuseum.com,

BD-10	T-114(CT)	Lancaster Project	Zenair Zenith
F-5(CF)	T-134(CT)	Osprey	
F-105(CF)Rep	DH-82 Project	Sea Prince	
S2F(CF)	Hurricane 5/8 Rep	Ultimate 100	

Wildwood Park, Derry Rd, NE of Lester B Pearson Int'l Airport, (416) 247-7678, F-100(CF)

Trenton – Holiday Inn, Sidney St & Hwy 401 (Glen Miller Interchange) Exit 526, F-5(CF)

RCAF Memorial Museum, Quinte West, 8 Wing, RCAF Rd, K0K 1B0, Mail: POB 1000, Stn Forces, Astra,
K0K3W0, Exit 526 on Hwy 401, (613) 965-2140, 965-2208, Fax: 965-7352, May 1-Oct 1 Daily 10-5,
Oct 1-May 1 Wed-Sun 10-5, Free Adm, www.rcafmuseum.on.ca

Argus 732	DHC 1B (CT-120)	F-104D(CF)	OH-58
Auster AOP Mk6	F-100(CF) MkIV	Handley-Page Halifax	T-33(CT) MkIII
C-47	F-101B(CF) 2ea	Hawker Hunter Mk9	T-114(CT)
Canadair Mk.2	F-86D MkVI	Lancaster	T-133(CT)
CL-41	F-5B(CF)	MiG-21 MF	T-134(CT)

Town Arena, South of Dundas St, F-86

Wellington – Hwy 33 East of Town, On Garage Roof, F4U (1/3 Scale)

Windsor – Canadian Aviation Historical Society Windsor, Windsor Airport
Airport Rd, N8V 1A2, (519) 737-9461,

DHC-1	Fleet Fawn	Mosquito Project	Stearman

Jackson Park, Tecumseh Rd East, Lancaster

PRINCE EDWARD ISLAND

Summerside – Heritage Aircraft Society, 173 Victoria Rd, C1N 2G8

Argus 739(CP-107)	F-101(CF)	Tracker 131(CS2F)

QUEBEC
Bagotville Alouette - CFB, F-5(CF), F-86, F-100(CF), F-101(CF)

La Baie - Air Defence Museum, Hwy 170, Mail: POB 5000 Station Bureau-Chief
Alouette, QC, G0V 1A0, (418) 677-4000 Ext 8159, Fax 677-4073, Mid-June to
Labour Day Tue-Sun 9-5m Off-Season by Appt, Adm Adult $4, Child & Snr $3,
Under 5 Free, CF-18,   CF-86,   MiG-23,

Knowlton - Brome County Historical Society, POB 690, J0E 1V0
Near Brome, 243-6782, Fokker D.VII

St Esprit - RB-57

St Hubert - CFB, CF-100

St Jean-sur-Richelieu - Airport, CFB, CF-100   CF-104
College Military Royal, CF-100

SASKATCHEWAN
Assiniboia - Harry & Anne Whereatt, POB 31, S0H 0B0,

Moose Jaw - Western Development Museum, 50 Diefenbaker Dr, (306) 693-5989,
Mail: POB 185, S6H 4NB, Daily 9-5, Adm Adult $7.25, Snrs 65 $6.25, Student $5.25,
Child 6-12 $2, Under 6 Free, Family $16, Gift Shop, www.wdm.ca/mj.html

Aeronca K	Cessna 195	H-10	Stinson 105
Avro Anson	DH 53	Harvard Mk IV	Spitfire Parts
Avro F-100(CF)	DH 60M	Hawker Hurricane	T-33A
B-25	DH 82C	JN-4	T-50
Beech D18D	DH C-1	Jodel D-9	Waco YKS
BT-14 Yale	Fleet Finch	Mead C-III	Zogling Glider
C-64 CF-SAM	Fleet Fort	PT-19	

Regina - C-45

Saskatoon - T-33(CT)

YUKON TERRITORY
Whitehorse - Yukon Transportation Museum, Mile 917 Alaska Hwy, Y1A 5L6, (403) 668-4792
Fax: 633-5547, May 22-Spet 5 Dayily 10-7, Adm Adult $3, 60+ $2.50, Child 12+ $2.50,
6-12 $2, Family $7, Ryan NYP, DC-3

CITY DISPLAYED AIRCRAFT

(AP) = Airport; (AM) = American Legion; (VWF) = Verterans of Foreign Wars

ALABAMA	Atmore	T-33A		ILLINOIS	Aurora Airport	F-105D
	Florala	T-33A			Brookfield	F-86L
	Mobile	T-33A,			Elhert Park, Rte 34(Elm St)	
		F-105			Centralia	T-33A
	Monroeville	T-33A			Danville Airport F-86	
	Montgomery	F-84F			Edwardsville	
	"	F-86L 3ea			(RC Stille Twnp Park), A-7E	
	Ozark	RF-84F			Granite City	F-84F, DC-3
	Selma	T-33A 2ea			Highland	T-33A
	Tuscaloose AP	T-33A			Lindenhurst VFW	A-7
	" I-20/59	A-7,			Pekin	F-84F
		UH-1,			Pinckneyville	T-33A
		M60			Quincy	T-33A
					Versailles	T-33A
ARIZONA	Apache Junction	T-33A			Wenona	F-84F
	Chandler	F-86D				
	Douglas	RF-101C		INDIANA	Churubusco	F-86H
Airport	Gila Bend	RF-101C 2ea			Green Castle	Buzz Bomb
	Glendale	F-100D			Hoagland	F-84F
	Globe(VFW 1704)	F-86D			Huntington	T-33A
	Peoria US 60(AL)	F-84F			Indianapolis	F-86E
					Monroeville	F-84F
ARKANSAS	Gravette	T-33A			Montpelier	F-84F
	Harrison	F-84F			South Whitley	F-84F
	Helena	T-33A				
	Pocahontas	MGM-13B		IOWA	Burlington	T-33A
	Rogers	V-101B		(Vet Memorial)	Cedar Rapids	F-84F, T-33A
					Correctionville	F-84F, A-7D
CALIFORNIA	Bakersfield	T-38 (2ea)			Fairfield	F-84F
	Banning	XGAM-67			Harlan	RF-84F
	Burbank	F-104D			Iowa City	F-86L
	Los Gatos	T-33A		(Airport)	Sheldon	A-7D, T-33A
	Madera	T-33A			Sigourney	T-33A
	Porterville	A-4				
	Torrance (AP)	T-33		KANSAS	Dodge City	B-26C
	Tulare AMVet 56	B-17			Independence	T-33A
	West Covina	F-86D			Lynn	F-84F
COLORADO	Flagler	T-33A		KENTUCKY	Fulton	T-33A
	"	TGM-13, Mace			Sturgis	F-86D
	Monte Vista	XQ4				
				LOUISIANA	Alexandria	F-80
DELAWARE	Dover(AL P-2)	T-33A			Houma	T-33A
				(VFW Hwy 6)	Many	M4 Sherman
FLORIDA	Arcadia	T-33A			Mansfield	T-33A
	Callaway	F-101			Springhill	T-33A
	DeFuniak	T-33A				
(Holiday Park)	Ft. Lauderdale	F-86H		MAINE	Blaine	AGM-28B
	Ft.Walton Bch	CQM-10A			Marshill A.L. Post 118	
	Homestead	F-4			Waterville	F-89J
(I-75N Exit 81)	Lake City	A-7E				
	Milton	T-28		MARYLAND	Cumberland	T-33A
	Oelwein	T-33A			Handcock Nike-Ajax APC	
	Orlando	B-52			Pocomoke City	T-33A
	Panacea	CGM-13B			Rockville	T-33A
(Am Leg Post2)	Wauchula	F-84F				
(Am Leg Post18)	Wildwood	CGM-13B		MICHIGAN	Breckenridge	T-33A
					Escanaba	F-84F
GEORGIA	Athens VFW	F-84F			Grand Haven	F-100A
	Cochran	Missile			Grayling	T-33A
	Douglas	T-33A			Hart	T-33A
	Griffin	T-33A			Iron Mountain	T-33A
	Hawkinsville	MGM-1			Monroe	F-86D, UH-1
	Thomasville	T-33A			Rosebush	T-33A
	Valdosta	F-86L			Sebewaing	T-33A
	Warner Robins	CGM-13B				
	Waynesboro	T-33A		MINNESOTA	Albert Lea	T-33A
	Willacoochee	T-33A			Alexanderia	T-33A
					Buffalo	T-33A
IDAHO	Burley	T-33A			Duluth	T-38
	Idaho Falls	F-86L			Hector	T-33A
	Lewiston	T-33A			Minnesota Lake	T-33A
	Malad	T-33A			Proctor	F-101F
(Carl Miller Park)	Mountain Home	F-111				
	Nampa	F-89B		MISSISSIPPI	Columbia	T-33A
	Pocatello Airport	F-101		(Hwy 51)	Greneda HS	A-7F
	Sheldon Airport	T-33A				
	Twin Falls	T-33A		MISSOURI	Caruthersville	T-33A
					LaPlata	F-86H
					Monett	F-4

CITY DISPLAYED AIRCRAFT

State	City	Aircraft
MISSOURI	Mountain View	T-33A
	Richmond	T-33A
	St. Charles	T-33A
	St. Louis	T-33A
MONTANA	Butte	F-86L
	Glasgow	T-33A
	Great Falls	T-33A
NEBRASKA	Beatrice	T-33A
	Creighton	F-84F
	David City	RF-84F
	Fairbury City	T-33A
	Franklin	T-33A
	Kimball	Titan 1
	Mc Cook	F-86H
	Neligh	RF-84F
	S Sioux City	A-7D
	Valley	RF-84F
	York	RF-84F
NEVADA	Indian Springs	F-84F
	Reno Lions Park	Jet
	Winemucca	F-86D,
		UH-1B,
		M-3 Tank
NEW MEXICO	Alamogordo	F-80F,
		XQ-4
	Artesia Hwy 285	F-84F
	Manchester	F-86H-10-NH
	Melrose	F-100A
	Truth	T-33A
NEW YORK	Baldwinsville	F-102A-80
	Buffalo	F-4J,101F
	Central Square	F-86H
	Manchester	F-86H
	Monroe	F-86L
	Tonawanda	F-9
N CAROLINA	Fayetteville	F-94C
	Goldsboro	F-86H
	Kings Mountain	F-105
(Carolina Beech Rd)	Wilmington	T-33A
N DAKOTA	Dickenson	T-33A
	Grand Forks	F-86L
	Hatton	T-33A
	Hettinger	F-86H
Airport	Jamestown	F-86H
	Vela	T-33A
	Walhalla	F-86H
	Wahpeton	A-7D
OHIO	Brooklyn	T-33A
	Cincinnati	F-86H
	Marietta	T-33A
	Wadsworth	T-33A
OKLAHOMA	Comanche	T-33A
	Hattiesburg	RF-84F, RF-101C
	Hazlehurst	F-86L
	Jackson	F-105
(VFW382)	El Reno	A-26
	Elk City	T-33A
	Midwest	GAM-63
	Oklahoma City	AGM-28,
		B-52F 2ea, WB-47E
OREGON	Nyssa	F-86L
	Vale	F-86L
	Woodburn	T-33A
PENNSYLVANIA		
	Beaver Falls	F-86H
	Cory	F-94C
	Imperial	F-86L
	Mildred	MACE

State	City	Aircraft
PENNSYLVANIA		
	New Kensington	T-33A
	N Huntington	T-33A
	Waterford	F-94
S CAROLINA	Greenville	F-86H
	Hartsville	T-33A
	Huron	T-33A
	Lake Norden	T-33A
TENNESSEE	Athens VFW 5146	F-4
	Crossville	T-33A
	Dayton	T-33A
	Johnson City	T-33A
	Knoxville	F-86D
	Nashville	F-86L
	Pulaski	T-33A
TEXAS	Bastrop VFW	F-4
(Court House)	Beeville	F-80
	Del Rio Commerce	T-33A
	Denison	F-86L
	Eagle Pass	T-33A
VFW	Ellington	F-84G
	Kingsville NAS	A4D
(VFW 3377)	Manchaca	F-4
	Muenster	F-84F
	Sherman	F-86L
	Texarkana	T-33A
UTAH	Murray	T-33A
VIRGINIA	Hampton	CIM-10A
	"	F-84F
	"	F-86L
		F-89JC
		F-100C
		F-104C
WASHINGTON	Brewster	YIM-99B
	Bridgeport	F-86L
		XGAM-67
Oak Harbor City Beach Park		EA-6B
	Othello	T-33A
	Spokane	T-33A
	Reedsville	T-33A
	River Falls	AGM-28A
	Sherwood	T-33A
	Stoughton	T-33A
W. VIRGINIA	Milton	F-86L
	Vienna	F-84H
WISCONSIN	Appleton	F-86L
	Argyle	F-86H
	Brillion	T-33A
	Fall River	T-33A
	Janesville	F9F
	Madison	T-33A
(Twining Park)	Monroe	F-86D
(Am. Leg 80)	New Richmond	P-80
	Prentice	T-33A
WYOMING	Buffalo	AGM-28A
	Milwaukee	B-25
	New Richmond	T-33A
I-80	Rock Springs	F-101

Canada

Alberta	Vulcan	Starship Enterprise
Brititsh Columbia	St James	Junkers W34
Ontario	Moonbeam	Flying Saucer
	Windsor	Flying Saucer

RESTAURANTS

The following are restaurants with one or more aircraft in or around them or have been converted into a restaurant.

ARKANSAS **Hot Springs** Granny's Kitchen, 332 Central Ave, 71901, (501) 624-6183
Daily 6:30-8pm, Closed January, Home Cooking At Moderate
Prices, Daily Breakfast Special, Daily Lunch Special
Full Lunch and Dinner Menu With 12 Vegetables,
Specialty - Blackberry Cobbler. Hanging From Ceiling Are:

A6M Zero	Ju 87 Stuka	Pitts S-1	RC-3
DHC. 1	Nieuport 28	PT-19	Super Chipmunk
Flybaby Biplane	Nieuport 17	PT-19	UC-78
J-3	P-38		

CALIFORNIA **Calabasas** Sagebrush Cantina, 3527 Calabasas Rd, 91302, (818) 222-6062
Mon-Thur 11am-10pm, Fri-Sat 11am-11pm, Sun 9am-2pm,
Bar: Fri-Sat 9am-1:30am, Sun-Thur 9am-Midnight,
Appetizers Avg $6, Soups and Salads$4-9, BBQ Ribs $15
Mexican Specialties $8-11, Charcaol Broiler $9-17
Bede BD-5J N007JB Ontop Restaurant

Camarillo Camarillow Airport Cafe, Breakfast, Sandwichs

Hawthorne Pizza Hut, 5107 El Segundo Blvd, 90250-4139, (424) 676-1100
1 Mile from Northrop Plant, Space & Aviation Artifacts

Los Angeles Proud Bird Restaurant, 11022 Aviation Blvd, 90045, (818) 670-3093
Leave 405 Freeway on Century Off Ramp, West To Aviation
Blvd, South To 11022 (Just East of LAX South Runway)
Sun-Thur 11-10, Fri-Sat 11-11, Main Dinning Room, 8 Ballrooms
Seats 25-1200 People

F4U	P-40	MiG 15	X-1
F6F	P-47	SBD	
F-86	P-51D	Spad XIII	
P-38	Me-109	Spitfire V	

Sacramento Aces Restaurant, Holiday Inn, 5321 Date Ave, 95841-2597
(800) 388-9284, www.basshotels.com/h/d/hi/hr/sacne
Breakfast/Lunch/Dinner, Steaks, Seafood, P-51 Replica Above Roof

Santa Ana Nieuport 17 Restaurant, 1615 E 17th , (714) 547-9511

San Diego 94th Aero Sqd, 8885 Balboa Ave, 92123, (619) 560-6771

San Jose 94th Aero Sqd, 1160 Coleman Ave, 95110, (408) 287-6150, Airplane there

Santa Monica DC-3 Restaurant, 2800 Donald Douglas Loop North, 90405
(310) 399-2323, Mon & Sun Lunch, Tue-Sat Lunch & Dinner
Specialty - Steaks
Douglas - Sunbeam - Harley Davidson Motorcycle Display

Torrance Doolittle's Raiders, 2780 Skypark, 90505, (428) 539-6203
Manager: Keith Sulesky

Tulare Aero Dogs, 240 North L St, (559) 685-1230, Mon-Sat 10:30-8:00pm
Seats 18, email: schoenau@comcast.net, Convair 240 (T-29)

Tustin Nieuport 17 Restaurant, 13051 Newport Ave, 92780 (714) 731-5130

Van Nuys 94th Aero Sqd, 16320 Raysner Ave, 91406, (818) 994-7437

COLORADO **Greeley** State Armory, 6148 8th Ave, 80631, (970) 352-7424,
Burgers, Steaks, B-17 Hanging from Ceiling.

CO Springs Solo's Restaurant, 1665 N Newport Rd, 80916, (Off Fountain Blvd, One
block East of Powers Blvd), CO Springs Mncpl Airport, (719) 570-7656,
Sun 12-8, Mon-Sat 11-9, Eat inside a KC-97, Burgers to Steaks, Pasta,
Ribs, Sea Food, $7-20, Owner: Steve Kanatzar, KC-97, Model 8' B-17

CONNECTICUT **Bridgeport** Captains Cove, 1 Bostwick Ave, Restaurant (203) 335-7104,

Gostave Whitehead Model 21, 1901 Glider, (203) 335-1433,

DELAWARE **New Castle** Air Transport Command Greater Wilmington Airport,
143 N du Pont Hwy(US Hwy 13), 19720, (302) 328-3527, C-47

FLORIDA	**Clearwater**	(Restaurants Continued) 94th Aero Sqd, 94 Fairchild Dr, 33520, (727) 536-0409
	Ft Lauderdale	Aviator's Tavern & Grille, Ft Lauderdale Int'l Airport, Under the Control Tower on the SW Side of the Airport, 1050 Lee Wagner Blvd, 33315, (954) 359-0044
		95th Bomb Grp, 2500 NW 62nd St, 33309, (954) 491-4570
	Miami	94th Aero Sqd, 1395 NW 57th Ave, 33126, (305) 261-4220
		Mayday's, 7501 Pembroke Rd, S Side of North Perry Airport, 33024, (305) 989-2210, Manager: Mark Siple,
		Spirit Restaurant, 7250 NW 11th St., 33126, (305) 262-9500 Pres Denise Noe, Lunch Specials Daily $4-7, Mon-Fri Dinner 5pm Mon-Sat $7-11, Happy Hour Mon-Fri & D.J. Fri/Sat, Steaks - Seafood - Pasta's - Salads - Mexican - Cuban, Artifacts & 5' Models of Eastern & Pan Am Airlines DC-3, DC-10, 727, 747, 757,
	Orlando	4th Fighter Grp, 4200 E Colonial Dr, 32803, (305) 898-4251
		Off-The-Wall, Night Club, 4893 S Orange Blossom Tr, 305-851-3962, Fokker D.VII Fokker DR.I SE-5A
	Sarasota	306th Bomb Grp, 8301 N Taniani Trail, 33580, (941) 355-8591
	West Palm Beach	391st Bomb Grp, 3989 Southern Blvd, 33406, (561) 683-3919 C-47
GEORGIA	**Atlanta**	57th Fighter Grp, 3829 Clairmont Rd, 30341, (404) 457-7757
		Air Superiorty Group, DeKalb-Peachtree Airport, POB 566726, 31156, AT-6, C-47, P-51, Rides in a N2S-3
IOWA	**Cedar Rapids**	Flyin Weenie, Downtown, PA-22 On Roof
ILLINOIS	**Decatur**	Decatur Airport Restaurant, R/C Aircraft Hanging From Ceiling,
	Moline	Bud's Skyline Inn, 2621 Airport Rd, Rt 6 & 150, 61265, (309) 764-9128, Lunch Mon-Sat 11am, Dinner: Ribs, Catfish, Steaks, Email: skyline@qconline.com, Artifacts, Models
	Wheeling	94th Aero Sqdn, 1070 S Milwaukee Ave, 60090, 847-459-3700 P-38 Replica P-47 Replica P-51 Replica
INDIANA	**Muncie**	Vince's Gallery, 5201 N Walnut, Muncie Airport, 47303, (765) 284-6364, Mon-Thur 11-10, Fri 11-11, Sat 7-11, Sun 7-9, Dinners Average: 10.00-12.00, Artifacts (Restaurants Continued)
	Valparaiso	Strongbow Turkey Inn, 2405 Hwy 30 E, (219) 462-5121, 11-10pm
MARYLAND	**College Park**	94th Aero Sqd, 5240 Calvert Rd, 20740, (301) 699-9400, Replicas: Bf-109F, F4U, P-40, P-47, P-51D
MICHIGAN	**Flint**	Mister Gibby's Food & Spirits, Mister Gibby's Inn, Best Western, G 3129 Miller Rd, At I-75 & US 23, 48507, (810) 235-8561, (800) 528-1234, 1/3 Scale Wings of DR.1 in Cocktail Lounge, Bi-Plane Wings Outside Wall of Building. Steaks, Seafood and Salad Bar.
Minnesota	**Alexandria**	Doolittle Restaurant, 4409 Hwy 29 South, 56308, (320) 759-0885, Steaks, Ribs, Pasta, Seafood, Sandwiches, www.doolittlesaircafe.com, R/C Aircraft, Artifacts, T-33
	Coon Rapids	Doolittle Restaurants, 3420 129nd Ave NW, 55448, (612) 576-0575 Steaks, Ribs, Pasta, Seafood, Sandwiches, www.doolittlesaircafe.com, R/C Aircraft, Artifacts,
	Eagan	Doolittle Restaurants, 2140 Cliff Rd, 55122, (651) 452-6627 Steaks, Ribs, Pasta, Seafood, Sandwiches, www.doolittlesaircafe.com, R/C Aircraft, Artifacts,
	Golden Valley	Doolittle Restaurants, 550 Winnetka Ave North, 55427, (612) 542-1931 Steaks, Ribs, Pasta, Seafood, Sandwiches, www.doolittlesaircafe.com, R/C Aircraft, Artifacts,
	Plymouth	Doolittle Restaurants, 15555 34th Ave North, 55447, (612) 577-1522 Steaks, Ribs, Pasta, Seafood, Sandwiches, www.doolittlesaircafe.com, R/C Aircraft, Artifacts,
MISSOURI	**Berkeley**	94th Aero Sqd, 5933 McDonnell Blvd, 63134, (314) 731-3300

		(Restaurants Continued)
NEW JERSEY	Caldwell	94th Bomb Grp, 195 Passaic Ave, 07006, (973) 882-5660

NEW YORK   Buffalo   Inn of the Port, Buffalo Greater Int'l Airport, (716) 632-5050,
                         P-40 Replica

            Cheektowaga Flying Tigers, 100 Amherst Villa Rd, 14225-1432
                         (716) 631-3465, Seats 200, Smoking & Handicapped Sections,
                         P-40: Tail Rudders - Parts of Wing - Propellers
                         Assistant General Manager: Matthew Rickrode
                         Appetizers: $2.95-$6.95   Entrees: $10.95-$15.95
                         Soups & Salads: $2.95   Desserts: $ 1.95-$ 3.95
                         (Restaurants Continued)

        E Farmingdale   56th Fighter Grp, Republic Airport Gate 1, Route 110
                         11735, (631) 694-8280,   P-47 Replica

NORTH DAKOTA Grand Forks John Barley'Corn, 123 Columbia Mall, (701) 775-0501, Lunches
                         $5.50 to Dinners $14.00, Hamburger to Lobster EAA Biplane,
                         Hanging From Ceiling In Lounge, 11:30 am -1 am

            Fargo   Doolittle Restaurants, 2112 25 th St South, 58103, (701) 478-2200
                         Steaks, Ribs, Pasta, Seafood, Sandwiches, www.doolittlesaircafe.com,
                         R/C Aircraft, Artifacts,

OHIO   Cleveland   100th Bomb Grp, 20000 Brookpark Rd, 44135, (216) 267-1010, P-51

            Columbus   94th Aero Sqd, Port Columbus Int'l Airport
                         5030 Sawyer Rd, 43219, (419) 237-9093

            North Canton 356th Fighter Grp, Akron-Canton Airport, 2787 Mt Pleasant Rd,
                         44720, (330)494-3500, Lounge Seats 170, Banquet
                         Seats 60, Non-Smoking & Handicapped Sections,
                         Daily : Lunches $4.95-7.95; Dinners $10.95-22.95

OREGON   Milwaukie   Lacey's Bomber Inn, 13515 SE. McLoughlin Blvd, Hwy 99E,
                         97222, (503) 654-6491, B-17G (485790) Breakfast Mon-Sat
                         6am-1:45, 12:45 Sun, $2.25-6.95 Lunch 11am-5, $3.25-6.50,
                         25 Selections Dinner 11am-8:30, Till 9 Thr-Sat, $4.95-8.95
                         12 Selections Daily Specials: Ribs, Seafood, Italian,
                         Steak & Prime Rib, www.thebomber.com

PENNSYLVANIA Reading   Dutch Colony Motor Inn, Antique Airplane Restaurant and
                         Rudder Bar, 4635 Perkiomen Ave, 19606, (610) 779-2345
                         Co-Owner: R.H. Breithaupt, Suspended In Dinning Room
                         1927 Monocoupe, Left Wing From A Piper Cub From WWII,
                         1917 Curtiss OX-5 Engine, 1930 Zekely Engine, & Artifacts

            Philadelphia 94th Aero Sqd, N Philadelphia Airport, 2750 Red Lion Rd, 19154,
                         (215) 671-9400

Tennesee   Nashville   101st Airborne Restaurant, 1362-A Murfreesboro Pike, 37217,
                         (717) 361-4212, DC-3

                         Sam's Place, 7648 Hwy 70 South, (615) 662,7474,
                         Large Models Hanging from Ceiling

TEXAS   Pittsburg   Warrick's Restaurant, 142 Marshall St, 75686,
                         (903) 856-7881 Tue-Thur 11-9, Fri-Sat 11-10, 1902 Ezekiel
                         Airship Replica Appetizers, Side Orders, Desserts,
                         Sandwiches, Salads & Soups, Seafood $6-9, Specialty Dishes
                         $7-14, Steaks & Chicken $6-13, Child Menus $3-4

WISCONSIN   Dodgeville   Don Q's INN, Highway 23 N, PO BOX 53533, (608) 935-2321,
                         This has a KC-97 in front of the motel.

USS NAVAL SHIP MUSEUMS

ALABAMA
  Chickasaw   USS LST 325 Ship Memorial, Inc, LST325 Hook Term, Hardwood Ln,Off Rt 43
                   (251) 452-3255, 402-1225, Mon-Fri 10-3, www.lstmemorial.org

  Mobile   Battleship Memorial Park, POB 65, 2703 Battleship Parkway, 36601,
                   (251) 433-2703, Daily 8-Sunset, Adm Adult $5, Child 6-12 $2.50, Gift Shop,
                   Located On Battleship Parkway Between Exit #27 & #30, USS Alabama, Uss Drum, YF-17

CALIFORNIA
  Alameda Point USS Hornet Museum, Pier 3, Mail: POB 460, 94501, (510) 521-8448, Wed-Mon 10-5,
                   Tue 10-3, Closed TD, CD, ND, Adm Adult $14, Snrs 65 & Mil $12, Child 5-17 $6,
                   Under 5 Free, Groups Rates, Gift Shop, www.uss-hornet.org,

A-4A	FJ-2	US2B
F-7U3	H-34	Apollo Lunar Lander
F-14A	HUP-1	BP1102A
F8U-1(F-8A)	SBD-4	MQU-004 (Apollo 14)
F9F-5P	TBM-3	

  Long Beach   SS Queen Mary , Pier J, 1126 Queens Way, POB 8, 90801,
                   (424) 435-4747, Mon-Thur 10-4:30, Fri-Sun 10-5, Adm Adult $23-31, Snrs/Mil $20-28,
                   Child 5-11 $12-20, Overnight Stay on Queen Mary for one person $31 - $94.
                   www.queenmary.com   SS Queen Mary,   Russian Foxtrot Submarine "Scorpion" $10/$9/$9

                   Naval Ship Visitation Tours, Terminal Island Naval Complex, Pier T
                   (800) 262-7838, USS Mobile, Tours change Monthly, Call for current ship.

                   USS Roncador, 7950 Deering Ave, Canoga Park, 91304

  Oakland   USS Potomac Museum, 540 Water St, 94607, Mail: POB 2064, 94604, (866) 468-1215
                   Mon-Tue 9-1, Wed-Fri 9-5, Adm $20-40, www.usspotomac.org

  Richmond   Richmond Museum of History, POB 1267, 94802, (510) 237-2933,
                   SS Red Oak Victory Ship

  San Diego   San Diego Aircraft Carrier Museum, 1355 North Harbor Dr, 92101
                   (619) 544-9600, Daily 10-5, Closed TD, CD, Adm Adult $13, Snrs 62+ $10,
                   Child 6-17 $7, Under 6 Free, Gift Shop 544-9600 ext 244, www.midway.org,

A-4C	F-4N	F/A-18	SH-2F
A-4F	F-4S 2ea	H-1B(UH)	SH-3
A-6E	F-9F-8P	H-46(HH)	SNJ-7
A-7B	F-9F-5	RA-5C	T-2C
C-1A	F9F-8T	S-3B	
E-2C	F-14A	SBD-1	

  San Francisco National Maritime Museum , Fisherman's Wharf Pier 32-47 Changes Seasonally,
                   POB 470310, 94147, (415) 775-1943, Oct-May Sun-Thur 9-6, Fri-Sat 9-8,
                   May-Oct Tue-Mon 9-8, Wed 9-6, Adm Adult $9, Snrs 62 $5, Mil $4, Child 6-12 $3,
                   Familt $20, www.maritime.org/pamphome.htm, Contact: Dave Lerma,
                   USS Roncador (Submarine SS-301), USS Pamanito (Submarine SS-383)

                   National Liberty Ship Memorial, Ft Mason Center, Bldg A, 94123, (415) 441-3101

                   Daily 10-4, Adm Adult $8, Snrs $5, Child 6-14 $4, Mil/Child Under 6 Free, Family
                   $20, www.ssjeremiahobrien.org/   SS Jeremiah O'Brian (Liberty Ship)

  San Pedro   US Merchant Marine Veterans of WW2, POB 629, 90733, (424) 519-9545,
                   SS Lane Victory Ship

CONNECTICUT
  Groton   Submarine Force Museum, X-1

  New London   Nautilus Memorial & Submarine Force Library & Museum, New London
                   Submarine Base, Mail: Box 571, 06349-5000, (800) 343-0079, (860) 449-3174,
                   449-3558, Mid-April to Mid Oct Daily 9-5, Tue 1-5, Nov 1-May 14 Daily 9-4,
                   Closed TueClosed: TD, CD, May 1st Week, Oct 1st Week, Free Adm,
                   www.ussnautilus.org, USS Nautilus SSN 571, Bushnells Turtle
                   Mato-8 (Japanese Midget Sub), Maiale (Italian Midget Sub),
                   Seahund (German Midget Sub)

DISTRICT OF
  COLUMBIA   The Navy Museum, 805 Kidder Breese St, 20374-5071, (202) 433-4882, Mon-Fri 9-4,
                   Sat-Sun 10-5, Closed: TD, CD, ND, Adm Free, Tours Dahlgren Ave, 8th & Main St,
                   Gift Shop, www.history.navy.mil

FG-1D	MXY7 Trainer	Posedon Missile USS Barry
Maiale SSB	Turtle	USS Roncador Tower
LCVP Higgins	Balao Fairwater	

FLORIDA	
Tampa	(US Naval Museums Continued)
	American Victory Mariners Memorial & Museum Ship, 705 Channelside Dr, 33602,
	(813) 228-8766, Mon-Sat 10-4, Sun 12-4, Adm Adult $8, Mil/Snrs/Adult $7,
	Child 3-12 $4, Under 3 Freewww.americanvictory.org, SS American Victory

HAWAII	
Honolulu	USS Arizona Memorial BB-39, Shoreline Dr. Pearl Harbor Navy Base off I-99
	(808) -422-0561, 422-2771, 1 Arizona Memorial Place, 96818-3145,
	Daily 7:30-5, Closed TD, CD, ND, Free Adm, Theater, www.nps.gov/usar/ USS Arizona,
	USS Utah Memorial, www.ussutah.org, Aeronca 65TC,
	USS Missouri BB-63, Uss Missouri Memorial Assoc, POB 6339, 96818, (808) 423-2263,
	Adult $16, Child $8, www.ussmissouri.com, Aeronca 65TC
	USS Bowfin Submarine Museum & Park, 11 Arizona Memorial Dr.,
	Pearl Harbor, 96818, (808) 423-1341, Next to USS Arizona Visitor
	Center, Daily 8-5, Adm Adult $8, Snrs/Mil $6, Child 4-12 $3, Gift Shop,
	www.bowfin.org, USS Bowfin SS-287, Missile & Rockets

LOUISIANA	
Baton Rouge	Louisiana Naval War Memorial, 305 S River Rd, 70802, (225) 342-1942
	Daily 9-5, Closed CD, Adm Adult $7, Snrs 60 $6, Mil $5, Child 5-12 $4,
	Under 5 Free, (Camping aboard available groups of 20), www.usskidd.com
	USS KIDD, P-40

MARYLAND	
Baltimore	Baltimore Maritime Museum, Pier 4 Pratt St, Inn Harbor, 21202,
	(410) 396-5528, Mail: 802 S Carolina St, 21231, Summer Dailt 10-6
	Spring/Fall Daily 10-5, Winter Fri-Sun 10-5, Adm Adult $7, Snrs $6
	Child 6-14 $4, Under 6 Free, www.usstorsk.org
	USS Torsk, Lightship "Chesapeak", USCG "Taney"
	Liberty Ship Project, Highland Station, Pier One, 2000 block of South Clinton St,
	Mail: Project Liberty Ship, POB 25846 Station, 21224-0546, (410) 558-0646
	www.liberty-ship.com, email: john.w.brown@usa.net, SS John Brown,
	Cruises Available
	USS Constellation, DockPier One, 301 E Pratt, 21202, (410) 539-1797,
	May-Oct Daily 10-6, Oct-April Daily 10-4, Adm Adult $7.50, Snrs 60 $6,
	Child 6-14 $3.50, Under 6 Free, www.constellation.org, USS Constellation

MASSACHUSETTS	
Boston	USS Constitution Museum, Boston National Historic Park, Charlestown Navy Yard,
	02129, (508) 242-5601, Daily 10-5, www.ussconstitution.navy.mil,
	USS Constition, USS Cassin Young, PT-619, PT-796
Fall River	Fall River - Battleship Cove, 02721, (508) 678-1100, I-95 Exit 5 to Braga Bridge,
	April-July 9-5, July-Sept Daily 9-5:30, Sept-Oct 9-5, Nov-April 9-4:30,
	Closed TD, CD, ND, Adm Adult $14, Snrs $12, Child 6-14 $8, Mil/Child Under 6 Free,
	www.battleshipcove.com

USS Cassin Young	USS Fall River	PT-796 Patrol Boat
USS Lionfish	Japanese Suicide Sub	T-28
USS Joseph P Kenndey Jr	PT-617 Patrol Boat	UH-1M
USS Massachusetts	PT-617 Patrol Boat	LCM

Quincy	US Naval & Shipbuilding Museum, 739 Washington St, Next to Fore River Bridge Rte 3A
	(617) 479-7900, Voice 7686, Fax 479-8792, Sat-Sun 10-4, Closed Holidays, Adm Adult
	$6, Snrs & Child 4-12 $4, Under 4 Free, www.uss-salem.org, USS Salem CA 139

MICHIGAN	
Muskegon	USS Silversides SS-236, S Channel Wall, Pere Marquette Park, 134 Bluffton St,
	(231) 755-1230, Fax 755-5883, All Year Sat-Sun 10-5:30, May Weekdays 1-5, June-Aug
	Daily, 10-5:30, Sept, Weekdays 1-5:30, Oct Sat-Sun Only, Adm Adults $7.00,
	Snrs 62 $5.50, Child 12-18 $6, 5-11 $5, Under 5 Free, www.silversides.org
	USS Silversides SS-236, USCGC, LST 393

NEBRASKA	
Omaha	Freedom Park, 2497 Freedom Park Rd, 68110, (402) 345-1959, From I-29 Go W
	on I-480 Then N on Freedom Park Rd, Apr 15-Oct 31, Daily, 10-5, Adm Adult $4,
	Snr $3, Child $2.50, Goup Rates, USS Hazard AM-240 Mine Sweeper

A-4D	H-1(UH)	USS Marlin SST-2 (Submarine)	
A-7	SH-3	USS Towers DDG-9	USS LSM-45 Landing Ship

New Hampshire	
Portsmouth	Portsmouth Maritime Museum, 600 Market St, 03801, (603) 436-3680, USS Albacore Sub

NEW JERSEY	
Camden	The Battleship New Jersey BB-62, Home Port Alliance, 2500 Broadway,
	08104, 856-966-1652, Jan-Feb Fri-Mon 9-3, Oct-Dec Daily 9-3,
	April-Sept Daily 9-5, Oct-Dec Daily 9-3, Adm Adult $13.50,
	Snrs & Child 6-11 $9, Under 6 Free, www.bb62museum.org/
	www.battleshipnewjersey.org, USS New Jersey BB-62

NEW JERSEY	(US Naval Museums Continued)
Hackensack	Hackensack - US Naval Museum/Submarine USS Ling, 150 River St, 07601, Mail: POB 375, 07682, (201) 342-3268, Sat-Sun 10-4, Adm Adult $7, Child Under 12 $3, www.njnm.com USS Ling (SS-297)(Submarine), German Seehund, Japanese Kaiten
Sea Grit	New Jersey National Guard Militia Museum, Intelligent Whale

NEW YORK	
Albany	USS Slater (DE-766), POB 1926, 12201, (518) 431-1943, April-Nov Wed-Sun 10-4 Adm Adult $6, Snrs 65 $5, Child 6-14 $4, Under 6 Free, www.ussslater.org
Buffalo	Buffalo & Erie County Naval & Servicemen's Park, 1 Naval Park Cove, 14202, (716) 847-1773, April 1-Oct 31 10-5, Nov Sat-Sun 10-4, Adm Adult $8.00, Snrs 60 & Child 6-12 $5, Under 6 Free, Gift Shop, www.buffalonavalpark.org, PTF-17 Boat, USS Croaker SSK-246, USS Little Rock (CLG-4),USS Sullivans
New York City	Intrepid Sea-Air-Space Museum, 1 Intrepid Plaza, Pier 86, 46th & 12th, 10036, (212) 245-0072, 2533, MD-LD 10-5, RoY Wed-Sun 10-5, Closed TD, CD, ND, Adm Adult $4.75, Snr $4, Child 7-13 $2.50, Under 6 Free www.intrepid-museum.com, USS Intrepid, USS Growler, USS Edson

NORTH CAROLINA	
Kinston	CSS Neuse & Governor Caswell Memorial, 2612 W Vernon Ave (US Bus 70) Mail: POB 3043, 28502, (252) 522-2091, Apr-Oct Mon-Sat 9-5, Sun 1-5 Nov-Mar Tus-Sat 10-4, Sun 1-4, Free Adm, Hull of Iron Clad Gunboat CSS Neuse 1862 www.ah.dcr.state.nc.us/sections/Hs/neuse/neuse.htm
Wilmington	Wilmington - USS North Carolina Battleship Memorial, POB 417, 28402, (910) 762-1829, May-Sept 8-8, Sept May 8-5, Adm Adult $9, Snrs 65 $8, Child 6-11 $4.50 Under 6 Free, www.battleshipnc.com USS North Carolina OS2U

OHIO	
Cleveland	Submarine USS COD, 1089 N. Marginal Dr, Lakefront Between E & 9th St, 44114, (216) 566-8770, N41, 30.6'/W81 41.5', May-Sept Daily 10-5, Adm Adult $6, Snrs $5, Child $3, Under 6 Free, www.usscod.org, USS Cod
Newcomerstown	National Naval Museum, 132 W Canal St, I-77 Exit 65, 43832, (740) 498-4446, www.ussradford446.org, R/C Helicopter, USS Radford & USS Helena Artifacts

OKLAHOMA	
Muskogee	Muskegee - War Memorial Park, POB 253, 74401, (918) 682-6294, Mar 15-Oct 15 Mon, Wed-Sat 9-5, Sun 1-5, Adm Adult $5, Snrs $3, Child $2, www.batfish.org, USS Batfish (Submarine)

OREGON	
Astoria	Ft Stevens Historical Military Museum & Trails, Ft. Stevens State Park, Off US101, 10 Miles West of Astoria, (800) 551-6949, (503) 861-1671, Adm $3, www.oregonstateparks.org/park_179.php; 5 Inch 38 Caliber Navy Gun Sites WWII. Deloria Beech Rd., WWII Japanese I-25 Submarine Siting Plaque
Portland	OMSI Oregon Museum of Science & Industry, Washington Park, 1945 SE Water Ave, 97208, (503) 797-4600, Sept-June Daily 10-4:30 Adm $5, www.omsi.edu, USS Blueback Sub

Pennsylvania	
Philadelphia	Independence Seaport Museum, 131 N Dlwr Avenue & Chstnt, 19104 (215) 923-9129, Mail: POB 928, Daily 10-5, Adm Adult $ 9, Snrs 65 $8 Child 3-12 $6, Free Adm Sun 10-12, www.phillyseaport.org USS Becuna USS Olympia
Pittsburgh	Carnegie Science Center, One Allengeny Ave, 15212-5850, (412) 237-3400, Sun-Fri 10-5, Sat 10-7, Adm Adult $14, Snrs & Child 3-18 $10, www.carnegiesciencecenter.org, 45 Min Tours Every 15 Min, USS Requin SS-481 Submarine

Rhode Island	
Newport	USS Saratoga Museum, Coddington Cove, Naval Station Newport, Next to Quonset Air MuseumPOB 28581, 02908, (401) 831-8696, www.saratogamuseum.org, email: SaveSara@aol.com, Not at site until 2002, Aircraft Carrier CV-60

SOUTH CAROLINA	
Mt Pleasant	Patriots Point Museum, 40 Patriots Point Rd, 29464-4377, Mail: POB 986, 29464, (800) 248-3508, (843) 884-2727, Daily 9-5, Closed CD, Adm Adult $14, Snrs $12, Child 6-11 $7, www.state.sc.us/patpt, UH-1 (2ea) USCG Ingham USS Clamagore SS-343, USS Laffey, USS Yorktown, MARK I Patrol Boat,

TEXAS   (US Naval Museums Continued)
Corpus Christi USS Lexington Museum, 2914 Shoreline Dr, Mail: POB 23076, 78403-3076,
                   (361) 888-4873, Daily 9-5, Adm Adult $11.95, Snrs/Mil $9.95, Child 4-12 $6.95,
                   Under 4 Free, Closed CD, Gift Shop, Food Court, www.usslexington.com,
                   USS Lexington, USS PINTA,   USS MARIA

Galveston   Seawolf Park, Pelican Island, Mail: POB 1575, 77550, (409) 744-5738,
                   Daily 9-5, Adm Charged, www.cavalla.org,
                   USS Cavalla (Submarine), USS Stewart (Destroyer), F-86

Houston   USS Houston Museum, (800) 231-7799, 8:30-5,

La Porte   USS TEXAS BB-35 Battleship SMS, 3527 Battleground Rd, 77571,(218) 479-4414,
                   Daily 10-4, Adm Adult $7, Snrs $4, Child Under 12 Free,
                   www.tpwd.state.tx.us/park/battlesh/

Orange   Southeast Texas War Memorial, 2606 Eddleman Rd, 77632, (409) 883-8346,
                   Mon-Sat 10-3, Sun 11-3, Adm Adult $3, Child 6-16 $2, Under6 Free, www.ussorleck.org,
                   USS Orleck

VIRGINIA
Newport News   USS Savannah

Norfolk   Battleship Wisconsin Foundation, National Maritime Center, 224 E Main, 23510,
                   (757) 233-6464, Memorial Day-Labor Day, Daily 10-6, RoY Tue-Sat 10-5, Sun 12-5
                   www.battleshipwisconsin.org, www.nauticus.org, USS Wisconsin (BB-64)

WASHINGTON
Bremerton   Puget Sound Naval Shipyard, 130 Washington Ave, 98337, (360) 479-7447,
                   Tue-Sat 10-5, Sun & Holidays 1-5, One Block from Port Orchard Ferry
                   or Hwy 304 These Ships Change and May Be Gone, Check Ahead. www.psns.navy.mil
                   USS Camden   (AOE-2)   Others Included:
                   USS Nimitz   (CVN-68)   Destroyers
                   USS Sacramento (AOE-1)   Battleships

                   Bremeerton Historic Ship Assn, 300 Washington Beach Ave, 98337, (360) 792-2457
                   North of Ferry at Waterfront, May 1 - Sept 30 Daily 10-5, RoY Sat-Sun 10-4,
                   Adm Adult $8, Snt $7, Child 5-12 $6, USS Turner Joy (DD-951) Destroyer,

Ft Columbia   Ft Columbia, 6 Inch Guns

WASHINGTON
Keyport   Naval Undersea Museum, End of Route 308, POB 408, 98345-5000,
                   (360) 396-4148, Daily 10-4 Summer, Closed Tue Oct-May, Free Adm
                   Kaiten Japanese Suicide Mini-Sub   USS Etlah Netlayer
                   Trieste II Deep Submerge Vehicle   USS Safeguard Salvage Vessel

WISCONSIN
Manitowoc   Wisconsin Maritime Museum, 75 Maritime Dr, 54220-6823, (920) 684-0218,
                   Nov-March Daily 9-5, April-Oct 9-6, Closed NYD, ED, TD, CD
                   Adm Adult $12, Child 6-15 $10, Under 6 Free, www.wimaritimemuseum.org/
                   USS Cobia Submarine

Canada
Alberta
 Calgary   Naval Museum of Alberta - 1820-24th St SW, T2T 0G6, (403) 242-0002,
                   July-Aug Daily 10-5, Sept-June Tue-Fri 1-5, Sat-Sun 10-5, Closed: CD, ND,
                   Adm Adult $5, Snrs $3, Child Under 12 $2, Family $12, www.navalmuseum.ab.ca
                   F2H-3, Hawker FB.11 Sea Fury, Supermarine Seafire Mk XV, T-33

ONTARIO
 Hamilton   HMCS Haida Tribal Class Destroyer WWII # G63

ARMORED VEHICLE & ARTILLERY MUSEUMS

HAWAII
Honolulu   Historic Battery Randolf, US Army Museum,, Kalia Rd Ft. DeRussy
(808) 438-2821, Mail: POB 8064, 96830-0064, Tue-Sun 10-4:30,
Closed Mon, CD, Nd, Free Adm, Gift Shop 955-9552, AH-1, Japanese Tank, 14" Gun

ILLINOIS
Salem   Route 37 North of Salem,   WWI Howitzer

Wheaton   Cantigny 1st Divison Museum, 1S151 Winfield Rd, 60187, (630) 668-5161
10-5 Tue-Sun Memorial-Labor Day, 10-4 Tue-Sun Remaining Year, Free Adm

M5	M47	T26E4	M1896
M4A3E8	M48	M24	M113A2
M41A3	M60	M1917	Howitzer 75mm
M46	M551	M1902	

INDIANA
Brooksburg   City Hall, Main St, Cannon 120 mm

Cromwell   North of Rail Road Track,   Patton Tank

Huntington   Huntington Memorial Park, W Park & Bartlett St, T-33A,   M4A1 Tank

Michigan City   Great Lakes Museum of Military History, 1710 E Hwy 20,
Evergreen Plaza 46360, (219) 872-2702, May 20-Labor Day Tue-Fri 10-5,
Sat 10-4, Sun 10-2: Labor Day-May 20 Tue-Sat 12-4:
Closed ES, TD, CD, Military Vehicles

Scottsburg   Indiana National Guard Center, Sherman Tank

Sunman   Aerican Legion, St Leon Exit, M4A3(75)VVSS Sherman Tank,

Van Buren   VFW, I-69, Army Tank

Warsaw   City Court House, WWII Tank

MARYLAND
Aberdeen   VFW Post 10028, 821 Old Philadelphia Rd, POB T, 21001, Tank

Crisfield   VFW Post 8274, Somerset County memorial Post, Rocket

Federalsburg   VFW Post 5246, 203 Vernon Ave, 21632, (410) 754-5020, Tank

Grasonville   VFW Post 7464, Grasonville Memorial, Tank

Jarrettsville   VFW Post 8672, Manor Memorial, 3713 Federal Hill Rd, 21084-9998, Tank

Port Deposit   VFW Post 8185, Jerry Skrivanes Post, Tank

Powellville   VFW Post 2996, East Side Memorial Post, POB 51, 21850,
(410) 835-8785, M-64 Tank

NORTH CAROLINA
Camp Lejeune   Camp Lejeune,Visitors Center (Bldg 812)at Main Gate on Holcomb Blvd, Off NC 24,

(910) 451-2197, www.lejeune.usmc.mil or www.ci.jacksonville.nc.us
M-48 & M-60 Tank Infront of Bldg 407, At Courthose Bay: LVTPX12,
LVTP-4, LVTP-5A1, BMP-76PB (From Desert Storm)

Camp Mackall   4 Acres of WWII Jeeps, 10 Miles West of Fort Bragg
Near Addor, NC Just Off US 1, Between Southern Pines and Hoffman
Places where to purchase Military Aircraft, Vehicles:

Greenville   VFW Post 7032, PO Box 8387, 27835, Tank

OHIO
Hubbard   World War II Vehicle Museum, 5959 W Liberty St (Rt 304), 44425,
(330) 534-8125, Fax 534-3695, Mon-Fri 9-12 & 1-5, Adm Adult $5,
Child 10 & Under $3, Tanks: M4A1E8, M4A3, M7B1, M19, LVT(A)4
Half Track 3ea, 8 Inch Howitzer, DUKW, 6 Towed Guns 37mm to 175mm

Virginia
Danville   American Armoured Foundation Tank Museum, 3401 US Hwy 29, 24540,
(434) 836-5323, Fax: 836-532, Mon-Sat 10-5, Closed TD, CD, Adm Adult $10,
Snr & Child Under 12 $8, Gift Shop, Tanks: M5A1, M42A1, M551A1, T54-55
M110A1, M-20, Daimler Dingo

Petersburg   Fort Lee, Army Quartermaster Museum, 1201 22ed St, 23801-1601
(804) 734-4203, Tue-Fri 10-5, Sat-Sun 11-5, Closed TD, CD, ND, Free Adm
http://www.qmmuseum.lee.army.mil/index.html, Artifacts

Virginia

(Armored & Artilary Museums Continued)

Fort Lee, US Army Women's Museum, 2100 Adams Ace, Bldg P-5219, 23801-2100
Tue-Fri 10-5, Sat-Sun 11-4:30, Closed TD, CD, ND, Free Adm, Gift Shop 734-4636

WISCONSIN
Racine

American Legion K Rd, Exit 329 Off I-94, Tank, Cannon

HISTORICAL LANDMARKS

CALIFORNIA
Point Loma

Cabrillo National Monument, 1800 National Monument Dr, San Diego,
92106, (619) 557-5450, Daily 9-5:15, Adm Charged, Two 16" Gun Mounts
& Station used for WWII Costal Defenses.

San Francisco

Battery Davis Fort Funston, Pacific Side of City, 16" Gun Bunker.

Fort Point National Historical Site, 3" Gun Observation Posts,
South End Under the Golden Gate Bridge,

San Miguel
Island

Green Mountain, Channel Island National Park, B-24 Crash Remains
Story on VHS "Wreckfinding, Lost But Not Forgotten".

Ventura

Battery 2 & Camp Seaside, Emma Wood State Beach, Panama Gun Mounts,
West 100 Yards from the Ventura River Mouth.

DELAWARE
Lewes

(Historical Landmarks Continued)
Cape Henlopen State Park, 42 Cape Henlopen Dr, 19958, (302) 645-8983
This is where you'll find a 12 Inch Gun & Tower 4A, a WWII observation
tower that was used to spot enemy submarines & vessels. These towers
helped direct eight 16 inch guns buried in sand along the coast.
The guns had a range of 24 miles but were never called upon.
At the end of the war a German sub surrendered in the area,
which claimed the sinking of 400 vessels along the east coast.

FLORIDA
Clearwater

Ft Desoto Museum, Tampa Bay, 12 Inch Motar

Miami

Dade Metro Zoo. Here you will find still standing a tall blimp
support that was part of the NAS Hangar in Richmond during WWII.

New Smyrna

Target Rock, Rings of Port, WWII Gunnery & Bombing Target, Beach 13
Miles S of H-1A Hwy, Along Canaveral National Seashore, Remains of
an F6F Target, See Ranger Station on Directions.

MICHIGAN

Porcupine Mountain Wilderness State Park, On April 19, 1944 a B-17
crashed inside the wilderness where you can still find remains of
small parts along with the marks. To see this stop at the park
visitor center near junction of M-107 and South Boundary Rd.

NEBRASKA
Mc Cook

Mc Cook Air Base Historical Box 29 or Box B-337, 69001-0029
(308) 345-3200, under restoration of the facility. Training base
for B-24 & B-29 Bomb Groups. Remains are the buildings, hangars,
water tower, runways and aprons.

NEW JERSEY
Sandy Hook

The Gunnery, Sandy Hook State Park, Long Branch area,
Formerly Ft Hancock, 6" Shore Battery & Bunker System,
Tour Bunkers Used To Protect NY Harbor, Slide Show Twice,
Twice per Season Only, All Evening Tour

OREGON
Brookings

Siskiyou National Forest, From Hwy 101 - S Bank Chetco River Rd 6mi
Right on Forest Rd 1205 - At 12.7 mi - Take Wheeler Creek Research
Natural Area (#260) - This is a incendiary bomb site of a Japanese
aircraft launched off of a submarine near Gold Beach.

Hillsboro

Bruce Campbell, 15270 SW Holly Hill Rd, 97123-9074, (503) 628-2936
Home Built Out of a Boeing 727

Tillamook

Municipal Airport, Blimp Hangar, Used for patrol along the west
coast during WWII.

WASHINGTON
Coupeville

Fort Casey State Park, 1280 S Fort Casey Rd, 98239, (360) 678-4519
Apr 1-Oct 31 Daily 6:30-Dusk, Oct 16-Mar 31 Daily 8-Dusk, Free Adm,
Manager: John Harris, 2 each 3" WWII Guns, 2 each 6" WWII Guns

Port Townsend Coast Artillery Museum, 200 Battery Way, 98368, (360) 385-0373
Daily 12-4, Artifacts from Fort Casey, Fort Flager & Fort Worden

AIRCRAFT RIDES

AZ, Scottsdale - Sun Air Aviation, Inc, 15115 Airport Dr, Scottsdale Airpark, 85260,
(480) 991-0611, (800) 382-5030, Rides In The Following Aircraft:
Pitts Special   T-34   Waco   Helicopter & Balloon

CA - Chino - Planes of Fame Air Museum, 7000 Merrill Ave, #17, 91710, (909) 597-3722
Fax 597-4755, www.planesoffame.org/member-flights.php, P-38, P-40, P-51, B-25, SBD, SNJ
See web for details.

Fullerton - Air Combat USA, 230 N Dale Pl, Mail: POB 2726, 92633-2524,
(800) 522-7590 Fly Laser Dog Fights in the SIAI Marchetti SF260. $695 Phase I/II,
$1295 Full Day Training & 2 Flight Missions & G-1 Jacket.
Flights Offer In The Following Cities:

Batavia	NY	Dallas	TX	Nashville	TN
Nend	OR	Detroit	OH	Phoenix	AZ
Boston	MA	Kansas City	KS	Portland	OR
Chicago	IL	Lancaster	PA	San Jose	CA
Cincinnati	OH	Leesburg	VA	Seattle	WA
Fullerton	CA	Long Island	NY	St. Louis	MO

CO, Aurora - Airpower West, 2850 Kerr Gulch Rd, Mail: 3641 S Yampa St, 80013,
(303) 674-7864, Fax 670-6529, Airshow Coordinator: Mike Baldwin, apwrwest@rmi.net
Scheduled Airshows Flying: A-1, A-37, AT-6's, Beechcraft D17S & 18S, N2S, OV-1

FL, Kissimmee - Awesome Balloon FLights, Inc, (843) 215-7990, 1 Hr Flights, 24 Reservation Notice

St Augustine - North American Top Gun, 270 Estrella Ave, 32095, (800) 257-1636,
AT-6 Rides $190-550, www.natg.com, AT-6G,   AT-6D/G,   SNJ-4,   SNJ-5,   SNJ-6

Stallion 51 Corp, 804 N Hoagland Blvd, 34741, (407) 846-4400,
Fax 846-0414, Mon-Fri 9-5, Ride/Fly a TF-51 (Dual Cockpit) www.stallion51.com

Warbird Adventures, Ramp 66, Grand Strand Airport, Adjacent to Flying Tigers Warbird
Restoration Museum, (800) 386-1593, (407) 870-7366, www.warbirdadventures.com,
E-mail: programs@warbirdmuseum.com,   AT-6/SNJ Rides

GA, Atlanta - Air Superiorty Group, DeKalb-Peachtree Airport, POB 566726, 31156, Rides in a N2S-3

CAF - Dixie Wing, Falcon Field Airport, Bldg #410, Kennesaw, 30144,
(678) 354-1110, Mon-Sat 9-4, www.dixiewing.org, Rides Available in:
 C-45 $75, P-51D $750, PT-26 $100, SBD $400

Sky Warriors, Inc, 3996 Aviation Circle, Hangar B-3, Fulton County
Airport, Brown Field, 30336, (404) 699-7000, Fax 699-7200,
T-34A Aerial Laser Combat (75 Minute Flights)

ID, Driggs - Teton Aviation Center. 675 Airport Rd, Off Hwy 33, Mail: POB 869, 83422
(800) 472-6382, (208) 354-3100, Fax 354-3200, Daily 8-5, Closed TD, CD, Free Adm
www.tetonaviation.com, Glider Rides Available & Aviat Husky A-1 Rides

KS, Wichita - CAF Jayhawk Wing, 2558B S Kessler, Westport Airport, 67217, (316) 943-5510,
www.cafjayhawks.org, Rides available = C-78(UC) $60, PT-23 $60

KY, Louisville, Bowman Field, (502) 368-6524, AT-6

MO, Maryland Heights - Historic Aircraft Restoration Museum, Dauster Flying Field,
Creve Coeur Airport, 3127 Creve Coeur Mill Rd, 63146, (314) 434-3368, Fax 878-6453
Sat-Sun 10-4,Rides: SNJ $100, Stearman $75, www.historicaircraftrestorationmuseum.org

NC, Durham - Carolina Barnstormers, Durham Skypark Airport, 4340 Ger St, 27704 Off I-85,
(919) 680-6642, Owner: Mike Ratty, Rides: Waco YPF-7 and PT-17

NY, Horsehead - Wings of Eagles Discovery Center, 17 Aviation Dr, Elmira-Corning Regional Airport,
14845, (607) 739-8200, Mon-Fri 10-4, Sat 9-5, Sun 11-5, Closed TD, CD, ND,
Rides: AT-6 $225, PT-17 $150, PT-19 $99, www.wingsofeagles.com

Rhinebeck - Old Rhinebeck Aerodrome, 44 Stone Church Rd, Mail: BOX 229, 12572
(845) 752-3200, Fax: 758-6481, May 15-Oct31, Daily 10-5, www.oldrhinebeck.org/
1929 New Standard Biplane Rides 15 Min $40 Per Person

OH, Miamisburg - Wright B Flyer Museum, 10550 Springboro Pike, Off Rte 741, Wright Brothers Airport
(Dayton General Airport), 45342, (937) 885-2327, Tue,Thur,Sat 9-2:30,
Closed Holidays, www.wright-b-flyer.org, Wright B Flyer Flyable Rides for $150

VA, Bealeton - Flying Circus Aerodrome, 15S. Route 17, BOX 99, 22712, (540) 439-8661,
Daily 11-Sunset, Adm Adult $9, Child $3, Open Cockpit Rides $25,
Acrobatic Rides $50, Cub Rides $17.50,

Manassas - CAF - National Capital Squadron, Mail: NCS, POB 185, Falls Church, VA 22040,
www.natlcapsq.org, Funeral Flyovers & Ash Dispersals Available, Rides Available:BT-13A,L-5

(Aircraft Rides Continued)

WA, Vashon - Olde Thyme Aviation Inc, 21704 141st. Avenue SW, 98070, Rides starting at
$125 and up, 2 Travel Airs, 2 Waco UPF-7s, 2 Stearman Kaydets (1944 N2S-4 Navy
& 1944 PT-17 Army), and 2 Cabin Waco Biplanes (1936 YKS-6 & 1937 YKS-7),
http://www.oldethymeaviation.com/index.html, email: Waco@oldethymeaviation.com,

WI, Oshkosh - EAA Air Adventure Museum, Wittman Airfield, 3000 Poberezny Rd,
POB 3065, 54903-3065, US 41 Exit 44, (920) 426-4818, Mon-Sat 8:30-5, Sun 11-5,
Closed TD, CD, ND,

Ford Tri-Motor Adult $30, Child $20	Travel Air E-4000 Biplane $50
Waco YKS-7 Biplane $40, 2 for $70, 3 for $90	Bell 47 $30 , 2 for $50
Spirit of St Louis Replica $100	New Standard D-25 Biplane $50

Canada - **Ontario, Collingwood** - Collingwood Classic Aircraft Foundation,
Collingwood Mncpl Airport, Mail: Box 143, L9Y 3Z4, (705) 445-7545, Thur 9-4, Adm Free,
www.classicaircraft.ca/homepage.htm, Smith Miniplane, Stinson 105
Rides in: Aeronca Champ 7AC, DH 82A, Fleet Canuck

DC-3 RIDES

CA, San Clemente, Air Cruise America, 1 Via Pasa, 92673-2750, (949) 661-8410
DC-3 (Rides Available)

CA, San Leandro, Otis Spunkmeyer Air, 8433 Earhart Rd, Kaaiser Air Jet Center,
Mail: 14490 Catalina St, 94577, 800-938-1900, (510) 649-5900, DC-3 & C-41

FL, Marco Island - South Florida Sea Ventures, Inc, 2 Marco Lake Dr, #6, 33907,
(800) 835-9323, DC-3 Flights in 1940 Interiors From Naples To Key West,
Ft Meyers to Key West, Naples to Ft Lauderdale, Round Trip $139-169.

GA, Griffin, Alexander Aeroplane Co, 118 Huff Daland Cir, 30223, (770) 228-3901,
(800) 831-2949,

KY, Louisville, Bowman Field, (502) 368-6524, DC-3/C-47 Flights

OK, Ames, Bygone Aviation, POB 22, 73718, (580) 753-4445, DC-3 Rides Available

YUKON TERRITORY
Whitehorse - Whitehorse Airport, (403) 667-8440, DC-3(3ea) Flights To:
Dawson City, Fairbanks, Juneau, Old Crow

CREDITS

Carry Patrick from Waukegan, IL
Has provided me with endless letters each month with lots of useful
information on museums & aircraft. He saved me Months of work.

I would like to thank all museums who have sent me information on their
facility and for the following people who have provided me with
information for this edition.

Alexander	Rick	Bangor	ME
Bachle	Carl F	Jackson	MI
Baleria	Dave	Rapid City	SD
Barrows	Peter	Versailles	KY
Baumann	Richard	Encino	CA
Colleen	G	Woonsocket	SD
Cox	Ron D	Panama City	FL
Deeds	Kelly	Kansas City	KS
Eschweiler	Ron	Wilmington	DE
Evelsizr	Darwin L	Mascoutah	IL
Hulslander	Curt	Kent	WA
Kashiwagi	Kuni	Tokyo	Japan
McKenzie	Dan W	El Cajon	CA
Moss	Phillip	Manly Vale	Australia
Omlid USN RET	Chuck	Pensacola	FL
Repke	Dennis K	Annapolis	MD
Robinson	Terry	Ramona	CA
Saxon Jr	Col Vernon P	Boron	CA
White	Brent	San Jose	CA
Workman	Grant	Abbotsford	BC

Last I want to thank my wife **Sylverta M Blaugher**
for her help and support in my long hours and months putting
this edition together.

UH-1 Huey
Houston Welcome Center
15121 S US 231
N of FL State Line
Slocomb, AL 36273
by - Thomas Buuck
Ft. Wayne, IN

B-24 Nose Section
Fantasy of Flight
1400 Broadway Blvd. SE
Polk City, FL 33868
by - Linda & Pat Carry
Waukegan, IL

P-38 Lightning
Major Thomas B.
McQuire Jr. Memorial
McGuire AFB, NJ
by - Linda &
Pat Carry
Waukegan, IL

Aircraft Type	State	City Abv.	Museum Abv.	Manufacture	Aircraft Name/ SN, N#, Tail#, Side#, Sq#, Nick Name
A-1	CO	Puebl	PWAM	Martin-Marietta	Pershing 15
A-1	FL	Pensa	USNAM	Curtiss	Triad
A-1	OH	S.Euc	USAM	Curtiss	Triad
A-1 EAA	WI	Oshko	EAAAAM	Curtiss	Triad N6077V
A-1(BTD-1)	NY	Horseheads	NWM	Douglas	Skyraider 04959
A-1A(AD-1)	VA	VBeac	ONAS	Douglas	Skyraider 9102, 500, VA-176
A-1A(AD-1H)	CA	El Cajon	WW	Douglas	Skyraider
A-1C(AD-3)	WI	Oshko	EAAAAM	Douglas	Skyraider 122811
A-1D	CO	Denver	69thB	Douglas	Skyraider Tail: TT822
A-1D(AD-4N)	CA	Chino		Douglas	Skyraider
A-1D(AD-4N)	CT	Winds	NEAM	Douglas	Skyraider
A-1D(AD-4N)	WA	Eastsound	FHC	Douglas	Skyraider 126924, N2692
A-1D(AD-4N)	VA	Suffolk	FF	Douglas	Skyraider 123827, VA-195
A-1D(AD-4NA)	MI	Kalam	KAHM	Douglas	Skyraider 127888, N92334
A-1D(AD-4W)	NV	Fallon	NASF	Douglas	Skyraider 132261, VA-145, 500, NK
A-1D(AD-4W)	OR	Tillamook	TAM	Douglas	Skyraider
A-1E(AD-5)	CA	Lemoore	LNAS	Douglas	Skyraider
A-1E(AD-5)	CA	Sacra	McCelAFB	Douglas	Skyraider 132463, 552, Twin Seater
A-1E(AD-5)	FL	FtWal	HF	Douglas	Skyraider 52-598, Twin Seater
A-1E(AD-5W)	NY	Geneseo	1941AG	Douglas	Skyraider
A-1E(AD-5)	OH	Dayto	USAFM	Douglas	Skyraider 52-13264, 9, Twin Seater, 52-132649
A-1E(AD-5)	OH	Newbu	WASAC	Douglas	Skyraider 165273, Twin Seater
A-1E(AD-5)	SC	MtPleasant	PPM	Douglas	Skyraider Twin Seater
A-1E(AD-5)	TX	Midla	CAFFM	Douglas	Skyraider Twin Seater
A-1E(AD-5)	TX	Slaton	TAM	Douglas	Skyraider SN BU132443, Twin Seater
A-1E(AD-5)	UT	Ogden	HAM	Douglas	Skyraider
A-1E(AD-5)	WA	Olympia	OFM	Douglas	Skyraider Side # 21
A-1E(AD-5)	WI	Oshko	EAAAAM	Douglas	Skyraider 132789, Twin Seater
A-1F(AD-5Q)	AZ	Tucso	PAM	Douglas	Skyraider 135018, VR703, Twin Seater
A-1H(AD-6)				Douglas	Skyraider N39606, 39606, D, VA-145
A-1H(AD-6)	FL	Pensa	USNAM	Douglas	Skyraider
A-1H(AD-7)	MD	Silve	PEGF	Douglas	Skyraider 135300, NL405, VA-25
A-2	CA	Ridgecrest	CLNWC	Lockheed	Polaris
A-2	VA	Hampt	APM	Lockheed	Polaris
A-2	VA	Quant	MCAGM	Lockheed	Polaris
A-3A(A3D-1)	FL	Pensa	USNAM	Douglas	Skywarrior 135418, 70
A-3B(EA-3B)(A3D-2)	MD	Ft Meade	NVP	Douglas	Skywarrior
A-3B(A3D-2)	CT	Winds	NEAM	Douglas	Skywarrior 142246
A-3B(A3D-2)	NY	NYC	ISASM	Douglas	Skywarrior
A-3D(A3D-1)	AZ	Tucso	PAM	Douglas	Skywarrior 130361
A-3D(A3D-4)	CA	Rosam	EAFB	Douglas	Skywarrior 135434
A-3D(A3D-4)	NY	NYC	ISASM	Douglas	Skywarrior "Whale"
A-3D(KA-3B)	CA	Oakla	OWAM	Douglas	Skywarrior
A-3D(KA-3B)	TX	C Christi	USS Lexi	Douglas	Skywarrior
A-4J(TA)	Al	Birmingham	SMoF	McDonnell-Douglas	Skyhawk
A-4	AZ	Yuma	YUSMAB	McDonnell-Douglas	Skyhawk SC01
A-4	CA	Alame	ANAS	McDonnell-Douglas	Skyhawk
A-4	CA	El Centro	ECNAF	McDonnell-Douglas	Skyhawk Sn 159798
A-4	CA	Inglewood	PBR	McDonnell-Douglas	Skyhawk
A-4	CA	Lemoore	LNAS	McDonnell-Douglas	Skyhawk
A-4	CA	S.Mon	MoF	McDonnell-Douglas	Skyhawk "Blue Angels", #4
A-4	CA	Twentynine	TPMC	McDonnell-Douglas	Skyhawk 5133
A-4	FL	Kissi	FTWAM	McDonnell-Douglas	Skyhawk
A-4	FL	Orlan	ONTC	McDonnell-Douglas	Skyhawk
A-4	IL	Great Lakes	GLNTC	McDonnell-Douglas	Skyhawk
A-4	LA	Reser	AMHFM	McDonnell-Douglas	Skyhawk
A-4	NB	Omaha	FP	McDonnell-Douglas	Skyhawk
A-4	NC	Charl	CHAC	McDonnell-Douglas	Skyhawk
A-4	NC	CPoin	CPMB	McDonnell-Douglas	Skyhawk
A-4	NC	Havelock	HI	McDonnell-Douglas	Skyhawk
A-4	NH	Nashu	FAAATCC	McDonnell-Douglas	Skyhawk
A-4	NJ	Millville	MAAFM	McDonnell-Douglas	Skyhawk
A-4	NJ	Rio Grande	NASW	McDonnell-Douglas	Skyhawk
A-4	NV	Fallon	NASF	McDonnell-Douglas	Skyhawk 142100, VFC-13, 01
A-4	NV	Fallon	NASF	McDonnell-Douglas	Skyhawk
A-4	NY	Brooklyn	FAAATCC	McDonnell-Douglas	Skyhawk
A-4	SC	Mt Pleasant	PPM	McDonnell-Douglas	Skyhawk 149623, VA 163 USS Oriskany, 353, Tail AH
A-4	TX	Beevi	CrtHouse	McDonnell-Douglas	Skyhawk
A-4	TX	San A	CityPark	McDonnell-Douglas	Skyhawk
A-4	VA	Norfolk	NMM	McDonnell-Douglas	Skyhawk
A-4(Tail Only)	TN	Memph	LS	McDonnell-Douglas	Skyhawk
A-4A	CA	Alameda	USSHM	McDonnell-Douglas	Skyhawk 139929
A-4A	CA	Hawth	WMoF	McDonnell-Douglas	Skyhawk
A-4A	CA	Paso Robles	EWM	McDonnell-Douglas	Skyhawk 137826
A-4A	CA	S.Mon	MoF	McDonnell-Douglas	Skyhawk
A-4A	CT	Winds	NEAM	McDonnell-Douglas	Skyhawk 2219 , 36
A-4A	IL	Ranto	OCAM	McDonnell-Douglas	Skyhawk 139947, 52-0898, Blue Angle #6 "Lucy"
A-4A	KS	Liberal	MAAM	McDonnell-Douglas	Skyhawk
A-4A Cockpit	KS	Topeka	CAM	McDonnell-Douglas	Skyhawk 142168
A-4A	MD	Annap	USNAM	McDonnell-Douglas	Skyhawk
A-4A	NY	NYC	ISASM	McDonnell-Douglas	Skyhawk 2833, AF, 300
A-4A	TX	Kings	CityPark	McDonnell-Douglas	Skyhawk
A-4A	TX	Paris	FTAM	McDonnell-Douglas	Skyhawk
A-4B(TA)(A4D-2)	AZ	Tucso	PAM	McDonnell-Douglas	Skyhawk 14928
A-4B	CA	Bishop	INP	McDonnell-Douglas	Skyhawk 142790, Tail 7L, Side 49
A-4B	CA	Chino	PoF	McDonnell-Douglas	Skyhawk
A-4B	CA	Chino	YAM	McDonnell-Douglas	Skyhawk
A-4B	CA	San Diego	SDAM	McDonnell-Douglas	Skyhawk NP302, VA-212
A-4B	DC	Washi	NA&SM	McDonnell-Douglas	Skyhawk
A-4B	IN	Indianapolis	RAM	McDonnell-Douglas	Skyhawk 142834
A-4B(A4D-2)	MI	Kalamazoo	KAHM	McDonnell-Douglas	Skyhawk 057182, 145011
A-4B	MI	Mt Clemens	SMAM	McDonnell-Douglas	Skyhawk 142761, Side # 01
A-4B	NY	NYC	ISASM	McDonnell-Douglas	Skyhawk
A-4B	OR	Tillamook	TAM	McDonnell-Douglas	Skyhawk
A-4B	TN	Crossville	CCHS	McDonnell-Douglas	Skyhawk 148572, "Blue Angles"
A-4B	TX	C Christi	USS Lexi	McDonnell-Douglas	Skyhawk
A-4B	TX	C Christi	USS Lexi	McDonnell-Douglas	Skyhawk
A-4B	TX	Rio Grande V	TAM	McDonnell-Douglas	Skyhawk
A-4B	WI	Oshko	EAAAAM	McDonnell-Douglas	Skyhawk 685
A-4C	AR	Fayet	AAM	McDonnell-Douglas	Skyhawk 147733
A-4C	AZ	Tucso	PAM	McDonnell-Douglas	Skyhawk N401FS, 148571
A-4C	CA	El Cajon	SDAMGF	McDonnell-Douglas	Skyhawk 201, NM

Type	State	City	Code	Manufacturer	Name	Notes
A- 4C	CA	Miramar	FLAM	McDonnell-Douglas	Skyhawk	DT, VMA-242, "Advisory"
A- 4C	CA	San Diego	SDACM	McDonnell-Douglas	Skyhawk	148517
A- 4C	CA	S.Mon	MoF	McDonnell-Douglas	Skyhawk	
A- 4C	FL	Clear	FMAM	McDonnell-Douglas	Skyhawk	
A- 4C	FL	Jacks	NASCF	McDonnell-Douglas	Skyhawk	147708, AK 301, VA-106
A- 4C	NJ	Lumberton	AVM	McDonnell-Douglas	Skyhawk	145072
A- 4C	NY	NYC	ISASM	McDonnell-Douglas	Skyhawk	
A- 4C	RI	NKing	QAM	McDonnell-Douglas	Skyhawk	"Mighty Midget", 147790
A- 4D	IN	Goshen	AM	McDonnell-Douglas	Skyhawk	
A- 4D	NB	Omaha	FP	McDonnell-Douglas	Skyhawk	149618, "USS Enterprise", 601, Tail AE, VA-64
A- 4D-2	CO	Puebl	PWAM	McDonnell-Douglas	Skyhawk	147702
A- 4E	CA	Chino	YAM	McDonnell-Douglas	Skyhawk	
A- 4E(A4D)	FL	Pensa	USNAM	McDonnell-Douglas	Skyhawk	149656, VA-164, Tail "AH", #303
A- 4E(A4D)	FL	Pensa	USNAM	McDonnell-Douglas	Skyhawk	"Blue Angels", 150076 154180 1
A- 4E	HI	Oahu	BPNAS	McDonnell-Douglas	Skyhawk	150023 (Hl Hist Avia Fndt)
A- 4E	HI	Oahu	BPNAS	McDonnell-Douglas	Skyhawk	153689 (MCBH)
A- 4E	HI	Oahu	BPNAS	McDonnell-Douglas	Skyhawk	151030 (Pacific Aerospace Museum)
A- 4F(NT)	CA	Ridgecrest	CLNWC	McDonnell-Douglas	Skyhawk	
A- 4F	CA	San Diego	SDACM	McDonnell-Douglas	Skyhawk	154977
A- 4F	NY	Glenville	ESAM	McDonnell-Douglas	Skyhawk	155009
A- 4F	RI	NKing	QAM	McDonnell-Douglas	Skyhawk	155027
A- 4F	VA	VBeac	ONAS	McDonnell-Douglas	Skyhawk	155176, VF- 43
A- 4F	WA	Seatt	MoF	McDonnell-Douglas	Skyhawk	"Blue Angels", 154180 4
A- 4F(A4D)	FL	Pensa	USNAM	McDonnell-Douglas	Skyhawk	"Blue Angels", 154217 4
A- 4F(A4D)	FL	Pensa	USNAM	McDonnell-Douglas	Skyhawk	"Blue Angels" , 155033 3
A- 4F(A4D)	FL	Pensa	USNAM	McDonnell-Douglas	Skyhawk	"Blue Angels" , 154983 2
A- 4L	AL	Mobil	BMP	McDonnell-Douglas	Skyhawk	147787
A- 4J(TA)	CA	Palm Springs	PSAM	McDonnell-Douglas	Skyhawk	154649, VC-8
A- 4J(TA)	IL	Sugar Grove	ACM	McDonnell-Douglas	Skyhawk	153678
A- 4J(TA)	IN	Elkhart	NIAM	McDonnell-Douglas	Skyhawk	153671, VT-7, CTW-1, Nose 716
A- 4J(TA)	KS	Topeka	CAM	McDonnell-Douglas	Skyhawk	158716, , Side # 771, Tail A, VT-7(CTW-1)
A- 4J(TA)	MD	Lexington	USNTPS	McDonnell-Douglas	Skyhawk	158106, Side # 8, TPS Tail
A- 4J(TA)	MD	Middle River	GLMAM	McDonnell-Douglas	Skyhawk	
A- 4J(TA)	TX	Beevi	CFAFB	McDonnell-Douglas	Skyhawk	
A- 4J(TA)	TX	FWort	NASFWJRB	McDonnell-Douglas	Skyhawk	
A- 4L	KS	Liberal	MAAM	McDonnell-Douglas	Skyhawk	149635
A- 4L	KY	Lexington	AMoK	McDonnell-Douglas	Skyhawk	147708
A- 4L	MS	Greneda	HS	McDonnell-Douglas	Skyhawk	160255, NMF-213
A- 4L	SC	Beauf	MAS	McDonnell-Douglas	Skyhawk	147772, EX 01, MALS-31
A- 4M	CA	Oakla	OWAM	McDonnell-Douglas	Skyhawk	SI 59
A- 4M	ME	Lexin	PNAT&EM	McDonnell-Douglas	Skyhawk	
A- 4M	NC	Havelock	HTC	McDonnell-Douglas	Skyhawk	
A- 4M	PA	Willo	WGNAS	McDonnell-Douglas	Skyhawk	WA 00
A- 4M	RI	NKing	QAM	McDonnell-Douglas	Skyhawk	158148
A- 4M	TX	FWort	NASFWJRB	McDonnell-Douglas	Skyhawk	
A- 5	FL	KeyWe	NASKW	NA-Rockwell	Vigilante	
A- 5	FL	Orlan	MGNTC	NA-Rockwell	Vigilante	
A- 5C	FL	Sanford	Airport	NA-Rockwell	Vigilante	
A- 5(A3J)	MD	Lexington	PRNAM	NA-Rockwell	Vigilante	156643, Side# 643, NATC Tail
A- 5A(A3J)	MD	Lexington	SWD	NA-Rockwell	Vigilante	146697
A- 5	TN	Millington	NASM	NA-Rockwell	Vigilante	
A- 6	GA	Marietta	NASA	Grumman	Intruder	
A- 6	MI	Lapee	YAFDLA	Grumman	Intruder	
A- 6	NV	Fallon	NASF	Grumman	Intruder	155627
A- 6	NY	NYC	ISASM	Grumman	Intruder	147867
A- 6	PA	Smethport	AAAM	Grumman	Intruder	
A- 6	VA	Norfolk	NASN	Grumman	Intruder	
A- 6	WA	Oak Harbor	City Park	Grumman	Intruder	
A- 6 Simulator	CA	Oakla	OWAM	Grumman	Intruder	
A- 6A	AL	Starke	CBM	Grumman	Intruder	155661, VA-35, 507, Tail 07, "USS America"
A- 6A	MD	Lexington	PRNAM	Grumman	Intruder	156997, 500, NAWC/AD Tail,
A- 6A	MI	Belleville	YAM	Grumman	Intruder	156981, "Flight of the Intruder" Movie
A- 6A	NY	NYC	ISASM	Grumman	Intruder	162185
A- 6B	CA	Chino	YAM	Grumman	Intruder	
A- 6B	SC	Mt Pleasant	PPM	Grumman	Intruder	152599
A- 6D(KA-6D)	CA	Oakla	OWAM	Grumman	Intruder	
A- 6E	AZ	Tucso	PAM	Grumman	Intruder	155713, NJ 562, VA-128
A- 6E	CA	Paso Robles	EWM	Grumman	Intruder	154717
A- 6E	CA	Ridgecrest	CLNWC	Grumman	Intruder	
A- 6E	CA	Miramar	FLAM	Grumman	Intruder	NAWC
A- 6E	CA	Palm Springs	PSAM	Grumman	Intruder	154162, #500, VA-36, AJ, USS Theodore Roosevelt
A- 6E	CA	S.Mon	MoF	Grumman	Intruder	
A- 6E	CA	SRosa	PCAM	Grumman	Intruder	
A- 6E	CA	El Cajon	SDAMGF	Grumman	Intruder	151782
A- 6E	CO	Grand Junction	CAF-RMW	Grumman	Intruder	VMA-533, #7
A- 6E	FL	Pensa	USNAM	Grumman	Intruder	155610
A- 6E	FL	Tittusville	VACM	Grumman	Intruder	
A- 6E	RI	NKing	QAM	Grumman	Intruder	155629
A- 6E	TX	C Christi	USS Lexi	Grumman	Intruder	151579, AC501, VA- 75
A- 6E	VA	VBeac	ONAS	Grumman	Intruder	151579, AC501, VA- 75
A- 6E	WA	Seatt	MoF	Grumman	Intruder	158794
A- 6E(EA)	WA	Tacoma	City Beach Park	Grumman	Intruder	152907, VA-128, NJ, Side # 800
A- 6F	NY	Garde	CoAM	Grumman	Intruder	162184
A- 7	AL	Starke	CBM	Vought	Corsair II	157503, Nose 301, Tail NE 01, Lt PS Clark
A- 7	AL	Tuscalloose	I-20/59	Vought	Corsair II	400
A- 7	AR	Pocahontas	PMA	Vought	Corsair II	153150, 300, Tail NL, VA-22, USS Nmitz
A- 7	CA	Alame	ANAS	Vought	Corsair II	400
A- 7	CA	Chino	YAM	Vought	Corsair II	
A- 7(LTV)	FL	Kissimmee	FTWRM	Vought	Corsair II	
A- 7	FL	Orlan	ONTC	Vought	Corsair II	
A- 7	FL	Titus	VACM	Vought	Corsair II	
A- 7	GA	Calhoun	MAM	Vought	Corsair II	145326, 7B, #9
A- 7	IA	Des Moines	ING	Vought	Corsair II	75403
A- 7	IA	Greenfield	IAM	Vought	Corsair II	
A- 7	LA	New Orleans	Belle Chasee NAS	Vought	Corsair II	
A- 7	MD	Lexin	PNA&EM	Vought	Corsair II	
A- 7	NB	Omaha	FP	Vought	Corsair II	
A- 7	NC	Charl	CHAC	Vought	Corsair II	
A- 7	NC	CPoin	CPMB	Vought	Corsair II	
A- 7	ND	Minot	DTAM	Vought	Corsair II	
A- 7	NV	Fallon	NASF	Vought	Corsair II	154420, 00
A- 7	NV	Fallon	NASF	Vought	Corsair II	
A- 7	OH	Alliance	AHS	Vought	Corsair II	153142, VA-86

Type	State	City	Code	Mfr	Model	Notes
A-7A	FL	Tittusville	VACM	Vought	Corsair II	
A-7A	IL	Bloom	PAM	Vought	Corsair II	NJ412
A-7B	CA	El Cajon	SDAMGF	Vought	Corsair II	154370
A-7B	NJ	Lumberton	AVM	Vought	Corsair II	154550
A-7B	NC	Hickory	HRA	Vought	Corsair II	144345, VA-82
A-7B	TX	C Christi	USS Lexi	Vought	Corsair II	154431
A-7B	TX	Slaton	TAM	Vought	Corsair II	154431
A-7C	CA	Ridgecrest	CLNWC	Vought	Corsair II	
A-7C	CA	Paso Robles	EWM	Vought	Corsair II	156739
A-7C	WI	Kenos	KMM	Vought	Corsair II	156751, VAQ33, #120
A-7C(TA)	NM	Albuq	NAM	Vought	Corsair II	
A-7D	AZ	Tucso	DMAFB	Vought	Corsair II	
A-7D	AZ	Tucso	PAM	Vought	Corsair II	Sn 70-973, "Big D"
A-7D	AZ	Tucso	TANG	Vought	Corsair II	
A-7D	CA	S.Mon	MoF	Vought	Corsair II	
A-7D	CA	Riverside	MAFM	Vought	Corsair II	69-6188
A-7D	CA	Sacra	McCelAFB	Vought	Corsair II	70-998
A-7D	CO	Aurora	WOTR	Vought	Corsair II	
A-7D	IA	Altoona	SWYC	Vought	Corsair II	71334, Tail IA AF
A-7D	IA	Carroll	Airport	Vought	Corsair II	
A-7D	IA	Corre	CityPark	Vought	Corsair II	
A-7D	IA	Johnston	CD	Vought	Corsair II	75403, Tail IA, AF,
A-7D	IA	SBluf	MAAM	Vought	Corsair II	
A-7D	IA	Sheld	CityPark	Vought	Corsair II	
A-7D	IA	Sioux	SCANG	Vought	Corsair II	
A-7D	IL	Ranto	OCAM	Vought	Corsair II	69-6190
A-7E	LA	Alexandria	EAB	Vought	Corsair II	69-234, EL 23TFW
A-7D	MD	Middl	GLMAM	Vought	Corsair II	
A-7D	MI	Mt Clemens	SMAM	Vought	Corsair II	72-0261
A-7D	MT	Helena	FFTC	Vought	Corsair II	
A-7D	NC	Fayet	PAFB	Vought	Corsair II	
A-7D	ND	Wahpe	CityPark	Vought	Corsair II	
A-7D	NE	S.Sio	CityPark	Vought	Corsair II	
A-7D	NE	SSiou	MA	Vought	Corsair II	
A-7D	NM	Albuquerque	KAFB	Vought	Corsair II	72045
A-7D	NY	Horsehead	WoE	Vought	Corsair II	69-6200
A-7D	OH	Dayto	USAFM	Vought	Corsair II	69-6192
A-7D	OH	Lockb	RANGB	Vought	Corsair II	73-999
A-7D	OH	Lockb	RANGB	Vought	Corsair II	73-1006
A-7D	OK	Oklah	45IDM	Vought	Corsair II	72-0240
A-7D	RI	NKing	QAM	Vought	Corsair II	75-0408
A-7D	SC	McEnt	MEANGB	Vought	Corsair II	
A-7D	SD	Huron	Airport	Vought	Corsair II	
A-7D	SD	McEnt	MEANGB	Vought	Corsair II	
A-7D	SD	Pierr	SDNGM	Vought	Corsair II	
A-7D	SD	Sioux	SDANGSF	Vought	Corsair II	
A-7D	SD	Tea	Airport	Vought	Corsair II	
A-7D	TX	Burnet	HLS-CAF	Vought	Corsair II	
A-7D	VA	Richm	SMAM	Vought	Corsair II	72-0
A-7D	VA	Sands	VAM	Vought	Corsair II	"Death Dealer"
A-7D	WI	CDoug	WNGML&M	Vought	Corsair II	
A-7D(YA)	CA	Rosam	EAFB	Vought	Corsair II	67-14583
A-7D-3-CV	MI	Belleville	YAF	Vought	Corsair II	69-6193
A-7E	Al	Birmingham	SMoF	Vought	Corsair II	
A-7E	AZ	Tucso	PAM	Vought	Corsair II	160713
A-7E	CA	Lemoore	LNAS	Vought	Corsair II	
A-7E	CA	Oakla	OWAM	Vought	Corsair II	NJ250
A-7E	FL	Colum	CityPark	Vought	Corsair II	158003
A-7E	FL	Jacks	NASCF	Vought	Corsair II	158662, AC301, VA-37
A-7E	FL	Jacks	NASCF	Vought	Corsair II	152650, 301, VA-46
A-7E	FL	LakeCity	CityPark	Vought	Corsair II	Thunderbird colors
A-7E	FL	Pensa	USNAM	Vought	Corsair II	160714
A-7E	GA	Marietta	NASA	Vought	Corsair II	158842
A-7E	IL	Sugar Grove	ACM	Vought	Corsair II	158842
A-7E	IL	Edwardsville	CityPark	Vought	Corsair II	159303, #401
A-7E	IL	Linco	HIFM	Vought	Corsair II	
A-7E	KS	Liberal	MAAM	Vought	Corsair II	73009
A-7E	LA	Baton Rouge	LNWM	Vought	Corsair II	160724
A-7E	LA	Reser	AMHFM	Vought	Corsair II	
A-7E	NM	STere	WEAM	Vought	Corsair II	
A-7E	NV	Fallo	NAS	Vought	Corsair II	
A-7E	NY	NYC	ISASM	Vought	Corsair II	AE 401
A-7E	SC	Mt Pleasant	PPM	Vought	Corsair II	Side 301
A-7E	TN	Memph	MBMA	Vought	Corsair II	160869, 401, VA-27
A-7E	VA	Hampt	APM	Vought	Corsair II	157500, AC-300, VA-37
A-7E Cockpit	OR	Tillamook	TAM	Vought	Corsair II	
A-7F	OR	Tillamook	TAM	Vought	Corsair II	
A-7F(YA)	CA	Rosam	EAFB	Vought	Corsair II	71-344
A-7F(YA)	UT	Ogden	HAFBM	Vought	Corsair II	
A-7K	IA	SBluf	MAAM	Vought	Corsair II	
A-9A(YA)	CA	Riverside	MFAM	Northrop		71-1368
A-10	KY	Ft Campbell	DFPMM	Fairchild	Thunderbolt II	
A-10	LA	Alexandria	EAB	Fairchild	Thunderbolt II	23-3667, EL 23TFW
A-10	LA	New Orleans	Belle Chasse NAS	Fairchild	Thunderbolt II	
A-10	CT	Windsor	ANG	Fairchild	Thunderbolt II	
A-10 Cockpit	TX	Big Springs	H25	Fairchild	Thunderbolt II	
A-10	WI	CDoug	WNGML&M	Fairchild	Thunderbolt II	
A-10 Wing	WI	Oshko	EAAAAM	Mitchell	Wing	
A-10(YA)	OH	Dayto	USAFM	Fairchild	Thunderbolt II	71-1370
A-10A	AZ	Tucso	DMAFB	Fairchild	Thunderbolt II	
A-10A	AZ	Tucso	PAM	Fairchild	Thunderbolt II	75-298
A-10A	CA	Sacra	McCelAFB	Fairchild	Thunderbolt II	76-540
A-10A	CT	Winds	NEAM	Fairchild	Thunderbolt II	173
A-10A	FL	Shali	USAFAM	Fairchild	Thunderbolt II	77-205, NO
A-10A	IN	Peru	GAFB	Fairchild	Thunderbolt II	77-228
A-10A	NC	Fayet	PAFB	Fairchild	Thunderbolt II	
A-10A	NY	Garde	CoAM	Fairchild	Thunderbolt II	760535
A-10A	NY	Horseheads	NWM	Fairchild	Thunderbolt II	
A-10A	NY	Glenville	ESAM	Fairchild	Thunderbolt II	75-263
A-10A	OH	Dayto	USAFM	Fairchild	Thunderbolt II	78-681, TWF-23
A-10A	PA	Willow	WGNAS	Fairchild	Thunderbolt II	
A-10A	TX	San A	LAFB	Fairchild	Thunderbolt II	76-547
A-10A	UT	Ogden	HAFBM	Fairchild	Thunderbolt II	

Type	State	City	Facility	Manufacturer	Name	Notes
A-10A	WA	Tacoma	MAFB	Fairchild	Thunderbolt II	270
A-10A(OA)	NC	Fayet	PAFB	Fairchild	Thunderbolt II	
A-10B(YA)	CA	Rosam	EAFB	Fairchild	Thunderbolt II	73-1664
A-12	AL	Birmingham	SMoF	Lockheed	Blackbird	60-6937
A-12	AL	Huntsville	HSRM	Lockheed	Blackbird	60-6930
A-12	AL	Mobil	BMP	Lockheed	Blackbird	60-6938
A-12	CA	Los Angeles	CMoS	Lockheed	Blackbird	60-6927
A-12	CA	Palmd	PAFB	Lockheed	Blackbird	60-6924
A-12	CA	San Diego	SDAM	Lockheed	Blackbird	60-6933
A-12	MN	Minneapolis	MAGM	Lockheed	Blackbird	60-6931
A-12	NY	New York City	ISASM	Lockheed	Blackbird	60-6925
A-12	OH	Dayton	USAFM	Lockheed	Blackbird	60-6935
A-12(M-21)	WA	Seatt	MoF	Lockheed	Blackbird	60-6940
A-17A	OH	Dayto	USAFM	Northrop	Nomad	36-207
A-20	AZ	Tucson	PA&SM	Douglas	Havoc	43-21627
A-20G	OH	Dayto	USAFM	Douglas	Havoc	43-22200
A-20G	TX	Galve	LSFM	Douglas	Havoc	43-21709, N3WF
A-20H	PA	Beave	AHM	Douglas	Havoc	44-0020
A-20	FL	Polk City	FoF	Douglas	Havoc	43-22197
A-24	IL	Chicago	MAP	Douglas	Dauntless	
A-24B(RA)	TX	Midla	CAFFM	Douglas	Dauntless	
A-24B-15-DT(SBD-5)	OH	N Canton	MAM	Douglas	Dauntless	42-54654
A-25A (See SB2C)	MN	Blaine	ACBA	Curtiss	Helldiver	Owner: Mike Rawson
A-25A (See SB2C)	OH	Dayton	USAFM	Curtiss	Helldiver	
A-26	AL	Birmingham	SMoF	Douglas	Invader	
A-26	AL	Troy	TMA	Douglas	Invader	
A-26	AR	PineB	CAF-RW	Douglas	Invader	N2268N
A-26	AZ	PBluf	RWCAF	Douglas	Invader	
A-26	BC-C	Sidne	BCAM	Douglas	Invader	
A-26	CA	Marys	BAFB	Douglas	Invader	
A-26(JD-1)	CA	Palm Sprg	PSAM	Douglas	Invader	43-5721, N94257, Target Tug, Tail BP
A-26	CA	SRosa	PCAM	Douglas	Invader	
A-26	FL	Kissi	FTWAM	Douglas	Invader	
A-26(JD-1)	FL	Pensa	USNAM	Douglas	Invader	44-6928, 77141, UH2, VU-5, Target Tug
A-26	LA	New Orleans	FoJBMM	Douglas	Invader	Sn 44-35937
A-26	MA	Stow	BCF	Douglas	Invader	
A-26	MS	Jacks	ThompANG	Douglas	Invader	
A-26	NM	STere	WEAM	Douglas	Invader	
A-26	NY	Cheec	CSCA	Douglas	Invader	
A-26(VA)	OH	Newbu	WASAC	Douglas	Invader	
A-26	OK	ElRen	VFW	Douglas	Invader	"Sonny"
A-26	ON-C	Bradford	GoAR	Douglas	Invader	
A-26	ON-C	Oshaw	MT	Douglas	Invader	
A-26	ON-C	Oshaw	OAM&IM	Douglas	Invader	
A-26C	OR	McMinnville	EAV	Douglas	Invader	44-35439, N74833
A-26	OR	Tillamook	TAM	Douglas	Invader	44-35439, N3222T
A-26	TX	SMarc	CTWCAF	Douglas	Invader	
A-26	TX	Waco	WRA	Douglas	Invader	N240P
A-26	WY	Greyb	H&PA	Douglas	Invader	
A-26A	SC	Flore	FA&MM	Douglas	Invader	
A-26B	CA	Rosam	EAFB	Douoglas	Invader	44-34165
A-26B(VB)	MD	Silve	PEGF	Douglas	Invader	
A-26B	MS	Jacks	JANG	Douglas	Invader	
A-26B(VA)	NE	Ashland	SACM	Douglas	Invader	44-34665
A-26B	NM	Las Cruces	SA	Douglas	Invader	
A-26B	NY	Horseheads	NWM	Douglas	Invader	41-39516, N237Y, VA ANG
A-26B	OH	Carroll	HAS	Douglas	Invader	44-34104, N99420
A-26B	OK	Fredi	AAM	Douglas	Invader	
A-26B	TX	Midla	CAFFM	Douglas	Invader	
A-26B	UT	Ogden	HAM	Douglas	Invader	44-35617
A-26B	VA	Suffolk	FF	Douglas	Invader	Project,
A-26B	UT	Ogden	HAFBM	Douglas	Invader	
A-26C	AR	Mesa	CAFAW	Douglas	Invader	
A-26C	AZ	Grand	PoFGCVA	Douglas	Invader	39359
A-26C	AZ	Tucso	PAM	Douglas	Invader	43-22494
A-26C	AZ	Tucso	PAM	Douglas	Invader	44-35372, N8028E, "Grim Reaper"
A-26C	CA	Atwater	CAM	Douglas	Invader	43-5648
A-26C(RA)	CA	Chino	PoF	Douglas	Invader	44-35323
A-26C	CA	Riverside	MFAM	Douglas	Invader	44-35224, "Midnight Endeavors", BC-224
A-26C	CO	Puebl	PWAM	Douglas	Invader	44-35892
A-26C	CT	Winds	NEAM	Douglas	Invader	
A-26C	FL	Miami	WOM	Douglas	Invader	N3941
A-26C(TB)	GA	Warner Robin	MoF	Douglas	Invader	44-35732, BC-732
A-26C(RB)	HI	Oahu	HAFB	Douglas	Invader	44-35596/BC-596
A-26C	KS	Dodge	CityPark	Douglas	Invader	
A-26C(GA)	MI	Mt Clemens	SMAM	Douglas	Invader	43-5884 (43-5986)
A-26C	ND	Grand	GFAFB	Douglas	Invader	
A-26C	OH	Dayto	USAFM	Douglas	Invader	44-35733, "Dream Girl"
A-26C	OH	Dayto	USAFM	Douglas	Invader	44-35439
A-26C	TX	Abile	DLAP	Douglas	Invader	44-35913
A-26C	TX	San Antonio	LAFB	Douglas	Invader	44-35918
A-26C	WA	Seattle	MoF	Douglas	Invader	
A-26C	CA	Fairf	TAFB	Douglas	Invader	
A-36A	OH	Dayto	USAFM	North American	Apache	42-83665
A-37	CO	Denver	69thB	Cessna	Dragonfly	
A-37	FL	Clear	FMAM	Cessna	Dragonfly	
A-37	TX	San Antonio	LAFB	Cessna	Dragonfly	
A-37A	GA	Warner Robin	MoF	Cessna	Dragonfly	67-14525
A-37A	PA	Willow	WGNAS	Cessna	Dragonfly	
A-37A(GY)	TX	Wichi	SAFB	Cessna	Dragonfly	
A-37A(YA)	OH	Dayto	USAFM	Cessna	Dragonfly	62-5951
A-37B(NA)	CA	Rosam	EAFB	Cessna	Dragonfly	
A-37B(OA)	CA	Woodland	Airport	Cessna	Dragonfly	73-1114
A-37B	FL	Mary Esther	HF	Cessna	Dragonfly	70-1293
A-37B	NY	Horseheads	NWM	Cessna	Dragonfly	71-0826
A.E.G.GIV	ON-C	Ottaw	CAM	Allquemeine/Elektrizitat/Gesellschaft		574/18
A.W.650-101	MI	Belleville	YAF	Armstrong-Whitworth	Argosy	6651, N896U, "City of Leamington Spa"
A6M-2B	FL	Pensa	USNAM	Mitsubishi	Zero	5450
A6M2	ND	Fargo	FAM	Mitsubishi	Zero	
A6M2	OH	Dayto	USAFM	Mitsubishi	Zero	51553
A6M2	CA	Camarillo	CAF-SCW	Mitsubishi	Zero	5356, N58245
A6M2	WA	Olympia	OFM	Mitsubishi	Zero	9403
A6M3	CA	Camarillo	CAF-SCW	Mitsubishi	Zero	Sn 58245, N712Z, "E111-142"

Model	State	City	Code	Manufacturer	Type	Notes
A6M3	CA	S.Mon	MoF	Mitsubishi	Zero	N58245
A6M3	ID		T&S	Mitsubishi	Zero	3318 Model 32
A6M3	ID		T&S	Mitsubishi	Zero	3685 Model 22
A6M3	OR	Mc Minnville	TNSAM	Mitsubishi	Zero	3318
A6M3	WA	Eastsound	FHC	Mitsubishi	Zero	3852, N3852
A6M5	CA	Chino	PoFAM	Mitsubishi	Zero	5357, N46770
A6M5	CA	Chino	PoFAM	Mitsubishi	Zero	4400
A6M5	CA	S.Mon	MoF	Mitsubishi	Zero	N58245
A6M5	DC	Washi	NA&SM	Mitsubishi	Zero	4340
A6M5	FL	Miami	WOM	Mitsubishi	Zero	4043
A6M5	WA	Eastsound	FHC	Mitsubishi	Zero	1303, N1303
A6M5	WA	Eastsound	FHC	Mitsubishi	Zero	4400, N652Z
A6M7	CA	San Diego	SDAM	Mitsubishi	Zero	23186
Air Command Autogyro	PA	WChester	AHM	Air Command	Autogyro	
Abernathy Streaker	FL	Polk	FoF	Abernathy	Streaker	
Abrams Explorer	MD	Silve	PEGF	Abrams	Explorer	
Acro Sport P-8 EAA	WI	Oshko	EAAAAM	Acro	Sport	N9PH
Acro Sport P-8 EAA	WI	Oshko	EAAAAM	Acro	Sport	N1AC
Acro Sport S1	WI	Oshko	EAAAAM	Acro	Sport	N15HS
Acro Sport Super	WI	Oshko	EAAAAM	Acro	Super Sport	N76BM
Adams Wilson Hobbycopter	CA	Ramona	CR	Adams Wilson	Hobbycopter	
ADOCK	WA	Vancouver	PAM		Bi-plane	
Addventura	AR	Little Rock	AEC	Arnet Peryra	Ultrlight	
AEC Ace	NY	Garde	CoAM	Aircraft Eng Co	Ace 1	1
Aero Vodochody L-39C	AL	Birmingham	SMoF	Aero	Albatros	931332, N4679B
Aero Commander	TX	Laredo	Airport	Rockwell	Commander	
Aero Commander 500U	IL	Springfield	ACM	Aero	Commander	
Aero Commander 520	KS	Liberal	MAAM	Aero	Commander	
Aero Commander 520	OK	Fredi	AAM	Aero	Commander	
Aero Commander 680	AL	Birmingham	SMoF	Aero	Commander	
Aero Commander 680	LA	Patte	WWMAM	Aero	Commander	
Aero Commander 690B	KS	Liberal	MAAM	Aero	Commander	
Aero Commander 690B	OK	Fredi	AAM	Aero	Commander	
See Also (U-4)(U-9)						
Aero Sport	FL	St. A	EM	Aero	Sport	
Aero Sport Champ	FL	Lakel	SFAF	Aero	Sport Champ	N25130
Aero Sport-3	WA	Seatt	MoF	Aero	Sport	12, N23JF
Aero Star	IL	Springfield	ACM	Aero	Starr	
Aerobat Corp 1-A	TX	San Antonio	TAM	Aerobat		NX17638
Aerocar	MN	Blaine	GWFM	Taylor	Aerocar	
Aerocar	WA	Seatt	MoF	Taylor	Aerocar	1, N100D
Aerocar Model	ID	Athol	NAM	Taylor	Aerocar	
Aerojet Aerobee	OH	Dayton	USAFM	Aerojet	Aerobee Rocket	
Aerojet V-260	WI	Oshko	EAAAAM	Aerojet-General	Aerojet	V-260
Aeromarine 39B	NY	Rhine	ORA	Aeromarine		Navy Two Seater Biplane
Aeromarine AKL-26A	NY	Rhine	ORA	Aeromarine-Klemm		AKL-26A
Aeronaut	KS	Liberal	MAAM	Armstrong	Aeronaut	
Aeronca 7AC	GA	Warner Robin	MoF	Aeronca	Champ	
Aeronca 7AC	IA	Ottumwa	MAAM	Aeronca	Champ	7AC-6740, N3144E
Aeronca 7AC	KS	Liberal	MAAM	Aeronca	Champ	
Aeronca 7AC	NY	Bayport	BA	Aeronca	Champ	
Aeronca 7AC	NY	River	TFAC	Aeronca	Champ	
Aeronca 7AC	OH	Madis	CFR	Aeronca	Champ	
Aeronca 7AC	OH	Wapak	NAA&SM	Aeronca	Champ	
Aeronca 7AC	OK	Fredi	AAM	Aeronca	Champ	
Aeronca 7AC	ON-C	Collingwood	CCAF	Aeronca	Champ	
Aeronca 7AC	WA	Port Townsend	PTAM	Aeronca	Champ	6597, N3011E
Aeronca 7AC	WA	Port Townsend	PTAM	Aeronca	Champ	732, N82106
Aeronca 11AC	AL	Birmingham	SMoF	Aeronca	Chief	
Aeronca 11AC	BC-C	Langley	CMoF	Aeronca	Chief	1261, N9622E, CF-HGN
Aeronca 11AC	IA	Ottumwa	AM	Aeronca	Chief	11AC-956, N9318E
Aeronca 11AC	NY	Bayport	BA	Aeronca	Chief	
Aeronca 65C	HI	Honolulu	PHNB	Aeronca	Super Chief	Airborne During 12/07/41 Attack
Aeronca 65C	IN	LVill	LVA	Aeronca	Super Chief	Aeronca 65C
Aeronca 65C	KS	Liberal	MAAM	Aeronca	Super Chief	Aeronca 65C
Aeronca 65C	MD	College Park	CPAM	Aeronca	Super Chief	
Aeronca 65C	MI	Kalam	KAHM	Aeronca	Super Chief	12231
Aeronca 65C	OK	Fredi	AAM	Aeronca	Super Chief	Aeronca 65C
Aeronca 65CA	IA	Ottumwa	AM	Aeronca	Super Chief	N29427
Aeronca 65LA	IA	Ottumwa	AM	Aeronca	Chief	L-750, N24276
Aeronca 65LB	IL	L-14881, N3449Cul		OCAM	Aeronca	Chief
Aeronca 65TC	HI	Oahu	USSMO	Aeronca	Super Chief	Aeronca 65TC
Aeronca 7DC	NC	Hende	WNCAM	Aeronca	Champ	N4537E
Aeronca C-2	IA	Ottumwa	APM	Aeronca	Robin	301-44
Aeronca C-2	MD	Silve	PEGF	Aeronca	Robin	
Aeronca C-2	ON-C	Ottaw	CAM	Aeronca	Robin	N525
Aeronca C-2	WA	Port Townsend	PTAM	Aeronca	Robin	
Aeronca C-2	WA	Seatt	MoF	Aeronca	Robin	301-23, N30RC
Aeronca C-2N	VA	Sands	VAM	Aeronca	Robin	Sn 151,N11417
Aeronca C-2N	WI	Oshko	EAAAAM	Aeronca	Robin	NC13089
Aeronca C-3	CA	Hayward	VAM	Aeronca	Duplex	N13094
Aeronca C-3	CA	San Diego	SDAM	Aeronca	Duplex	
Aeronca C-3	FL	Kissi	FTWAM	Aeronca	Duplex	
Aeronca C-3	FL	Lakel	SFAF	Aeronca	Duplex	N17449
Aeronca C-3	IA	Ottumwa	APM	Aeronca	Duplex	A-405, NC14098
Aeronca C-3	MN	Blaine	GWFM	Aeronca	Duplex	
Aeronca C-3	NC	Hende	WNCAM	Aeronca	Duplex	NC11923
Aeronca C-3	NY	Bayport	BA	Aeronca	Duplex	
Aeronca C-3	NY	Rhine	ORA	Aeronca	Duplex	
Aeronca C-3	NY	River	RE	Aeronca	Duplex	
Aeronca C-3	PA	Bethel	GAAM	Aeronca	Master	
Aeronca C-3	PA	Readi	MAAM	Aeronca	Master	
Aeronca C-3	PA	Tough	CFCM	Aeronca	Duplex	
Aeronca C-3	VA	Sands	VAM	Aeronca	Duplex	Sn 426, NC14640
Aeronca C-3B	WA	Port Townsend	PTAM	Aeronca	Duplex	A673, NC16529
Aeronca C-3B	WA	Vancouver	PAM	Aeronca	Duplex	Flying Bathtub
Aeronca C-3	WI	Oshko	EAAAAM	Aeronca	Duplex	NC16291
Aeronca C-3 (Fuse)	NS	Halifax	ACAM	Aeronca	Duplex	
Aeronca K	AL	Birmingham	SMoF	Aeronca	Scout	
Aeronca K	IA	Ottumwa	APM	Aeronca	Scout	K-147, NC18872, Model 8135
Aeronca K	KS	Liberal	MAAM	Aeronca	Scout	
Aeronca K	KY	Lexington	AMoK	Aeronca	Scout	K165, NC18896
Aeronca K	OK	Fredi	AAM	Aeronca	Scout	

Aeronca K	PA	Readi	MAAM	Aeronca	Scout	
Aeronca K	SK-C	MJaw	WDM	Aeronca	Scout	
Aeronca K	WI	Oshko	EAAAAM	Aeronca	Scout	NC19732
Aeronca LC	IA	Ottumwa	APM	Aeronca	LC	90 Hp Warner Junior
Aeronca LC	WI	Oshko	EAAAAM	Aeronca	LC	NC17484, 90 Hp Warner Junior
Aeronca Sedan Floats	AL	Birmingham	SmoF	Aeronca	Sedan	On Floats
Aerospatial SA-341G	CA	Ramona	CR	Aerospatial	Gazelle	1408, N505NM
Aerospatial Tampico	FL	Dayto	ERAU	Aerospatial	Tampico	
Aerosport Quail	AZ	Tucso	PAM	Aerosport	Quail	54716941, Q547169410
Aerosport Scamp	FL	Lakeland	SNFAM	Aerosport	Scamp	
Aetna-Timm #4	IA	Greenfield	IAM			
AEW.3	AZ	Tucson	PAM	Fairey-Gannet	Gannet	AS.1-4 1949 Anti-Sub
AEW.3	CT	Winds	NEAM	Fairey-Gannet	Gannet	AS.1-4 1949 Anti-Sub
AF-2S(G-82)	AZ	Mesa	CAF-AW	Grumman	Guardian	N9993Z
AF-2S(G-82)	WA	Seattle	MoF	Grumman	Guardian	
AF-2S(G-82)	AZ	Mesa	CAF-AWM	Grumman	Guardian	
AF-2S(G-82)	AZ	Tucso	PAM	Grumman	Guardian	129233, N9995Z
AF-2S(G-82)	FL	Pensa	USNAM	Grumman	Guardian	123100, SK30, VS-25
AG Tiger	FL	Dayto	ERAU	American-General	Tiger	
Agena Space Vehicle	OH	Dayton	USAFM	Agena	Space Vehicle	
Aichi D3A Val	TX	Frede	NMofPW	Aichi	Val	
Aichi D3A2 Val	CA	Chino	PoFAM	Aichi	Val	
Alien Blimp	OR	Tillamook	TAM		Blimp	
AJ-2	FL	Pensa	USNAM	North American	Savage	130418
Akerman Tailless	MD	Silve	PEGF	Akerman	Tailless	
Albatros D.Va	AZ	Mesa	CFM	Albatros	Scout	
Albatros D.Va	WA	Seattle	MoF	Albatros	Scout	NX36DV
Albatros D.Va Rep	CA	San Diego	SDAM	Albatros	Scout	AA, 106, N3767A
Albatros D.Va	DC	Washi	NA&SM	Albatros	Scout	
Albatros D.Va	NY	Rhine	ORA	Albatros	Scout	
Albatros D.Va	OH	Dayton	USAFM	Albatros	Scout	
Albatros D.VII	AL	Gunte	LGARFM	Albatros	Scout	
Alexander Primary Glider	CA	Santa Martin	WoHAM	Alexander	Primary Glider	Year 1930, NC205Y
Alexander Eagle Rock A-14	CO	Denve	DIA	Alexander	Eagle Rock	NC205Y
Alexander Eagle Rock	CO	Denve	DIA	Alexander	Eagle Rock	469, N4648, Combo Wing
Alliance Argo	MN	Blaine	GWFM	Alliance	Argo	
Alliance Argo	WY	Jackson	GWFM	Alliance	Argo	
Allied Aerospace UAV	CA	Ramona	CR	Allied Aerospace	UAV	
Allison Sport	PA	Bethel	GAAM	Allison	Sport	
AM-1	FL	Pensa	USNAM	Martin	Mauler	122397
AM-1	OR	Tillamook	TAM	Martin	Mauler	N7163M 22275
AM-1	TX	Midla	CAF-Hq	Martin	Mauler	N5586A
American Aerolights	IL	Rantoul	OCAM	AmEagle	American Aerolights	
American Aerolights	MD	Silve	PEGF	AmEagle	American Aerolights	
American Aerolights	PA	Readi	MAAM	AmEagle	American Aerolights430R, "Double Eagle"	
American BAT	TX	Frede	NMofPW		American Bat	
American Eagle 230	AR	Fayetteville	AAM	American	American Eagle	
American Eaglet A-101	AZ	Tucson	PAM	American	American Eagle	Sn 538
American Eaglet	CA	Santa Martin	WoHAM	AmEagle	American Eaglet	
American Eaglet	FL	Lakel	SFAF	AmEagle	American Eaglet	N5AQ
American Eaglet	KS	Wichita	KAM	AmEagle	American Eaglet	8-129
American Eaglet	NY	Rhine	ORA	AmEagle	American Eaglet	
American Eaglet	OK	Oklah	KCASM	AmEagle	American Eaglet	
American Eagle A 1	CA	Chino	YAM	AmEagle	American Eagle	
American Eaglet A 1	CA	San Diego	SDAM	AmEagle	American Eagle	N4289
American Eaglet B-31	IA	Ottumwa	APM	AmEagle	American Eaglet	1111, N17007
AN-2	AZ	Grand	GCNPA	Antonov	Colt	
AN-2	CA	Chino	PoFAM	Antonov	Colt	
AN-2	CA	Riverside	MAFM	Antonov	Colt	ANATDSR-IR-16550, N22AN
AN-2	FL	Titusville	VACM	Antonov	Colt	
AN-2	MN	Blaine	AWAM	Antonov	Colt	
AN-2	MO	Maryland Hts	HARM	Antonov	Colt	
AN-2	NC	Charl	CHAC	Antonov	Colt	
AN-2	NY	Geneseo	1941AG	Antonov	Colt	
AN-2	NC	CPoin	CPMB	Antonov	Colt	
AN-2	ON-C	Hamilton	CWHM	Antonov	Colt	
AN-2	WA	Seattle	MoF	Antonov	Colt	1G17527, N615L
AN-2	WA	Vancouver	PAM	Antonov	Colt	
Anderson Greenwood 14	WI	Oshko	EAAAAM	Anderson-Greenwood		N314AG
Anderson Z	IA	Ottumwa	APM	Anderson		2A, N12041
Antoinette	ME	Owls Head	OHTM	Antoinette		
Anglin Spacewalker II	FL	Lakel	SFAF	Anglin	Spacewalker II	N168CM
Anzani Longester Rep	OR	Eugen	OAM	Anzani	Longester	
Apollo	AR	Little Rock	AEC	North American	Command Module	
Apollo	AZ	Flags	MC	North American	Command Module	
Apollo	CA	Chino	PoFAM	North American	Command Module	
Apollo	CA	San Diego	SDAM	North American	Command Module	
Apollo	FL	Shali	USAFAM	North American	Command Module	
Apollo	GA	Atlan	FSC	North American	Command Module	
Apollo	NY	NYC	ISASM	North American	Command Module	
Apollo	OH	Dayton	USAFM	North American	Command Module	
Apollo	OK	Oklah	KCASM	North American	Command Module	
Apollo	WA	Seatt	MoF	North American	Command Module	
Apollo	WA	Vanco	PAM	North American	Command Module	
Apollo 8	IL	Chica	MoS&I	North American	Command Module	First Moon Orbit
Apollo 8	KY	Louis	MoH&S	North American	Command Module	First Moon Orbit
Apollo 12	VA	Hampt	VA&SC	North American	Command Module	Last Apollo
Apollo 13	KS	Hutch	KC&SC	North American	Command Module	
Apollo 14 BP1102A	CA	Alameda	USSHM	North American	Command Module	Training
Apollo 14 MQF004	CA	Alameda	USSHM	North American	Mobile Quarantine Facility	
Apollo Skylab III	OH	Cleve	NASALRC	North American	Skylab III	
Applebay Zuni II	MD	Silve	PEGF	Applebay	Zuni	
Arado Ar.196A	FL	Pensa	USNAM	Arado	Ar.196A	
Arado Ar.196A	MD	Silve	PEGF	Arado	Ar.196A	
Arado Ar.234B-2	MD	Silve	PEGF	Arado	Blitz(Lightning)	
Argo D-4	VA	Hampt	APM	Argo	Javelin Launcher	4 Stage Launch Vehicle
Arlington Sisu 1A	MD	Silve	PEGF	Arlington	Sisu	
Arrow Sport	CA	San F	SFIA	Arrow	Sport	
Arrow Sport	MD	Silve	PEGF	Arrow	Sport	
Arrow Sport	MN	Blaine	GWFM	Arrow	Sport	
Arrow Sport	ND	Minot	DTAM	Arrow	Sport	
Arrow Sport F	CA	Oakla	OWAM	Arrow	Sport	
Arrow Sport F	IA	Ottumwa	APM	Arrow	Sport	18, N18000

Type	State	City	Code	Manufacturer	Model	Notes
Arrow Monoplane	ND	Minot	DTAM	Arrow	Monoplane	
AS.10 MKII	AB-C	Calga	AMoC	Airspeed	Oxford	Pilot,Radio,Navigator Trainer
AS.65	ON-C	Ottaw	CAM	Airspeed	Consul	
ASG-21	CA	San Diego	SDAM	Albatross	Sails HG	Hang Glider 1976
ASV-3	OH	Dayton	USAFM	ASSET		Lifting Body
AT-6	AB-C	Calgary	ASMoC	North American	Harvard	
AT-6 (AT-16)	AB-C	Nanton	NLSAM	North American	Harvard	
AT-6	AB-C	Claresholm	CFB	North American	Harvard	
AT-6	AB-C	Edmonton	AAM	North American	Harvard	
AT-6	AZ	Mesa	CAFM	North American	Texan	
AT-6	AZ	Phoenix	DVA	North American	Texan	
AT-6	AZ	PBluf	RWCAF	North American	Texan	
AT-6	AZ	Tempe	AHSM	North American	Texan	
AT-6	CA	Atwater	CAM	North American	Texan	Side # TA-684
AT-6	CA	Shafter	MFAM	North American	Texan	"Miss T-N-T"
AT-6	CA	Shafter	MFAM	North American	Texan	"Warlock"
AT-6	CO	Denve	JWDAS	North American	Texan	
AT-6	CT	Winds	NEAM	North American	Texan	
AT-6	FL	Titusville	VACM	North American	Texan	
AT-6	GA	Atlanta	ASG	North American	Texan	
AT-6	GA	Douglas	LF	North American	Texan	
AT-6	GA	Marietta	NASA	North American	Texan	
AT-6	IL	Aurora	RH	North American	Texan	
AT-6	IL	Cahok	PCUSL	North American	Texan	
AT-6	IN	Ft. W	FWAS	North American	Texan	
AT-6	KS	New Century	CAF-HoAW	North American	Texan	49-3349
AT-6	KY	Louis	BF	North American	Texan	
AT-6	MA	Stow	BCF	North American	Texan	
AT-6	MB-C	Brand	CATPM	North American	Harvard	2557
AT-6	MB-C	Winni	WCAM	North American	Harvard	20301
AT-6	MB-C	Winni	WCAM	North American	Harvard	
AT-6	MB-C	Winni	WCAM	North American	Harvard	
AT-6	MD	Hager	HRegAirP	North American	Texan	
AT-6	MI	Kalam	KAHM	North American	Texan	49-3509, 112493
AT-6	MN	Minne	JJ	North American	Texan	
AT-6	MO	SChar	CAF-MW	North American	Texan	N9627C
AT-6	MO	SLoui	SLAM	North American	Texan	
AT-6	MO	StCha	CAFMW	North American	Texan	
AT-6	ND	Fargo	FAM	North American	Texan	
AT-6	ND	Fargo	WEAM	North American	Texan	
AT-6	NM	STere	WEAM	North American	Texan	
AT-6	NY	Farmingdale	AAM	North American	Texan	
AT-6	ON-C	Dunnville	CL	North American	Harvard	2766
AT-6	ON-C	Kingtons	CFBK	North American	Harvard	AJ-693
AT-6	ON-C	Smith Falls	WCAM	North American	Harvard	Xx443
AT-6	ON-C	Tillsonburg	CHAA	North American	Harvard	HWX
AT-6	ON-C	Tillsonburg	CHAA	North American	Harvard	MTX
AT-6	ON-C	Tillsonburg	CHAA	North American	Harvard	RWN
AT-6	ON-C	Tillsonburg	CHAA	North American	Harvard	WPK
AT-6	ON-C	Tillsonburg	CHAA	North American	Harvard	MKA
AT-6	ON-C	Tillsonburg	CHAA	North American	Harvard	NDB
AT-6	OR	Tillamook	TAM	North American	Texan	
AT-6	TX	Breck	BAM	North American	Texan	
AT-6	TX	C Christi	USS Lexi	North American	Texan	
AT-6	TX	Addison	CFM	North American	Texan	
AT-6	TX	D Rio	LAFB	North American	Texan	
AT-6	TX	FtWorth	VFM	North American	Texan	
AT-6	TX	Galve	LSFM	North American	Texan	77-4601, N78RN
AT-6	TX	Houst	CAF-GCW	North American	Texan	N4447
AT-6	TX	Houst	CAF-GCW	North American	Texan	N15797
AT-6	TX	Houst	CAF-GCW	North American	Texan	N11171
AT-6	TX	Houst	CAF-GCW	North American	Texan	N15799
AT-6	TX	Houst	CAF-GCW	North American	Texan	N9097
AT-6	TX	Houst	CAF-GCW	North American	Texan	N3725G
AT-6	TX	Houst	CAF-WHS	North American	Texan	"Ace In The Hole", N97902
AT-6	TX	Paris	FTAM	North American	Texan	
AT-6	TX	SMarc	CAF-WF	North American	Texan	N2047
AT-6	UT	Ogden	HAFBM	North American	Texan	
AT-6	WA	Olympia	OFM	North American	Texan	Side # 6N6
AT-6	WA	Vanco	PAM	North American	Texan	"Scrap Iron IV", 486
AT-6	WI	Bosco	BA	North American	Texan	
AT-6	WV	Bride	BA	North American	Texan	
AT-6 (BC-1A)	MN	Minne	MAGM	North American	Texan	40-2122, 798
AT-6 (P-64)	TX	Galve	LSFM	North American	Texan	
AT-6 (SNJ)	AR	Fayetteville	AAM	North American	Texan	
AT-6 (SNJ)	VA	Suffolk	FF	North American	Texan	
AT-6 (SNJ)	AZ	PBluf	RWCAF	North American	Oxford	
AT-6 (SNJ)	CA	Oakland	CAF-GGW	North American	Harvard	51697
AT-6 (SNJ)	ID	Driggs	TAC	North American	Texan	Side # 69
AT-6 (SNJ)	MO	Maryland Hts	HARM	North American	Texan	
AT-6 (SNJ)	PA	Tough	CFCM	North American	Texan	
AT-6 (SNJ)	TX	C Christi	CCMOS&H	North American	Texan	
AT-6 (SNJ)	TX	C Christi	USS Lexi	North American	Texan	
AT-6 (SNJ)	WA	Seattle	MoF	North American	Texan	
AT-6 (SNJ-3)	FL	Kissi	FTWAM	North American	Texan	
AT-6 (SNJ-4)	CA	Riversideside	MFAM	North American	Texan	51360, N6411
AT-6 (SNJ-4)	FL	Kissi	FTWAM	North American	Texan	
AT-6 (SNJ-4)	FL	St Augustine	NATG	North American	Texan	N55A
AT-6 (SNJ-4)	IN	Elkhart	NIAM	North American	Texan	
AT-6 (SNJ-4)	NM	Hobbs	CAF-RB	North American	Texan	N7024C
AT-6 (SNJ-4)	OH	Elyri	CAF-CW	North American	Texan	N224X
AT-6 (SNJ-4)	OR	Mc Minnville	EAEC	North American	Texan	88-13466, N33CC
AT-6 (SNJ-4)	VA	Suffolk	FF	North American	Texan	
AT-6 (SNJ-5)	AZ	Mesa	CAF-AW	North American	Texan	N3246G
AT-6 (SNJ-5)	CA	Oklan	CAF-GGS	North American	Texan	N3195G
AT-6 (SNJ-5)	CA	Camarillo	CAF-SCW	North American	Texan	N89014, Side Number 290
AT-6 (SNJ-5)	CA	Chino	PoFAM	North American	Texan	39
AT-6 (SNJ-5)	CA	Chino	YAM	North American	Texan	
AT-6 (SNJ-5)	CA	Miramar	FLAM	North American	Texan	WD, VMT-2
AT-6 (SNJ-5)	CA	S. Mon	MoF	North American	Texan	90952, N3204G, "Big Thunder"
AT-6 (SNJ-5)	FL	St Augustine	NATG	North American	Texan	N1617F
AT-6 (SNJ-5)	MI	Kalamazoo	KAHM	North American	Texan	91005
AT-6 (SNJ-5)	NC	Hendersonville	WNCAM	North American	Texan	

AT- 6 (SNJ-5)	TX	C Christi	USS Lexi	North American	Texan	
AT- 6 (SNJ-5)	TX	Midla	CAFFM	North American	Texan	
AT- 6 (SNJ-5)	VA	Quant	MCAGM	North American	Texan	84962
AT- 6 (SNJ-5B)	IN	Indianapolis	AMHF	North American	Texan	43963
AT- 6 (SNJ-5B)	MD	Ft Meade	QM	North American	Texan	
AT- 6G(SNJ-6)	FL	Kissi	FTWAM	North American	Texan	
AT- 6G(SNJ-6)	FL	Miami	WOM	North American	Texan	
AT- 6 (SNJ-7)	CA	San Diego	SDACM	North American	Texan	91091
AT- 6 Mk IV	KS	Topek	CAM	North American	Harvard	N-294CH, 29, CCF-4-85
AT- 6A(SNJ-4A)	MD	Silve	PEGF	North American	Texan	
AT- 6A	CO	Auror	BANGB	North American	Texan	
AT- 6A	MN	Eden Prairie	WotN	North American	Texan	N77TX, #42
AT- 6B	AZ	Tucso	PAM	North American	Texan	41-17246
AT- 6B-NT	IL	Ranto	OCAM	North American	Texan	41-17372
AT- 6B	TX	Midla	CAFFM	North American	Texan	
AT- 6B(SNJ-4B)	PA	Readi	MAAM	North American	Texan	88-12281, N24554
AT- 6C	AB-C	Wetas	RM	North American	Harvard Mk.II	
AT- 6C	FL	Miami	WOM	North American	Harvard Mk.II	
AT- 6C	NY	Geneseo	1941AG	North American	Harvard Mk.II	
AT- 6C	NS-C	Shear	CFBS	North American	Harvard Mk.II	
AT- 6C	AB-C	Nanton	NLSAM	North American	Harvard Mk.II	
AT- 6C	ON-C	Ottaw	CAM	North American	Harvard Mk.II	66-2265
AT- 6C	TX	Midla	NAM	North American	Texan	
AT- 6C(SNJ-5C)	FL	Pensa	USNAM	North American	Texan	51849
AT- 6C(SNJ-5C)	NC	Charl	CHAC	North American	Texan	
AT- 6C(SNJ-5C)	NC	CPoin	CPMB	North American	Texan	
AT- 6D	AK	Ancho	KANGB	North American	Texan	
AT- 6D	DE	Dover	DAFB	North American	Texan	41-33070, Side U238,
AT- 6D/G	FL	St Augustine	NATG	North American	Texan	N1364N
AT- 6D	FL	Polk	FoF	North American	Texan	
AT- 6D	IN	Bippu	PAC	North American	Texan	
AT- 6D-NT	MI	Belleville	YAF	North American	Texan	42-85377, N555Q
AT- 6D	MI	Detro	WR	North American	Texan	
AT- 6D	NY	eads	NWM	North American	Texan	41-16667
AT- 6D	NY	longl	TC	North American	Texan	
AT- 6D	OH	Batavia	TSWM	North American	Texan	"Tweety"
AT- 6D(SNJ-5)	TN	Sevierville	TMoA	North American	Texan	49-2977, N29963 Flyable
AT- 6D	TX	San A	LAFB	North American	Texan	
AT- 6D	TX	San A	RAFB	North American	Texan	
AT- 6D	WI	Oshko	EAAAAM	North American	Texan	42-44629
AT- 6D(T-6)	OH	Dayto	USAFM	North American	Texan	42-84216
AT- 6D-NT	MI	Belleville	YAF	North American	Texan	42-84678, N7095C, 26, "Turtle Bay"
AT- 6D-NT	MI	Belleville	YAF	North American	Texan	44-81346, N6637C
AT- 6F	AB-C	Calga	NAM	North American	Harvard Mk.IV	
AT- 6F Mk IIB	BC-C	Langley	CMoF	North American	Harvard Mk.IV	07-144, RCAF 3275, YRI
AT- 6F	NY	Ghent	POMAM	North American	Harvard Mk.IV	
AT- 6F	ID	Zellw	BWA	North American	Texan	
AT- 6F	OK	Fredi	AAM	North American	Texan	
AT- 6F	MN	StPau	CAF-SMW	North American	Harvard Mk IV	N13595
AT- 6F	ON-C	Hamilton	CWH	North American	Harvard Mk.IV	20431, CF-UZW
AT- 6F	ON-C	Hamilton	CWH	North American	Harvard Mk.IV	3372
AT- 6F	ON-C	Hamilton	CWH	North American	Harvard Mk.IV	20213, RAF, CF-UUU
AT- 6F	ON-C	Ottaw	CAM	North American	Harvard Mk.IV	20387
AT- 6F	ON-C	Ottaw	CAM	North American	Harvard Mk.II	81-4107
AT- 6F	SK-C	MJaw	WDM	North American	Harvard Mk.IV	20456
AT- 6F	NS-C	Halifax	ACAM	North American	Harvard Mk.VI	
AT- 6F	TX	Galve	LSFM	North American	Texan	20247 NX 1811B
AT- 6F	TX	Midla	CAFFM	North American	Texan	
AT- 6F	TX	San Antonio	TAM	North American	Texan	SN112501, N9806C
AT- 6F(T-6)	TX	Abile	DLAP	North American	Texan	44-81819
AT- 6G	AL	Birmingham	SMoF	North American	Texan	
AT- 6G	AR	Fayet	AAM	North American	Texan	N6FD
AT- 6G	AZ	Grand Canyon	PoFGCVA	North American	Texan	
AT- 6G	AZ	Marana	SAW	North American	Texan	
AT- 6G	CA	Sacra	McCelAFB	North American	Texan	51-5124
AT- 6G (SNJ-5)	FL	Kissi	FTWAM	North American	Texan	
AT- 6G	FL	St Augustine	NATG	North American	Texan	N49NA
AT- 6G (SNJ-6)	FL	St Augustine	NATG	North American	Texan	N1044C
AT- 6G	GA	Warner Robin	MoF	North American	Texan	
AT- 6G	IL	Danville	MAM	North American	Texan	
AT- 6G	IN	Hunti	WoF	North American	Texan	53- 4568, N153NA, 13, TA-568, "Lackland"
AT- 6G	IN	Valparaiso	IAM	North American	Texan	51-14726
AT- 6G	NC	Asheboro	PFAC	North American	Texan	
AT- 6G	NJ	Trent	MGAFB	North American	Texan	
AT- 6G	OH	Newbu	WASAC	North American	Texan	
AT- 6G	ON-C	Hamilton	CWH	North American	Harvard	
AT- 6G(SNJ-5)	MI	Kalam	KAHM	North American	Texan	91005, N333SU, 1
AT- 6G(T-6)	AL	Birmi	Southe	North American	Texan	TA-963
AT- 6G (SNJ)	CA	Palm Sprg	PSAM	North American	Harvard	49-3402, N85JR
AT- 6G(T-6)	GA	Warner Robin	MoF	North American	Texan	49-3217, TA 217
AT- 6G(T-6)	LA	Reser	AMHFM	North American	Texan	
AT- 6G(T-6)	MI	Ypsil	YAF	North American	Texan	
AT- 6G(T-6)	OH	Dayto	USAFM	North American	Texan	49-3368
AT- 6G(T-6)	OH	Dayto	USAFM	North American	Texan	50-1279
AT- 6G(T-6)	TX	Gilmer	PotP	North American	Texan	
AT- 6G(T-6)	VA	Manassas	CAFNCS	North American	Texan	
AT- 6H	WA	Olympia	MAHSM	North American	Texan	Side # 25, Tail ZE
AT- 9	OH	Dayto	USAFM	Curtiss-Wright	Fledgling Jeep	41-12150
AT- 9A	AZ	Tucso	PAM	Curtiss-Wright	Fledgling Jeep	42-56882
AT- 10	OH	Dayto	USAFM	Beech		42-35143
AT- 10	OH	Dayto	USAFM	Beech		42-35180
AT-11(Beech D18S)	AZ	Tucso	PAM	Beech	Kansan	41-9577, N6953C
AT-11(Beech D18S)	CA	Fairf	TAFB	Beech	Kansan	
AT-11(Beech D18S)	CA	Paso Robles	EWM	Beech	Kansan	
AT-11(Beech D18S)	CA	Sacra	SWAM	Beech	Kansan	
AT-11(Beech D18S)	CA	Santa Martin	WoHAM	Beech	Kansan	
AT-11(Beech D18S)	CO	Denve	JWDAS	Beech	Kansan	9639, 619
AT-11(Beech D18S)	FL	Clear	FMAM	Beech	Kansan	
AT-11(Beech D18S)	FL	Lakeland	SNF	Beech	Kansan	
AT-11(Beech D18S)	FL	Polk	FoF	Beech	Kansan	
AT-11(Beech D18S)	GA	Warner Robin	MoF	Beech	Kansan	41-27391
AT-11(Beech D18S)	IL	Springfield	ACM	Beech	Kansan	
AT-11(Beech D18S)	IN	Auburn	HW	Beech	Kansan	

AT-11-BH(Beech D18S)	MI	Belleville	YAF	Beech	Kansan	43-10404, N7340C
AT-11(Beech D18S)	MI	GRapi	CAF-WMW	Beech	Kansan	N320A
AT-11(Beech D18S)	OH	Dayto	USAFM	Beech	Kansan	41-27561
AT-11(Beech D18S)	OH	Newbu	WASAC	Beech	Kansan	41-27332
AT-11(Beech D18S)	TX	Big Springs	H25	Beech	Kansan	
AT-11(Beech D18S)	TX	Galve	LSFM	Beech	Kansan	42-37240, N81Y
AT-11(Beech D18S)	WI	Janes	YAFS	Beech	Kansan	
AT-12A/2PA	CA	Chino	PoFAM	Sikorsky	Guardian	
AT-19	AK	Ancho	AAHM	Stinson	Gullwing	
AT-19-VW(V-77)	MI	Belleville	YAM	Stinson	Reliant	43-44165, N15JH
AT-19	NC	Morga	CWCAF	Stinson	Gullwing	
AT-19	NC	S.Pin	CAF-CW	Stinson	Gullwing	1335, V77-333, N60634
AT-19	NM	STere	WEAM	Stinson	Gullwing	
AT-19	NV	Las Vegas	CAFNW	Stinson	Gullwing	
AT-19	OK	Fredi	AAM	Stinson	Gullwing	
AT-19	PA	Beave	AHM	Stinson	Gullwing	
AT-19	TX	Slaton	TAM	Stinson	Gullwing	477
AT-19	TX	Midland	AAPM	Stinson	Gullwing	N67227
AT-19(V-77)	AK	Fairb	APAM	Stinson	Reliant	"Peter Pan", NC60924
AT-19(V-77)	CA	S.Mon	MoF	Stinson	Reliant	
AT-19(V-77)	TX	Lancaster	CAF-DFW	Stinson	Reliant	
AT-301	TX	Rio Grande V	TAM	Air Tractor	Air Tractor	SN301-0051, N43925
AT-301	TX	Rio Grande V	TAM	Air Tractor	Air Tractor	SN301-0053, N43935
AT-301	TX	Rio Grande V	TAM	Air Tractor	Air Tractor	SN301-0062, N44026
Atlas Mercury	NY	Coron	NYHoS	Atlas	Mercury	
Auster	AB-C	Wetas	RM	Auster		
Auster AOP Mk6	BC-C	Langley	CMoF	Auster		16685, N2863
Auster AOP Mk6	ON-C	Trenton	RCAFMM	Auster		VF-582, C-FLWK
Auster AOP.9 Mk.IX	FL	Lakel	SFAF	Auster		N408XN
Auster MK.V1-J	PA	Readi	MAAM	Auster		
Auster	ON-C	Hamilton	CWH	Auster		16652
Auster Mk.VI	ON-C	Ottaw	CAM	Auster		16652
AV-2	TX	Amari	EFA&SM		Balloon Launch	
AV-8	AZ	Yuma	YUSMAB	McDonnell	Harrier	
AV-8	NC	Havel	CPMCAS	McDonnell	Harrier	
AV-8	TX	Big Springs	H25	McDonnell	Harrier	
AV-8A	CA	Ridgecrest	CLNWC	McDonnell	Harrier	
AV-8A	ONT-C	Ottawa	CAM	McDonnell	Harrier	
AV-8B	AL	Huntsville	AC	McDonnell-Douglas	Harrier	
AV-8B	IL	Cahokia	GSLA&SM	McDonnell-Douglas	Harrier	
AV-8B	MD	Lexington	PRNAM	McDonnell-Douglas	Harrier	161396, Side # 623, SD Tail
AV-8C	AZ	Tucso	PAM	McDonnell-Douglas	Harrier	159241
AV-8C	CA	Oakla	OWAM	McDonnell-Douglas	Harrier	
AV-8C	FL	Pensa	USNAM	McDonnell-Douglas	Harrier	158975, WF
AV-8C	NY	NYC	ISASM	McDonnell-Douglas	Harrier	
Avian Falcon II	AZ	Tucson	PAM	Avian	Falcon II	Man Sn 12, N4369Z, N3AV
Aviat A-1	ID	Driggs	TAC	Aviat	Huskey	
Aviatik D.II	AZ	Mesa	CFM	Aviatik	Berg Scout	101,40
Aviatik D.II	WA	Seattle	MoF	Aviatik	Berg Scout	101,40
Avid Flyer	MI	Kalamazoo	KAHM	Wings An Things	Avid Flyer	
Avid Flyer	OK	Fredi	AAM	Leak	Avid Flyer	
Avid Flyer	WI	Oshko	EAAAAM	Wings An Things	Avid Flyer	N4636J
Avitor Hermes, Jr.	CA	SCarl	HAM	Avitor	Hermes Jr.	
Avro 504 (3 ea)	ON-C	Ottaw	CAM	Avro	Gosport	D-8971
Avro 504J/K	FL	Polk	FoF	Avro	Gosport	
Avro 504K	MB-C	Winni	WCAM	Avro	Gosport	
Avro 504K	NY	Rhine	ORA	Avro	Gosport	
Avro 504K	OH	Dayton	USAFM	Avro	Gosport	
Avro 504K Replica	MB-C	Winni	WCAM	Avro	Gosport	
Avro 581	AB-C	Wetas	RM	Avro	Avian	
Avro 581	MN	Blaine	GWFM	Avro	Avian	
Avro 595	CA	Santa Martin	WoHAM	Avro	Avian	Cirrus Engine
Avro 616 Mk.IV M	ON-C	Ottaw	CAM	Avro	Avian	
Avro 652 (See also: AT-20; C.18; C.19; T-20; T-21; T-22)						
Avro 652	AB-C	Nanton	NLSAM	Avro	Anson	
Avro 652	SK-C	MJaw	WDM	Avro	Anson	
Avro 652	MB-C	Brandon	CATPM	Avro	Anson	
Avro 652 Mk.I	MB-C	Winni	WCAM	Avro	Anson	
Avro 652 Mk.II	AB-C	Calga	AMoC	Avro	Anson	
Avro 652 Mk.II	AB-C	Edmonton	AAM	Avro	Anson	
Avro 652 Mk.II	AB-C	Wetas	RM	Avro	Anson	
Avro 652 Mk.II	BC-C	Langley	CMoF	Avro	Anson	7139
Avro 652 Mk.II	MB-C	Winni	WCAM	Avro	Anson	
Avro 652 Mk.II	NS-C	Greenwood	GMAM	Avro	Anson	
Avro 652 Mk.V	BC-C	Langley	CMoF	Avro	Anson	12032
Avro 652 Mk.V	MB-C	Winni	WCAM	Avro	Anson	12518
Avro 652 Mk.V	ON-C	Ottaw	CAM	Avro	Anson	
Avro 652 Mk.VI	ON-C	Hamilton	CWH	Avro	Anson	
Avro 652A Mk.VI	TX	San Antonio	TAM	Avro	Anson	SN266324
Avro 683 Mk.X	AB-C	Calga	AMoC	Avro	Lancaster	FM136, BX
Avro 683 Mk.X	AB-C	Nanto	TBGLTD	Avro	Lancaster	FM159
Avro 683 Mk.X	AB-C	Nanto	NLS	Avro	Lancaster	
Avro 683 Mk.X	NB-C	Edmunston	EA	Avro	Lancaster	KB882
Avro 683 Mk.X	NS-C	Greenwood	GMAM	Avro	Lancaster	KB829
Avro 683 Mk.X	ON-C	Hamilton	CWH	Avro	Lancaster	BX
Avro 683 Mk.X	ON-C	Ottaw	CAM	Avro	Lancaster	BX
Avro 683 Mk.X	ON-C	Toronto	TAM	Avro	Lancaster	
Avro 683 Mk.X	ON-C	Trenton	JP	Avro	Lancaster	
Avro 683 Mk.X	ON-C	Windsor		Avro	Lancaster	FM212
B-1	CA	Chino	YAM	Mahoney-Ryan		141, NC6956
B-1	WA	Seatt	SHSM	Boeing	Flying Boat	I-13, M-92, Model 6, "U.S. Mail"
B-1A	CO	Aurora	WOTR	Boeing	Stealth	
B-1A	NE	Ashland	SACM	Rockwell	Lancer	76-174
B-1B	OH	Dayto	USAFM	Rockwell	Lancer	84-0051
B-1B	SD	Rapid City	SDA&SM	Rockwell	Lancer	83-0067
B-2	PA	WChes	AHM	Brantly-Hynes	Model 305	
B-2	OH	Dayton	USAFM		Spirit	
B-3	OH	Dayton	USAFM	Northrop	Bomber	
B-5	CA	San Diego	SDAM	Ryan	Brougham	NC9236
B-10	AK	Fairb	APAM	Mitchell	Wing	
B-10	AZ	Tucson	PAM	Mitchell	Wing	Sn 285, N4232A
B-10	NM	Moriarty	SSM	Mitchell	Wing	
B-10	OH	Dayto	USAFM	Martin	Bomber	

Type	State	City	Code	Manufacturer	Name	Details
B-17	CO	Greel	SA	Boeing	Flying Fortress	
B-17 Ball Turret	FL	Lakeland	SNF	Boeing	Flying Fortress	
B-17	FL	Polk City	FoF	Boeing	Flying Fortress	44-83525, Suzy Q", Storage
B-17	WA	Arlington	GPAM	Boeing	Flying Fortress	
B-17D	MD	Silve	PEGF	Boeing	Flying Fortress	40-3097, "Swoose"
B-17E	OH	Cincinatti	BR	Boeing	Flying Fortress	41-9032, 2504, "My Gal Sal"
B-17E	IL	Marengo	MK	Boeing	Flying Fortress	41-2595, 2406, "Desert Rat"
B-17E	WA	Eastsound	FHC	Boeing	Flying Fortress	41-9210, N8WJ, 2682
B-17F	IA	Offutt	OAPB	Boeing	Flying Fortress	42-30230, "Homesick Angel", Blk H/W Sq/Yel L
B-17F	TN	Memph	MBMA	Boeing	Flying Fortress	41-24485, 3170, "Memphis Belle"
B-17F	WA	Seatt	MoF	Boeing	Flying Fortress	42-29782, N17W , 4896, "Boeing Bee"
B-17G	AZ	Mesa	CAF-AW	Boeing	Flying Fortress	44-83514, N9323Z, U, 32155, "Sentimental Journey"
B-17G(PB-1G)	AZ	Tusco	390thMM	Boeing	Flying Fortress	44-85828, N9323R ,JDIH "I'll Be Around"
B-17G	CA	Atwater	CAM	Boeing	Flying Fortress	43-38635, N3702G, A-N, 9613, "Virgin's Delight",
B-17G	CA	Chino	PoFAM	Boeing	Flying Fortress	44-83684, N3713G, 32325, "Picadilly Lilly"
B-17G-105VE	CA	Palm Sprg	PoF	Boeing	Flying Fortress	44-85778, N3509G, 8687, "Miss Angela"
B-17G	CA	Riverside	MFAM	Boeing	Flying Fortress	44-6393, "Starduster II", "Return to Glory"
B-17G	CA	Tular	VMVETS56	Boeing	Flying Fortress	44-85738, K,8647, "Reston's Pride"
B-17G	DC	Dulle	AP	Boeing	Flying Fortress	44-83814, NASM/Storage
B-17G	DE	Dover	DAFB	Boeing	Flying Fortress	44-83624, 381BG, 32265, "Sleepy Time Gal"
B-17G	GA	Douglas	LF	Boeing	Flying Fortress	44-83790
B-17G	GA	Douglas	LF	Boeing	Flying Fortress	44-85734, N5111N, 8643, "Liberty Belle"
B-17G	FL	Polk	FoF	Boeing	Flying Fortress	44-83542, N9324Z, 32183, "Picadilly Princess"
B-17G	FL	Shali	USAFAM	Boeing	Flying Fortress	44-83863, 32504, "Gremlins Hideout"
B-17G	IN	Peru	GAFB	Boeing	Flying Fortress	44-83690,XK-D,305BG, "Miss Liberty Bell"
B-17G	LA	Bossi	BAFB	Boeing	Flying Fortress	44-83884, 32525 / 333284, "Yankee Doodle II",
B-17G	MA	Stow	BCF	Boeing	Flying Fortress	44-83575, N93012, OR-R, Resembles Scraped, "909"
B-17G-110-VE	MI	Belleville	YAF	Boeing	Flying Fortress	44-85829, N3193G, "Yankee Lady", Side GD, Tail L Y
B-17G	NE	Ashland	SACM	Boeing	Flying Fortress	44-83559, EP-B, 32200 / 23474, "King Bee"
B-17G	NY	Farmingdale	AAM	Boeing	Flying Fortress	44-83563, N95637, "Fuddy Duddy"
B-17G-35-BO	OH	Dayto	USAFM	Boeing	Flying Fortress	42-32076, 7190, 91, "Shoo Shoo Baby"
B-17G	OR	Milwa	BG	Boeing	Flying Fortress	44-85790, "Lacey Lady"
B-17G	OR	McMinnville	EAEC	Boeing	Flying Fortress	44-83785, N207EV , K32426, "Shady Lady"
B-17G(DB)	TX	Abile	DLAP	Boeing	Flying Fortress	44-85599, 8508, 238133
B-17G	TX	FWort	BCVintag	Boeing	Flying Fortress	44- 8543, N3701G, 7943, 44- 8543A, "Chuckie",
B-17G	TX	Galve	LSFM	Boeing	Flying Fortress	44-85718, N900RW, BN-U, "Thunder Bird"
B-17G	TX	Houst	CAF-GCW	Boeing	Flying Fortress	44-83872, N7227C, 32513, "Texas Raiders"
B-17G	TX	San A	LAFB	Boeing	Flying Fortress	44-83512, HT, 32153, "Heavens Above"
B-17G	UT	Ogden	HAFBM	Boeing	Flying Fortress	44-83663, 32304, "Short Bier",
B-17G-VE	WI	Oshko	EAAAAM	Boeing	Flying Fortress	44-85740, N5017N, FU-D, "Aluminum Overcast"
B-17 Parts	CO	Denve	JWDAS	Boeing	Flying Fortress	
B-17G (Parts)	CA	Wells	Ocotillo	Boeing	Flying Fortress	44-83722, 32363
B-17G (Parts)	FL	Kissi	FTWAM	Boeing	Flying Fortress	44-85813
B-18A	CA	Atwater	CAM	Douglas	Bolo	37-029, Tail # BI
B-18A	CO	Aurora	WOTR	Douglas	Bolo	
B-18A	OH	Dayto	USAFM	Douglas	Bolo	37-469
B-18A	WA	Tacoma	MAFB	Douglas	Bolo	37-505, N18AC
B-18B	AZ	Tucso	PAM	Douglas	Bolo	38-593, N66267
B-23	CA	Atwater	CAM	Douglas	Dragon	39-45, Tail # 112MD
B-23	OH	Dayto	USAFM	Douglas	Dragon	39-37
B-23	FL	Polk City	FoF	Douglas	Dragon	
B-23	WA	Tacoma	MAFB	Douglas	Dragon	1089R
B-23(UC-67)	AZ	Tucso	PAM	Douglas	Dragon	39-51, N534J
B-24 *One Tail version See PB4Y*						
B-24M-5-CO	CA	Atwater	CAM	Consolidated	Liberator	44-41916, RE,Tail B, "Shady Lady"
B-24(LB-30)	TX	Midla	CAF-B29	Consolidated	Liberator	AM927, N24927, "Diamond Lil"
B-24J Nose	MD	Ft Meade	QM	Consolidated	Liberator	44-40332
B-24L Fuse	MD	Ft Meade	QM	Consolidated	Liberator	44-50022
B-24M Replica	TX	San Antonio	LAFB	Consolidated	Liberator	
B-24 Cockpit	GA	Savan	MEHM	Consolidated	Liberator	
B-24 Nose	GA	Pooler	M8thAFHM	Consolidated	Liberator	42-40557
B-24 Nose	VA	Hampt	VA&SC	Consolidated	Liberator	"Old Bessie"
B-24 Nose Turret	MI	Lansi	MHM	Consolidated	Liberator	
B-24D-160-CO	OH	Dayto	USAFM	Consolidated	Liberator	42-72843, "Strawberry Bitch"
B-24D	UT	Ogden	HAFB	Consolidated	Liberator	40-2367, N58246, Project
B-24J-90-CF	AZ	Tucso	PAM	Consolidated	Liberator	44-44175, N7866, KH304,"Bungay Buckaroo"
B-24J-95-CF	FL	Polk City	FoF	Consolidated	Liberator	44-44272, N94459, 250551,"Joe"
B-24J-25-FO	LA	Bossi	BAFB	Consolidated	Liberator	44-48781, "Laden Maiden"
B-24J	MA	Stow	BCF	Consolidated	Liberator	44-44052, N224J, JHK191, "All American"
B-24L-20-FO	ON-C	Ottaw	CAM	Consolidated	Liberator	44-50154, 11130
B-25	AB-C	Westaskiwin	RM	North American	Mitchell	44-86726
B-25	AL	Troy	TMA	North American	Mitchell	
B-25	AZ	Mesa	CAF-AW	North American	Mitchell	43-35972N9552Z
B-25	CA	Fierbaugh	HEM	North American	Mitchell	44-30748, "Heavenly Body"
B-25	CA	Marysville	BAFB	North American	Mitchell	43-28222
B-25	CA	Rialt	KA	North American	Mitchell	44-29199, N9117Z, "In The Mood"
B-25	CA	San Diego	MCAS	North American	Mitchell	44-86727
B-25	FL	Pensacola	NMoNA	North American	Mitchell	44-29035
B-25	FL	Polk City	FoF	North American	Mitchell	43-28059, "Apache Princess"
B-25	OH	Dayton	USAFM	North American	Mitchell	43- 3374
B-25				North American	Mitchell	44-86725, N25NA
B-25	MO	SChar	CAF-MW	North American	Mitchell	44-31385, N3481G, "Show Me"
B-25	MT	Great Falls	MAFB	North American	Mitchell	44-30493
B-25	MB-C	Brandon	CATPM	North American	Mitchell	44-86724
B-25	MB-C	Winnipeg	AFHM	North American	Mitchell	5203
B-25	NC	Charl	CHAC	North American	Mitchell	
B-25	NB	Ashland	SASM	North American	Mitchell	43-30772
B-25	ND	Fargo	FAM	North American	Mitchell	
B-25	ND	Wahpe	TSA	North American	Mitchell	
B-25	OH	N Canton	MAM	North American	Mitchell	44-30324
B-25	ND	Fargo	FAM	North American	Mitchell	44-30010, N9641C
B-25	OK	Tulsa	RA	North American	Mitchell	"Martha Jean"
B-25	ON-C	Ottaw	CAM	North American	Mitchell	44-86699
B-25	OR	Tillamook	TAM	North American	Mitchell	44-30456, N43BA, "Silver Lady"
B-25D-NC	SC	Mt Pl	PPM	North American	Mitchell	41-29784, "Furtile Turtle"
B-25	TX	Breck	BAM	North American	Mitchell	
B-25	TX	Addison	CFM	North American	Mitchell	44-28925, N7687C, 380BS, 310BG, "How Boot That"
B-25	TX	FtWor	CAF-JH	North American	Mitchell	44-86758, N9643C , "Devil Dog"
B-25	TX	Galve	LSFM	North American	Mitchell	44-86734, N333RW, "Special Delivery"
B-25	TX	Pendleton	PAM	North American	Mitchell	44-30243
B-25	WA	Arlington	FHCM	North American	Mitchell	44-30254, N41123
B-25	WI	Milwaukee	GMF	North American	Mitchell	44-30444
B-25 Nose	WA	Tacoma	MAFB	North American	Mitchell	

B-25 Simulator	MN	Duluth	CAF-LSS	Curtiss Dehmel	Simulator	
B-25A	CA	Atwater	CAM	North American	Mitchell	44-86891, "Lazy Daisy Mae"
B-25C	CA	Lanca	MoFM	North American	Mitchell	41-13251
B-25C	SC	Colum	SCSM	North American	Mitchell	41-13285
B-25C(PBJ-1C)	CA	Miramar	FLAM	North American	Mitchell	44-46727
B-25C(PBJ-1C)	TX	Pampa	PAAF	North American	Mitchell	43-3308
B-25D-35-NC	MI	Belleville	YAF	North American	Mitchell	43- 3634, NX3774, "Yankee Warrior"
B-25D(PBJ-1) Nose	VA	Quant	MCAGM	North American	Mitchell	43-3308
B-25G	ND	Grand	GFAFB	North American	Mitchell	44-28834
B-25H	AL	Mobil	BMP	North American	Mitchell	44-31004, NC44310004
B-25H	CT	Winds	NEAM	North American	Mitchell	43-4999, "Dog Daze"
B-25H	TX	San A	LAFB	North American	Mitchell	44-29835J, 35103
B-25J	AL	Montg	MAFB	North American	Mitchell	44-30649
B-25J	AZ	Tucso	PAM	North American	Mitchell	43-27712
B-25J(PBJ)	CA	Camarillo	CAF-SCW	North American	Mitchell	44-30988, N5865V, "Big Ole Brew"
B-25J	CA	Chino	PoFAM	North American	Mitchell	44-30423, N3675G
B-25J	CA	Chino	YAM	North American	Mitchell	44-86791, N6116X
B-25N	CA	Palm Sprg	PSAM	North American	Mitchell	44-86747, N8163H, A, "Mitch the Witch II"
B-25J	CA	Riverside	MFAM	North American	Mitchell	44-31032, "Problem Child"
B-25J	DC	Dulle	DA	North American	Mitchell	44-29887, "Carol Jean", Storage
B-25J	FL	Kissimmee	FTWAM	North American	Mitchell	44-86697, "Killer B"
B-25J	FL	Shali	USAFAM	North American	Mitchell	44-30854, "Doolittle Raider"
B-25J	GA	Warner Robin	MoF	North American	Mitchell	44-86872, N2888G, "little King"
B-25J	HI	Hickm	HAFB	North American	Mitchell	44-31504
B-25J-25-NA	IL	Ranto	OCAM	North American	Mitchell	44-30635, "Whiskey Pete"
B-25J	IN	Peru	GAFB	North American	Mitchell	44-86843, "Pasionate Paulette"
B-25J	KS	Liberal	MAAM	North American	Mitchell	44-30535, N9462Z, "Iron Laiden Maiden"
B-25J	MA	Stow	BCF	North American	Mitchell	44-28932, N3478G, "Tondelayo"
B-25J	MI	Kalam	KAHM	North American	Mitchell	43-4899
B-25	MN	StPau	CAF-SMW	North American	Mitchell	44-29869, N27493, "Miss Mitchell"
B-25J	NC	Asheboro	NAC	North American	Mitchell	44-28866
B-25J	ND	Grand	GFAFB	North American	Mitchell	44-28834
B-25J	IL	Springfield	ACM	North American	Mitchell	45-8898, "Axis Nightmire"
B-25J	OH	Newbu	WASAC	North American	Mitchell	44-31121
B-25J	OK	Fredi	AAM	North American	Mitchell	
B-25J	ON-C	Hamilton	CWH	North American	Mitchell	45-8883, C-GCWM, "Grumpy"
B-25J	TX	Frede	NMofPW	North American	Mitchell	44-86880
B-25J	TX	Midla	CAFFM	North American	Mitchell	43-27868, N25YR, "Yellow Rose"
B-25J	UT	Ogden	HAFBM	North American	Mitchell	44-86772
B-25J	VA	Suffolk	FF	North American	Mitchell	44-30129
B-25J	WI	Oshko	EAAAM	North American	Mitchell	43-4432, N10V, "City of Burlington"
B-25J(TB)-NC	NE	Ashland	SACM	North American	Mitchell	44-30363, Desert Boom"
B-25J(VB)	SD	Rapid	SDA&SM	North American	Mitchell	43-4030
B-25J-10-NA	PA	Readi	MAAM	North American	Mitchell	44-29939, N9456Z, 9D, Model 108, "Briefing Time"
B-25M	MT	Great	MAFB	North American	Mitchell	44-50493
B-25N	FL	FtWal	HF	North American	Mitchell	
B-25N	NY	Farmingdale	AAM	North American	Mitchell	40-2168, "Miss Haps"
B-25N(TB)	FL	Kissi	FTWAM	North American	Mitchell	44-30077
B-25N(TB)	TX	San Angelo	GAFB	North American	Mitchell	44-28875
B-26	FL	Polk	FoF	Martin	Marauder	40-1464 N 4297J
B-26	OH	North Canton	MAM	Martin	Marauder	40-1459
B-26	AZ	Tucson	PAM	Martin	Marauder	40-1501
B-26	UT	Ogden	HAM	Martin	Marauder	40-1370
B-26G-MO	DC	Washi	NA&SM	Martin	Marauder	41-31773, "Flak Bait"
B-26G-MO	OH	Dayto	USAFM	Martin	Marauder	43-34581, "Shootin In"
B-26K	AZ	Tucson	PAM	Douglas	Counter Invader	64-17653 / 41-39378
B-26K	FL	FtWal	HF	Martin	Marauder	64-666
B-26K	OH	Dayton	USAFM	Douglas	Counter Invader	41-39596
B-26K	SD	Ellsworth	A&SM	Martin	Marauder	44-35896, 64-17640
B-29	CA	Fairf	TAFB	Boeing	Super Fortress	42-65281, R, "Miss America 62"
B-29	CO	Puebl	PWAM	Boeing	Super Fortress	44-62022, "Peachy"
B-29	FL	Polk City	WAM	Boeing	Super Fortress	44-70049, Nose at Borrego Springs, CA
B-29	FL	Polk City	WAM	Boeing	Super Fortress	44-84084, at Borrego Springs, CA
B-29 Nose	FL	Lakeland	SNF	Boeing	Super Fortress	Nose
B-29	GA	Cordele	GVMSP	Boeing	Super Fortress	42-93967
B-29	GA	Marie	DAFB	Boeing	Super Fortress	44-70113, "Sweet Loise"
B-29	LA	Bossi	BAFB	Boeing	Super Fortress	44-87627
B-29	MD	Chantilly	NASM	Boeing	Super Fortress	44-86292, "Enola Gay"
B-29	MO	White	WAFB	Boeing	Super Fortress	44-61671, 89, 509BW, "The Geat Artist"
B-29	NM	Albuq	NAM	Boeing	Super Fortress	45-21748, "Duke of Albuquerque"
B-29	OH	Dayto	USAFM	Boeing	Super Fortress	44-27297, "Bockscar"
B-29 Cockpit	OH	Dayto	USAFM	Boeing	Super Fortress	42-24791, Forward Half only, "Big Time Operator"
B-29 Cockpit & Bomb Bay	OH	Dayto	USAFM	Boeing	Super Fortress	44-62139, "Command Decision"
B-29	OK	Tinke	TAFB	Boeing	Super Fortress	44-27343, "Tinker Heritage"
B-29	SD	Rapid	SDA&SM	Boeing	Super Fortress	44-87779, "Legal Eagle II"
B-29	UT	Ogden	HAFBM	Boeing	Super Fortress	44-86408, "Haggerty's Hag"
B-29	WA	Seatt	MoF	Boeing	Super Fortress	44-69729, "T-Squre 54"
B-29(TB)	AZ	Tucso	PAM	Boeing	Super Fortress	44-70016, "Sentimental Journey"
B-29-60-BA(TB)	NE	Ashland	SACM	Boeing	Super Fortress	44-84076, "Man O" War"
B-29A(B-50)	CA	Atwater	CAM	Boeing	Super Fortress	44-61535, "Raz'n Hell" 49-351, 46-010
B-29A	CA	Riverside	MFAM	Boeing	Super Fortress	44-61669, E, "Flag Ship 500"
B-29A	CT	Winds	NEAM	Boeing	Super Fortress	44-61975, "Jack'S Hack"
B-29A	TX	Midla	CAF-B29	Boeing	Super Fortress	44-62070, N5298, "FiFi"
B-29A	TX	San A	LAFB	Boeing	Super Fortress	44-62220
B-29B-55	GA	Warner Robin	MoA	Boeing	Super Fortress	44-87627
B-36A(YB)	OH	Newbu	WASAC	Convair	Peacemaker	42-13571
B-36J	OH	Dayto	USAFM	Convair	Peacemaker	52- 2220
B-36J-111-10	TX	FWort	AHM	Convair	Peacemaker	52-2827A
B-36H(RB)	CA	Atwater	CAM	Convair	Peace Maker	51-13730, Circle W
B-36J-65-CF	NE	Ashland	SACM	Convair	Peacemaker	52-2217A
B-37(RB)	AB-C	Edmonton	AAM	Lockheed	Ventura	5324
B-37(RB)	AB-C	Edmonton	VMFA	Lockheed	Ventura	2195, CF-FAV, CAF447
B-37(RB)	CO	Puebl	PWAM	Lockheed	Ventura	342-17
B-37(RB)	QU-C	St Esprit	Airport	Lockheed	Ventura	CF-SEQ
B-377SG	AZ	Tucso	PAM	Aer0 Spacelines	Super Guppy 201	52-2693, N940NS
B-42A(XB)	MD	Silve	PEGF	Douglas	Mixmaster	
B-43(XB)	MD	Silve	PEGF	Douglas	Jetmaster	
B-45A	AZ	Tucso	PAM	North American	Tornado	47-63
B-45A	CA	Atwater	CAM	North American	Tornado	47-008, Tail B
B-45C	OH	Dayto	USAFM	North American	Tornado	48-10
B-45C(RB)	NE	Ashland	SACM	North American	Tornado	48-0017
B-47	OK	Oklah	SFG	Boeing	Stratojet	012387
B-47	SD	Rapid	SDA&SM	Boeing	Stratojet	52-410

B-47A Nose	AZ	Tucso	PAM	Boeing	Stratojet	49-1901, 450002
B-47B	CA	Rosam	EAFB	Boeing	Stratojet	51-2075
B-47B	MO	Knob	WAFB	Boeing	Stratojet	51-2120
B-47B(WB)	GA	Pooler	M8thAFM	Boeing	Stratojet	50-062
B-47B	IN	Peru	GAFB	Boeing	Stratojet	51-2315
B-47E	AR	Littl	LRAFB	Boeing	Stratojet	52-595, 384th BW
B-47E	CA	Atwater	CAM	Boeing	Stratojet	52-0166, 0166, "Spirit"
B-47E Nose	CA	Riverside	MFAM	Boeing	Stratojet	Used in movie "Strategic Air Command"
B-47E	CA	Riverside	MFAM	Boeing	Stratojet	53-2275, "Betty Boop"
B-47E	CO	Puebl	PWAM	Boeing	Stratojet	53-2104
B-47E(RB)	UT	Ogden	HAFB	Boeing	Stratojet	51-2360
B-47E	KS	Wichita	McCAFB	Boeing	Stratojet	53-4213
B-47E	LA	Bossi	BAFB	Boeing	Stratojet	53-2276
B-47E	NY	Platt	PAFB	Boeing	Stratojet	53-2385
B-47E	OH	Dayton	USAFM	Boeing	Stratojet	53-2280
B-47E	OK	Altus	City	Boeing	Stratojet	51-7071
B-47E(WB)	WA	Seatt	MoF	Boeing	Stratojet	51-7066
B-47E(EB)	AZ	Tucso	PAM	Boeing	Stratojet	53-2135, 44481
B-47E(XB)	IL	Ranto	OCAM	Boeing	Stratojet	46-0066
B-47E(EB)	OK	Tinke	TAFB	Boeing	Stratojet	53-4257
B-47E(EB)	TX	Abile	DLAP	Boeing	Stratojet	52-4120
B-47E(RB)	TX	Midla	CAFFM	Boeing	Stratojet	
B-47E(WB)	OK	Oklah	CityPark	Boeing	Stratojet	51-2387
B-47E-35-DT	NE	Ashland	SACM	Boeing	Stratojet	52-1412
B-47H(RB)	OH	Dayton	USAFM	Boeing	Stratojet	53-4299
B-47N(RB)	FL	Shali	USAFAM	Boeing	Stratojet	53-4296
B-50(WB)	CA	Atwater	CAM	Boeing	Superfortress	49-351
B-50A Fuse	CA	Chino	PoFAM	Boeing	Superfortress	46-010
B-50D(WB)	OH	Dayto	USAFM	Boeing	Superfortress	49-310
B-50J(KB)	AZ	Tucso	PAM	Boeing	Superfortress	49-372
B-50J(KB)	FL	Tampa	MAFB	Boeing	Superfortress	49-389, Side 48-114A, Tail 0-80114
B-52 Gunner Trainer	CA	Riversideside	MAM	Boeing	Stratofortress	Gunner Trainer
B-52	NE	Offut	OAFB	Boeing	Stratofortress	
B-52	LA	Bossie City	BAFB	Boeing	Stratofortress	
B-52	LA	Bossie City	BAFB	Boeing	Stratofortress	
B-52	OK	Oklah	SFG	Boeing	Stratofortress	70038
B-52 Nose	TX	Big Springs	H25	Boeing	Stratofortress	
B-52A(NB)	AZ	Tucso	PAM	Boeing	Stratofortress	52-3
B-52B	NM	Albuq	NAM	Boeing	Stratofortress	
B-52B(GB)	CO	Aurora	WOTR	Boeing	Stratofortress	
B-52B(RB)-15-BO	NE	Ashland	SACM	Boeing	Stratofortress	52-8711
B-52C Cockpit	IL	Ranto	OCAM	Boeing	Stratofortress	
B-52D	AL	Montg	MAFB	Boeing	Stratofortress	
B-52D	AZ	Tucso	DMAFB	Boeing	Stratofortress	
B-52D	AZ	Tucso	PAM	Boeing	Stratofortress	55-67
B-52D	CA	Atwater	CAM	Boeing	Stratofortress	56-0612
B-52D	CA	Fairf	TAFB	Boeing	Stratofortress	
B-52D	CA	Rosam	EAFB	Boeing	Stratofortress	56-585
B-52D	CO	CSpri	USAFA	Boeing	Stratofortress	"Diamond Lil"
B-52D	FL	Orlan	OIAMP	Boeing	Stratofortress	
B-52D	KS	Wichita	KAM	Boeing	Stratofortress	
B-52D	GA	Warner Robin	MoF	Boeing	Stratofortress	55-85
B-52D-25-BW	MI	Belleville	YAF	Boeing	Stratofortress	55-677, N464024, "Clyde"
B-52D	MI	Marqu	KISAFB	Boeing	Stratofortress	
B-52D	MI	Ypsil	YAF	Boeing	Stratofortress	
B-52D	OH	Dayto	USAFM	Boeing	Stratofortress	56-665
B-52D	OK	Tinke	TAFB	Boeing	Stratofortress	
B-52D	SD	Rapid	SDA&SM	Boeing	Stratofortress	56-0657
B-52D	TX	Abile	DLAP	Boeing	Stratofortress	56-685
B-52D	TX	FWort	SAM	Boeing	Stratofortress	
B-52D	TX	San A	LAFB	Boeing	Stratofortress	55-68
B-52D	TX	Wichi	SAFB	Boeing	Stratofortress	
B-52D	VA	Hampt	LAFB	Boeing	Stratofortress	
B-52D	WA	Spoka	FAFBHM	Boeing	Stratofortress	
B-52D(GB)	CA	Riverside	MFAM	Boeing	Stratofortress	55-0679
B-52D-40BW	MO	White	WAFB	Boeing	Stratofortress	56-683, 683, 509BG, "Necessary Evil"
B-52F (2 ea)	OK	Oklah	CityPark	Boeing	Stratofortress	
B-52G	AZ	Tucso	PAM	Boeing	Stratofortress	58-183
B-52G	FL	Shali	USAFAM	Boeing	Stratofortress	80185
B-52G	ND	Grand	GFAFB	Boeing	Stratofortress	
B-52G	NY	Rome	MVBM	Boeing	Stratofortress	58-0225
B-52G	TX	Wichi	SAFB	Boeing	Stratofortress	
B-52G	UT	Ogden	HAFBM	Boeing	Stratofortress	
B-52G	WA	Seattle	MoF	Boeing	Stratofortress	59-2584, 17066
B-52G Nose	CA	S.Mon	MoF	Boeing	Stratofortress	
B-52G-105-BW	NY	Rome	GAFBM	Boeing	Stratofortress	80225, "Mohawk Valley"
B-52N	AL	Mobil	BMP	Boeing	Stratofortress	55071, "Calamity Jane"
B-57	AZ	Mesa	CAFM	Martin	Canberra	
B-57	KS	Topek	FF	Martin	Canberra	
B-57	MI	Kalam	KAHM	Martin	Canberra	52-1584
B-57	OH	Newbu	WASAC	Martin	Canberra	
B-57A(RB)	UT	Ogden	HAFBM	Martin	Canberra	
B-57A(RB)	CT	Winds	NEAM	Martin	Canberra	52-1488
B-57A(RB)	GA	Warner Robin	MoF	Martin	Canberra	52-1475A
B-57A(RB)	MD	Middl	GLMAM	Martin	Canberra	
B-57A(RB)-MA	MI	Belleville	YAF	Martin	Canberra	52-1426
B-57A(RB)	MI	Mt Clemens	SMAM	Martin	Canberra	52-1485
B-57A(RB)	NY	Horseheads	NWM	Martin	Canberra	52-1459
B-57A(RB)	SC	Flore	FA&MM	Martin	Canberra	
B-57A(RB)	TX	Midla	CAFFM	Martin	Canberra	
B-57A(RB)	UT	Ogden	HAM	Martin	Canberra	
B-57B	CA	Rosam	EAFB	Martin	Canberra	52-1576
B-57B	FL	Shali	USAFAM	Martin	Canberra	52-1516
B-57B(EB)	CA	Riverside	MFAM	Martin	Canberra	52-1519
B-57B(EB)	DC	Dulle	DA	Martin	Canberra	
B-57B(EB)	MT	Great	MAFB	Martin	Canberra	52-1505
B-57B(EB)	OH	Dayto	USAFM	Martin	Canberra	52-1499
B-57B(EB)	SD	Rapid	SDA&SM	Martin	Canberra	
B-57B(EB)	TX	D Rio	LAFB	Martin	Canberra	
B-57B(EB)	VT	Nurli	BANG	Martin	Canberra	
B-57C(EB)	AR	Littl	LRAFB	Martin	Canberra	53-521
B-57C(EB)	TX	Abile	DLAP	Martin	Canberra	52-1504
B-57D(RB)	AZ	Tucso	PAM	Martin	Canberra	53-3982

B-57E(EB)	AZ	Tucso	PAM	Martin	Canberra	55-4274	
B-57E(EB)	CA	Atwater	CAM	Martin	Canberra	54-00253	
B-57E(EB)	CO	CSpri	EJPSCM	Martin	Canberra	55-4279	
B-57E(EB)	CO	Aurora	WOTR	Martin	Canberra		
B-57E(EB)	NE	Ashland	SACM	Martin	Canberra	55-4244, MA	
B-57F(WB)	AZ	Tucso	PAM	Martin	Night Intruder	63-13501, N925NA	
B-57F(WB)	GA	Warner Robin	MoF	Martin	Canberra	63-13293A	
B-58A	AZ	Tucso	PAM	Convair	Hustler	61-2080	
B-58A	IL	Ranto	OCAM	Convair	Hustler	55-0666, "Greased Lightning"	
B-58A Escape Capsule	MD	Silver Hill	PEGF	Convair	Hustler		
B-58A	OH	Dayto	USAFM	Convair	Hustler	59-2458	
B-58A	TX	San Antonio	KAFB	Convair	Hustler	59-2437	
B-58A(N)	CA	Rosam	EAFB	Convair	Hustler	55-665, "Snoopy"	
B-58A(TB)	IN	Peru	GAFB	Convair	Hustler	55-663	
B-58A(TB)	TX	FWort	SAM	Convair	Hustler		
B-58A(TB)	TX	Galve	LSFM	Convair	Hustler	55-668	
B-58A-CF	NE	Ashland	SACM	Convair	Hustler	61-2059	
B-66(RB)	TX	Abile	DLAP	Douglas	Destroyer	53-0466	
B-66(RF)	TX	Austi	BAFMlark	Douglas	Destroyer		
B-66(WB)	SC	Flore	FA&MM	Douglas	Destroyer		
B-66A(RB)	SC	Sumte	SAFB	Douglas	Destroyer		
B-66B(RB)	OH	Dayto	USAFM	Douglas	Destroyer	53-475	
B-66D	IL	Ranto	OCAM	Douglas	Destroyer	53-0412, BB	
B-66D(WB)	AZ	Tucso	PAM	Douglas	Destroyer	55-395	
B-66D(WB)	GA	Warner Robin	MoF	Douglas	Destroyer	55-392, RB	
B-66D(WB)	TX	San A	LAFB	Douglas	Destroyer	55-390	
B-69A(RB)	GA	Warner Robin	MoF		Neptune]	54-4037	
B-70(XB)	OH	Dayto	USAFM	North American	Valkyrie	62-1	
B.2 Mk.II	LA	Bossi	BAFB	Avro	Vulcan	Model 698	
B.2 Mk.II	NB	Belle	SAC	Avro	Vulcan	Model 698	
B.2 Mk.II	NE	Ashland	SACM	Avro	Vulcan	XM573	
B.2 Mk.II	CA	Atwater	CAM	Avro	Vulcan		
B.E.2c	ON-C	Ottaw	CAM	Royal Aircraft	B.E.2c	4112	
B.H. 305	BC-C	Langley	CMoF	Brantley-Haynes	Model 305	B-2B only 5 Seater Helicopter	
B290	WI	Oshko	EAAAAM	Bauman	Brigadier	N90616	
B6N2	MD	Silve	PEGF	Nakajima	Jill (Tenzan)	Jill	
B7A1	MD	Silve	PEGF	Aichi	Grace (Ryusei)		
BAC-167	WA	Olympia	OFM	Bachem	Strikemaster		
Ba 349	CA	Chino	PoFAM	Bachem	Natter		
Ba 349	MD	Silve	PEGF	Bachem	Natter		
Backstrom EPB-1A	NY	Elmire	NSM	Cleave	Flyinh Plank	N7634B	
Backstrom EPB-1C	NY	Elmire	NSM	Cleave	Flyinh Plank	N19C	
BAe Mk 53	GA	Warner Robin	MoF	British	Lightning		
Baby Great Lakes	KS	Liberal	MAAM	Baby	Great Lakes Bi		
Baby Great Lakes	OR	McMinnville	EAM	Baby	Great Lakes Bi	6907M-187, N44ET	
Backstrom Plank	IA	Ottumwa	APM	Backstrom	Plank	1, N20WB	
Bagjo BG12	AB-C	Calga	AMoC	Bagjo	Glider		
Baker 001 Special	WI	Oshko	EAAAAM	Baker	Special	N3203	
Baker McMillen Cadet	NY	Elmire	NSM	Baker McMillen	Cadet	G10265	
Baking Duce II (F.M.1)	AK	Fairb	APAM	Baking	Duce II	N75FD	
Baldwin Red Devil	MD	Silve	PEGF	Baldwin	Red Devil		
Ballistic Silo	IL	Ranto	OCAM		Ballistic Silo		
Balloon Basket	CT	Winds	NEAM	Blanchard	Balloon Basket		
Balloon Basket	VA	Quantico	MCAGM		Balloon Basket	Year 1919	
Balloon Capsule	SD	Mitch	S&TIB&AM		Balloon Capsule	"Zanussi"	
Balloon D	TX	FWort	BCVintag				
Balloon Gondola	SD	Mitch	S&TIB&AM		Balloon Gondola	"Super Chicken"	
Balloon Helium	IA	India	USNBM		Balloon Helium		
Balloon Hot Air	IA	India	USNBM		Balloon Hot Air		
Balloon Hot Air	SD	Mitch	S&TIB&AM		Balloon Hot Air	"Hilda"	
Balloon Hot Air	SD	Mitch	S&TIB&AM		Balloon Hot Air	"Chic I Boom"	
Balloon Hot Air	SD	Mitch	S&TIB&AM		Balloon Hot Air	"Chesty"	
Balloon Hot Air	SD	Mitch	S&TIB&AM		Balloon Hot Air	"Matrioshk"	
Balloon Hot Air	SD	Mitch	S&TIB&AM		Balloon Hot Air	"Uncle Sam"	
Balloon Hot Air	SD	Mitch	S&TIB&AM		Balloon Hot Air	"Aero Star"	
Balloon Montgolfiere	CA	San Diego	SDAM	Montgolfiere	Balloon		
Balloon WWI Gas	SD	Mitch	S&TIB&AM		Balloon Gas		
Balloon Works Firefly 7	AZ	Tucson	PAM	Balloon Works	Firefly 7	N4065D	
Barlow Acapella	WI	Oshko	EAAAAM	Barlow	Acapella	N455CB	
Baracuda	MI	Oscoda	YAF	Baracuda	Homebuilt	N29M	
Barrage Kite	WI	Oshko	EAAAAM		Barrage Kite		
Bates Tractor	WI	Oshko	EAAAAM	Bates	Tractor		
BC-12D	AZ	Tucso	PAM	Taylorcraft	T-Craft	N43584	
BD-10	ON-C	Toronto	TAM				
Beachy Little Looper	CA	S.Mon	MoF	Betchy	Little Looper		
Bede BD-4	AL	Birmingham	SMoF	Bede	Micro		
Bede BD-4	AZ	Tucson	PAM	Bede	Micro		
Bede BD-4	FL	Lakel	SFAF	Bede	Micro	N8826	
Bede BD-4	IA	Ottumwa	APM	Bede	Micro		
Bede BD-4	WI	Oshko	EAAAAM	Bede	Micro	N200SS	
Bede BD-5	AZ	Tucso	PAM	Bede	Micro		
Bede BD-5	CA	Santa Rosa	PCAM	Bede	Micro		
Bede BD-5	WI	Oshko	EAAAAM	Bede	Micro	N500BD	
Bede BD-5B	AL	Birmingham	SMoF	Bede	Micro		
Bede BD-5B	CA	Oakla	OWAM	Bede	Micro		
Bede BD-5B	FL	Lakel	SFAF	Bede	Micro	N51GB	
Bede BD-5B	MD	Silve	PEGF	Bede	Micro		
Bede BD-5B	OR	McMinnville	EAV	Bede	Micro	2392, N110CJ	
Bede BD-5B	PA	Readi	MAAM	Bede	Micro	N5BE	
Bede BD-5	AZ	Tucso	PAM	Bede	Micro	N505MR	
Bede BD-5J	CA	Calab	SC	Bede	Micro		
Bede BD-5J	CA	S.Mon	MoF	Bede	Micro		
Bede BD-5V	AZ	Grand	PoFGCVA	Bede	Micro	N64DS	
Bede XBD-2	WI	Oshko	EAAAAM	Bede	Micro	N327BD	
Bee Honey Bee	WI	Oshko	EAAAAM	Bee	Honey Bee	N90859	
Beech A17R	TN	Tulla	SMF	Beech	Staggerwing		
Beech B17S	TN	Tulla	SMF	Beech	Staggerwing		
Beech C17L	DC	Washi	NA&SM	Beech	Staggerwing		
Beech C17S	TN	Tulla	SMF	Beech	Staggerwing		
Beech D17A	OR	Mc Minnville	EAEC	Beech	Staggerwing		
Beech D17S	CA	Santa Monica	MoF	Beech	Staggerwing		
Beech D17S	CA	Santa Paula	SPAA	Beech	Staggerwing		
Beech D17S	ID	Zellw	BWA	Beech	Staggerwing		

Beech D17S	KS	Liberal	MAAM	Beech	Staggerwing	
Beech D17S	KS	Wichita	KAM	Beech	Staggerwing	
Beech D17S	LA	Patte	WWMAM	Beech	Staggerwing	
Beech D17S	NC	Fargo	FAM	Beech	Staggerwing	
Beech D17S	TN	Tulla	SMF	Beech	Staggerwing	
Beech D18D	BC-C	Langley	CMoF	Beech	Twin Beech	2307
Beech D18D	RK-C	MJaw	WDM	Beech	Twin Beech	
Beech D18H-4D	TX	Ralve	LSFM	Beech	Twin Beech	670, N954
Beech D18H	TX	Fulsh	CTA	Beech	Twin Beech	
Beech D18S *See AT-11*				Beech	Kansan	
Beech D18S See Also (C-45)				Beech	Twin Beech	
Beech D18S	AB-C	Calga	AMoC	Beech	Expediter	Twin Beech
Beech D18S	AB-C	Edmonton	AAM	Beech	Twin Beech	2366, CA-245
Beech D18S	AB-C	Nanton	NLSAM	Beech	Twin Beech	
Beech D18S	AB-C	Wetas	RM	Beech	Twin Beech	
Beech D18S	AZ	Tucso	PAM	Beech	Twin Beech	N55681
Beech D18S	CO	Aurora	WOTR	Beech	Twin Beech	
Beech D18S	FL	Deland	FW-CAF	Beech	Twin Beech	
Beech D18S	IN	Ft. W	BAI	Beech	Twin Beech	
Beech D18S	LA	Bossier City	BAFB	Beech	Twin Beech	
Beech D18S	MB-C	Winni	WCAM	Beech	Twin Beech	
Beech D18S	MD	Silve	PEGF	Beech	Twin Beech	
Beech D18S	NF-C	Gander	NAAM	Beech	Twin Beech	
Beech D18S	OK	Fredi	AAM	Beech	Twin Beech	
Beech D18S	ON-C	Campbellford	MMM	Beech	Twin Beech	
Beech D18S	ON-C	Ear FAlls	EFM	Beech	Twin Beech	
Beech D18S	ON-C	Ignace	City	Beech	Starship	
Beech D18S	ON-C	Sault Ste Marie	CBHC	Beech	Twin Beech	CF-MGY
Beech D18S	ON-C	Sault Ste Marie	CBHC	Beech	Twin Beech	CF-UWE
Beech D18S	ON-C	Sault Ste Marie	CBHC	Beech	Twin Beech	Cockpit Only
Beech D18S	TN	Gatlinburg	PHLTG	Beech	Twin Beech	
Beech D18S	TX	Ft Worth	VFM	Beech	Twin Beech	
Beech D18S	TX	Gilmer	PotP	Beech	Twin Beech	
Beech D18S	TX	Houston	1940AT	Beech	Twin Beech	
Beech D18S	TX	Midla	CAFFM	Beech	Twin Beech	
Beech D18S	WA	Seatt	MoF	Beech	Twin Beech	
Beech D18S	WI	Janesville	BHA	Beech	Twin Beech	
Beech D18S(AT-7)	AZ	Tucso	PAM	Beech	Twin Beech	Sn 42-2438, N8073H, Navigation Trainer
Beech E17S	TN	Tulla	SMF	Beech	Staggerwing	
Beech F17S	TN	Tulla	SMF	Beech	Staggerwing	
Beech G17S	TN	Tulla	SMF	Beech	Staggerwing	
Beech 3NM	AR	Fayetteville	AAM	Beech	Canadian Queen	
Beech 23 (See C-45)						
Beech 73	KS	Wichita	KAM	Beech	Mentor	Jet
Beechcraft 35	FL	Dayto	ERAU	Beechcraft	Bonanza	
Beechcraft 35	GA	Calho	Mercer A	Beechcraft	Bonanza	
Beechcraft 35	KS	Liberal	MAAM	Beechcraft	Bonanza	
Beechcraft 35	KS	Wichita	KAM	Beechcraft	Bonanza	
Beechcraft 35	MD	Silve	PEGF	Beechcraft	Bonanza	"Waikiki Beach"
Beechcraft 35	OK	Fredi	AAM	Beechcraft	Bonanza	
Beechcraft 35	OR	McMinnville	EAV	Beechcraft	Bonanza	D-1111, N3870N
Beechcraft 35	TX	Laredo	AAM	Beechcraft	Bonanza	
Beechcraft 35(N)	AZ	Tucso	PAM	Beechcraft	Bonanza	N9493Y
Beechcraft 36 (See QU-22B)						
Beechcraft 50(L-23)	IN	Mento	LB	Beechcraft	Seminole	Twin Bonanza Model 50
Beechcraft 50(L-23)	OK	Fredi	AAM	Beechcraft	Seminole	Twin Bonanza Model 50
Beechcraft 50(L-23D)(U-8D)	AZ	Tucso	PAM	Beechcraft	Seminole	Twin Bonanza Model 50, 56- 3701
Beechcraft 50(RU-8D)	GA	Calho	Mercer A	Beechcraft	Seminole	Twin Bonanza Model 50
Beechcraft 50(RU-8D)	KS	Topek	CAM	Beechcraft	Seminole	Twin Bonanza Model 50, "Lonely Ringer"
Beechcraft 50(RU-8D)	MD	Ft Mead	NVP	Beechcraft	Seminole	Twin Bonanza Model 50,
Beechcraft 50(RU-8D)	VA	FtEus	USATM	Beechcraft	Seminole	58-3051
Beechcraft 50(U-8A)	AL	Ozark	USAAM	Beechcraft	Seminole	Twin Bonanza Model 50
Beechcraft 50(U-8A)	AL	Ozark	USAAM	Beechcraft	Seminole	Twin Bonanza Model 50, 52- 1700
Beechcraft 50(U-8D-5J)	SD	Rapid	SDA&SM	Beechcraft	Seminole	Twin Bonanza Model 50
Beechcraft 50(U-8F)	GA	Hampton	AAHF	Beechcraft	Seminole	Twin Bonanza Model 50
Beechcraft 55(T-42)	AL	Ozark	USAAM	Beechcraft	Baron	65-12685
Beechcraft 55(T-42)	IN	Valparaiso	IAM	Beechcraft	Baron	
Beechcraft 55(T-42A)	GA	Hampton	AAHF	Beechcraft	Baron	
Beechcraft 58P	MT	Misso	AFDSC	Beechcraft	Baron	
Beechcraft 99	MT	Misso	AFDSC	Beechcraft	Airliner	
Beechcraft Dutches	FL	Dayto	ERAU	Beechcraft	Dutches	
Beechcraft 2000A	AZ	Tucson	PAM	Beechcraft	Starship	NC-23, N39TU
Beech 2000A	KS	Wichita	KAM	Beech	Starship	
Beagle B.206	AL	Birmingham	SmoF	Beagle	B.206	
Bell 204	CO	Denve	JWDAS	Bell	Model 204	
Bell 205A	BC-C	Langley	CMoF	Bell	Iroquois (Huey)	
Bell 206	FL	Starke	ACAM	Bell	Long Ranger	
Bell 206B	NS	Halifax	ACAM	Bell	Long Ranger	
Bell 206L	MD	Silve	PEFG	Bell	Long Ranger	
Bell 214	CA	Miramar	FLAM	Bell	Huey Super	
Bell 260(TH-67)	CA	Ramona	CR	Bell	Model 260	Bell 206 Jet Ranger
Bell 260	MD	Silve	PEGF	Bell	Model 260	Bell 206 Jet Ranger
Bell 260	PA	WChester	AHM	Bell	Model 260	Bell 206 Jet Ranger
Bell 47B-3	CA	Ramona	CR	Bell	Ranger	
Bell 47B-3	NY	Niagara Falls	NIA	Bell	Ranger	
Bell 47	WA	Seatt	PSC	Bell	Ranger	
Bell 47B	PA	WChes	AHM	Bell	Sioux	NC5H
Bell 47D (H-13)	AB-C	Calga	AMoC	Bell	Sioux	
Bell 47D (H-13)	ON-C	Sault Ste Marie	CBHC	Bell	Sioux	Sn 665-8
Bell 47D-1(H-13)	BC-C	Sidne	BCAM	Bell	Sioux	CD-FZX
Bell 47D-1(H-13)	CA	Chino	YAM	Bell	Sioux	51-4175, N55230
Bell 47D-1(H-13)	CT	Winds	NEAM	Bell	Sioux	LV AEF
Bell 47D-1(H-13)	ON-C	Sault Ste Marie	CBHC	Bell	Sioux	Replica CF-ODM
Bell 47D-1(H-13)	PA	WChes	AHM	Bell	Sioux	
Bell 47D-1(H-13)	TX	Ft Worth	FWSH	Bell	Sioux	
Bell 47D-5(H-13)	NY	Niagara Falls	NAM	Bell	Sioux	
Bell 47G (HTL-6)	ON-C	Ottaw	CAM	Bell	Sioux	1387
Bell 47G-5(HTL-5)	CA	LAnge	CMoS&I	Bell	Sioux	
Bell 47G	CO	Pueblo	PWAM	Bell	Sioux	
Bell 47G	TX	Laredo	Airport	Bell	Sioux	
Bell 47H-1	NY	Niagra Falls	NAM	Bell	Ranger	
Bell 47H-1	PA	WChester	AHM	Bell	Ranger	
Bell 47J	PA	WChes	AHM	Bell	Ranger	

108

Aircraft	State	City	Museum	Manufacturer	Model	Notes
Bell 47J-2	BC-C	Langley	CMoF	Bell	Ranger	
Bell 47J-2(H-13)	NS	Halifax	ACAM	Bell	Sioux	
Bell ATV VTOL	MD	Silve	PEGF	Bell	VTOL	
Bell Boeing Tiltrotor RPV	PA	WChester	AHM	Bell	RPV	
Bell Model 30	MD	Silve	PEGF	Bell	Model 30	
Bell Model 30	PA	WChes	AHM	Bell	Model 30	NX41867
Bell Rocket Belt	MD	Silve	PEGF	Bell	Rocket Belt	
Bell Rocket Belt	VA	FtEus	USATM	Bell	Rocket Belt	
Bellanca	NV	Carso	YF	Bellanca		
Bellanca 14-9	FL	Lakeland	SNF	Bellanca		
Bellanca 14-9L	NC	Charlotte	CAM	Bellanca	Crusair	N1KQ
Bellanca 14-13-2	AZ	Tucso	PAM	Bellanca	Crusair	Sn 1551, XB-FOU
Bellanca 14-13-2	AZ	Tucso	PAM	Bellanca	Crusair	Sn 1073, N46LW
Bellanca 14-13-3	KS	Liberal	MAAM	Bellanca	Crusair	
Bellanca 14-13-3	MD	Silve	PEGF	Bellanca	Crusair	
Bellanca 14-13-3	OK	Fredi	AAM	Bellanca	Crusair	
Bellanca 14-19C (260)	OK	Fredi	AAM	Bellanca	Cruisemaster	
Bellanca 190	KS	Liberal	MAAM	Bellanca	Cruisemaster	
Bellanca 31-55A	BC-C	Langley	CMoF	Bellanca	Skyrocket	
Bellanca CH-400(1-87)	VA	Sands	VAM	Bellanca	Skyrocket	Sn 187, NX237, "Columbia"
Bellanca 66-75 BTW	MB-C	Winni	WCAM	Bellanca	Aircruiser	
Bellanca 66-75 BTW	OR	Tillamook	TAM	Bellanca	Aircrusier	
Bellanca C.F.	MD	Silve	PEGF	Bellanca		
Bellanca CH.300	AK	Ancho	AAHM	Bellanca		
Bellanca Pacemaker	ON-C	Ottaw	CAM	Bellanca	Pacemaker	
Bellanca Replica	ME	OwlsH	OHTM	Bellanca		
Bennett Matiah M-9	MD	Silve	PEGF	Bennett	Matiah M-9	
Bennett Model 162	MD	Silve	PEGF	Bennett	Model 162	
Bennett Phonix 6	MD	Silve	PEGF	Bennett	Phonex 6	
Bennett Phonix 6B	MD	Silve	PEGF	Bennett	Phonex 6B	
Bennett Phonix Viper	MD	Silve	PEGF	Bennett	Phonix Viper	
Bennett Streak 130	MD	Silve	PEGF	Bennett	Streak 130	
Bennett (See also Rogallo)						
Benoist Air Boat 1914	FL	Largo	HPPCHM	Benoist	Air Boat	
Benoist-Korn	MD	Silve	PEGF	Benoist-Korn		
Bensen B- 6	MD	Silve	PEGF	Bensen	Gyro-Glider	
Bensen B- 6	NE	Minde	HWPV	Bensen	Gyro-Glider	
Bensen B- 7	BC-C	Langley	CMoF	Bensen	Gyro-Glider	
Bensen B- 7	NE	Minde	HWPV	Bensen	Gyro-Glider	
Bensen B- 7M	MB-C	Winni	WCAM	Bensen	Gyro-Copter	
Bensen B- 8M	AL	Birmingham	SMoF	Bensen	Gyro-Copter	
Bensen B- 8M	BC-C	Langley	CMoF	Bensen	Gyro-Copter	
Bensen B- 8M	CA	Riverside	MAFM	Bensen	Gyro-Copter	
Bensen B- 8M	CT	Winds	NEAM	Bensen	Gyro-Copter	
Bensen B- 8M	MD	Silve	PEGF	Bensen	Gyro-Copter	
Bensen B- 8M	OH	Dayto	USAFM	Bensen	Gyro-Copter	Model X-25A
Bensen B- 8M	OR	Eugen	OAM	Bensen	Gyro-Copter	
Bensen B- 8M	WA	Seatt	MoF	Bensen	Gyro-Copter	1, N8533E
Bensen B-11	CA	Chino	PoFAM	Bensen	Gyro-Copter	
Bensen B-11	WI	Oshko	EAAAAM	Bensen	Gyro-Copter	N63U
Bensen B-8M	NC	Ralei	NCMoH	Bensen	Gyro-Copter	
Bensen Gyro-Copter	FL	Lakel	SFAF	Bensen	Gyro-Copter	
Bensen Sport Autogyro	PA	Wchester	AHM	Bensen	Gyro-Copter	
Bergfalke 11 Glider	PA	Tough	CFCM	Bergfalke	Glider	
Berkshire Concept 70	NY	Elmire	NSM	Berkshire	Concept 70	
Berliner Helicopter	MD	College Park	CPAM	Berliner	Helicopter	
Berliner Helicopter	MD	Silve	PEGF	Berliner	Helicopter	
Bertelson Aeromobile Hover	MD	Silve	PEGF	Bertelson	Aeromobile Hover	
Bf 109	GA	Savan	MEHM	Messerschmitt	Gustav	
Bf 109	MD	Silve	PEGF	Messerschmitt	Gustav	
Bf 109	ON-C	Ottaw	CAM	Messerschmitt	Gustav	471-39
Bf 109	OR	Tillamook	TAM	Messerschmitt	Gustav	
Bf 109 (1/2 Scale)	LA	Patte	WWMAM	Messerschmitt	Gustav	
Bf 109E-7	VA	Suffolk	FF	Messerschmitt	Gustav	Out of Country Until 2003, "Black 9"
Bf 109G	DC	Washi	NA&SM	Messerschmitt	Gustav	
Bf 109G-5	OH	Dayto	USAFM	Messerschmitt	Gustav	C.4K- 64
Bf 109G	TX	Addison	CFM	Messerschmitt	Gustav	N48157, 14
Bf 109G-10/U4	AZ	Grand	PoFGCVA	Messerschmitt	Gustav	13
Bf 109G-10	OR	Mc Minnville	EAEC	Messerschmitt	Gustav	610937, N109EV
Bf 109G-14(Mock Up)	CA	San Diego	SDAM	Messerschmitt	Gustav	
BFC-2(F11C)	FL	Pensa	USNAM		Goshawk	9332 2-B-13
BG-12BD	NY	Elmira	NSM	Brieglab	Sailplane	162, N12RK
Biplane	IN	India	CMoI		Biplane	"Lil Chil"
Biplane	KS	Topek	KSHS		Biplane	
Biplane	TX	C Christi	USS Lexi		Biplane	
Bird Biplane	IL	Harva	BA	Bird	Biplane	
Bird CK	PA	Bethel	GAAM	Bird	CK	
Birdwing Imperial	NY	River	RE	Birdwing	Imperial	1930
Blanik	ID	Driggs	TAC	Blanik	Glider	
Blanik L-13	NM	Hobbs	NSF	Blanik	Glider	
Blaty	CA	Chino	PoFAM	Blaty	Orion Hang Glider	
Bleriot X	NY	Rhine	ORA	Bleriot		
Bleriot XI	CA	San Diego	SDAM	Bleriot		
Bleriot XI	CT	Winds	NEAM	Bleriot		
Bleriot XI	DC	Washi	NA&SM	Bleriot		"Domenjoz"
Bleriot XI	FL	Pensa	USNAM	Bleriot		
Bleriot XI	IA	Des M	ISHD	Bleriot		
Bleriot XI	MA	Stow	BCF	Bleriot		
Bleriot XI	MD	College Park	CPAM	Bleriot		
Bleriot XI	ME	OwlsH	OHTM	Bleriot		
Bleriot XI	MI	Dearb	HFM	Bleriot		1, "Boneshaker"
Bleriot XI	NY	Bayport	BA	Bleriot		153
Bleriot XI	NY	River	RE	Bleriot		Original
Bleriot XI	OH	Dayto	USAFM	Bleriot		1909
Bleriot XI	ON-C	Ottaw	CAM	Bleriot		
Bleriot XI	TX	Kingbury	VAHF	Bleriot		
Bleriot XI	TX	San Antonio	TAM	Bleriot		
Blimp (2ea)	OR	Tillamook	TAM			
Block IV Satellite	OH	Dayton	USAFM	Block	IV Satellite	
BobCat	GA	Woodstock	NGWS		BobCat Kit	
Boeing 100	WA	Seattle	MoF	Boeing	Boeing 247D	1143, N872H
Boeing 247D(C-73)	DC	Washi	NA&SM	Boeing	Boeing 247D	1930 - 10 Passenger
Boeing 247D(C-73)	ON-C	Ottaw	CAM	Boeing	Boeing 247D	1930 - 10 Passenger

Boeing 247D(C-73)	WA	Seattle	MoF	Boeing	Boeing 247D	1729, NC13347, "Cpt George Juneau"
Boeing 367-80	VA	Sterling	UHC	Boeing	Boeing 367	
Boeing 367-80	WA	Seatt	MoF	Boeing	Boeing 367	
Boeing 377(C-97)	OR	Tillamook	TAM	Boeing	Mini Guppy	
Boeing 40B-2	MI	Dearb	HFM	Boeing	Boeing 40B	NC285
Boeing 40B-2 (727-100)	IL	Chica	MoS&I	Boeing	Boeing 40B	7017, "United Airlines"
Boeing 707 Cockpit	NY	NYC	ISASM	Boeing	Boeing 707	
Boeing 707 Cockpit	TX	Ft Worth	FWSH	Boeing	Boeing 707	
Boeing 707-131B	AZ	Tucso	PAM	Boeing	Boeing 707	Sn 99-18390, N751TW
Boeing 707 Air Force 1	CA	Simi VAlley	RL	Boeing	Boeing 707	Air Force One, 27000
Boeing 720	NV	Las Vegas	LBAHSM	Boeing	Boeing 720	"Kay O"ll", Cockpit Only
Boeing 727	IL	Chicago	MoS&I	Boeing	Boeing 727	
Boeing 727-22	WA	Seattle	MoF	Boeing	Boeing 727	18293, N7001U
Boeing 727-25C	MI	Kalamazoo	KAHM	Boeing	Boeing 727	19301, N119FE
Boeing 727	OR	Hillsboro	BC	Boeing	Boeing 727	Home
Boeing 727-100	KS	Wichita	KAM	Boeing	Boeing 727	
Boeing 727-100	WA	Seattle	MoF	Boeing	Boeing 727	N7001U, 1st Built
Boeing 737-130	WA	Seattle	MoF	Boeing	Boeing 727	19437, 515
Boeing 737-200	KS	Wichita	KAM	Boeing	Boeing 737	
Boeing 737-200	WA	Seatt	MoF	Boeing	Boeing 737	
Boeing 747 Cockpit	CA	San Carlos	HAM	Boeing	Boeing 747	
Boeing 747-121	WA	Seatt	MoF	Boeing	Boeing 747	20235, N747001
Boeing 747 Fuse	DC	Washington	NASM	Boeing	Boeing 747	
Boeing 80A-1	WA	Seatt	MoF	Boeing	Tri-Motor	1082, NC224M
Boeing B&W Replica	WA	Seatt	MoF	Boeing	B&W	N1916
Boeing B-100	FL	Polk	FoF	Boeing	B-100	
Boeing Bird of Prey	OH	Dayton	USAFM	Boeing	Bird of Prey	
Boeing Condor	CA	San Carlos	HAM	Boeing	Condor	
Boeing E75N1	WI	Oshkosh	EAAAAM	Boeing		
Boeing Inertial Upper Stage	WA	Seattle	MoF	Boeing	Upper Stage	
Boeing Lunar Rover	WA	Seattle	MoF	Boeing	Lunar Rover	
Boeing MIM-10B	ON-C	Ottaw	CAM	Boeing	Super Bomarc	60446
Boeing SST	CA	San Carlos	HAM	Boeing	SST	
Boeing SST	FL	CapeC		Boeing	SST	
Bolkow Bo 102	CA	CR	CR	Bolkow		
Bolkow Bo 208A-1 Jr	IA	Ottumwa	APM	Bolkow		525, N208JR
Boost Glide Reentry Vehicle	OH	Dayton	USAFM		Reentry Vehicle	
Bowers 1-A	CA	S.Mon	MoF	Bowers	Fly Baby	
Bowers Fly Baby	FL	Lakel	SFAF	Bowers	Fly Baby	
Bowers Flybaby 1-A	AZ	Tucso	PAM	Bowers	Flybaby	N49992
Bowers Flybaby 1-A	BC-C	Langley	CMoF	Bowers	Flybaby	
Bowers Flybaby 1-A	CA	Santa Martin	WoHAM	Bowers	Flybaby	
Bowers Flybaby 1-A	CA	S.Mar	SMMoF	Bowers	Flybaby	
Bowers Flybaby 1-A	CA	San Diego	SDAM	Bowers	Flybaby	
Bowers Flybaby 1-A	ND	WFarg	Bonanzav	Bowers	Flybaby	
Bowers Flybaby 1-A	OH	Madis	CFR	Bowers	Flybaby	
Bowers Flybaby 1-A	WA	Seatt	MoF	Bowers	Flybaby	68-15, N4339
Bowlus Albatross	CA	Santa Martin	WoHAM	Bowlus	Falcon	
Bowlus Albatross	NY	Elmir	NSM	Bowlus	Falcon	N6219Y, 25
Bowlus Albatross	VA	Hampt	APM	Bowlus	Falcon	
Bowlus Albatross I	MD	Silve	PEGF	Bowlus	Falcon	
Bowlus Albatross SP-1	CA	San Diego	SDAM	Bowlus	Falcon	
Bowlus BB-1	BC-C	Langley	CMoF	Bowlus	Bumblebee	506, N34922, CF-MB/CF-VFA
Bowlus Baby Ace	CA	Santa Martin	WoHAM	Bowlus	Baby Ace	
Bowlus Baby Ace	NM	Kirkl	KA	Bowlus	Baby Ace	
Bowlus BA-100	NY	Elmira	NSM	Super Bowlus	Baby Ace	N33658
Bowlus BA-100	NY	Elmira	NSM	Bowlus	Baby Ace	
Bowlus BA-102	NY	Elmira	NSM	Bowlus	Baby Ace	N33630
Bowlus Senior Albatross	NY	Elmira	NSM	Bowlus	Senior Albatross	NC219Y
Bowlus Baby Albatross	WA	Seattle	MoF	Bowlus	Baby Albatross	N25605
Bowlus Super Albatross	CA	M.Maria	WoHAM	Bowlus	Super Albatross	
Brantly 305	CA	Ramona	CR	Brantly	305	
Breese Penquin	NY	Garde	CoAM	Breese	Penquin	33622
Breguet G-3	NY	Rhine	ORA	Breguet		1911, 3 Seater Biplane
Brewster B-1	IA	Ottumwa	APM	Brewster		Sn 1, NC-20699
Brewster Bermuda	AZ	Tucson	PAM	Brewster	Bermuda	
Bristol Beaufighter	ON-C	Ottaw	CAM	Bristol	Beaufighter	RD 867
Bristol Beaufighter Mk.Ic	OH	Dayto	USAFM	Bristol	Beaufighter	A19-43
Bristol Beaufighter	TX	Kingbury	VAHF	Bristol	Beaufighter	
Bristol Beaufighter	TX	Kingbury	VAHF	Bristol	Beaufighter	Project
Bristol Beufort Mk.I	TX	Hawki	RRSA	Bristol	Beaufort	Torpedo-Bomber 1939
Bristol Blenheim Mk.IV	AB-C	Nanton	NLSAM	Bristol	Blenheim	
Bristol Bolingbroke	AB-C	Wetas	RM	Bristol	Bolingbroke	Model 149
Bristol Bolingbroke Mk IV	BC-C	Sidne	BCAM	Bristol	Bolingbroke	Model 149
Bristol Bolingbroke	BC-C	Langley	CMoF	Bristol	Bolingbroke	Model 149
Bristol Bolingbroke	CA	Chiriaco	GPM	Bristol	Bolingbroke	RCAF 9048
Bristol Bolingbroke	MB-C	Brand	CI	Bristol	Bolingbroke	Model 149
Bristol Bolingbroke	MB-C	Brand	CATPM	Bristol	Bolingbroke	9944
Bristol Bolingbroke	MB-C	Winni	WCAM	Bristol	Bolingbroke	Model 149
Bristol Bolingbroke Mk.IVT	ON-C	Ottaw	CAM	Bristol	Bolingbroke	Model 149, 9892
Bristol Bolingbroke Mk.IV	WON-C	Hamilton	CWH	Bolingbroke	Bolingbroke	Model 149, 903
Bristol Bolingbroke	NS-C	Greenwood	GMAM	Bristol	Bolingbroke	Model 149
Bristol F.2B	AL	Gunte	LGARFM	Bristol	Brisfit	
Bristol F.2B Rep	AZ	Grand	PoFGCVA	Bristol	Brisfit	PWZ
Bristol 170 Freighter Mk.31	NT-C	Yellowknife	YA	Bristol	Freighter	13137, CF-TFX
Bristol Type 170 Mk.31	MB-C	Winni	WCAM	Bristol	Freighter/Wayfarer	
Brock Keb 8BM Gyroplane	WI	Oshko	EAAAAM	Brock	Gyro-Plane	N2303
Broussard MH.1512	CA	SRosa	PCAM	Broussard	MH.1512	
Brown B-1	IL	Chica	MoS&I	Brown	B-1 Racer	
Brown B-1	WI	Oshko	EAAAAM	Brown	B-1 Racer	NR 83Y
Brown-Bushby-Robinson	WI	Oshkosh	EAAAAM	Brown-Bushby-Robinson	Suzie Jane 19	
Brown Star Lite	WI	Oshko	EAAAAM	Brown	Star Lite	N81197
Brugioni Mario	WI	Oshko	EAAAAM	Brugioni Mario	Cuby	
Brunner-Winkle Bird	NY	Bayport	BA	Brunner-Winkle	Bird	
Brunner-Winkle Bird	NY	Garde	CoAM	Brunner-Winkle	Bird	NC78K
Brunner-Winkle Bird	PA	Bethel	GAAM	Brunner-Winkle	Bird	NC726N
Brunner-Winkle Bird BK	VA	Sands	VAM	Brunner-Winkle	Bird	20250-96, N83!W
Brunner-Winkle Bird BK	CA	Chino	YAM	Brunner-Winkle	Bird	
Brunner-Winkle Bird BK	CA	San Diego	SDAM	Brunner-Winkle	Bird	N731Y
Brunner-Winkle Bird CK	NY	Rhine	ORA	Brunner-Winkle	Bird	
Brunner-Winkle Bird CK	NY	River	TFAC	Brunner-Winkle	Bird	
BT-9B	OH	Dayton	USAFM			
BT-12(YB)	OH	Newbu	WASAC	Fleetwings	Model 23	

Type	State	City	Code	Manufacturer	Model	Notes
BT-13	AZ	PBluf	RWCAF	Vultee	Valiant	
BT-13	CA	Atwater	CAM	Vultee	Valiant	42-16978, Side # E-205
BT-13	CA	Shafter	MFAM	Vultee	Valiant	
BT-13	CA	Fairf	TAFB	Vultee	Valiant	
BT-13	CT	Winds	NEAM	Vultee	Valiant	
BT-13	DE	Dover	DAFB	Vultee	Valiant	K-11
BT-13	IL	Danville	MAM	Vultee	Valiant	
BT-13	IN	Mento	LB	Vultee	Valiant	
BT-13	KS	New Century	CAF-HoAW	Vultee	Valiant	41-21216, N56665, "Good Vibrations"
BT-13	KS	New Century	CAF-HoAW	Vultee	Valiant	N2808
BT-13	KS	Topek	CAM	Vultee	Valiant	
BT-13	MN	Blaine	ACBA	Vultee	Valiant	44-30535
BT-13	MN	Minne	JJ	Vultee	Valiant	
BT-13	MS	Petal	MWHMM	Vultee	Valiant	
BT-13	NM	STere	WEAM	Vultee	Valiant	
BT-13	NV	Carso	YF	Vultee	Valiant	
BT-13	NY	Geneseo	1941AG	Vultee	Valiant	
BT-13	TX	Brown	RGVW-CAF	Vultee	Valiant	
BT-13	TX	Brown	RGVW-CAF	Vultee	Valiant	
BT-13	OH	Carroll	HAS	Vultee	Valiant	
BT-13	TX	Houst	CAF-GCW	Vultee	Valiant	N67208
BT-13 (SNV-1)	MI	Kalam	KAHM	Vultee	Valiant	11676
BT-13 (SNV-1VU)	MI	Ypsil	YAF	Vultee	Valiant	
BT-13 (SNV-2)	TX	Addison	CFM	Vultee	Valiant	13
BT-13	TX	RioHo	CAF-NCS	Vultee	Valiant	
BT-13A	AZ	Tucso	PAM	Vultee	Valiant	42-42353
BT-13A	CA	Riverside	MFAM	Vultee	Valiant	41-1414, Side BI-211
BT-13A	CA	Riverside	MFAM	Vultee	Valiant	41-1306, 21487
BT-13A	GA	Warner Robin	MoF	Vultee	Valiant	42-90018
BT-13A	KS	Liberal	MAAM	Vultee	Valiant	
BT-13A	KS	New Century	CAF-HoAW	Vultee	Valiant	N57486
BT-13A	IN	Indianapolis	AMHF	Vultee	Valiant	"Vibrator"
BT-13A	MB-C	Winni	WCAM	Vultee	Valiant	
BT-13A	MN	StPau	CAF-SMW	Vultee	Valiant	N52411
BT-13A	NC	Asheboro	PFAC	Vultee	Valiant	
BT-13A	OH	Newbu	WASAC	Vultee	Valiant	44- 9642
BT-13A	OK	Fredi	AAM	Vultee	Valiant	
BT-13A	SD	Rapid	SDA&SM	Vultee	Valiant	41-22204
BT-13A	TX	San Angelo	GAFB	Vultee	Valiant	42-04130
BT-13A	TX	Houst	CAF-GCW	Vultee	Valiant	N56336
BT-13A	TX	Houst	CAF-WHS	Vultee	Valiant	N27003
BT-13A	TX	Midla	CAFFM	Vultee	Valiant	
BT-13A(SNV-1)	VA	Manassas	CAFNCS	Vultee	Valiant	
BT-13A(SNV-1)	PA	Readi	MAAM	Vultee	Valiant	41-22441, N60277, 42
BT-13B	AL	Birmingham	SMoF	Vultee	Valiant	
BT-13B	CA	Chino	YAM	Vultee	Valiant	79-326, N4425V
BT-13B	OH	Dayto	USAFM	Vultee	Valiant	42-17800
BT-14 (NA-64)	AB-C	Nanton	NLSAM	North American	Yale	
BT-14 (NA-64)	AB-C	Wetas	RM	North American	Yale	
BT-14 (NA-64)	AZ	Tucso	PAM	North American	Yale	3397, N4735G
BT-14 (NA-64)	MB-C	Winni	WCAM	North American	Yale	
BT-14 (NA-64)	OH	Dayto	USAFM	North American	Yale	38-224
BT-14 (NA-64)	OH	Toled	TSA	North American	Yale	
BT-14 (NA-64)	ON-C	Dunnville	RCAFDA	North American	Yale	
BT-14 (NA-64)	ON-C	Hamilton	CWH	North American	Yale	CF-CWZ, 3350
BT-14 (NA-64)	ON-C	Tillsonburg	CHAA	North American	Yale	3399
BT-14 (NA-64)	SK-C	MJaw	WDM	North American	Yale	
BT-14 (NA-64)	TX	Midla	CAF-Hq	North American	Yale	N4574Y
BT-15	MN	Eden Prairie	WotN	Vultee	Valiant	
BT-15	OH	Newbu	WASAC	Vultee	Valiant	42-41597
BT-15	TX	Midla	CAFFM	Vultee	Valiant	
Bu.131	TX	Gilmer	PotP	Bucker		
Bu.133	FL	Polk	FoF	Bucker	Jungmeister	
Bu.133	ID	Athol	NAM	Bucker	Jungmeister	
Bu.133	MD	Silve	PEGF	Bucker	Jungmeister	
Bu.133	OK	Oklah	A&SM	Bucker	Jungmeister	
Bu.133	OK	Oklah	KCASM	Bucker	Jungmeister	
Bu.133-C	VA	Sands	VAM	Bucker	Jungmeister	Sn 251N133BU
Bu.133L	WI	Oshko	EAAAAM	Bucker	Jungmeister	N515
Bu.133L	WI	Oshko	EAAAAM	Bucker	Jungmeister	N258H
Bu.181	MD	Silve	PEGF	Bucker	Bestmann	
Bugatti 100	WI	Oshkosh	EAAAAM	Bugatti	100	
Buhl Sport	MN	Blaine	GWFM	Buhl	Airsedan	
Buhl Sport	ON-C	Sault Ste Marie	CBHC	Buhl	Airsedan	CF-OAT
Buhl Sport	ON-C	Sault Ste Marie	CBHC	Buhl	Airsedan	CF-OAR Wreckage
Buhl Sport	WY	Jackson	GWFM	Buhl	Airsedan	
Bunce-Curtiss Pusher	CT	Winds	NEAM	Bunce-Curtiss	Pusher	
Bunker 154	OK	Oklah	KCASM	Bunker	Model 154	
Burgess-Curtis SC	MD	Silve	PEGF	Burgess-Curtiss	SC	
Burgess-Dunne Rep	ON-C	Trenton	RCAFMM	Burgess-Dunne		
Burgess Twister	WI	Oshkosh	EAAAAM	Burgess-Knight	Twister Imperial	
Burgess-Wright B	ME	OwlsH	OHTM	Burgess-Wright	Flyer	
Burgess-Wright F	UT	Ogden	HAM	Burgess-Wright	Flyer	
Bushby Mustang I	KY	Louis	MoH&S	Bushby	Mustang I	
Bushby Mustang II	AL	Birmi	SMoF	Bushby	Mustang II	
Bushby Mustang II(MM-2)	AZ	Tucso	PAM	Bushby	Mustang Mk.2	Man Sn 581, N53RM
Bushby Mustang II	KS	Liberal	MAAM	Bushby	Mustang II	
Bushmaster 2000	MN	Blaine	GWM	Bushmaster	2000	
BV 155B	MD	Silve	PEGF	Blohm & Voss	Model 155B	
C- 1	FL	Kissi	FTWAM	Grumman	Trader	
C- 1A	CA	San Diego	SDACM	Grumman	Trader	146036
C- 1A	FL	Pensa	USNAM	Grumman	Trader	136754, 754, "Bicentenial"
C- 1A	PA	Willo	WGNAS	Grumman	Trader	62
C- 1A	CA	Palm Sprgs	PoFAM	Grumman	Cod Twin Tail	
C- 1A	RI	NKing	QAM	Grumman	Cod Twin Tail	136792
C- 1A	SC	Flore	FA&MM	Grumman	Cod Twin Tail	
C- 1A	TX	Galve	LSFM	Grumman	Cod Twin Tail	N 81193 146052
C- 2	CA	San Diego	NINAS			Tail RW, Nose 30, Side VRC 30
C- 2	OK	Tulsa	TA&SC		Spartan	
C- 3	OK	Tulsa	TA&SC		Spartan	
C- 5A	DE	Dover	DAFB	Lockheed	Galaxy	
C- 5A	NS-C	Halifax	ACAM	Lockheed	Galaxy	
C- 5A Simulator	NM	STere	WEAM	Lockheed	Galaxy	

Model	State	City	Code	Mfr	Type	Serial/Reg
C- 6A(VC)	IA	Sioux City	MAAM	Beechcraft	King Air	
C- 6A(VC)	NM	Las Cruces	WSMP	Beechcraft	King Air	
C- 6A(VC)	OH	Dayto	USAFM	Beechcraft	King Air	66-0943
C- 7	NC	Fayet	FBADM	de Havilland	Caribou	
C- 7A	CA	Fairfield	TAFB	de Havilland	Caribou	
C- 7A	CT	Winds	NEAM	de Havilland	Caribou	62-4188
C- 7A	DE	Dover	DAFB	de Havilland	Caribou	
C- 7A(CV2B)	GA	Hampton	AAHF	de Havilland	Caribou	
C- 7A	GA	Warner Robin	MoF	de Havilland	Caribou	63-9756, 756, "Dixie Pub"
C- 7A	OH	Dayto	USAFM	de Havilland	Caribou	62-4193
C- 7A	TX	Abile	DLAP	de Havilland	Caribou	58-82
C- 7A	TX	Amarillo	EFA&SM	de Havilland	Caribou	63-9719
C- 7A	UT	Ogden	HAFBM	de Havilland	Caribou	
C- 7A(CV-7)	VA	FtEus	USATM	de Havilland	Caribou	57-3079, (Golden Knights)
C- 7B	CA	Rosam	EAFB	de Havilland	Caribou	63-9765
C- 7B	DE	Dover	DAFB	de Havilland	Caribou	KA-760
C- 14(YC)	AZ	Tucso	PAM	Boeing		72- 1873
C- 15(YC)	AZ	Tucso	PAM	McDonnell		72- 1875
C- 21B(CH)	AK	Palme	MOAT&I			
C- 35 (XC)	MD	Silve	PEGF	Lockheed	Electra	
C- 36(UC)	AZ	Tucso	PAM	Lockheed	Lockheed 10	43-56638, N4963C
C- 37	AB-C	Wetas	RM	Airmaster		
C- 37	MB-C	Winni	WCAM	Airmaster		
C- 39A	OH	Dayto	USAFM	Douglas		38-515
C- 40	CA	Chino	YAM	Lockheed		
C- 41	CA	SLean	OSA	Douglas		2053, NC41HQ, "General Hap Arnold"
C- 43(UC)	CA	Chino	YAM	Beech	Traveler	4890, N51746
C- 43(UC)	OH	Dayto	USAFM	Beech	Traveler	44-76068
C- 45	AR	Mesa	CAFAW	Beech	Twin Beech	
C- 45	WA	Seattle	MoF	Beech	Twin Beech	51-11696, N115ME
C- 45	AZ	Mesa	CAF-AW	Beech	Twin Beech	N145AZ
C- 45	AZ	PBluf	RWCAF	Beech	Twin Beech	
C- 45	CA	Fairf	TAFB	Beech	Twin Beech	
C- 45	GA	Atlan	CAF-DW	Beech	Twin Beech	N70GA
C- 45	IL	Linco	HIFM	Beech	Twin Beech	
C- 45	KS	Liberal	MAAM	Beech	Twin Beech	
C- 45	LA	Reser	AMHFM	Beech	Twin Beech	
C- 45	MI	Selfridge	PAM	Beech	Twin Beech	42-37511
C- 45	MN	Minne	MAGM	Beech	Twin Beech	51-338
C- 45	MN	Winoma	WTI	Beech	Twin Beech	N3785
C- 45	MO	Missoula	MMF	Beech	Twin Beech	
C- 45	MS	Canto	CAF-MW	Beech	Twin Beech	N4207
C- 45	NM	Hobbs	CAF-NMW	Beech	Twin Beech	N79AG
C- 45	NC	Asheboro	PFAC	Beech	Twin Beech	
C- 45	NY	Brooklyn	PFAC	Beech	Twin Beech	90536
C- 45(SNB-5)	OH	N Canton	MAM	Beech	Twin Beech	67103, N200KU
C- 45	OH	Newbu	WASAC	Beech	Twin Beech	N99662
C- 45	OH	S.Euc	USAM	Beech	Twin Beech	
C- 45	OK	Enid	CAF-CSW	Beech	Twin Beech	N40074
C- 45	SD	Rapid	SDA&SM	Beech	Twin Beech	
C- 45	TX	Ladero	Airport	Beech	Twin Beech	
C- 45 (2 EA)	CO	Denve	JWDAS	Beech	Twin Beech	
C-45(CT-134)	CA	Santa Martin	WoHAM	Beech	Musketeer	Model 23
C-45(CT-134)	AB-C	Wetaskawin	CFB	Beech	Musketeer	134232
C-45(CT-134)	MB-C	Brandon	CATPM	Beech	Musketeer	
C-45(CT-134)	MB-C	Portage	S	Beech	Musketeer	134201
C-45(CT-134)	MB-C	Portage	S	Beech	Musketeer	134238
C-45(CT-134)	MB-C	Winni	WRCFB	Beech	Musketeer	134228
C-45(CT-134)	ON-C	Campbellford	CFB	Beech	Musketeer	134219
C-45(CT-134)	ON-C	Picton	CFB	Beech	Musketeer	134211
C-45(CT-134)	ON-C	Toronto	TAM	Beech	Musketeer	
C-45(CT-134)	ON-C	Trenton	RCAFMM	Beech	Musketeer	23
C-45(CT-134A)	ON-C	Brockville	Park	Beech	Musketeer	
C-45(CT-134A)	ON-C	Campbellford	MMM	Beech	Musketeer	
C-45(CT-134A)	ON-C	Prairie LP	PA	Beech	Musketeer	11400
C-45(CT-134A)	ON-C	Prairie LP	FLPRM	Beech	Musketeer	
C-45(CT-134A)	SK-C	Regina		Beech	Musketeer	A141
C-45(CT-128)	MB-C	Winnipeg	AFHP	Beech	Expediter	
C- 45	WY	Greyb	H&PA	Beech	Expediter	
C- 45 (D-18 / CT-128)	MB-C	Brandon	CATPM	Beech	Expediter	
C- 45 (JRB)	AR	Fayetteville	AAM	Beech	Expediter	
C- 45 (JRB Mk.III)	MB-C	Portage	S	Beech	Expediter	1560
C- 45 (JRB Mk.III)	MB-C	Winni	WCAM	Beech	Expediter	1528
C- 45(JRB)	OH	Leroy	PRA	Beech	Expediter	
C- 45 (JRB Mk.III)	VT	Burli	BANG	Beech	Expediter	
C- 45 (SNB) Trainer	AR	Walnut Ridge	WRAFSM	Beech	Kansan	
C- 45 (SNB)	CA	Chino	PoFAM	Beech	Kansan	BG-33
C- 45 (SNB)	KS	Topek	CAM	Beech	Kansan	
C-45H(SNB)	NY	Horseheads	NWM	Beech	Kansan	52-01539
C- 45 (SNB-5)	AZ	Tucso	PAM	Beech	Kansan	N40090, 39213
C-45(SNB-5)	AZ	Marana	SAW	Beech	Twin Beech	
C- 45 (UC)	AK	Fairb	APAM	Beech	Twin Beech	N9199Z
C-45A	CA	Atwater	CAM	Beech	Twin Beech	51-1897
C-45F(JRB-4)	CA	Riverside	MFAM	Beech	Expediter	44588, 52-10588A
C-45F(UC)	AK	Ancho	AAHM	Beech	Twin Beech	
C-45F(UC) Cockpit	MD	Ft Meade	QM	Beech	Twin Beech	
C-45G	DE	Dover	DAFB	Beech	Twin Beech	
C-45G	IN	Ligonier	ZF	Beech	Twin Beech	AF95, British
C-45H	AK	Ancho	AAHM	Beech	Twin Beech	
C-45H	AL	Ozark	USAAM	Beech	Expediter	51-11638
C-45H	FL	Titusville	VACM	Beech	Twin Beech	
C-45H	GA	Warner Robin	MoF	Beech	Expediter	51-11653, N141ZA
C-45H	IL	Belle	SAFB	Beech	Twin Beech	
C-45H	OH	Dayto	USAFM	Beech	Twin Beech	52-10893
C-45H	UT	Ogden	HAFBM	Beech	Twin Beech	
C-45J	IL	Belle	SAFB	Beech	Twin Beech	
C-45J	ND	Fargo	FANG	Beech	Twin Beech	
C-45J	TX	Midla	CAFFM	Beech	Twin Beech	
C-45J(UC)	TX	San A	LAFB	Beech	Twin Beech	29639, #637
C-45J(RC)(SNB-5P)	FL	Pensa	USNAM	Beech	Kansan	9771, 4P, NATTU, PNCL
C-45J(RC)	GA	Woodstock	NGWS	Beech	Twin Beech	
C-45J(UC)	AL	Ozark	USAAM	Beech	Expediter	43-9767
C-45J(UC)	CA	Sacra	McCelAFB	Beech	Twin Beech	51-291

Type	State	City	Code	Mfr	Name	Notes
C-45J(UC)	ON-C	Hamilton	CWH	Beech	Twin Beech	
C-45J(UC)	TX	D Rio	LAFB	Beech	Twin Beech	
C-45J(UC)(SNB-2)	CA	Rosam	EAFB	Beech	Twin Beech	67161
C-45J(UC)(SNB-2C)	AZ	Tucso	PAM	Beechcraft	Expeditor	43-50222, N1082
C-45J(YC)(SNB-5)	AZ	Tucso	PAM	Beechcraft	Expeditor	Sn 39123, N75018, 29585
C-46	CA	Chino	YAM	Curtiss	Commando	43-47218
C-46	NM	Las Cruces	LCIA	Curtiss	Commando	
C-46	NM	Las Cruces	SA	Curtiss	Commando	
C-46(EC)(R5C)	FL	Pensa	USNAM	Curtiss	Commando	398, N611Z, 39611, 14, 398CK
C-46(EC)(R5D-2Z)	CA	Miramar	FLAM	Curtiss	Commando	MARS-37
C-46A	GA	Warner Robin	MoF	Curtiss	Commando	42-10119, 198S, 42-101198
C-46D	AZ	Tucso	PAM	Curtiss	Commando	44-77635
C-46D	AZ	Tucso	PAM	Curtiss	Commando	44-78019, N32229
C-46D	CA	Atwater	CAM	Curtiss	Commando	44-77575
C-46D	FL	FtWal	HF	Curtiss	Commando	44-424
C-46D	OH	Dayto	USAFM	Curtiss	Commando	44-78018
C-46F	CA	Camarillo	CAF-SCW	Curtiss	Commando	78774, N53594, "China Doll"
C-46F(NC)	NC	Fayet	FBADM	Curtiss	Commando	44-78573
C-47 *See C-53*				Douglas	Sky Train	
C-47 *See R4D*				Douglas	Sky Train	
C-47	AA	Starke	CBM	Douglas	Sky Train	12436, nose Z7
C-47	AZ	Tucso	PAM	Douglas	Sky Train	41-7723, 4201
C-47	CA	Chino	YAM	Douglas	Sky Train	
C-47	CA	Palm Springs	PSAM	Douglas	Sky Train	0106, N60154, #44
C-47	DE	New Castle	ATC	Douglas	Sky Train	"Kilroy Was Here"
C-47	FL	Clear	FMAM	Douglas	Sky Train	
C-47	FL	Kissimmee	FTWRM	Douglas	Sky Train	
C-47	FL	Polk	FoF	Douglas	Sky Train	
C-47	FL	Stark	CB-FANTC	Douglas	Sky Train	
C-47	FL	Titus	VACM	Douglas	Sky Train	2100591, S U 5, "Tico Belle"
C-47	FL	WPalm	391FG	Douglas	Sky Train	
C-47	GA	Atlanta	ASG	Douglas	Sky Train	
C-47	GA	Calho	MAM	Douglas	Sky Train	45-928, N54599
C-47	GA	Douglas	LF	Douglas	Sky Train	
C-47(R4D-6R)	IL	Chica	CAF-GLW	Douglas	Sky Train	99854, N227GB
C-47(AC)	KS	Topeka	SS	Douglas	Sky Train	45-1120, N2805J, "Spooky"
C-47	KY	FKnox	FC	Douglas	Sky Train	
C-47	MB-C	Winnipeg	WRCAFB	Douglas	Sky Train	
C-47	MI	Kalam	KAHM	Douglas	Sky Train	42-93168
C-47	ND	Minot	DTAM	Douglas	Sky Train	
C-47 Cockit	ND	Minot	DTAM	Douglas	Sky Train	
C-47(SC)	NM	Albuquerque	KAFB	Douglas	Sky Train	035732
C-47(SC)	NM	Albuq	KAFB	Douglas	Sky Train	035732
C-47	NY	Brooklyn	Bonanzav	Douglas	Sky Train	
C-47	NY	Geneseo	HAGM	Douglas	Sky Train	
C-47(R4D-5)	NY	Horsehead	WoE	Douglas	Sky Train	43-13860, N293WM
C-47	OK	Oklah	SFG	Douglas	Sky Train	892953, , "U7", T
C-47	OH	N Canton	MAM	Douglas	Sky Train	45-0928, N54599, "Raptured Duck"
C-47	ON-C	Ottaw	CAM	Douglas	Sky Train	
C-47	ON-C	Petawawa	CFBPMM	Douglas	Sky Train	
C-47	ON-C	Trenton	RCAFMM	Douglas	Sky Train	
C-47	OR	Tillamook	TAM	Douglas	Sky Train	43-15512, N62376
C-47	TX	Burnet	HLSCAF	Douglas	Sky Train	
C-47	TX	FWort	PMoT	Douglas	Sky Train	
C-47	TX	Houston	1940ATM	Douglas	Sky Train	
C-47(EC)	TX	San Antonio	VMP	Douglas	Sky Train	43-48415 as 43-49201
C-47	VA	Peter	FL	Douglas	Sky Train	
C-47 (R4D)	CO	Puebl	PWAM	Douglas	Sky Train	17217
C-47 Simulator	NY	Garde	CoAM	Douglas	Sky Train	
C-47(UH)	MS	Petal	MWHMM	Douglas	Sky Train	
C-47(VC)	CA	Riverside	MFAM	Douglas	Sky Train	43-15579, "Golden Bear"
C-47(VC)	ND	WFarg	Bonanzav	Douglas	Sky Train	
C-47A	AK	Ancho	KANGB	Douglas	Sky Train	
C-47A	AK	Palme	MOAT&I	Douglas	Sky Train	
C-47A	AZ	Marana	SAW	Douglas	Sky Train	
C-47A	CA	Atwater	CAM	Douglas	Sky Train	43-15977, Tail N, Side L7
C-47A	DE	Dover	DAFB	Douglas	Sky Train	292841, Q9, R, "Turf & Sport Special"
C-47A	LA	Bossi	BAFB	Douglas	Sky Train	"Hi Honey"
C-47A-90-DL(DC-3-C)	MO	Missoula	MMF	Douglas	Dakota	43-15731, 20197, N24320
C-47A	NY	Glenville	ESAM	Douglas	Sky Train	43-12061
C-47A	SD	Rapid	SDA&SM	Douglas	Sky Train	N226GB
C-47A	TX	Abile	DLAP	Douglas	Sky Train	41-8808
C-47A RAF	NWTC	HayRi	BA	Douglas	Dakota	12327, C- GWZS
C-47A RAF	NWTC	HayRi	BA	Douglas	Dakota	13155, C- FLFR
C-47A RAF	NWTC	HayRi	BA	Douglas	Dakota	13333, C- GPNR
C-47A(AC)	FL	FtWal	HF	Douglas	Sky Train	42-510, AH
C-47A(AC)	FL	Shali	USAFAM	Douglas	Sky Train	43-10, O
C-47A(R4D-6)	GA	Warner Robin	MoF	Douglas	Sky Train	43-48957, 15090 EL, "Saylor's Trailer"
C-47A(VC)	MO	SLoui	NMoT	Douglas	Sky Train	43-15635
C-47A(VC)	ND	WFarg	Bonanzav	Douglas	Sky Train	42-93800
C-47A-30-DK	NE	Ashland	SACM	Douglas	Sky Train	43-48098
C-47B	AL	Montg	GAFB	Douglas	Sky Train	
C-47B	MN	Minne	MAGM	Douglas	Sky Train	44-7462
C-47B	NC	Fayet	FBADM	Douglas	Sky Train	
C-47B	NC	Fayet	PAFB	Douglas	Sky Train	
C-47B	ND	Fargo	FANG	Douglas	Sky Train	
C-47B(TC)	WA	Tacoma	MAFB	Douglas	Sky Train	
C-47D	AZ	Tucso	PAM	Douglas	Sky Train	Sn 41-7723
C-47D	IL	Ranto	OCAM	Douglas	Sky Train	43-49336
C-47D	IN	Peru	GAFB	Douglas	Sky Train	43-49270
C-47D	KS	Topek	CAM	Douglas	Sky Train	45-1074, 476582, 17077 / 34344, "Kilroy", J8
C-47D	MI	Belleville	YAF	Douglas	Sky Train	44-76716, N33048, "Yankee Doodle Dandy"
C-47D	MI	Ypsil	YAF	Douglas	Sky Train	
C-47D	OH	Dayto	USAFM	Douglas	Sky Train	43-49507
C-47D	TX	San A	LAFB	Douglas	Sky Train	44-76671
C-47D	WA	Spoka	FAFBHM	Douglas	Sky Train	
C-47D(VC)	AL	Mobil	BMP	Douglas	Sky Train	40-76326
C-47D(VC)	SC	Charl	CAFB	Douglas	Sky Train	
C-47D(VC)	TX	Midla	CAFFM	Douglas	Sky Train	
C-47D(VC)	UT	Ogden	HAFBM	Douglas	Sky Train	43-49281
C-47H	AL	Ozark	USAAM	Douglas	Gooney Bird	41-12436
C-47H(R4D-5)	FL	Pensa	USNAM	Douglas	Sky Train	12418, 18
C-47J	GA	Warner Robin	MoF	Douglas	Sky Train	43-49442, N50811

113

Model	State	City	Museum	Manufacturer	Name	Notes
C- 50	CT	Winds	NEAM	Douglas	Sky Train	
C- 53	CA	Rosam	EAFB	Douglas	Skytrooper	
C- 53D	CA	Sacra	McCelAFB	Douglas	Skytrooper	42-68835
C- 54	CA	Riverside	WFAM	Douglas	Skymaster	42-72636
C- 54	NJ	Farmi	BAHF	Douglas	Skymaster	"Spirit of Freedom"
C- 54	NY	Brooklyn	BAHF	Douglas	Skymaster	
C- 54	SD	Rapid	SDA&SM	Douglas	Skymaster	42-72592
C- 54	TX	Brown	RGVW-CAF	Douglas	Skymaster	
C- 54	WA	Seattle	MoF	Douglas	Skymaster	
C- 54	WY	Greyb	H&PA	Douglas	Skymaster	
C- 54B(R5D-2)	MA	NAndo	AW	Douglas	Skymaster	N44914, 56498, "Air Transport Command"
C- 54C(VC)	OH	Dayto	USAFM	Douglas	Skymaster	42-10745, 1, 42-107451, "Sacred Cow"
C- 54D(DC-4)	AZ	Tucso	PAM	Douglas	Skymaster	42-72488
C- 54D	CA	Riverside	MAFB	Douglas	Skymaster	42-72636, 56514, N67062
C- 54D	CA	Sacra	McCelAFB	Douglas	Skymaster	42-72449
C- 54D	TX	Midla	CAFFM	Douglas	Skymaster	
C- 54D-1-DL	NE	Ashland	SACM	Douglas	Skymaster	42-72724
C- 54E	CA	Atwater	CAM	Douglas	Skymaster	1373
C- 54G	GA	Warner Robin	MoF	Douglas	Skymaster	45-579, A
C- 54G	UT	Ogden	HAM	Douglas	Skymaster	45-502
C- 54M	DE	Dover	DAFB	Douglas	Skymaster	
C- 54Q	CA	Fairf	TAFB	Douglas	Skymaster	
C- 56 (L.18)	CA	Atwater	CAM	Lockheed	Lodestar	
C- 56 (L.18)	CA	Fairf	TAFB	Lockheed	Lodestar	
C- 60 (L.18)	BC-C	Langley	CMoF	Lockheed	Lodestar	
C- 60 (L.18)	CA	Chino	PoFAM	Lockheed	Lodestar	
C- 60 (L.18)	CA	SAnto	CAF-AW	Lockheed	Lodestar	N6371C
C- 60 (L.18)	TX	Houston	1940AT	Lockheed	Lodestar	
C- 60 (L.18)	VA	Chesa	CAF-ODS	Lockheed	Lodestar	N30N
C- 60A(L.18)(PV1)(R50)	CO	Westminster	CAF	Lockheed	Lodestar	43-16438
C- 60A(L.18)	GA	Warner Robin	MoF	Lockheed	Lodestar	42-55918, N18198
C- 60A(L.18)	OH	Dayto	USAFM	Lockheed	Lodestar	43-16445, Military Version L.18
C- 60A(L.18)	VA	Chesapeake	CAFODW	Lockheed	Lodestar	
C- 60C(L.18C)	CA	Atwater	CAM	Lockheed	Lodestar	
C- 61(UC)(FC-24)	AK	Ancho	AAHM	Fairchild	Argus	
C- 61(UC)(FC-24)	KS	Liberal	MAAM	Fairchild	Argus	
C- 61(UC)(FC-24)	PA	Reading	MAAM	Fairchild	Argus	NC19133
C- 61(UC)(FC-24)	VA	Sands	VAM	Fairchild	Argus	Sn 2983, Model G, N19123
C- 61(UC)(FC-24)	WA	Seatt	MoF	Fairchild	Argus	
C- 61(UC)(FC-24)	AB-C	Edmonton	AAM	Fairchild	Argus	
C- 61(UC)(FC-24)	ON-C	Greenwood	GMAM	Fairchild	Argus	
C- 61B(UC)(FC-24J)	AK	Fairb	APAM	Fairchild	Argus	NC20617, "Pollack Flying Service"
C- 61F(UC)(FC-24R)	ON-C	Hamilton	CWH	Fairchild	Argus	C-FGZL, 4809
C- 61G(UC)(FC-24H)	OK	Fredi	AAM	Fairchild	Argus	
C- 61G(UC)(FC-24W)	AL	Birmi	Southe	Fairchild	Argus	
C- 61G(UC)(FC-24W)	OK	Fredi	AAM	Fairchild	Argus	
C- 61G(UC)(FC-24W-46)	MB-C	Winni	WCAM	Fairchild	Argus	
C- 61G(UC)(FC-24W-46)	WI	Oshko	EAAAAM	Fairchild	Argus	N81318
C- 61G(UC)(FC-2W) Frame	AK	Ancho	AAHM	Fairchild	Argus	
C- 61J(UC)(FC-24 C8)	WI	Oshko	EAAAAM	Fairchild	Argus	N13191
C- 61J(UC)(FC-24C-8A)	WI	Oshko	EAAAAM	Fairchild	Argus	N957V
C- 61K(UC)	KS	Topek	CAM	Fairchild	Argus	N-18395
C- 64	AB-C	Edmonton	AAM	Noorduyn	Norseman	
C- 64	ON-C	Red Lake	HB	Noorduyn	Norseman	
C- 64A Mk.I	ON-C	Sault Se Marie	CBHC	Noorduyn	Norseman	CF-AYO
C- 64	AK	Ancho	AAHM	Noorduyn-CCF	Norseman	N725M
C- 64	BC-C	Sidne	BCAM	Noorduyn-CCF	Norseman	"Thunder Chicken"
C- 64A Mk.IV	ON-C	Sault Ste Marie	CBHC	Noorduyn-CCF	Norseman	Sn 17, CF-BFT
C- 64	SK-C	MJaw	WDM	Noorduyn-CCF	Norseman	
C- 64(UC)	CO	Denve	JWDAS	Noorduyn	Norseman	
C- 64(YC)	MD	Silve	PEGF	Noorduyn	Norseman	
C- 64(YC) Mk.IV	MD	Silve	PEGF	Noorduyn	Norseman	
C- 64A Mk.IV	AB-C	Wetas	RM	Noorduyn-CCF	Norseman	
C- 64A Mk.IV	MB-C	Winnipeg	WCAM	Noorduyn-CCF	Norseman	
C- 64A Mk.IVW	BC-C	Langley	CMoF	Noorduyn-CCF	Norseman	
C- 64A Mk.V	AB-C	Calga	AMoC	Noorduyn-CCF	Norseman	
C- 64A Mk.V	BC-C	Langley	CMoF	Noorduyn-CCF	Norseman	
C- 64A Mk.VI	AK	Fairb	APAM	Noorduyn-CCF	Norseman	N55555, "Alaska Airways"
C- 64A Mk.VI	ON-C	Ottaw	CAM	Noorduyn-CCF	Norseman	
C- 64A(UC)	OH	Dayto	USAFM	Noorduyn	Norseman	44-70296
C- 78(UC) See Also AT-17	AZ	Tucso	PAM	Cessna	Bobcat	42-39162, N66794,
C- 78(UC) See Also (T-50)	CA	Atwater	CAM	Cessna	Bobcat	
C- 78(UC)	CA	Fairf	TAFB	Cessna	Bobcat	
C- 78(UC)	CO	Denve	JWDAS	Cessna	Bobcat	3806 806
C- 78(UC)	MD	Cambr	CA	Cessna	Bobcat	
C- 78(UC)	NY	River	RE	Cessna	Bobcat	
C- 78(UC)	PA	Readi	MAAM	Cessna	Bobcat	N 41793
C- 78(UC)	TX	Midla	CAF-Hq	Cessna	Bobcat	N 44795
C- 78(UC)	TX	SMarc	CTWCAF	Cessna	Bobcat	
C- 78B(UC)	AZ	Tucso	PAM	Cessna	Bobcat	42-71830
C- 78B(UC)	GA	Warner Robin	MoF	Cessna	Bobcat	42-71714
C- 78B(UC)	OH	Dayto	USAFM	Cessna	Bobcat	42-71626
C- 82	OH	Newbu	WASAC	Fairchild	Packet	44-22991
C- 82	WA	Tacoma	MAFB	Fairchild	Packet	
C- 82	WY	Greyb	H&PA	Fairchild	Packet	
C- 82A	AZ	Tucso	PAM	Fairchild	Packet	44-23006, N6997C
C- 82A	OH	Dayto	USAFM	Fairchild	Packet	48-581
C- 97(KC)	CO	Colorado Sprs	SR	Boeing	Stratocruiser	3-0283
C- 97(KC)	OH	Newbu	WASAC	Boeing	Stratocruiser	235
C- 97(KC)	WI	Dodge	Restaura	Boeing	Stratocruiser	
C- 97(KC)	WY	Greyb	H&PA	Boeing	Stratocruiser	
C- 97G	AZ	Tucso	PAM	Boeing	Stratocruiser	Sn 52-2626, HB-ILY
C- 97G	CA	Lanca	MoFM	Boeing	Stratocruiser	
C- 97G	IL	Ranto	OCAM	Boeing	Stratocruiser	52-0898
C- 97G(KC)	AZ	Tucso	PAM	Boeing	Stratocruiser	53-151
C- 97G(KC)	MO	White	WAFB	Boeing	Stratotanker	0-30327
C- 97G(KC)	NJ	Farmi	BAHF	Boeing	Stratocruiser	52- 2718, N117GA, "Deliverance"
C- 97G(KC)	NV	Las Vegas	LBAHSM	Boeing	Stratocruiser	53-0317, N971HP, #377, Cockpit
C- 97G(KC)	OR	Medford	RVIA	Boeing	Stratocruiser	2-0895
C- 97G(KC)	TX	Midla	CAFFM	Boeing	Stratocruiser	
C- 97G(KC)-BN	NE	Ashland	SACM	Boeing	Stratocruiser	53-0198
C- 97K(KC)	SC	Flore	FA&MM	Boeing	Stratocruiser	
C- 97L(KC)	CA	Atwater	CAM	Boeing	Stratocruiser	0-0354,

C-97L(KC)	CA	Marys	BAFB	Boeing	Stratocruiser	
C-97L(KC)	CA	Riverside	MFAM	Boeing	Stratotanker	53-0363
C-97L(KC)	GA	Warner Robin	MoF	Boeing	Stratotanker	53-298
C-97L(KC)	IN	Peru	GAFB	Boeing	Stratocruiser	52-2297
C-97L(KC)	LA	Bossi	BAFB	Boeing	Stratocruiser	0240
C-97L(KC)	MD	Silve	PEGF	Boeing	Stratocruiser	
C-97L(KC)	MT	Great Falls	MAFB	Boeing	Stratocruiser	53-360, 0-30354, 2638
C-97L(KC)	NH	Ports	PAFB	Boeing	Stratocruiser	
C-97L(KC)	OH	Dayto	USAFM	Boeing	Stratocruiser	52-2630
C-97L(KC)	TX	Abile	DLAP	Boeing	Stratocruiser	53-282
C-97L(KC)	TX	FWort	NASFWJRB	Boeing	Stratocruiser	
C-97L(KC)	TX	FWort	SAM	Boeing	Stratocruiser	
C-97L(KC)	WI	CDoug	WNGML&M	Boeing	Stratocruiser	905
C-103A	AZ	Tucso	DMAFB			
C-117D *See R4D*						
C-118	WY	Greyb	H&PA	Douglas	Liftmaster	
C-118(VC)	OH	Dayto	USAFM	Douglas	Liftmaster	46-505
C-118(YO)	CA	Fairf	TAFB	Douglas	Liftmaster	
C-118A	NJ	Trent	MGAFB	Douglas	Liftmaster	
C-118A	TX	San A	LAFB	Douglas	Liftmaster	51-17640
C-118A(VC)(DC-6)	AZ	Tucso	PAM	Douglas	Liftmaster	53-3240, 33240, "Air Force One"
C-118B(R6D-1)	OK	Altus	AAFB	Douglas	Liftmaster	
C-118B(R6D-1)	FL	Pensa	USNAM	Douglas	Liftmaster	128424, 424
C-119	CO	Puebl	PWAM	Fairchild	Flying Boxcar	131688
C-119	GA	FtBen	IM	Fairchild	Flying Boxcar	
C-119	KY	FKnox	FC	Fairchild	Flying Boxcar	
C-119	NV	Battl	BMAM	Fairchild	Flying Boxcar	N5216R, 137
C-119F	PA	Readi	MAAM	Fairchild	Flying Boxcar	N175ML, VMR-52
C-119	TX	FWort	PMoT	Fairchild	Flying Boxcar	0-12675
C-119	WI	Milwa	MANG	Fairchild	Flying Boxcar	
C-119	WY	Greyb	H&PA	Fairchild	Flying Boxcar	
C-119(R4Q-2)	CA	Miramar	FLAM	Fairchild	Flying Boxcar	708, VMR-352
C-119B	CA	Rosam	EAFB	Fairchild	Flying Boxcar	48-352
C-119B	GA	Warner Robin	MoF	Fairchild	Flying Boxcar	51-2566
C-119C	AZ	Tucso	PAM	Fairchild	Flying Boxcar	49-0157
C-119C	AZ	Tucso	PAM	Fairchild	Flying Boxcar	49-132, N13743
C-119C	CA	Atwater	CAM	Fairchild	Flying Boxcar	49-199, N13744
C-119C	TX	Midla	CAFFM	Fairchild	Flying Boxcar	
C-119F	NY	Geneseo	1941AG	Fairchild	Flying Boxcar	10678
C-119G	CA	Fairf	TAFB	Fairchild	Flying Boxcar	134
C-119G	CA	Riverside	MFAM	Fairchild	Flying Boxcar	RCAF 22122, 452 TCW
C-119G	CA	Sacra	McCelAFB	Fairchild	Flying Boxcar	52-114
C-119G	DE	Dover	DAFB	Fairchild	Flying Boxcar	
C-119G	FL	FtWal	HF	Fairchild	Flying Boxcar	33144
C-119G	IN	Peru	GAFB	Fairchild	Flying Boxcar	52- 5850, "Hash-2-Zero"
C-119G	UT	Ogden	HAFBM	Fairchild	Flying Boxcar	
C-119J	AR	Littl	LRAFB	Fairchild	Flying Boxcar	53-8084, 314th TAW
C-119J	OH	Dayto	USAFM	Fairchild	Flying Boxcar	51-8037
C-119L	NC	Fayet	FBADM	Fairchild	Flying Boxcar	
C-121 (EC)(L-1049)	TX	San Antonio	LAFB	Lockheed	Constellation	54115
C-121 (L-0749)	MA	Stow	BCF	Lockheed	Constellation	
C-121 (L-0749)	MO	River	SACI	Lockheed	Constellation	"TWA"
C-121 (L-0749)	MT	Helena	CoT	Lockheed	Constellation	52-3417
C-121A(L-0749)	AZ	Tucso	PAM	Lockheed	Constellation	48-614, USAF Constellation
C-121A(L-0749A)	AZ	Scott	CG	Lockheed	Constellation	48-609, 2601, USAF Constellation MATS
C-121A(VC)(L-0749)	AL	Ozark	USAAM	Lockheed	Constellation	48-613, USAF Constellation
C-121A(VC)(L-0749)	AZ	Grand	PoFGCVA	Lockheed	Constellation	48-613, N422NA, Constellation, "Bataan"
C-121C(L-0749)	CA	Lanca	CHS	Lockheed	Constellation	54-156, N73544, USAF Constellation
C-121C(L-0749)	SC	Charl	CAFB	Lockheed	Constellation	USAF Constellation
C-121D(EC)(L-1049)	OH	Dayto	USAFM	Lockheed	Warning Star	53-555, USAF Super Constellation
C-121E(VC)(L-0749)	OH	Dayto	USAFM	Lockheed	Constellation	53-7885
C-121G(L-0749)	DE	Dover	DAFBHC	Lockheed	Constellation	
C-121K(EC)	FL	Pensa	USNAM	Lockheed	Warning Star	143221, VT 86
C-121K(EC)(L-1049)	GA	Warner Robin	MoF	Lockheed	Warning Star	141297, USAF Super Constellation
C-121S(EC)	TX	San A	LAFB	Lockheed	Super Constellation	54- 155,
C-121T(EC)(L-1049)	AZ	Tucso	PAM	Lockheed	Warning Star	53-554, USAF Constellation
C-123B	AZ	Tucso	PAM	Fairchild	Provider	55-4505
C-123J	AK	Ancho	KANGB	Fairchild	Provider	
C-123J	AK	Palme	MOAT&I	Fairchild	Provider	N98
C-123K	AZ	Phoenix	DVA	Fairchild	Provider	
C-123K	AZ	Tucso	PAM	Fairchild	Provider	54-580, N3142D, 731TAS, "War Wagon"
C-123K	AZ	Tucso	PAM	Fairchild	Provider	Sn 54-0659, N2129J
C-123K	CA	Atwater	CAM	Fairchild	Provider	54-512, Tail WX
C-123K	CA	Riverside	MFAM	Fairchild	Provider	54-612, "The Chief"
C-123K	CA	Rosam	EAFB	Fairchild	Provider	54-683
C-123K	CA	Fairfield	TAFB	Fairchild	Provider	
C-123K	DE	Dover	DAFB	Fairchild	Provider	WM
C-123K	FL	Titusville	AAF	Fairchild	Provider	54-674
C-123K(UC)	FL	FtWal	HF	Fairchild	Provider	55- 533
C-123K(UC)	NY	Farmingdale	AAM	Fairchild	Provider	55- 4533
C-123K	MN	Blaine	Airport	Fairchild	Provider	N681DG
C-123K	MN	Blaine	Airport	Fairchild	Provider	54603, NX-4254H, #603, "Cat House", Air America"
C-123K	MN	Minneapolis	MAGM	Fairchild	Provider	
C-123K	NC	Fayet	FBADM	Fairchild	Provider	
C-123K	NC	Fayet	PAFB	Fairchild	Provider	
C-123K	NJ	Trent	MGAFB	Fairchild	Provider	
C-123K	OH	Dayto	USAFM	Fairchild	Provider	56-4362
C-123K	PA	Beave	AHM	Fairchild	Provider	"Thunder Pig"
C-123K	TX	Abile	DLAP	Fairchild	Provider	54-604 A
C-123K	TX	D Rio	LAFB	Fairchild	Provider	
C-123K	TX	San A	LAFB	Fairchild	Provider	54-668
C-123K	UT	Ogden	HAFBM	Fairchild	Provider	
C-123K(UC)	GA	Warner Robin	MoF	Fairchild	Provider	54-633
C-124	NV	L.Veg	LB	Douglas	Globemaster	
C-124	NV	L.Veg	MIA	Douglas	Globemaster	
C-124	NV	LasVe	MIAHM	Douglas	Globemaster	
C-124C	AZ	Tucso	PAM	Douglas	Globemaster	52-1004
C-124C	CA	Fairf	TAFB	Douglas	Globemaster	
C-124C	GA	Warner Robin	MoF	Douglas	Globemaster	51-89
C-124A	OH	Dayto	USAFM	Douglas	Globemaster	51-0135
C-124C	SC	Charl	CAFB	Douglas	Globemaster	
C-124C	TX	Midla	CAFFM	Douglas	Globemaster	
C-124C	UT	Ogden	HAFBM	Douglas	Globemaster	

Model	State	City	Code	Manufacturer	Name	Serial/Notes
C-124C	WA	Tacoma	MAFB	Douglas	Globemaster	20994, MATS
C-125A(YC)	AZ	Tucso	PAM	Northrop	Raider	48-0636 N 2573B
C-125B(YC)	OH	Dayto	USAFM	Northrop	Raider	48-0626 N 2566B
C-126A(LC)	CA	Fairf	TAFB	Cessna	Businessliner	Model 195
C-126A(LC)	OH	Dayto	USAFM	Cessna	Businessliner	49-1949, Model 195
C-126A(LC)	TX	Denton	H10FM	Cessna	Businessliner	
C-130	AR	Littl	LRAFB	Lockheed	Hercules	
C-130 Fuse Only 2ea	LA	Alexandria	EAP	Lockheed	Hercules	
C-130	GA	Colum	FB	Lockheed	Hercules	
C-130	MN	Minne	MAGM	Lockheed	Hercules	70485
C-130	NS-C	Greenwood	GMAM	Lockheed	Hercules	70485
C-130	OR	Mc Minnville	EAEC	Lockheed	Hercules	
C-130A	AZ	Tucso	PAM	Lockheed	Hercules	57-457
C-130A	CA	Hemet	HAAB	Lockheed	Hercules	
C-130A	DC	Dulle	DA	Lockheed	Hercules	
C-130A	IL	Ranto	OCAM	Lockheed	Hercules	55-0037, MA ANG
C-130A	MD	Ft Meade	NVP	Lockheed	Hercules	60528, 60528
C-130A	MI	Mt Clemens	SMAM	Lockheed	Hercules	57-0514
C-130A	TX	Abile	DLAP	Lockheed	Hercules	55-23
C-130A	TX	Wichi	SAFB	Lockheed	Hercules	
C-130A	WY	Greyb	H&PA	Lockheed	Hercules	
C-130A(AC)	FL	Shali	USAFAM	Lockheed	Spectre Gunship	
C-130A(AC)	OH	Dayto	USAFM	Lockheed	Spectre Gunship	54-1626
C-130A(JC)	OH	Dayto	USAFM	Lockheed	Hercules	54-1630
C-130A(YMC)	GA	Warner Robin	MoF	Lockheed	Hercules	55-14
C-130B	UT	Ogden	HAFBM	Lockheed	Hercules	
C-130D	AZ	Tucso	PAM	Lockheed	Hercules	57-493
C-130E	TX	Wichi	SAFB	Lockheed	Hercules	
C-130H(YMC)	GA	Warner Robin	MoF	Lockheed	Hercules	74-1686
C-131	CA	Fairf	TAFB	Convair	Samaritan	Model 340
C-131	MN	Minne	MAGM	Convair	Samaritan	54-757, Model 340
C-131D	SD	Rapid	SDA&SM	Convair	Samaritan	55-0292, Model 340
C-131(VC)	CA	Sacra	McCelAFB	Convair	Samaritan	54- 2822 Model 340
C-131A(HC)	AR	Littl	LRAFB	Convair	Samaritan	Model 340
C-131A(HC)	VT	Burli	BANG	Convair	Samaritan	
C-131A(T-29A)	CA	Chino	PoFAM	Convair	Samaritan	Model 240
C-131A(T-29A)	MD	Silve	PEGF	Convair	Samaritan	"Caroline" Model 240
C-131A(T-29A) Nose	TX	Rio Grande V	TAM	Convair	Samaritan	Model 240
C-131A(VC)(T-29A)	AZ	Tusco	HA	Convair	Samaritan	Allison Model 580
C-131B	CA	Chino	PoFAM	Convair	Samaritan	Model 340
C-131B	DE	Dover	DAFB	Convair	Samaritan	Model 340
C-131B	FL	Shali	USAFAM	Convair	Samaritan	Model 340
C-131D	CA	Camarillo	CAF-SCW	Convair	Samaritan	N131CW, "samaritan"
C-131D	CA	Riverside	MFAM	Convair	Samaritan	54-2808
C-131D	MI	Mt Clemens	SMAM	Convair	Samaritan	52-0293, Model 340
C-131D	OH	Dayto	USAFM	Convair	Samaritan	55- 301 Model 340
C-131D	UT	Ogden	HAFBM	Convair	Samaritan	Model 340
C-131E	OH	Lockb	RANGB	Convair	Samaritan	55- 4751
C-131F(R4Y-1)	AZ	Tucson	PAM	Convair	Samaritan	141017
C-131F(R4Y-1)	AZ	Tucson	PAM	Convair	Samaritan	141025
C-131F(R4Y-2)	FL	Pensa	USNAM	Convair	Samaritan	141015 615 Model 340
C-133A	IL	Ranto	OCAM	Douglas	Cargomaster	
C-133A	OH	Dayto	USAFM	Douglas	Cargomaster	56- 2008
C-133B	AZ	Tucso	PAM	Douglas	Cargomaster	59- 527
C-135C(EC)-BN	NE	Ashland	SACM	Boeing	Startotanker	63-8049
C-135 (EC)	OH	Dayton	USAFM	Boeing	Stratotanker	
C-135 (EC)	SD	Rapid	SDA&SM	Boeing	Stratotanker	61-0262
C-135(EC)	TX	Wichi	SAFB	Boeing	Looking Glass	
C-135J(EC)	AZ	Tucso	PAM	Boeing	Stratotanker	63-8057
C-135L(EC)	IN	Peru	GAFB	Boeing	Stratotanker	61-269, "Excalliber"
C-135(KC)	IL	Belle	SAFB	Boeing	Stratotanker	
C-135(KC)	LA	Bossi	BAFB	Boeing	Stratotanker	
C-135(KC)	NE	Offut	OAFB	Boeing	Stratotanker	
C-135(KC)	OK	Oklah	TAFB	Boeing	Stratotanker	
C-135A(KC)	AZ	Tucson	PAM	Boeing	Stratotanker	
C-135A(KC)	CA	Rosam	EAFB	Boeing	Stratotanker	
C-135A(KC)	CA	Atwater	CAM	Boeing	Stratotanker	55-3139
C-135A(KC)	CA	Riverside	MFAM	Boeing	Stratotanker	55-3130, "Old Grandad"
C-135A(KC)	TX	Abile	DLAP	Boeing	Stratotanker	56-3639
C-135A(NKC)	OH	Dayto	USAFM	Boeing	Stratotanker	55-3123
C-135E(KC)	KS	Wichita	KAM	Boeing	Stratotanker	
C-137B(VC)	AZ	Tucson	PAM	Boeing	Air Force One	58-6971, "Freedom One"
C-137B(VC)	OH	Dayton	USAFM	Boeing	Air Force One	
C-137B(VC)	WA	Seatt	MoF	Boeing	Air Force One	58-6970, 1958
C-140	IL	Belle	SAFB	Lockheed	Jetstar	
C-140(1329-8)	NS	Bedford	ACAM	Lockheed	Jetstar	
C-140	NS-C	Halifax	ACAM	Lockheed	Jetstar	
C-140	ON-C	Ottaw	CAM	Lockheed	Jetstar	
C-140	UT	Ogden	HAFBM	Lockheed	Jetstar	
C-140	WA	Seatt	MoF	Lockheed	Jetstar	
C-140(VC)	GA	Warner Robin	MoF	Lockheed	Jetstar	61-2488
C-140(VC)	IL	Belle	SAFB	Lockheed	Jetstar	
C-140A	CA	Fairf	TAFB	Lockheed	Jetstar	
C-140A	CA	Rosam	EAFB	Lockheed	Jetstar	59-5962
C-140B(VC)	AZ	Tucso	PAM	Lockheed	Jetstar	61-2489
C-140B(VC)	OH	Dayto	USAFM	Lockheed	Jetstar	61-2492
C-141	IL	Belle	SAFB	Lockheed	Starlifter	
C-141	CA	Riverside	MFAM	Lockheed	Starlifter	65-0257
C-141B(NC)	CA	Rosam	EAFB	Lockheed	Starlifter	65-0257
C-141A	DE	Dover	DAFB	Lockheed	Starlifter	
C-141B	AZ	Tucson	PAM	Lockheed	Starlifter	
C-141B	DE	Dover	DAFB	Lockheed	Starlifter	
C-141B	GA	Warner Robin	MoF	Lockheed	Starlifter	66-0180A
C-142(XC)(X-18)	CA	Redwo	HAM		VSTOL	
C-142A(XC)	OH	Dayto	USAFM		VSTOL	65-5924
C-144(CX)	MB-C	Winnipeg	CFB			144612
C6N1-S	MD	Silve	PEGF	Nakajima	Myrt (Saiun)	
CA-61 Mini-Ace	WI	Oshko	EAAAM	Cvjetkovic	Mini-Ace	N94283
Callair	MN	Blaine	GWFM	Callair	Callair	
Callair	WY	Afton	CAM	Callair	Callair	
CallAir A-2	WY	Jackson	GWFM	CallAir	A-2	
CAM 3	WA	Seatt	MoF	Swallow-Stearman		
Canard Quickie	PA	Phila	FI	Canard	Quickie	

Cangley Aerodome	VA	Hampt	VA&SC	Cangley	Aerodome	
Cap 231	FL	Polk	FoF	Cap	Cap	
Caproni CA 20	WA	Seattle	MoF	Caproni	Caproni	1
Caproni 36	OH	Dayto	USAFM	Caproni		Model 36 2378
Caquot Type R Balloon	OH	Dayton	USAFM	Caquot	Observation	
Caravelle VI-R	CT	Winds	NEAM	Caravelle	Sud	
Casade 180B	MD	Silve	PEGF	Casade	Kasperwing	
Casade 180B	WA	Seattle	MoF	Casade	Kasperwing	
Cassutt B Special	AZ	Tucson	PAM	Cassutt	B Special	
Cassutt B Special	NY	Garde	CoAM	Cassutt	B Special	
Caudron 276	AL	Gunte	LGARFM	Caudron	Model 276	
Caudron G.III	NY	Rhine	ORA	Caudron		France Biplane
Caudron G.IV	MD	Silve	PEGF	Caudron		France 2 Engine Bomber WWI
Cavalier	NY	Ghent	POMAM	Star	Cavalier	
Cavalier	OK	Oklah	KCASM	Star	Cavalier	
Cavalier Model B	PA	Bethel	GAAM	Star	Cavalier	
Cavalier Model E	PA	Bethel	GAAM	Star	Cavalier	
Cayley Glider	CA	San Diego	SDAM	Cayley	Glider	
Cayley Glider	ME	Owls Head	OHTM	Cayley	Glider	
CBY-3 Burnelli	CT	Winds	NEAM	Burnelli		
CCW-1	MD	Silve	PEGF	Custer	Channel Wing	
CCW-5	PA	Readi	MAAM	Custer	Channel Wing	Sn 1, N5855V
Cessna	MN	Winoma	WTI	Cessna		N6766S
Cessna	MN	Winoma	WTI	Cessna		N15153
Cessna	MO	SLoui	SLDPA	Cessna		
Cessna 120	AZ	Tucso	PAM	Cessna	Model 120	NC4191N
Cessna 120	IA	SBluf	MAAM	Cessna	Model 120	
Cessna 120	IL	Rantoul	OCAM	Cessna	Model 120	NC2660N
Cessna 120	KS	Liberal	MAAM	Cessna	Model 120	
Cessna 120	NC	Hendersonville	WNCAM	Cessna	Model 120	
Cessna 120	OK	Fredi	AAM	Cessna	Model 120	
Cessna 140	KS	Liberal	MAAM	Cessna	Model 140	
Cessna 140	NY	Bayport	BA	Cessna	Model 140	
Cessna 140A	NM	STere	WEAM	Cessna	Model 140A	
Cessna 145	KS	Liberal	MAAM	Cessna	Airmaster	NC32450
Cessna 150H	KY	Lexington	AMoK	Cessna	Commuter	N6598S
Cessna 150H	WI	Oshko	EAAAAM	Cessna	Commuter	N23107
Cessna 150K	WI	Oshko	EAAAAM	Cessna	Commuter	N5799G
Cessna 150L	AZ	Tucso	PAM	Cessna	Commuter	N18588
Cessna 150L	MD	Silve	PEGF	Cessna	Commuter	
Cessna 150M	PA	Readi	MAAM	Cessna	Commuter	N714GR
Cessna 165	KS	Liberal	MAAM	Cessna	Airmaster	
Cessna 172	FL	Dayto	ERAU	Cessna	Skylane	
Cessna 172	NV	LasVe	MIAHM	Cessna	Skylane	N9712B, "Hacienda"
Cessna 172Q	FL	Dayto	ERAU	Cessna	Skylane	
Cessna 175(T-41B)	OK	Fredi	AAM	Cessna	Mescalero	67-15140
Cessna 175(T-41B)	KS	Liberal	MAAM	Cessna	Mescalero	
Cessna 175(T-41B)	FL	Clear	FMAM	Cessna	Mescalero	
Cessna 175(T-41B)	OK	FtSil	USAFAM	Cessna	Mescalero	
Cessna 180	CA	Hayward	VAM	Cessna	Model 180	
Cessna 180	GA	Woodstock	NGWS	Cessna	Model 180	
Cessna 180	MD	Silve	PEGF	Cessna	Model 180	"Spirit of Columbus"
Cessna 180	OR	Tillamook	TAM	Cessna	Model 180	
Cessna 180F	FL	Pensa	USNAM	Cessna	Model 180F	N 2146Z, 18051246
Cessna 182RG	FL	Dayto	ERAU	Cessna	Model 182RG	
Cessna 182	GA	Woodstock	NGWS	Cessna	Model 182	
Cessna 182P	OH	Cleveland	FCAAM	Cessna	Model 182P	N20920
Cessna 185	PA	Tough	CFCM	Cessna	Model 185	
Cessna 195	KS	Liberal	MAAM	Cessna	Businessliner	
Cessna 195A	ND	Minot	DTAM	Cessna	Businessliner	
Cessna 195A	OK	Fredi	AAM	Cessna	Businessliner	
Cessna 195A	PA	Bethel	GAAM	Cessna	Businessliner	N195PD
Cessna 206	KS	Wichita	KAM	Cessna	Model 206	
Cessna 206	MI	Belle	AFDSC	Cessna	Model 206	
Cessna 303	FL	Dayto	ERAU	Cessna	Model 303	
Cessna 310 (U-3)	AZ	Tucso	PAM	Cessna	Blue Canoe	N182Z, U-3, L-27
Cessna 310F(U-3)	KS	Wichita	KAM	Cessna	Blue Canoe	U-3, L-27
Cessna 310 (U-3)	MO	SLoui	SLUPC	Cessna	Blue Canoe	U-3, L-27
Cessna 310 (U-3)	NY	Bayport	BA	Cessna	Blue Canoe	U-3, L-27
Cessna 310 (U-3)	OK	Fredi	AAM	Cessna	Blue Canoe	U-3, L-27
Cessna 310B(U-3)	IL	Bloom	PAM	Cessna	Blue Canoe	U-3, L-27
Cessna 320	MO	SLoui	SLUPC	Cessna	Skynight	
Cessna 401	PA	Beaver Falls	AHM	Cessna		
Cessna C-402	NV	Las Vegas	LBAHSM	Cessna		N59SA, Fuse Only, "Scenic Airlines"
Cessna AW	CA	Chino	YAM	Cessna	Model AW 167	N8782
Cessna AW	PA	Bethel	GAAM	Cessna	Model AW 167	
CF-CPY	YT-C	WHors	WA			
CG-15A	NC	Charl	CHAC	Waco	Cargo Glider	
CG-2	WI	Oshko	EAAAAM	Cessna	Primary Glider 1	86, V
CG-2A	WA	Seatt	MoF	Cessna	Primary Glider	50, N178V
CG-4	NY	Garde	CoAM	Waco	Hadrian	15574
CG-4A	AZ	Tucso	PAM	Waco	Hadrian	45-14647
CG-4A	CA	Atwater	CAM	Waco	Hadrian	
CG-4A	CA	Chino	YAM	Waco	Hadrian	45-13696
CG-4A	CT	Washi	TFC	Waco	Hadrian	
CG-4A	DE	Dover	DAFB	Waco	Hadrian	
CG-4A	GA	Ft Benning	AFBNIM	Waco	Hadrian	
CG-4A Nose	IN	Columbus	ABAM	Waco	Hadrian	
CG-4A	MI	Belleville	YAF	Waco	Hadrian	43-40833
CG-4A	MI	Greenville	FFMM	Waco	Hadrian	
CG-4A	MI	Kalam	KAHM	Waco	Hadrian	45-15965
CG-4A	MI	Oscoda	YAF	Waco	Hadrian	
CG-4A	NC	Fayetteville	A&SOM	Waco	Hadrian	
CG-4A	NJ	Fairf	YAFDCWA	Waco	Hadrian	
CG-4A	NY	Elmira	NSM	Waco	Hadrian	
CG-4A	OH	Dayto	USAFM	Waco	Hadrian	45-27948
CG-4A	OR	Hubbard	LC	Waco	Hadrian	
CG-4A	TX	Midla	CAFFM	Waco	Hadrian	
CG-4A	TX	Lubbock	SWM	Waco	Hadrian	
CH-113	NS-C	Greenwood	GMAM			
CH-135	ONT - C	Ottawa	CAM	Bell		
CH-136	ON-C	Kingston	CFBK			
CH-136	ON-C	Ottawa	CWM			

117

CH-136	ON-C	Trenton	RCAFMM			
CH-300	ON-C	Ottaw	CAM	Zenair	Tri-Zenith	
Chanute Glider	BC-C	Sidne	BCAM	Chanute	Glider	
Chanute Glider	CA	Chino	PoFAM	Chanute	Glider	
Chanute Glider	CT	Winds	NEAM	Chanute	Glider	
Chanute Glider	GA	Warner Robin	MoF	Chanute	Glider	
Chanute Glider	ME	Owls Head	OHTM	Chanute	Glider	
Chanute Glider	NY	Elmira	NSM	Chanute	Glider	
Chanute Glider	NY	Hammo	CM	Chanute	Glider	
Chanute Glider	NY	Rhine	ORA	Chanute	Glider	
Chanute Glider	WA	Seattle	MoF	Chanute	Glider	
Chanute Glider	WI	Oshko	EAAAAM	Chanute	Glider	
Chester Special	OH	Cleveland	FCAAM	Chester	Special Racer	NX-93-Y-Goon
Chester Special	WI	Oshko	EAAAAM	Chester	Special Racer	N12930, "Jeep"
Chief Oshkosh						
Chris-Tena	OR	Tillamook	TAM		Mini-Coupe	
Christen Eagle	CA	San Carlos	HAM	Christen Industries	Eagle	
Christen Eagle	CO	Aurora	WOTR	Christen Industries	Eagle	
Christen Eagle	TX	Addison	CFM	Christen Industries	Eagle	
Christen Eagle1	WI	Oshkosh	EAAAAM	Christen Industries	Eagle	
Christen Eagle1	WI	Oshkosh	EAAAAM	Christen Industries	Eagle	
Christen Eagle II	WI	Oshkosh	EAAAAM	Christen Industries	Eagle	
Christen Eagle 1F	WI	Oshkosh	EAAAAM	Christen Industries	Eagle	
Circa 1920	WI	Poplar Grove	VW&W	Circa		
CJ6A	FL	Miami	WOM			
CL-13	ON-C	Oshwa	OAM&IM	Canadair	Sabre	
CL-13	MB-C	Winnipeg	WRCAFB	Canadair	Sabre	
CL-13	ON-C	CFB Borden	BHT	Canadair	Sabre	
CL-13	NS	Halifax	ACAM	Canadair	Sabre	
CL-13 Sabre Mk.6	NJ	Lumberton	AVM	Canadair	Sabre Mk.6	31186
CL-13B Mk.6	ON-C	Ottaw	CAM	Canadair	Sabre	23455
CL-13B Mk.6	ON-C	Ottaw	CAM	Canadair	Sabre	23651
CL-13B Mk.6	WA	Seattle	MoF	Canadair	Sabre	23363, N8686F
CL-28(CP-107)	ON-C	Ottaw	CAM	Canadair	Argus Mk.1	10742
CL-28(CP-107)	ON-C	MtVie	MVRCAF	Canadair	Argus Mk.1	
CL-20(CP-107)	ON-C	Trenton	RCAFMM	Canadair	Argus Mk.1	10732
CL-28(CP-107)	PE-C	Summe	PEIHAS	Canadair	Argus Mk.1	20739
CL-28(CP-107) Mk I	NS	Greenwood	GMAM	Canadair	Argus	10717, 732
CL-28(CP-107)	NS	Halifax	ACAM	Canadair	Argus	
CL-84	MB-C	Winni	WCAM	Canadair	Dynavert	
CL-84	ON-C	Ottaw	CAM	Canadair	Dynavert	CX8402, Twin Engine 1970
CL-215	ON-C	Sault Ste Marie	CBHC	Canadair	Water Bomber	F-ZBBT
CL-475	AL	Ozark	USAAM	Lockheed	Rigid Rotor	56-4320, N6940C
Clark Bi Wing	ME	Owls Head	OHTM	Clark	Bi Wing	
Clemson Plane	SC	Colum	SCSM	Clemson		
CM-170R	TX	Brownsville	BIA	Fouga	Magister	N405DM, pVM 3362
CM-170	WA	Seattle	MoF	Fouga	Magister	N505DM
CMQ-10A	CO	Puebl	PWAM	Boeing	Bomarc	56-4029
CNA-40	PA	Readi	MAAM	Health	Midwing	
Coffman Glider	TX	Lubbock	SWM	Coffman	Glider	
Cole Flyer	CA	Redwo	HAM	Cole	Flyer	
Coleopter	CA	Redwo	HAM	Cole	Coleopter	
Collins Aerofoil Boat	WI	Oshkosh	EAAAAM	Collins	Aerofoil	
Colt	MN	Winoma	WTI	Colt		N1985AP
Comet Glider	CA	LAnge	CMoS&I	Comet	Glider	
Command-Aire 5-C-3	AR	Little Rock	AEC	Command-Aire		
Command-Aire	FL	Lakel	SFAF	Command-Aire		N345JA, "Little Rocket"
Commonwealth	NY	Garde	CoAM	Commonwealth	Skyranger	N92972
Commonwealth 185	PA	Readi	MAAM	Commonwealth		N93248
Continental R670	NY	River	TFAC	Continental		
Convair 240	CT	Hartford	PLoA	Convair	Convair 240	see also C-131
Convair 240 (T-29)	CA	Tulare	AD	Convair	Convair 240	
Convair 240	MD	Silve	PEGF	Convair	Convair 240	
Convair 340	TX	Ladero	Airport	Convair	Convair 340	
Convair 440 (2ea)	TX	Ladero	Airport	Convair	Convair 440	
Convair 880	NV	Las Vegas	LB	Convair	Golden Arrow	Sn 23, N817TW, Model 22
Convair Airliner	CO	Erie	BJStra	Convair		
Convair Airliner	TX	Ft Worth	VFM	Convair		
Corben Super Ace	WI	Madison	MTFMDCRA	Corben	Super Ace	
Corben Jr. Ace	NC	Hende	WNCAM	Corben	Baby Ace	N28LW
Corben Baby Ace	IL	Poplar Grove	VW&WM	Corben	Baby Ace	
Corben C-1	WI	Oshko	EAAAAM	Corben	Baby Ace	N9050C, "Box Full"
Corben D	WA	Port Twonsend	PTAM	Corben	Baby Ace	1, N49A
Corben D	WI	Oshko	EAAAAM	Corben	Baby Ace	N9017C, "Box Full"
Corben Jr. Ace	CT	Winds	NEAM	Corben	Jr. Ace	
Corben Jr. Ace	TX	Bealt	FCA	Corben	Jr. Ace	
Corben Jr. Ace	VA	Bealt	FCA	Corben	Jr. Ace	
Covertawings A	NY	Garde	CoAM	Convertawings		N63N
Coward Pacific D-8	NY	Elmira	NSM	Coward Pacific	Glider	N5053K
Co-Z Corp	WI	Oshkosh	EAAAAM	Co-Z Development Corp	Co-Z	
CP-40	IA	Ottumwa	APM	Porterfield		529, NC18743
CP-65	FL	Lakeland	SNFAM	Porterfield	Collegiate	
CP-107	NS-C	Greenwood	GMAM			
CQM-10A	FL	FtWal	CityPark			
CR-4	VA	Marti		Crosby		
Cranwell CLA4	AB-C	Edmonton	AAM	Cranwell		
Cricket MC-10	FL	Lakeland	SNF	Cricket	MC-10	
Cricket NC-2	CA	Chino	PoFAM	Cricket	Kid Display	
Croff Batwing	NY	Elmira	NSM	Croff	Batwing	
Crosley	KY	Lexington	AVoK	Crosley	Moonbeam	#4, NX147N
Crosley CR-4	WI	Oshkosh	EAAAAM	Crosley	CR-4	
Crowley Hydro-Air	MD	Silve	PEGF	Crowley	Hydro-Air	
CT-114	ON-C	Ottawa	CAM		Tutor	
CT-114	ON-C	Toronto	TAM		Tutor	
CT-114	ON-C	Trenton	RCAFMM		Tutor	
CT-114	NS-C	Greenwood	GMAM		Tutor	
Culver Cadet	CA	Santa Martin	WoHAM	Culver	Cadet	
Culver Cadet LCA	IA	Ottumwa	APM	Culver	Cadet	443, N-41725
Culver Cadet See PQ-14				Culver	Cadet	
Culver Dart	MN	Stewa	CCC	Culver	Dart	
Culver Dart	MO	HARM	CCC	Culver	Dart	
Culver V	KS	Liberal	MAAM	Culver	Cadet	
Culver V	OK	Fredi	AAM	Culver	Cadet	

Model	State	City	Museum	Manufacturer	Name	Notes
Cumulus Glider	AL	Birmingham	SmoF	Cumulus	Glider	
Curtiss	NE	Minde	HWPV	Curtiss		
Curtiss A-1	CA	San Diego	SDAM	Curtiss	Triad	
Curtiss Canuck	MI	Dearb	HFM	Curtiss	Canuck	1918
Curtiss Canuck	TX	Kingbury	VAHF	Curtiss	Canuck	1918
Curtiss E Boat	MD	Silve	PEGF	Curtiss		
Curtiss E-8.75	WI	Oshko	EAAAAM	Curtiss	Pusher	N24034, "Sweetheart"
Curtiss Golden Flyer	ND	Fargo	HIA	Curtiss	Flyer	
Curtiss H	NY	River	TFAC	Curtiss	America	OX-5 Engine
Curtiss J6-7	NY	River	TFAC	Curtiss		
Curtiss June Bug Rep	NY	Hammo	CM	Curtiss	June Bug	1908
Curtiss Little Looper	CA	San Diego	SDAM	Curtiss	Little Looper	N5599N
Curtiss MF	OH	Cleve	FCAAM	Curtiss	Seagull	1918
Curtiss MF	ON-C	Ottaw	CAM	Curtiss	Seagull	1918
Curtiss Monoplane 1912	AL	Birmi	Southe	Curtiss		
Curtiss N-9	NE	Minde	HWPV	Curtiss		
Curtiss N-9	NY	River	TFAC	Curtiss		Oxx-6 Engine
Curtiss N2C	NY	Rhine	ORA	Curtiss	Fledgling	
Curtiss NC-4	FL	Pensa	USNAM	Curtiss		A 2294 4
Curtiss Oriole	MN	Minne	MAGM	Curtiss	Oriole	
Curtiss Oriole	NY	Hammo	CM	Curtiss	Oriole	
Curtiss Pusher D	CA	SCarl	HAM	Curtiss	Curtiss Pusher D	
Curtiss Pusher D	DC	Washi	NA&SM	Curtiss	Curtiss Pusher D	
Curtiss Pusher D	IA	Des M	ISHD	Curtiss	Curtiss Pusher D	
Curtiss Pusher D	Il	Chica	MoS&I	Curtiss	Curtiss Pusher D	
Curtiss Pusher D	KS	Topek	KSHS	Curtiss	Curtiss Pusher D	
Curtiss Pusher D	ME	OwlsH	OHTM	Curtiss	Curtiss Pusher D	
Curtiss Pusher D	NY	Hammo	CM	Curtiss	Curtiss Pusher D	
Curtiss Pusher D	NY	NYC	ISASM	Curtiss	Curtiss Pusher D	
Curtiss Pusher D	NY	Rhine	ORA	Curtiss	Curtiss Pusher D	
Curtiss Pusher D	OH	Dayto	USAFM	Curtiss	Curtiss Pusher D	
Curtiss Pusher D	OK	Oklah	AM	Curtiss	Curtiss Pusher D	
Curtiss Pusher D	OK	Oklah	KCASM	Curtiss	Curtiss Pusher D	
Curtiss Pusher D	OK	Weatherford	GTSM	Curtiss	Curtiss Pusher D	
Curtiss Pusher D	SC	MtPleasant	PN&MM	Curtiss	Curtiss Pusher D	
Curtiss Pusher D	TX	Rio Grande V	TAM	Curtiss	Curtiss Pusher D	
Curtiss Pusher D	WA	Vancouver	PAM	Curtiss	Curtiss Pusher D	
Curtiss Pusher D	WI	Milwa	MGoF	Curtiss	Curtiss Pusher D	
Curtiss Pusher D	WI	Oshko	EAAAAM	Curtiss	Curtiss Pusher D	N 37864
Curtiss Pusher D-5	AL	Birmingham	SMoF	Curtiss	Curtiss Pusher D	
Curtiss Robin	AK	Ancho	AAHM	Curtiss	Robin	
Curtiss Robin	AZ	Grand Canyon	PoFGCVA	Curtiss	Robin	
Curtiss Robin	IA	Greenfield	IAM	Curtiss	Robin 6	
Curtiss Robin	ID	Athol	NAM	Curtiss	Robin	
Curtiss Robin	MO	Maryland Hts	HARM	Curtiss	Robin	
Curtiss Robin	NV	Niagra Falls	NAM	Curtiss	Robin	
Curtiss Robin	NV	Carso	YF	Curtiss	Robin	
Curtiss Robin	NY	Hammo	CM	Curtiss	Robin	
Curtiss Robin J-1D	VA	Sands	VAM	Curtiss	Robin	Sn 733, "Ole Miss", NC532N
Curtiss Robin 4C-1A	NC	Hende	WNCAM	Curtiss	Robin	NC563N
Curtiss Robin B	FL	Delan	OHA	Curtiss	Robin	
Curtiss Robin B1	CA	San Diego	SDAM	Curtiss	Robin	N9265
Curtiss Robin B2	WI	Oshko	EAAAAM	Curtiss	Robin	N50H
Curtiss Robin C1	CA	Chino	YAM	Curtiss	Robin	538, N384K
Curtiss Robin C1	WA	Seatt	MoF	Curtiss	Robin	628, N979K
Curtiss Robin J1	NY	Niagara Falls	NAM	Curtiss	Robin	
Curtiss Robin 50C	NY	Garden	CoAM	Curtiss	Robin	
CV-580	PA	Readi	MAAM	Convair	Prop Jet	
CW A-14D	VA	Sandston	VAM	Curtiss-Wright	Speedwing	2009, N12329
CW A-22	OR	McMinnville	EAM	Curtiss	Falcon	A22-1, N500G
CW X-100	MD	Silve	PEGF	Curtiss-Wright	Robin	
CW-1	AR	Fayet	AAM	Curtiss	Junior	1930's
CW-1	CA	San Diego	SDAM	Curtiss-Wright	Junior	NC11850
CW-1	KS	Liberal	MAAM	Curtiss-Wright	Junior	
CW-1	MD	Silve	PEGF	Curtiss-Wright	Junior	
CW-1	NY	Mayvi	DA	Curtiss-Wright	Junior	
CW-1	NY	Rhine	ORA	Curtiss-Wright	Junior	
CW-1	NV	Carso	YF	Curtiss	Junior	1930's
CW-1	OK	Fredi	AAM	Curtiss-Wright	Junior	
CW-1	WA	Port Townsend	PTAM	Curtiss-Wright	Junior	N11809
CW-15	MO	Maryland Hts	Harm	Curtiss	Air Sedan	
CW 15-C	AZ	Tucson	PAM	Curtiss-Wright	Sedan	Man Sn 15C-2211. NC12302
CW 15-D	OR	McMinnville	EAM	Curtiss-Wright	Sedan	15-D-2214, N12314
Clyclo Crane	BC-C	Langley	CMoF	AeroLift Inc	Cyclocrane	N240AL
Clyclo Crane	CA	Ramona	CR	AeroLift Inc	Cyclocrane	1, Rotatory Blimp
D-25	NY	Rhine	ORA	New Standard		
D-25	OH	Chard	CA	New Standard		
D-558-1(H-76)	FL	Pensa	USNAM	Douglas	Skystreak	37970
D-558-2	CA	Chino	PoFAM	Douglas	Skyrocket	
D-558-2	CA	Lancaster	AVC	Douglas	Skyrocket	#3 Bu 37975
D-558-2	CT	Winds	NEAM	Douglas	Skyrocket	
D-588-2	DC	Washi	NA&SM	Douglas	Skyrocket	
D-9	SK-C	MJaw	WDM	Jodel		
D.H. 1	OR	McMinnville	EAEC	de Havilland		
D.H. 1A5	AL	Ozark	USAAM	Del Mar	Whirlymite	2
D.H. 2	CA	San Diego	SDAM	de Havilland	1915 Pusher	N32DH
D.H. 2	ID	Athol	NAM	de Havilland	1915 Pusher	
D.H. 4	DC	Washi	NA&SM	de Havilland	1915 Pusher	
D.H. 4	DC	Washi	USPM	de Havilland	1915 Pusher	
D.H. 4B	OH	Cleve	FCAAM	de Havilland	1915 Pusher	
D.H. 4 Rep	VA	Quant	MCAGM	de Havilland	1915 Pusher	
D.H. 4C	WA	Seattle	MoF	de Havilland	Comet	6424, N888WA, N6424
D.H. 4M-1	OR	Mc Minnville	EAEC	de Havilland	ET-4, N3258	
D.H. 4M	WA	Seatt	MoF	de Havilland	1915 Pusher	
D.H. 5	AL	Gunte	LGARFM	de Havilland	1915 Pusher	
D.H. 53	SK-C	MJaw	WDM	de Havilland	Hummingbird	
D.H. 60	AB-C	Wetas	RM	de Havilland	Moth	
D.H. 60	MT	Helen	MHSM	de Havilland	Moth 179	N617Y
D.H. 60	ON-C	Ottaw	CAM	de Havilland	Moth	
D.H. 60GM	AB-C	Wetas	RM	de Havilland	Cirrus Moth	
D.H. 60GM	BC-C	Langley	CMoF	de Havilland	Cirrus Moth	
D.H. 60GM	CA	El Cajon	SDAM	de Havilland	Cirrus Moth	N 917M
D.H. 60M	BC-C	Langley	CMoF	de Havilland	Moth Trainer	

D.H. 60M	SK-C	MJaw	WDM	de Havilland	Moth Trainer	
D.H. 61	TX	Brown	RGVW-CAF	de Havilland	Super Moth	
D.H. 80A	NY	Rhine	ORA	de Havilland	Puss Moth	
D.H. 80A	ON-C	Ottaw	CAM	de Havilland	Puss Moth	
D.H. 82	CA	Santa Maria	SMMoF	de Havilland	Tiger Moth	
D.H. 82	FL	Miami	WOM	de Havilland	Tiger Moth	
D.H. 82	NM	STere	WEAM	de Havilland	Tiger Moth	
D.H. 82	NY	Bayport	BA	de Havilland	Tiger Moth	
D.H. 82	OH	Dayton	USAFM	de Havilland	Tiger Moth	
D.H. 82	ON-C	Dunnville	RCAFDA	de Havilland	Tiger Moth	
D.H. 82	ON-C	Tillsonburg	CHAA	de Havilland	Tiger Moth	5030
D.H. 82	TX	Addison	CFM	de Havilland	Tiger Moth	R5130
D.H. 82	TX	Gilmer	PotP	de Havilland	Tiger Moth	
D.H. 82	WA	Vanco	PAM	de Havilland	Tiger Moth	
D.H. 82A	IA	Greenfield	IAM	de Havilland	Tiger Moth	Australian
D.H. 82A	ON-C	Collingwood	CCAF	de Havilland	Tiger Moth	86508, C-GSTP
D.H. 82A	WI	Oshko	EAAAAM	de Havilland	Tiger Moth	N16645, CF-IVO
D.H. 82A	PA	Toughkenamon	CFCM	de Havilland	Tiger Moth	N4808
D.H. 82B	WA	Port Townsend	PTAM	de Havilland	Tiger Moth	V4760, N2726A
D.H. 82C	AB-C	Calga	AMoC	de Havilland	Tiger Moth	
D.H. 82C	AB-C	Nanton	NLSAM	de Havilland	Tiger Moth	
D.H. 82C	AB-C	Wetas	RM	de Havilland	Tiger Moth	
D.H. 82C	BC-C	Langley	CMoF	de Havilland	Tiger Moth	C1178, RCAF5875, C-GFT
D.H. 82C	CA	Hawth	WMoF	de Havilland	Tiger Moth	
D.H. 82C	IA	Greenfield	IAM	de Havilland	Tiger Moth	Canadian
D.H. 82C	MB-C	Brand	CATPM	de Havilland	Tiger Moth	
D.H. 82C	MB-C	Winni	WCAM	de Havilland	Tiger Moth	
D.H. 82C	ME	OwlsH	OHTM	de Havilland	Tiger Moth	
D.H. 82C	ON-C	Hamilton	CWH	de Havilland	Tiger Moth	C-GCWT, 8922
D.H. 82C	ON-C	Ottaw	CAM	de Havilland	Tiger Moth	4861
D.H. 82C	SK-C	MJaw	WDM	de Havilland	Tiger Moth	
D.H. 83C	NT-C	Yellowknife	PWNHC	de Havilland	Fox Moth	
D.H. 83C	ON-C	S Ste Marie	CBHC	de Havilland	Fox Moth	CF-BNO Replica
D.H. 88 Rep	CA	Santa Martin	WoHAM	de Havilland	Comet	
D.H. 89	CA	Hayward	VAM	de Havilland	Dragon Rapide	
D.H. 89	MO	Maryland Hts	HARM	de Havilland	Dragon Rapide	
D.H. 89	ON-C	S Ste Marie	CBHC	de Havilland	Dragon Rapide	Sn 697, C-FAYE
D.H. 89A Mk.IV	WI	Oshko	EAAAAM	de Havilland	Dragon Rapide	N683DH
D.H. 89B	OH	Dayto	USAFM	de Havilland	Dragon Rapide	NR695
D.H. 94	TX	Brown	CAF-RVGW	de Havilland	Minor Moth	N940H
D.H. 94	TX	Brown	CAFRGVW	de Havilland	Moth Minor	
D.H. 98	AB-C	Calga	AMoC	de Havilland	Mosquito	
D.H. 98 Mk B35	AB-C	Edmonton	AAM	de Havilland	Mosquito	CF-HMQ, VP-189
D.H. 98	BC-C	Langley	CMoF	de Havilland	Mosquito	
D.H. 98	FL	Polk	FoF	de Havilland	Mosquito	
D.H. 98	OH	Dayto	USAFM	de Havilland	Mosquito	RS709
D.H. 98	ON-C	Ottaw	CAM	de Havilland	Mosquito	KB336
D.H. 98	ON-C	Windsor	CAHS	de Havilland	Mosquito	KB336
D.H. 98	TX	Midla	CAFFM	de Havilland	Mosquito	
D.H. 98 Mk.35	MD	Silve	PEGF	de Havilland	Mosquito	
D.H. 98 Mk.35	WI	Oshkosh	EAAAAM	de Havilland	Mosquito	
D.H. U-6	CA	SanLu	CSLO	de Havilland	Beaver	
D.H. U-6	MB-C	Winni	WCAM	de Havilland	Beaver	
D.H. U-6A	CA	Atwater	CAM	de Havilland	Beaver	
D.H. U-6A	CA	Rosam	EAFB	de Havilland	Beaver	53-2781
D.H. U-6A	CO	Denve	JWDAS	de Havilland	Beaver	
D.H. U-6A	CT	Winds	NEAM	de Havilland	Beaver	
D.H. U-6A	IL	Sugar Grove	ACM	de Havilland	Beaver	
D.H. U-6A	MO	SLoui	SLDPA	de Havilland	Beaver	153678
D.H. U-6A	ON-C	Ottaw	CAM	de Havilland	Beaver	
D.H. U-6A	ON-C	Sault Ste Marie	CBHC	de Havilland	Beaver	
D.H U-6A(L-10)	VA	FtEus	USATM	de Havilland	Beaver	58-1997
D.H U-6A	GA	Warner Robin	MoF	de Hallivand	Beaver	26087
D.H U-6A	OH	Dayto	USAFM	de Hallivand	Beaver	51-16501
D.H. U-6A(L-20A)	AZ	Tucso	PAM	de Havilland	Beaver	55-4595, N43906
D.H. U-6A(YU)	AL	Ozark	USAAM	de Havilland	Beaver	51-6263
D.H. U-6A6D(L-20A)	GA	Warner Robin	MoF	de Havilland	Beaver	52-6087, N30AR
D.H. U-6A(L-20A)	OK	Oklah	45IDM	de Havilland	Beaver	56-0367
D.H. U-6A(L-20A)	CA	Atwater	CAM	de Havilland	Beaver	
D.H. U-6A(L-20A)	FL	Clear	FMAM	de Havilland	Beaver	
D.H. U-6A(L-20A)	PA	Readi	MAAM	De Havilland	Beaver	52- 6112, N4957
D.H.100	AB-C	Calga	AMoC	de Havilland	Vampire	
D.H.100	BC-C	Langley	CMoF	de Havilland	Vampire	EEP42376, N6860D, RCAF17058
D.H.100	FL	Kissi	FTWAM	de Havilland	Vampire	
D.H.100	MB-C	Winni	WCAM	de Havilland	Vampire	
D.H.100	ON-C	Hamilton	CWH	de Havilland	Vampire	
D.H.100	OR	Mc Minnville	EAEC	de Havilland	Vampire	IB-1686, N174LA
D.H.100	WA	Seatt	MoF	de Havilland	Vampire	FLDH1367, N25776
D.H.100 Mk 35	WI	Oshko	EAAAAM	de Havilland	Vampire	N11926
D.H.100 Mk III	AZ	Grand	PoFGCVA	de Havilland	Vampire	17018
D.H.100 Mk VI	CA	Chino	PoFAM	de Havilland	Vampire	18
D.H.100 Mk. VI	ON-C	Ottaw	CAM	de Havilland	Vampire	17074, AAP
D.H.100 Mk.IIc	IN	India	IMoMH	de Havilland	Vampire	
D.H. 104	TX	Slaton	TAM	de Havilland	Dove	
D.H.C.-1	AB-C	Wetas	RM	de Havilland	Chipmunk	
D.H.C.-1	AZ	Tucso	PAM	de Havilland	Chipmunk	N48273
D.H.C.-1	KS	Ashla	HKAM	de Havilland	Chipmunk	
D.H.C.-1	ON-C	Hamilton	CWH	de Havilland	Chipmunk	B-2-S5, 035
D.H.C.-1	ON-C	Windsor	CAHS	de Havilland	Chipmunk	
D.H.C.-1	PA	Tough	CFCM	de Havilland	Chipmunk	
D.H.C.-1	SK-C	MJaw	WDM	de Havilland	Chipmunk	
D.H.C.-1	VA	Manassas	CAFNCS	de Havilland	Chipmunk	
D.H.C.-1A	MD	Silve	PEGF	de Havilland	Chipmunk	
D.H.C.-1B2	ON-C	Ottaw	CAM	de Havilland	Chipmunk	18070
D.H.C.-1B-2	ON-C	Trenton	RCAFMM	de Havilland	Chipmunk	
D.H.C.-1B2	WI	Oshko	EAAAAM	de Havilland	Chipmunk	N 1114V
D.H.C - 2 Mk.I	ON-C	Sault Ste Marie	CBHC	de Havilland	Beaver	Sn 2, CF-OBS
D.H.C - 2 Mk.II	ON-C	Sault Ste Marie	CBHC	de Havilland	Beaver	Sn 1650TB28, C-FOEK
D.H.C - 2 Mk.II	ON-C	Sault Ste Marie	CBHC	de Havilland	Beaver	Sn 1525TB1, C-FPSM
D.H.C.-3	AB-C	Calgary	ASMoC	de Havilland	Otter	
D.H.C.-3	MB-C	Winni	WCAM	de Havilland	Otter	9408
D.H.C.-3	ON-C	Ottaw	CAM	de Havilland	Otter	9408
D.H.C.-3	ON-C	Sault Ste Marie	CBHC	de Havilland	Otter	Sn 369, C-FODU

D.H.C.-3(U-1)NU-1B	FL	Pensa	USNAM	de Havilland	Otter	3824, 144672, F 699
D.H.C.-3(U-1A)	AL	Ozark	USAAM	de Havilland	Otter	57-6135
D.H.C.-3(U-1A)	VA	FtEus	USATM	de Havilland	Otter	55-3270
D.H.C.-5	ON-C	MtVie	MVRCAF	de Havilland	Buffalo	
D.H.C.-6	MT	Misso	AFDSC	de Havilland	Twin Otter	
D.H.C.-6	OH	N Canton	MAM	de Havilland	Twin Otter	
D.H.C.-6	ON-C	Ottaw	CAM	de Havilland	Twin Otter	
D.H.C.-6-300	CA	Carls	CAJM	de Havilland	Twin Otter	
DA-1W	FL	Miami	WOM	Davis		
DA-1W	IN	Richmond	WCHM	Davis		
DA-1W	NY	Rhine	ORA	Davis		
Daedalus 88	MD	Silver Hill	PEGF	Daedalus		
Dagling Primary 1	BC-C	Langley	CMoF	Dagling	Primary Glider	
Dagling Primary 1	NY	Elmira	NSMF	Dagling	Primary Glider	
Dart	OH	Dayton	USAFM	Dart	Aerial Target	
Dawydoff UT-1	NY	Elmira	NSM	Dawydoff	Cadet	N30422
D.A.S.H.	SC	MtPleasant	PPM		Drone Anti Sub Helio	
DC-2	WA	Seattle	MoF	Douglas	Dakota	1368, N1934D
DC-3 *See C-47*				Douglas	Dakota	
DC-3	AB-C	Calga	AMoC	Douglas	Dakota	
DC-3	AB-C	Harbor Grace	City	Douglas	Dakota	
DC-3	AL	Troy	TMA	Douglas	Dakota	
DC-3 Cockpit	AR	Fayetteville	AAM	Douglas	Dakota	
DC-3	BC-C	Langley	CMoF	Douglas	Dakota	
DC-3	CA	Ames	BA	Douglas	Dakota	
DC-3(R-4B)	CA	Chino	YAM	Douglas	Dakota	
DC-3	CA	SClem	ACA	Douglas	Dakota	11693, N7500A
DC-3	CO	Aurora	WOTR	Douglas	Dakota	
DC-3	CT	Winds	NEAM	Douglas	Dakota	"Taino Air"
DC-3	DC	Washi	NA&SM	Douglas	Dakota	
DC-3	GA	Atlanta	DATHM	Douglas	Dakota	NC28341, Ship 41
DC-3	GA	Calhoun	MAM	Douglas	Dakota	
DC-3A	GA	Dougl	BA	Douglas	Dakota	42-92606, N99FS
DC-3	GA	Griff	AAC	Douglas	Dakota	2239, N28AA
DC-3	IL	Bloom	PAM	Douglas	Dakota	N763A, "Ozark Airlines"
DC-3	IL	Grant	CityPark	Douglas	Dakota	
DC-3	IL	St. C	SCA	Douglas	Dakota	
DC-3	KY	Louis	BF	Douglas	Dakota	
DC-3(CC-129)	MB-C	Brandon	CATPM	Douglas	Dakota	
DC-3	MB-C	Winni	WCAM	Douglas	Dakota	12949
DC-3	MD	Hager	HRegAirP	Douglas	Dakota	
DC-3	MN	Minneapolis	MAG	Douglas	Dakota	
DC-3	MI	Dearb	HFM	Douglas	Dakota	Northwest Airlines
DC-3-362	MO	Kansas City	AHM	Douglas	Dakota	SN3294, NC1945
DC-3	MS	Petal	MWHMM	Douglas	Dakota	
DC-3	MT	Misso	AFDSC	Douglas	Dakota	
DC-3	NC	Charlotte	CAM	Douglas	Dakota	53-R1830 , 4900, "Piedmont Airlines"
DC-3	ND	Fargo	FAM	Douglas	Dakota	0-93800
DC-3	NF-C	Harbour Grace		Douglas	Dakota	6179
DC-3	NM	STere	WEAM	Douglas	Dakota	
DC-3	NV	Las Vegas	LBAHSM	Douglas	Dakota	3252, N19968, Cockpit Only, "Trans-Texas Airways"
DC-3	OK	Fredi	AAM	Douglas	Dakota	
DC-3	ON-C	Hamilton	CWH	Douglas	Dakota	C-GDAK, KN456, Z
DC-3	ON-C	Ottaw	CAM	Douglas	Dakota	
DC-3	OR	Mc Minnville	EAEC	Douglas	Dakota	1910, N16070, "United Airlines"
DC-3	TX	Brown	RGVW-CAF	Douglas	Dakota	
DC-3	TX	FWort	AACRS	Douglas	Dakota	
DC-3 (3ea)	TX	Ladero	Airport	Douglas	Dakota	
DC-3	WA	Seattle	MoF	Douglas	Dakota	2245, N138D, NC91008, "Alaska Airlines"
DC-3	WA	Vancouver	PAM	Douglas	Dakota	
DC-3	WI	Oshko	BFBO	Douglas	Dakota	
DC-3	WI	Oshko	EAAAM	Douglas	Dakota	N7772
DC-3	YK-C	White Horse	YTM	Douglas	Dakota	20833 C- GZOF, CF- IMA
DC-3	YK-C	White Horse	WA	Douglas	Dakota	CF-CPY
DC-3 Cockpit	CA	Chino	PoFAM	Douglas	Dakota	
DC-3 Cockpit	MD	Silve	PEGF	Douglas	Dakota	
DC-3 Cockpit	NF-C	Gander	NAAM	Douglas	Dakota	
DC-3 Fuseelage	FL	Polk	FoF	Douglas	Dakota	
DC-3 Parts	CO	Denve	JWDAS	Douglas	Dakota	
DC-3(R4D-1)	CA	S.Mon	MoF	Douglas	Dayliner	"Chas S Jones"
DC-3C	IN	Columbus	RA	Douglas	Dakota	19366, N141JR, 41, CFFCUC
DC-3C	IN	Columbus	RA	Douglas	Dakota	20550, N139JR, 40, Parts Missing, "Miss Daisy"
DC-3C	IN	Columbus	RA	Douglas	Dakota	26815, N140JR, 40
DC-3C(C-47A)	IN	Columbus	RA	Douglas	Dakota	32845, N142JR, 42-100903
DC-3C	TX	Midla	CAFFM	Douglas	Dakota	
DC-4	CA	Chiriaco	GPM	Canadair	North Star	
DC-4M	ON-C	Ottaw	CAM	Canadair	North Star	17515
DC-6(C-118)	CA	SRosa	PCAM	Cessna		
DC-6	NE	Minde	HWPV	Cessna		1929
DC-6B	MI	Belleville	YAF	Douglas		44913, N4913R, "Yankee Volunteer"
DC-7	DC	Washi	NA&SM	Douglas		
DC-7	MN	St Paul	MA&SM	Douglas		Looking for a Museum
DC-7B	OH	Newbu	WASAC	Douglas		44924
DC-7B	AZ	Tucso	PAM	Douglas		N 51701
DC-8-52	CA	LAnge	CMoS&I	McDonnell-Douglas	Jet Trader	
DC-8-55	MI	Oscoda	YAM	McDonnell-Douglas	Jet Trader	45856, N6161C
DC-9	VA	Hampton	VA&SM	Douglas		
DC-65	MI	Saginaw	YAF	Taylorcraft	Tandem	L-4874, N48102, "Yankee Hopper"
DC-65	NJ	Fairfield	YAF	Taylorcraft	Tandem	L-5041, N9666N
HZ-1	VA	FtEus	USATM	DeLackner	Aerocycle	
Damenjoz	ME	OwlsH	OHTM	Demenjos	Old Orchard Beach	
Deperdussin	ME	OwlsH	OHTM	Deperdussin		
Deperdussin	NV	Carso	YF	Deperdussin		
Deperdussin	NY	Rhine	ORA	Deperdussin		
Deperdussin Model C	CA	San Diego	SDAM	Deperdussin		
der Kricket	CO	Aurora	WOTR		der Kricket	
Dewoitine D.26	FL	Polk	FoF	Dewoitine		
DGA	CA	Santa Paula	SPAA	Howard	Nightingale	
DGA	ND	Wahpe	TSA	Howard	DGA	
DGA	TX	C Christi	USS Lexi	Howard		
DGA	TX	Denton	H10FM	Howard		
DGA	WA	Seatt	MoF	Howard	Nightingale	559, N52947
DGA 1A	FL	Lakel	SFAF	DGA	Sportfire	N37835

DGA 3	OH	Cleveland	FCAAM	Howard	Racer	"Pete"	
DGA 5	CA	Chino	PoFAM	Howard	Racer	"Ike"	
DGA 5	OH	Fremo		Howard	Racer	"Ike"	
DGA 6	AR	Fayet	AAM	Howard	Racer	NR273Y, "Mister Mulligan"	
DGA 11	AR	Fayet	AAM	Howard		NC18207	
DGA 15	BC-C	Langley	CMoF	Howard	Nightingale		
DGA-15	MB-C	Winni	WCAM	Howard	DGA		
DGA-15P	CA	S.Mon	MoF	Howard	Nightingale		
DGA 18K	AR	Fayet	AAM	Howard	Nightingale	N39668	
Diamond 1910	CA	San Carlos	HAM	Diamond	Bi Plane		
Diamond Katana	ON-C	Kitchener	KWRA	Diamond	Katana		
Diamond Katana	ON-C	London	AH	Diamond	Katana		
Diamond Katana	ON-C	London	LA	Diamond	Katana		
Dickerson	NY	Rhine	ORA	Diskerson	Primary Glider		
Do 335	MD	Silve	PEGF	Dornier	Pfeil		
Doman	CA	Redwo	HAM	Doman	Doman		
Dormoy Bathtub	PA	Bethel	GAAM	Dormoy	Bathtub		
Double Eagle II	MD	Silve	PEGF	Anderson	Double Eagle		
Double Eagle V	WI	Oshko	EAAAAM	Anderson	Double Eagle V		
DQ-14	MD	Silve	PEGF	Radioplane			
DQ-2A/TDD-1	MD	Silve	PEGF	Radioplane			
Driggers A 891H	WI	Oshko	EAAAAM	Driggers		"Sunshine Girl III"	
DSI/NASA RPRV	MD	Silve	PEGF				
DSP Satellite	OH	Dayton	USAFM		Satellite		
Dumont Demoiselle	NV	Carso	YF	Dumont	Demoiselle		
Dumont Demoiselle	NY	NYC	ISASM	Dumont	Demoiselle		
Durand Mk.V	WA	Seatt	MoF	Durand		5, N444JF	
DWC	AK	Palme	MOAT&I	Douglas	World Cruiser	"Seattle"	
DWC	DC	Washi	NA&SM	Douglas	World Cruiser	"Chicago"	
DWC-4	CA	S.Mon	MoF	Douglas	World Cruiser	"New Orleans"	
Dyndivic Sport	CT	Winds	NEAM	Dyndivic	Sport		
E-1	VA	Sands	VAM	Standard			
E-1	WI	Oshko	EAAAAM	Standard		N3783C	
E-1B	PA	Willo	WGNAS	Grumman	Tracer	146034	
E-1B	SC	MtPleasant	PPM	Grumman	Tracer	147225	
E-2	BC-C	Sidne	BCAM	Eastman	Sea Rover	Float Plane	
E-2	IL	Harva	BA	Taylor	Cub		
E-2	NC	Hende	WNCAM	Taylor	Cub	NC12644	
E-2	NJ	Lumberton	AVM	Taylor	Cub		
E-2	NY	Niagra Falls	NAM	Taylor	Cub		
E-2	ON-C	Ottaw	CAM	Taylor	Cub		
E-2	PA	Bethel	GAAM	Taylor	Cub	NC13146	
E-2	VA	Sandston	VAM	Taylorcraft	Cub	Sn 33, N15045	
E-2	WI	Oshko	EAAAAM	Taylor	Cub	N15045	
E-2B	FL	Pensa	USNAM	Grumman	Hawkeye	150540	
E-2B	ME	Lexin	PNAT&EM	Grumman	Hawkeye		
E-2C	CA	Chino	YAM	Grumman	Hawkeye		
E-2C	CA	San Diego	SDACM	Grumman	Hawkeye	161227	
E-2C	GA	Marietta	NASA	Grumman	Hawkeye	AA, 600, VAW-125	
E-2C	NV	Fallon	NASF	Grumman	Hawkeye	949603, NSAW	
E-2C	VA	Norfo	NNAS	Grumman	Hawkeye	AA, 600, VAW-125	
EAA Acro-Sport	FL	Lakeland	SNF	EAA	Acro-Sport		
EAA Biplane	ND	Grand	JBC	EAA	Biplane		
EAA P-9 Pober Pixie	OK	Fredi	AAM	EAA	Pober Pixie		
Eagle Eye	AR	Little Rock	AEC	Bell	UASV		
Eastern Rotorcraft Z-9	PA	Willow	WGNAS	Eastern	Rotorcraft		
Easy Riser	AZ	Tucso	PAM	Easy Riser	Hang Glider		
Easy Riser	CA	Chino	PoFAM	Easy Riser	Hang Glider		
Easy Riser	IA	Greenfield	IAM		Glider		
EC1 Aircoupe	PA	Readi	MAAM	Elias	Aircoupe		
Ecker Flying Boat	DC	Washi	NA&SM	Ecker	Flying Boat		
Eipper Cumulus	WA	Seatt	MoF	Eipper	Cumlus		
Eipper Cumulus 10	MD	Silve	PEGF	Eipper	Cumlus		
Eipper MX-1	WI	Oshko	EAAAAM	Eipper	Quicksilver	N87MX	
Eipper MXL-II	TX	Dallas	FoF	Eipper	Quicksilver		
EJ-4(F-1E)	FL	Pensa	USNAM	North American	Fury	N139486, 139486, NM 208, VA-192	
Elemdord A-1	WI	Oshko	EAAAAM	Elemdorf	Jackrabbit	NX264Y	
Emair Ultralight	TX	Rio Grande V	TAM	Emair	Ultralight		
Emigh Trojan	NY	River	RE	Emigh	Trojan	1951	
Enstrom F28A	PA	Wchester	AHM	Enstrom			
Epp's Monoplane	GA	Warner Robin	MoF	Epp	Monoplane		
Ercoupe 67	NE	Minde	HWPV	Erco	Ercoupe		
Ercoupe 415 F-1	AL	Birmi	Southe	Forney	Ercoupe		
Ercoupe 415	MD	College Park	CPAM	Erco	Ercoupe	NC93942	
Ercoupe 415	MD	Silve	PEGF	Erco	Ercoupe		
Ercoupe 415	ND	Minot	DTAM	Erco	Ercoupe		
Ercoupe 415	MN	Winoma	WTI	Erco	Ercoupe	N3920H	
Ercoupe 415	NY	Mayvi	DA	Erco	Ercoupe		
Ercoupe 415	OH	Dayto	USAFM	Erco	Ercoupe	86	
Ercoupe 415	WI	Fond du Lac	WAM	Erco	Ercoupe		
Ercoupe 415C	AZ	Tucson	PAM	Erco	Ercoupe	Sn 1188, N78X / N93865	
Ercoupe 415C	KS	Liberal	MAAM	Erco	Ercoupe		
Ercoupe 415C	MI	Kalam	KAHM	Erco	Ercoupe	1251	
Ercoupe 415C	NY	Geneseo	1941AG	Erco	Ercoupe		
Ercoupe 415CD	NC	Hendersonville	WNCAM	Erco	Ercoupe		
Ercoupe 415C	NS	Halifax	ACAM	Erco	Ercoupe		
Ercoupe 415C	OK	Fredi	AAM	Erco	Ercoupe		
Ercoupe 415C	WA	Seatt	MoF	Erco	Ercoupe	3569, N2944H	
Ercoupe 415C	WI	Oshko	EAAAAM	Erco	Ercoupe	NC28961	
Ercoupe 415D	CA	Chino	YAM	Erco	Ercoupe	4218, N3593H	
Ercoupe 415D	CA	Sands	VAM	Erco	Ercoupe	Sn 1766	
Ercoupe 415G	PA	Readi	MAAM	Erco	Ercoupe		
Ercoupe 415G	WI	Oshko	EAAAAM	Erco	Ercoupe	N94898	
Etrich Taube	ME	OwlsH	OHTM	Etrich	Taube		
Eurocopter Djinn SO.1221	PA	Wchester	AHM	Eurocopter			
Excelsior Gondola	OH	Dayton	Usafm	Excelsior	Gondola		
Experimental	KS	Topek	KSHS		Helicopter		
Explorer II	DC	Washi	NA&SM	Explorer	Gondola		
Extra 260	MD	Silve	PEGF	Extra	Extra		
Extra 300L	IL	Springfield	ACM	Extra	Extra		
Ezekiel Airship Rep	TX	Pitts	Restrant	Ezekiel	Airship		
F- 4	AL	Birmi	Southe	McDonnell	Phantom II		
F- 4	AR	FSmit	EANG	McDonnell	Phantom II		

Type	State	City	Code	Mfr	Model	Notes
F- 4	AZ	Mesa	CAF-AWM	McDonnell	Phantom II	
F- 4	CA	Boron	SAM	McDonnell	Phantom II	
F- 4	CA	Fresn	FANG	McDonnell	Phantom II	
F- 4	CA	Mojav	MA	McDonnell	Phantom II	
F- 4	CO	Cannon	CA	McDonnell	Phantom II	63-07551
F- 4	FL	KeyWe	NASKW	McDonnell	Phantom II	
F- 4	HI	Kaneohe	MB	McDonnell	Phantom II	
F- 4	Il	Sprin	SMAM	McDonnell	Phantom II	SI 468
F- 4	IN	Columbus	ABAM	McDonnell	Phantom II	64844 BA
F- 4	IN	FtWay	IANG	McDonnell	Phantom II	
F- 4	MD	Andrews	APG	McDonnell	Phantom II	AF66661
F- 4	MD	Lexin	PNA&EM	McDonnell	Phantom II	
F- 4	MD	Middl	GLMAM	McDonnell	Phantom II	
F- 4	MI	Sterling Hts	FHCMP	McDonnell	Phantom II	66-8755
F- 4	MN	Dulut	DIA	McDonnell	Phantom II	
F- 4	NC	CPoin	CPMB	McDonnell	Phantom II	
F- 4	NJ	Wrightstown	McGAFB	McDonnell	Phantom II	67-0270
F- 4	NV	Fallon	NASF	McDonnell	Phantom II	
F- 4	NV	Fallon	NASF	McDonnell	Phantom II	
F- 4	OH	N Canton	MAPS	McDonnell	Phantom II	
F- 4	OR	Klamath Falls	OANG	McDonnell	Phantom II	37479
F- 4	SC	McEnt	MEANGB	McDonnell	Phantom II	
F- 4	TN	Athen	VFW 5146	McDonnell	Phantom II	
F- 4	TX	Bastr	VFW 2527	McDonnell	Phantom II	
F- 4	TX	C Christi	USS Lexi	McDonnell	Phantom II	DC 3 VMFA-122
F- 4	TX	Dalla	DNAS	McDonnell	Phantom II	
F- 4	TX	Manch	VFW 3377	McDonnell	Phantom II	
F- 4	WA	Seattle	MoF	McDonnell	Phantom II	45-3016, 64-0776, NE 211, VF-21, "NAVY" Rear Fuse
F- 4	WA	Tacoma	MAFB	McDonnell	Phantom II	
F- 4	WI	Milwa	MANG	McDonnell	Phantom II	
F- 4 Cockpit	CA	Riverside	MFAM	McDonnell	Phantom II	
F- 4 Cockpit	ME	Lexin	PNAT&EM	McDonnell	Phantom II	
F- 4Cockppit	OH	Daton	USAFM	McDonnell	Phantom II	
F- 4 Cockpit	TX	C Christi	CCMOS&H	McDonnell	Phantom II	
F- 4 Cockpit	WI	Kenos	KMM	McDonnell	Phantom II	
F- 4(AF)	MI	Kalam	KAHM	McDonnell	Phantom II	74-0658
F- 4A	CO	Puebl	PWAM	McDonnell	Phantom II	
F- 4A	CT	Winds	NEAM	McDonnell	Phantom II	
F- 4A	FL	Clear	FMAM	McDonnell	Phantom II	
F- 4A	FL	Kissimmee	FTWAM	McDonnell	Phantom II	
F- 4A	MD	Silve	PEGF	McDonnell	Phantom II	"Sageburner"
F- 4A	NJ	Lumberton	AVM	McDonnell	Phantom II	148273
F- 4A	RI	NKing	QAM	McDonnell	Phantom II	
F- 4A	TX	C Christi	USS Lexi	McDonnell	Phantom II	
F- 4A	VA	Quantico	MCAGM	McDonnell	Phantom II	143388
F- 4B	CT	Winds	NEAM	McDonnell	Phantom II	
F- 4B	IL	Sugar Grove	ACM	McDonnell	Phantom II	148407
F- 4B	IL	Linco	HIFM	McDonnell	Phantom II	
F- 4B	NC	Hickory	HRA	McDonnell	Phantom II	148400
F- 4B	NY	Horseheads	NWM	McDonnell	Phantom II	152256, VF-21, NE2219
F- 4B	TX	San A	LAFB	McDonnell	Phantom II	149421
F- 4B	VA	VBeac	ONAS	McDonnell	Phantom II	7920, VF- 84
F- 4B(RF)	CA	Ridgecrest	CLNWC	McDonnell	Phantom II	
F- 4B(RF)	CA	Miramar	FLAM	McDonnell	Phantom II	RF, VMFP-3
F- 4B(RF)	NC	Havelock	HTC	McDonnell	Phantom II	
F- 4C	AK	Ancho	EAFB	McDonnell	Phantom II	
F- 4C	AL	Huntsville	AC	McDonnell	Phantom II	
F- 4C	AL	Mobile	BMP	McDonnell	Phantom II	637487
F- 4C	AL	Montg	MAFB	McDonnell	Phantom II	
F- 4C	AZ	Tucso	PAM	McDonnell	Phantom II	64-673
F- 4C	CA	Chino	YAM	McDonnell	Phantom II	
F- 4C	CA	Fairf	TAFB	McDonnell	Phantom II	
F- 4C	CA	Boron	VFW	McDonnell	Phantom II	66-7716
F- 4C	CA	Riverside	MFAM	McDonnell	Phantom II	63-7693
F- 4C	CA	Rosam	EAFB	McDonnell	Phantom II	63-7407
F- 4C	CA	Sacra	McCelAFB	McDonnell	Phantom II	64-705, MI40706
F- 4C	CA	Sacra	SWAM	McDonnell	Phantom II	
F- 4C	CA	San Luis	CSLO	McDonnell	Phantom II	64-0827
F- 4C	CA	SRosa	PCAM	McDonnell	Phantom II	
F- 4C(RF)	CA	Susanville	Airport	McDonnell	Phantom II	64-01022
F- 4C	CA	Tulare	AVP56	McDonnell	Phantom II	64-0912
F- 4C	CA	Victorville	GAFB	McDonnell	Phantom II	63-7519
F- 4C	CO	CSpri	EJPSCM	McDonnell	Phantom II	64-0799
F- 4C	CO	CSpri	USAFA	McDonnell	Phantom II	
F- 4C	CO	Aurora	WOTR	McDonnell	Phantom II	
F- 4C	FL	Panam	TAFB	McDonnell	Phantom II	63-7408
F- 4C	FL	Shali	USAFAM	McDonnell	Phantom II	40-813, XC
F- 4C	GA	Marie	DAFB	McDonnell	Phantom II	
F- 4C	GA	Pooler	M8AFHM	McDonnell	Phantom II	64-815
F- 4C	GA	Warner Robin	MoF	McDonnell	Phantom II	63-7465
F- 4C	HI	Oahu	HAFB	McDonnell	Phantom II	63-15796
F- 4C	HI	Oahu	HANG	McDonnell	Phantom II	40792, Blue
F- 4C	HI	Oahu	HAFBFU	McDonnell	Phantom II	64-00793
F- 4C	HI	Oahu	HAFBFU	McDonnell	Phantom II	66-07540
F- 4C	HI	Oahu	BPNAS	McDonnell	Phantom II	152291
F- 4C	IA	Marsh	CIAVM AM	McDonnell	Phantom II	
F- 4C	IN	Fairmount	ALP313	McDonnell	Phantom II	63-7623
F- 4C	IN	Peru	GAFB	McDonnell	Phantom II	64-783
F- 4C	IN	Terre Haute	THANG	McDonnell	Phantom II	63-565
F- 4C	LA	New Orleans	FoJBMM	McDonnell	Phantom II	
F- 4C-19-MC	MI	Belleville	YAF	McDonnell	Phantom II	63-7555
F- 4C	MI	Mt Clemens	SMAM	McDonnell	Phantom II	63-7534
F- 4C	NC	Golds	SJAFB	McDonnell	Phantom II	64-770 "Jeannie"
F- 4C	ND	Castl	CA	McDonnell	Phantom II	
F- 4C	NM	Alamo	HAFB	McDonnell	Phantom II	
F- 4C	NV	LasVe	NAFB	McDonnell	Phantom II	
F- 4C	NY	Niaga	NFANG	McDonnell	Phantom II	
F- 4C	OH	Newar	NAFM	McDonnell	Phantom II	
F- 4C	OH	Daton	USAFM	McDonnell	Phantom II	
F- 4C	SC	Charl	CAFB	McDonnell	Phantom II	
F- 4C	SC	Citid	CC	McDonnell	Phantom II	
F- 4C	TN	Arnol	AAFS	McDonnell	Phantom II	
F- 4C	TX	Austi	AGDTAG	McDonnell	Phantom II	

F- 4C	TX	Austi	BAFB	McDonnell	Phantom II	
F- 4C	TX	Addison	CFM	McDonnell	Phantom II	
F- 4C	TX	Dalla	FoF	McDonnell	Phantom II	64-0777, Tail AT, AF-477 Sq, Red Star
F- 4C	TX	San Antonio	TANG	McDonnell	Phantom II	63-7515
F- 4C	TX	Wichi	SAFB	McDonnell	Phantom II	
F- 4C	UT	Ogden	HAM	McDonnell	Phantom II	
F- 4C	WA	Seatt	MoF	McDonnell	Phantom II	
F- 4C	WI	CDoug	WNGML&M	McDonnell	Phantom II	
F- 4C(RF)	AR	Littl	LRAFB	McDonnell	Phantom II	64-0748, 389TFS/366TFW
F- 4C(RF)	CA	Riverside	MFAM	McDonnell	Phantom II	63-7746
F- 4C(RF) Cockpit	CA	Riverside	MFAM	McDonnell	Phantom II	Weapons System Trainer
F- 4C(NF)	CA	Rosam	EAFB	McDonnell	Phantom II	64-1004
F- 4C(RF)	FL	Shali	USAFAM	McDonnell	Phantom II	67-452 ET
F- 4C(RF)-14-MC	IL	Ranto	OCAM	McDonnell	Phantom II	62-12201
F- 4C(RF)	KY	Louisville	LANGS	McDonnell	Phantom II	64-081
F- 4C(RF)	MN	Minne	MAGM	McDonnell	Phantom II	64-61
F- 4C(RF)	MN	Minne	MAGM	McDonnell	Phantom II	64-665
F- 4C(RF)	NE	Lincoln	LANGB	McDonnell	Phantom II	64-0998, Tail Nebraska AF 64-998
F- 4C(RF)	OH	Dayto	USAFM	McDonnell	Phantom II	64-1047
F- 4C(RF)	OH	Lockb	RANGB	McDonnell	Phantom II	65-903
F- 4C(RF)	SC	Sumte	SAFB	McDonnell	Phantom II	
F- 4C(RF)	TX	San Angelo	GAFB	McDonnell	Phantom II	69-0367
F- 4C(RF)	TX	LV	LVAM	McDonnell	Phantom II	
F- 4C(RF)	TX	San A	VMP	McDonnell	Phantom II	63-7744 as 67-0467
F- 4C(RF)	UT	Ogden	HAFBM	McDonnell	Phantom II	
F- 4C(RF)	VA	Hampt	APM	McDonnell	Phantom II	69-0372, ZZ
F- 4D	FL	Homes	HAFB	McDonnell	Phantom II	
F- 4D	KS	Liberal	MAAM	McDonnell	Phantom II	66746
F- 4D	KS	Topek	CAM	McDonnell	Phantom II	268
F- 4D	KS	Wichi	K&HAP	McDonnell	Phantom II	66-0271
F- 4D	MA	Stow	BCF	McDonnell	Phantom II	
F- 4D	MN	Minne	MAGM	McDonnell	Phantom II	
F- 4D	ND	Fargo	FANG	McDonnell	Phantom II	
F- 4D	NY	Glenville	ESAM	McDonnell	Phantom II	65-626
F- 4D	OH	Enon	VFW	McDonnell	Phantom II	67-5550
F- 4D	OH	Fairborn	WPMCH	McDonnell	Phantom II	66-7554, "City of Fairborn", Tail: DO AF 66554
F- 4D	OH	Fairborn	WPMCH	McDonnell	Phantom II	66-7626, "City of Dayton, Tail: DO AF 66626
F- 4D	TX	Abile	DLAP	McDonnell	Phantom II	65-0796
F- 4D	TX	Corsicana	NC	McDonnell	Phantom II	65-0747
F- 4D	TX	FWort	NASFWJRB	McDonnell	Phantom II	
F- 4D	TX	Wichi	SAFB	McDonnell	Phantom II	
F- 4D	UT	Ogden	HAM	McDonnell	Phantom II	
F- 4D	VT	Burli	BANG	McDonnell	Phantom II	
F- 4D-1	AZ	Tucso	PAM	McDonnell	Phantom II	134748
F- 4D-1	VA	VBeac	ONAS	McDonnell	Phantom II	134950, 101, VF-41
F- 4D-1 Fuse	TN	Memph	LS	McDonnell	Phantom II	
F- 4D(XF)	CA	Ridgecrest	CLNWC	McDonnell	Phantom II	
F- 4E	AZ	Tucso	PAM	McDonnell	Phantom II	66-329
F- 4E(NF)	AZ	Tucso	PAM	McDonnell	Phantom II	66-0329
F- 4E	CA	Riverside	MFAM	McDonnell	Phantom II	68-0382
F- 4E	FL	Tampa	MAFB	McDonnell	Phantom II	
F- 4E	KS	Emporia	EMA	McDonnell	Phantom II	
F- 4E	MO	SLoui	MOANGSLL	McDonnell	Phantom II	
F- 4E	NC	Golds	SJAFB	McDonnell	Phantom II	74-649
F- 4E	OH	Cleveland	BLA	McDonnell	Phantom II	Thunder Birds #1
F- 4E	TX	FWort	NASFWJRB	McDonnell	Phantom II	
F- 4E	TX	Wichi	SAFB	McDonnell	Phantom II	
F- 4E	UT	Ogden	HAM	McDonnell	Phantom II	
F- 4E	VA	Hampt	VA&SC	McDonnell	Phantom II	67-392, JJ
F- 4E(NF)	MO	Monet	CityPark	McDonnell	Phantom II	
F- 4E(NF)	NV	Battl	BMAM	McDonnell	Phantom II	66-286, ED
F- 4E(RF)	MN	Minne	MAGM	McDonnell	Phantom II	
F- 4E(YF)	CA	Rosam	EAFB	McDonnell	Phantom II	
F- 4E(YF)	OH	Dayto	USAFM	McDonnell	Phantom II	62-12200
F- 4F	AZ	Mesa	CFM	McDonnell	Phantom II	3016, VF-21, Tail NE, 2118367 SH, VMFAT-101
F- 4F	MD	Annap	USNAM	McDonnell	Phantom II	
F- 4F	OR	Tillamook	TAM	McDonnell	Phantom II	
F- 4G	OH	Dayto	USAFM	McDonnell	Phantom II	64-829
F- 4J	FL	Tittusville	VACM	McDonnell	Phantom II	
F- 4J	MD	Lexington	PRNAM	McDonnell	Phantom II	153071, Side # 100, SD Tail
F- 4J	MO	Sikeston	SVP	McDonnell	Phantom II	153839, Tail NG (Black Eagle), 102, "USS Enterprise
F- 4J	NY	NYC	ISASM	McDonnell	Phantom II	
F- 4J	OH	Cleveland	BLA	McDonnell	Phantom II	153812, Blue Angeles #1
F- 4J	SC	Mt Pleasant	PPM	McDonnell	Phantom II	153077, VMFA 333, USS America, Nose 202
F- 4J(YF)	AZ	Tucso	PAM	McDonnell	Phantom II	151497
F- 4N	AL	Birmingham	SMoF	McDonnell	Phantom II	152996
F- 4N	AZ	Phoen	LAFB	McDonnell	Phantom II	
F- 4N	AZ	Tucso	DMAFB	McDonnell	Phantom II	
F- 4N	CA	San Diego	SDACM	McDonnell	Phantom II	153030
F- 4N	NY	NYC	ISASM	McDonnell	Phantom II	
F- 4N	SC	Beauf	MAS	McDonnell	Phantom II	152270, DW 2270, VMFA-251
F- 4N(F4H)	FL	Pensa	USNAM	McDonnell	Phantom II	153915, NK 101, VF-154
F- 4S Cockpit	CA	Paso Robles	EWM	McDonnell	Phantom II	155861
F- 4S	CA	San Diego	SDAM	McDonnell	Phantom II	153879
F- 4S	CA	San Diego	SDACM	McDonnell	Phantom II	153880
F- 4S	CA	Santa Maria	SMMoF	McDonnell	Phantom II	55014
F- 4S	DC	Dulle	DA	McDonnell	Phantom II	
F- 4S	HI	Kaneohe	KBMCAS	McDonnell	Phantom II	153689, VMFA-212
F- 4S	KY	Lexington	AMoK	McDonnell	Phantom II	153904, VFMA-321
F- 4S	TX	Slaton	TAM	McDonnell	Phantom II	
F- 5(CF)	MB-C	Brandon	CATPM	Northrop	Freedom Fighter	
F- 5(CF)	NS-C	Halifax	HAM	Northrop	Freedom Fighter	116748, 434 Bluenose Squadron
F- 5(CF)	AB-C	Cold Lake	CFB	Northrop	Freedom Fighter	116736
F- 5(CF)	AB-C	Grand Center	City	Northrop	Freedom Fighter	
F- 5(CF)	BC-C	Kamloops	CFB	Northrop	Freedom Fighter	116740
F- 5(CF)	ON-C	Bagotville	CFB-3WB	Northrop	Freedom Fighter	116733
F- 5(CF)	ON-C	Borden	TAM	Northrop	Freedom Fighter	116769
F- 5(CF)	ON-C	Kingston	CFBK	Northrop	Freedom Fighter	
F- 5(CF)	ON-C	Toronto	TAM	Northrop	Freedom Fighter	
F- 5(CF)	ON-C	Trenton	HI	Northrop	Freedom Fighter	
F- 5(CF)	ON-C	Trenton	RCAFMM	Northrop	Freedom Fighter	116721
F- 5L	MD	Silve	PEGF	FelixStow	America Flying Boat	
F- 5A	CA	Hawth	WMoF	Northrop	Freedom Fighter	

124

F- 5A	IN	Ft Wayne	Mercury	Northrop	Freedom Fighter	
F- 5A(YF)	OH	Dayto	USAFM	Northrop	Freedom Fighter	59-4989
F- 5A	ON-C	Hamilton	CWH	Northrop	Freedom Fighter	116757
F- 5A(YF)	WA	Seatt	MoF	Northrop	Freedom Fighter	59-4987
F- 5B	AZ	Tucson	PAM	Northrop	Freedom Fighter	C8123
F- 5B	TX	San A	LAFB	Northrop	Freedom Fighter	C8123
F- 5B-5-NO(T-38)	IL	Ranto	OCAM	Northrop	Freedom Fighter	63-8441
F- 5E	NV	LasVe	NAFB	Northrop	Freedom Fighter	
F- 5E	TX	Wichi	SAFB	Northrop	Freedom Fighter	
F- 10(EF)	VA	Quantico	MCAGM		Skyknight	124618
F- 11	MB-C	Winni	WCAM	Fairchild	Husky	
F- 11	ON-C	Sault Ste Marie	CBHC	Fairchild	Husky	Sn 12, CF-EIR
F- 11-2	BC-C	Langley	CMoF	Fairchild	Husky	
F- 11A	CO	Puebl	PWAM	Grumman	Tiger	
F- 11A	NC	Durha	NCMoLS	Grumman	Tiger	
F- 11A	NC	Newbe	CityPark	Grumman	Tiger	
F- 11A (F9F-9)	NY	Garde	CoAM	Grumman	Tiger	141832
F- 11A(F11F-1)	FL	Pensa	USNAM	Grumman	Tiger	141828, AD201, VF- 21
F- 11B	CA	Ridecrest	CLNWC	Grumman	Tiger	
F- 14	AL	Huntsville	AC	Grumman	Tomcat	
F- 14	CA	Riverside	MFAM	Grumman	Tomcat	157990, VF-1, Tail NE, Nose 100
F- 14	CA	Paso Robles	EAWM	Grumman	Tomcat	157990, VF-1, Tail NE, Nose 100
F- 14	CO	Aurora	WOTR	Grumman	Tomcat	
F- 14	NV	Fallon	NASF	Grumman	Tomcat	
F- 14	NY	NYC	ISASM	Grumman	Tomcat	
F- 14	PA	Willow Grove	WGNAS	Grumman	Tomcat	
F- 14	VA	Norfolk	NASN	Grumman	Tomcat	
F- 14	WA	Tillamook	TAM	Grumman	Tomcat	
F- 14	WI	Oshkosh	EAAAAM	Grumman	Tomcat	
F- 14A	AZ	Tucso	PAM	Grumman	Tomcat	160684, VF-124
F- 14A	CA	Alameda Pt	USSHM	Grumman	Tomcat	
F- 14A	CA	Camarillo	YAM	Grumman	Tomcat	16100, VX-9
F- 14A	CA	Chino	PoF	Grumman	Tomcat	160686
F- 14A	CA	Chino	YAM	Grumman	Tomcat	
F- 14A	CA	Hawth	WMoF	Grumman	Tomcat	
F- 14A	CA	Imperial	PM	Grumman	Tomcat	159620, Side # 100, Tail NJ
F- 14A	CA	PalmS	PSAM	Grumman	Tomcat	160898, Side # 101, AJ 41, USS Theodore Roosevelt
F- 14A	CA	S.Mon	MoF	Grumman	Tomcat	
F- 14A	CA	El Cajon	SDAMGF	Grumman	Tomcat	VF-24
F- 14A	CA	San Diego	SDACM	Grumman	Tomcat	158978
F- 14A	CA	SRosa	PCAM	Grumman	Tomcat	
F- 14A	FL	Pensa	USNAM	Grumman	Tomcat	157984, NK201, VF- 21
F- 14A	FL	Tittusville	VAC	Grumman	Tomcat	VF-41 Black Aces, "Tico Bell"
F- 14A	KS	Liberal	MAAM	Grumman	Tomcat	160903
F- 14A	KS	Topeka	CAM	Grumman	Tomcat	
F- 14A	OK	Tulsa	TA&SC	Grumman	Tomcat	
F- 14A	MD	Lexington	NASPR	Grumman	Tomcat	162595, Side # 221, SD Tail
F- 14A	MD	Lexington	PRNAM	Grumman	Tomcat	161623, Side # 220
F- 14A	MI	Kalam	KAHM	Grumman	Tomcat	160395
F- 14A	NJ	Lumberton	AVM	Grumman	Tomcat	
F- 14A	NY	Horseheads	NWM	Grumman	Tomcat	161605, VF-32, Tail AC, Side 100
F- 14A	NY	Calverton	GMP	Grumman	Tomcat	
F- 14A	NY	Garde	CoAM	Grumman	Tomcat	157982
F- 14A	TX	C Christi	USS Lexi	Grumman	Tomcat	
F- 14A	TX	FWort	NASFWJRB	Grumman	Tomcat	
F- 14A	TX	Slaton	TAM	Grumman	Tomcat	
F- 14A	WA	Seattle	MoF	Grumman	Tomcat	160382
F- 14A	VA	VBeac	ONAS	Grumman	Tomcat	157988, 9, VF-103
F- 14B	NY	NYC	ISASM	Grumman	Super Tomcat	
F- 15A	WA	Tacoma	MAFB	McDonnell-Douglas	Eagle	
F- 15A	AZ	Tucso	PAM	McDonnell-Douglas	Eagle	74-118
F- 15A	CO	CSpri	EJPSCM	McDonnell-Douglas	Eagle	76-024
F- 15A	HI	Honolulu	HAFB	McDonnell-Douglas	Eagle	76018
F- 15A	IL	Ranto	OCAM	McDonnell-Douglas	Eagle	71-0286
F- 15A	FL	Panam	TAFB	McDonnell-Douglas	Eagle	74-0095, 325 FW
F- 15A	FL	Shalimar	USAFAM	McDonnell-Douglas	Eagle	75-0033, 74-124, OT
F- 15A	FL	Tampa	MAFB	McDonnell-Douglas	Eagle	
F- 15A	GA	Warner Robin	MoF	McDonnell-Douglas	Eagle	73-85, RG
F- 15A	LA	NewOrleans	FoJBMM	McDonnell-Douglas	Eagle	
F- 15A	LA	NewOrleans	Belle Chasse NAS	McDonnell-Douglas	Eagle	
F- 15A	MO	SLoui	MOANGSLL	McDonnell-Douglas	Eagle	
F- 15A	OH	Dayto	USAFM	McDonnell-Douglas	Eagle	72-119
F- 15A	OH	Lockb	RANGB	McDonnell-Douglas	Eagle	77-68
F- 15A	OR	Klamath Falls	OANG	McDonnell-Douglas	Eagle	
F- 15A	OR	Mc Minnville	EAEC	McDonnell-Douglas	Eagle	76-0014
F- 15A	TX	San A	LAFB	McDonnell-Douglas	Eagle	71-280
F- 15A	TX	Wichi	SAFB	McDonnell-Douglas	Eagle	
F- 15A	UT	Ogden	HAFBM	McDonnell-Douglas	Eagle	
F- 15A(YF)	VA	Hampt	LAFB	McDonnell-Douglas	Eagle	
F- 15B	AZ	Phoen	LAFB	McDonnell-Douglas	Eagle	
F- 15B/E	NC	Goldsboro	SJAFB	McDonnell-Douglas	Eagle	77-0161
F- 16	CO	CSpri	USAFA	General Dynamics	Fighting Falcon	
F- 16	DE	Dover	AMCM	General Dynamics	Fighting Falcon	
F- 16	FL	Pinellas Park	FLP	General Dynamics	Fighting Falcon	80-0528
F- 16	NM	Albuq	KAFB	General Dynamics	Fighting Falcon	
F- 16	NM	Albuq	KAFB	General Dynamics	Fighting Falcon	
F- 16	ND	Fargo	FANG	General Dynamics	Fighting Falcon	
F- 16	NV	Fallon	NASF	General Dynamics	Fighting Falcon	
F- 16	NY	NYC	ISASM	General Dynamics	Fighting Falcon	
F- 16 Cockpit	OH	Dayton	USAFM	General Dynamics	Fighting Falcon	
F- 16	OK	Weatherford	GTSM	General Dynamics	Fighting Falcon	
F- 16	WI	Madison	MTFMDCRA	General Dynamics	Fighting Falcon	
F- 16A	AL	Mobile	BMP	General Dynamics	Fighting Falcon	79-0334
F- 16A	MI	Selfridge	SMAM	General Dynamics	Fighting Falcon	78-0059
F- 16A	NC	Sumter	SAFB	General Dynamics	Fighting Falcon	
F- 16A	VA	Hampt	LAFB	General Dynamics	Fighting Falcon	
F- 16A(YF)	OH	Dayto	USAFM	General Dynamics	Fighting Falcon	75-745, "Thunderbirds"
F- 16A	OR	Klamath Falls	OANG	General Dynamics	Fighting Falcon	81-759
F- 16A	OR	Medford	RVIA	General Dynamics	Fighting Falcon	81-759
F- 16A	UT	Ogden	HAFBM	General Dynamics	Fighting Falcon	Side # 399FW, Tail HL
F- 16A(YF)	VA	Hampt	VA&SC	General Dynamics	Fighting Falcon	1567
F- 16B	CA	Rosam	EAFB	General Dynamics	Fighting Falcon	
F- 16B	TX	San Antonio	LAFB	General Dynamics	Fighting Falcon	

F- 16C	FL	Shali	USAFAM	General Dynamics	Fighting Falcon	80-573, ET
F- 16N	CA	Palm Sprgs	PoFAM	General Dynamics	Fighting Falcon	163277
F- 16N	CA	El Cajon	SDAMGF	General Dynamics	Fighting Falcon	
F- 16N	CA	SRosa	PCAM	General Dynamics	Fighting Falcon	
F- 16N	TX	FWort	NASFWJRB	General Dynamics	Fighting Falcon	
F- 17(YF) Mock-Up	NY	NYC	ISASM	Northrop	Hornet	
F- 17(YF)(F/A18)	AL	Mobile	BMP	Northrop	Hornet	AC1002
F- 17(YF)(F/A18)	CA	Lemoore	LNAS	Northrop	Hornet	
F- 17(YF)(F/A18)	CA	Ridgecrest	CLNWC	Northrop	Hornet	
F- 17(YF)(F/A18)	CA	Hawth	WMoF	Northrop	Hornet	
F- 17(YF)(F/A18)	CA	Miramar	FLAM	Northrop	Hornet	SH, VMF AT-101
F- 17(YF)(F/A18)	CA	Lancaster	AVC	Northrop	Hornet	
F- 17(YF)(F/A18)	CA	San Diego	SDACM	Northrop	Hornet	162901
F- 17(YF)(F/A18)	FL	Jacks	NASCF	Northrop	Hornet	162462, AC401, VFA-105
F- 17(YF)(F/A18)	LA	New Orleans	Belle Chasse NAS	Northrop	Hornet	
F- 17(YF)(F/A18)	MD	Andrews	AAFB	Northrop	Hornet	151353, Side # 120, SD Tail
F- 17(YF)(F/A18)	MD	Lexington	PRNAM	Northrop	Hornet	151353, Side # 120, SD Tail
F- 17(YF)(F/A18)	MI	Kalamazoo	KAHM	Northrop	Hornet	161984
F- 17(YF)(F/A18)	NV	Fallon	NASF	Northrop	Hornet	
F- 17(YF)(F/A18)	TX	FWort	NASFWJRB	Northrop	Hornet	
F- 17(YF)(F/A18)	UT	Ogden	HAFBM	Northrop	Hornet	
F- 17A-25 (F/A18)	GA	Marietta	NASA	Northrop	Hornet	
F- 17A-25 (F/A18)	GA	Warner Robin	MoF	Northrop	Hornet	FS-604A
F- 17A(CF)(F/A18)	BC-C	La Baie	ADM	Northrop	Hornet	
F- 17A(CF)(F/A18)	ON-C	Borden	CFBBMM	Northrop	Hornet	
F- 17A(CF)(F/A18)	ON-C	Ottawa	CAM	Northrop	Hornet	
F- 17A(L)(F/A18)	WA	Seatt	MoF	Northrop	Hornet	
F- 20	CA	LAnge	CMoS&I	Northrop	Tigershark	
F- 20	CA	Rosam	EAFB	Northrop	Tigershark	
F- 23(YF)	CA	Hawth	WMoF	Northrop	Black Widow II	
F- 23(YF)	OH	Dayton	USAFM	Northrop	Black Widow II	
F- 80	AK	Anchr	KANGB	Lockheed	Shooting Star	
F- 80	IN	Columbus	VFW	Lockheed	Shooting Star	
F- 80	NM	Albuquerque	KAFB	Lockheed	Shooting Star	48501
F- 80	SC	McEnt	MEANGB	Lockheed	Shooting Star	
F- 80	TX	Beevi	CourtHse	Lockheed	Shooting Star	
F- 80 (P)	IN	South Bend	MHP	Lockheed	Shooting Star	
F- 80 (P)	MI	Kalam	KAHM	Lockheed	Shooting Star	44-85152
F- 80 (P)	NC	Charl	CHAC	Lockheed	Shooting Star	
F- 80 (P)	NC	CPoin	CPMB	Lockheed	Shooting Star	
F- 80 (P)(TV-1)	WA	Seatt	MoF	Lockheed	Shooting Star	47-1388, 33841
F- 80 (XP)	DC	Washi	NA&SM	Lockheed	Shooting Star	
F- 80 Cockpit	MI	Kalam	KAHM	Lockheed	Shooting Star	
F- 80-1D	FL	Shali	USAFAM	Lockheed	Shooting Star	49713
F- 80A	CA	Chino	PoFAM	Lockheed	Shooting Star	
F- 80A Mock-Up	UT	Ogden	HAFBM	Lockheed	Shooting Star	
F- 80A(P)	AZ	Mesa	WAFB	Lockheed	Shooting Star	
F- 80A(P)	CA	Chino	PoFAM	Lockheed	Shooting Star	
F- 80A(EF)	CA	Rosamond	EAFB	Lockheed	Shooting Star	
F- 80A(P)	FL	Pensa	USNAM	Lockheed	Seastar	44-85235, 29689
F- 80A(P)	GA	Warner Robin	MoF	Lockheed	Shooting Star	
F- 80A(P)	OH	Newbu	WASAC	Lockheed	Shooting Star	689
F- 80B	NM	Clovi	CAFB	Lockheed	Shooting Star	
F- 80B(P)	AZ	Tucso	PAM	Lockheed	Shooting Star	45-8612
F- 80B(P)	CA	Sacra	McCelAFB	Lockheed	Shooting Star	45-8704
F- 80B	CA	Atwater	CAM	Lockheed	Shooting Star	45-8490, Side FT-490
F- 80C	CA	Chino	YAM	Lockheed	Shooting Star	
F- 80C	FL	Shali	USAFAM	Lockheed	Shooting Star	53-2610
F- 80C	GA	Warner Robin	MoF	Lockheed	Shooting Star	45-8357 FN
F- 80C(P)	KS	Liberal	MAAM	Lockheed	Shooting Star	90710
F- 80C	KS	Wichita	K&HAP	Lockheed	Shooting Star	45-8612, "City of Wichita"
F- 80C	NC	Charl	CHAC	Lockheed	Shooting Star	
F- 80C	NM	Alamo	HAFB	Lockheed	Shooting Star	
F- 80C (P)	PA	Willo	WGNAS	Lockheed	Shooting Star	33824, 28
F- 80C	OH	Dayto	USAFM	Lockheed	Shooting Star	49-696
F- 80C	OH	Lockb	RANGB	Lockheed	Shooting Star	47-171
F- 80C	OK	Oklahoma City	45thIDM	Lockheed	Shooting Star	
F- 80C	TX	Austi	BAFB	Lockheed	Shooting Star	
F- 80C	WA	Seattle	MoF	Lockheed	Shooting Star	3841
F- 80C(EF)	CA	Rosam	EAFB	Lockheed	Shooting Star	49-851
F- 80C(GF)	WI	Oshko	EAAAAM	Lockheed	Shooting Star	48-868
F- 80F	NM	Alamo	CityPark	Lockheed	Shooting Star	
F- 80F	NY	NYC	ISASM	Lockheed	Shooting Star	
F- 80L	TX	Dalla	DNAS	Lockheed	Shooting Star	
F- 80L	TX	FWort	NASFWJRB	Lockheed	Shooting Star	
F- 82B(P)	OH	Dayto	USAFM	North American	Twin Mustang	44-65168, "Betty Jo", naca-132
F- 82E(EF)(P)	TX	San A	LAFB	North American	Twin Mustang	46-262
F- 84	AR	Little Rock	LRAFB	Republic	Thunderjet	0-37543
F- 84	CA	Chino	YAM	Republic	Thunderjet	
F- 84	CO	Puebl	PWAM	Republic	Thunderjet	71562
F- 84	IA	Des Moines	ING	Republic	Thunderjet	40-26497
F- 84	IA	SBluf	MAAM	Republic	Thunderjet	
F- 84	IN	Ft. W	MC	Republic	Thunderjet	50-19514
F- 84	TX	FWort	PMoT	Republic	Thunderjet	
F- 84 (XP)	MD	Silve	PEGF	Republic	Thunderjet	
F- 84(RF)	AR	FSmit	EANG	Republic	Thunderjet	
F- 84(RF)	IA	SBluf	MAAM	Republic	Thunderjet	
F- 84A(YP) Fuse	CA	Chino	PoFAM	Republic	Thunderjet	
F- 84A	IL	Ranto	OCAM	Republic	Thunderjet	45-59494
F- 84B	AZ	Grand	PoFGCVA	Republic	Thunderjet	45-59566
F- 84B	AZ	Tucso	PAM	Republic	Thunderjet	45-59554
F- 84B	NY	Garde	CoAM	Republic	Thunderjet	45-59504
F- 84B-35-RE	PA	Readi	MAAM	Republic	Thunderjet	
F- 84B	TX	San Antonio	Lackland	Republic	Thunderjet	
F- 84C	AZ	Tucso	PAM	Republic	Thunderjet	47-1433
F- 84C	CA	Riverside	MFAM	Republic	Thunderjet	47-1595
F- 84C	KS	Wichi	K&HAP	Republic	Thunderjet	47-1513
F- 84C	NM	Clovi	CAFB	Republic	Thunderjet	
F- 84C	OH	Sprin	OHANG	Republic	Thunderjet	
F- 84C	OH	Sprin	SMAM	Republic	Thunderjet	
F- 84C	WI	Oshko	EAAAAM	Republic	Thunderjet	51-9456
F- 84D	GA	Savan	SMAM	Republic	Thunderjet	
F- 84E	AZ	Tucson	AM 109	Republic	Thunderstreak	46-0294

126

Model	State	City	Location	Mfr	Name	Serial	Notes
F-84E	CA	Chino	PoFAM	Republic	Thunderjet	FU-849	
F-84E	HI	Oahu	HAFB	Republic	Thunderjet		
F-84E	OH	Dayto	USAFM	Republic	Thunderjet	50-1143	
F-84E	OH	Lockb	RANGB	Republic	Thunderjet	49-2348	
F-84E	OH	Newbu	WASAC	Republic	Thunderjet		
F-84E(RF)	AR	Littl	LRAFB	Republic	Thunderjet		
F-84E-25-RE	GA	Warner Robin	MoF	Republic	Thunderjet	51-604A	
F-84F	AL	Birmingham	SMoF	Republic	Thunderstreak		
F-84F	AL	Birmingham	SMoF	Republic	Thunderstreak		
F-84F	AL	Montg	CityPark	Republic	Thunderstreak		
F-84F	AR	Harri	VWF	Republic	Thunderstreak		
F-84F	AZ	Peori	VWF	Republic	Thunderstreak		
F-84F	AZ	Phoen	LAFB	Republic	Thunderstreak		
F-84F	AZ	Tucso	PAM	Republic	Thunderstreak	52-6563	Thunderbird Painted
F-84F	AZ	Tucso	TANG	Republic	Thunderstreak		
F-84F	CA	Atwater	CAM	Republic	Thunderstreak	51-9433, Side FS-433	
F-84F	CA	Fairf	TAFB	Republic	Thunderstreak	52-6359	FS-359
F-84F	CA	Riverside	MFAM	Republic	Thunderstreak	51-9432	
F-84F	CA	Rosam	EAFB	Republic	Thunderstreak	51-9350	
F-84F	CA	Sacra	McCelAFB	Republic	Thunderstreak	54-1772	
F-84F	CA	Santa Rosa	PCAM	Republic	Thunderstreak	52-6475, AF	
F-84F	FL	Shali	USAFAM	Republic	Thunderstreak	51-495	FS-495
F-84F	FL	Titusville	VAC	Republic	Thunderstreak		
F-84F	FL	Wauch	AL P-2	Republic	Thunderstreak		
F-84F	GA	Athen	VFW 2872	Republic	Thunderstreak		
F-84F	GA	Calhoun	MAM	Republic	Thunderstreak		
F-84F	GA	Corde	ALP-38	Republic	Thunderstreak		
F-84F	GA	Corde	GVMSP	Republic	Thunderstreak		
F-84F	GA	Dobbi	DAFB	Republic	Thunderstreak		
F-84F	GA	Marie	CCYM	Republic	Thunderstreak		
F-84F	IA	Corre	CityPark	Republic	Thunderstreak		
F-84F	IA	Fairf	CityPark	Republic	Thunderstreak		
F-84F	IA	FtDod	FtDIAANG	Republic	Thunderstreak		
F-84F	IA	Grime	GANG	Republic	Thunderstreak		
F-84F	IA	Sergant Bluff	SCANG	Republic	Thunderstreak		
F-84F	ID	Mount	MHAFB	Republic	Thunderstreak		
F-84F	IL	Cahok	PCUSL	Republic	Thunderstreak		
F-84F	IL	Grani	AMVETS51	Republic	Thunderstreak		
F-84F	IL	Peori	PANG	Republic	Thunderstreak		
F-84F	IL	Perki	CityPark	Republic	Thunderstreak		
F-84F	IL	Ranto	OCAM	Republic	Thunderstreak	51-9531	
F-84F	IL	Sprin	SMAM	Republic	Thunderstreak	2844	
F-84F	IL	Wenan	ALP1130	Republic	Thunderstreak		
F-84F	IN	Hagerstown	WWB	Republic	Thunderstreak	52-6993	
F-84F	IN	Hoagl	CityPark	Republic	Thunderstreak		
F-84F	IN	Monro	CityPark	Republic	Thunderstreak		
F-84F	IN	Montp	CityPark	Republic	Thunderstreak		
F-84F	IN	Peru	GAFB	Republic	Thunderstreak		
F-84F	IN	South	CityPark	Republic	Thunderstreak		
F-84F	IN	Terre Haute	THANG	Republic	Thunderstreak	027202	
F-84F	KS	Lynn	ALP237	Republic	Thunderstreak		
F-84F	KS	Wichita	KAM	Republic	Thunderstreak		
F-84F	KY	Frank	BNGC	Republic	Thunderstreak		
F-84F	LA	Alexandria	EHP	Republic	Thunderstreak	27080, FS-080, EL 23 TFW	
F-84F	LA	Bossi	BAFB	Republic	Thunderstreak	11386	
F-84F-25-GK	MI	Belleville	YAF	Republic	Thunderstreak	51-9361	
F-84F-35-GK	MI	Belleville	YAF	Republic	Thunderstreak	51-9501, N5006	
F-84F	MI	Escan	CityPark	Republic	Thunderstreak		
F-84F	MI	Lapee	YAFDLA	Republic	Thunderstreak		
F-84F	MI	Mt Clemens	SMAM	Republic	Thunderstreak	51-1664	
F-84F	MT	Great Falls	MAFB	Republic	Thunderstreak	52-6969	
F-84F	NE	Creig	CityPark	Republic	Thunderstreak		
F-84F	NJ	Wrightstown	McGAFB	Republic	Thunderstreak	27066, NJANG	
F-84F	NM	Alamo	HAFB	Republic	Thunderstreak		
F-84F	NM	Artes	CityPark	Republic	Thunderstreak		
F-84F	NM	STere	WEAM	Republic	Thunderstreak		
F-84F	NV	Indian Sprs	City Park	Republic	Thunderstreak	948051	
F-84F	NY	Garde	CoAM	Republic	Thunderstreak	948051	
F-84F	NY	NYC	ISASM	Republic	Thunderstreak		
F-84F	NY	Glenville	ESAM	Republic	Thunderstreak	51-1620	
F-84F	NC	Asheboro	PFAC	Republic	Thunderstreak		
F-84F	OH	Dayto	USAFM	Republic	Thunderstreak	52-6526	
F-84F	OH	Lockb	RANGB	Republic	Thunderstreak	51-1346	
F-84F	OH	Mansf	MANG	Republic	Thunderstreak		
F-84F	OH	Newbu	WASAC	Republic	Thunderstreak	52-6524	
F-84F	OH	Sprin	OHANG	Republic	Thunderstreak	51-1797	
F-84F	OH	Sprin	SMAM	Republic	Thunderstreak	92348	
F-84F	OH	Swant	TANG	Republic	Thunderstreak		
F-84F	PA	Pitts	PANG	Republic	Thunderstreak		
F-84F	SD	Rapid	SDA&SM	Republic	Thunderstreak	52-8886	
F-84F	TX	Abile	DLAP	Republic	Thunderstreak	51-9364	
F-84F	TX	Amarillo	EFA&SM	Republic	Thunderstreak	52-6553	
F-84F	TX	D Rio	LAFB	Republic	Thunderstreak		
F-84F	TX	Houst	ALP490	Republic	Thunderstreak		
F-84F	TX	Muens	CityPark	Republic	Thunderstreak		
F-84F	UT	Ogden	HAFBM	Republic	Thunderstreak		
F-84F	VA	Hampt	VA&SC	Republic	Thunderstreak	51-1786	FS-786
F-84F	VA	Richm	DGSC	Republic	Thunderstreak		
F-84F	VA	Richm	SMAM	Republic	Thunderstreak		
F-84F	VA	VBeac	VANG	Republic	Thunderstreak		
F-84F	WI	CDoug	WNGML&M	Republic	Thunderstreak		
F-84F	WI	Kenosha	GTAC	Republic	Thunderstreak	52-6370	
F-84F	WI	Oshko	EAAAAM	Republic	Thunderstreak	47-1498	
F-84F	WY	Cheye	WYANG	Republic	Thunderstreak		
F-84F	IA	Cedar	CityPark	Republic	Thunderstreak	51-9444	
F-84F (2ea)	KS	Topek	CAM	Republic	Thunderstreak	0-26458	
F-84F(RF)	MD	Middl	GLMAM	Republic	Thunderstreak		
F-84F(RF)	MI	Mt Clemens	SMAM	Republic	Thunderstreak	51-1896	
F-84F-30	NC	Asheb	AMA	Republic	Thunderstreak		
F-84F-30	VA	Hampt	APM	Republic	Thunderstreak	51-1786	
F-84F-35RE	MI	Kalam	KAHM	Republic	Thunderstreak	52-6486	
F-84F-RE	NE	Ashland	SACM	Republic	Thunderstreak	51-1714	
F-84F(RF)	AL	Ozark	CityPark	Republic	Thunderflash		

Model	State	City	Code	Manufacturer	Type	Notes
F-84F(RF)	AR	Littl	LRAFB	Republic	Thunderflash	
F-84F(RF)	AZ	Tucso	PAM	Republic	Thunderflash	51-1944
F-84F(RF)	GA	Warner Robin	MoF	Republic	Thunderflash	
F-84F(RF)	IA	Harla	CityPark	Republic	Thunderflash	
F-84F	IA	Sergant Bluff	SCANG	Republic	Thunderflash	
F-84F(RF)	MI	Belle	VFW4434	Republic	Thunderflash	
F-84F(RF)	MI	Lapee	YAFDLA	Republic	Thunderflash	
F-84F(RF)	MI	Ypsil	YAF	Republic	Thunderflash	
F-84F(RF)	MS	Hatti	CityPark	Republic	Thunderflash	
F-84F(RF)	MS	Jacks	JANG	Republic	Thunderflash	
F-84F(RF)	NC	Inca	IJHS	Republic	Thunderflash	
F-84F(RF)	NE	David	ALP125	Republic	Thunderflash	
F-84F(RF)	NE	Linco	LANG	Republic	Thunderflash	51-11259, Tail NEBR 0-11259
F-84F(RF)	NE	Nelig	CityPark	Republic	Thunderflash	
F-84F(RF)	NE	Valle	CityPark	Republic	Thunderflash	
F-84F(RF)	NE	York	CityPark	Republic	Thunderflash	
F-84F(RF)	OH	Dayto	USAFM	Republic	Thunderflash	49-2430
F-84F(RF)	OH	Newbu	WASAC	Republic	Thunderflash	52-7262
F-84F(RF)	TN	Nashv	NANG	Republic	Thunderflash	
F-84F(RF)	TX	Abile	DLAP	Republic	Thunderflash	51-1123
F-84F(RF)	TX	Austi	BAFB	Republic	Thunderflash	
F-84F(RF)	TX	Midla	CAFFM	Republic	Thunderflash	
F-84F-20-RE	GA	Warner Robin	MoF	Republic	Thunderflash	52-7244
F-84F-45-RE	GA	Warner Robin	MoF	Republic	Thunderflash	52-6701A FS-701
F-84G	IL	Ellington	EFM	Republic	Thunderjet	
F-84G	NY	Niagara Falls	NAM	Republic	Thunderjet	
F-84G	NC	Charl	CHAC	Republic	Thunderjet	
F-84G	UT	Ogden	HAFBM	Republic	Thunderjet	23275, FS-275
F-84H(XF)	OH	Dayton	USAFM	Republic	Thunderscreech	51-17059
F-84K(RF)	CA	Chino	PoFAM	Republic	Thunderjet	
F-84K(RF)	CO	Aurora	WOTR	Republic	Thunderjet	
F-84K(RF)-17-RE	OH	Dayton	USAFM	Republic	Thunderjet	52-7259, "Ypsi Gypsy Rose"
F-84K(RF)-17-RE	MI	Belleville	YAF	Republic	Thunderjet	52-7259
F-84K(RF)-17-RE	MI	Ypsil	YAF	Republic	Thunderjet	52-7260
F-84K(RF)	MI	Ypsil	YAF	Republic	Thunderjet	52-7259
F-84K(RF)	MI	Ypsil	YAF	Republic	Thunderjet	
F-84K(RF)	OH	Dayto	USAFM	Republic	Thunderflash	51-1847
F-85(XF)	OH	Dayto	USAFM	McDonnell	Goblin	46-0523
F-85(XF)-MC	NE	Ashland	SACM	McDonnell	Goblin	46-0524
F-86(QF)	CA	Ridgecrest	CLNWC	North American	Sabre	
F-86	CA	San Diego	SDAM	North American	Sabre	
F-86	CA	Santa Maria	SMMoF	North American	Sabre	
F-86	D.C.	Washington	USS&AH	North American	Sabre	
F-86	IL	Danville	DA	North American	Sabre	
F-86	IL	Joliet	RFA	North American	Sabre	52-4986, NX188RL, FU-584, "Mig Mad Marine"
F-86	KY	Middleboro	LS	North American	Sabre	31361, FU-361
F-86	MI	Frankenmuth	MOM&SM	North American	Sabre	
F-86	MI	Kalam	KAHM	North American	Sabre	52-5143
F-86	NC	CPoin	CPMB	North American	Sabre	
F-86	NM	STere	WEAM	North American	Sabre	
F-86	NV	Fallon	NASF	North American	Sabre	
F-86	NV	LasVe	NAFB	North American	Sabre	
F-86	OH	Cinncinnati	CMALF	North American	Sabre	
F-86	OK	Weatherford	GTSM	North American	Sabre	
F-86	AB-C	Bagotville	CFB	Canadair	Sabre	19454
F-86	BC-C	Sidney		Canadair	Sabre	23060
F-86	ON-C	Belle	ZPark	Canadair	Sabre	23053, Golden Hawks Colours
F-86	ON-C	Borden		Canadair	Sabre	23228
F-86	ON-C	Brockville	BIBM	Canadair	Sabre	23649
F-86	ON-C	Kingston	RMC	Canadair	Sabre	23221
F-86	ON-C	Hamilton	CWH	Canadair	Sabre	23651, GH
F-86	ON-C	Oshawa		Canadair	Sabre	23047, "City of Oshawa", 416
F-86	ON-C	Petersburg	RP&Z	Canadair	Sabre	23428
F-86	ON-C	Sarnia	GP	Canadair	Sabre	23164, Golden Hawks Colours, RCAF 428
F-86 Mk VI	ON-C	Trenton	MP	Canadair	Sabre	23641, Golden Hawks Colours
F-86	ON-C	Trenton	RCAFMM	Canadair	Sabre	23257, RCAF 428 Golden Hawks Colours
F-86	TN	Sevierville	TMoA	North American	Sabre	
F-86	TX	FWort	PMoT	North American	Sabre	
F-86	TX	FWort	VFM	North American	Sabre	
F-86	TX	Galveston	SP	North American	Fury	
F-86	TX	Inglewood	PBR	North American	Fury	
F-86	TX	Tulia	VFWP1798	North American	Sabre	
F-86	WA	Seatt	MoF	North American	Sabre	
F-86	WI	Monroe	TP	North American	Sabre	
F-86	MB-C	Winni	City	Canadair	Sabre	
F-86 Mk 3	MB-C	Winni	WCAM	Canadair	Sabre	
F-86 Mk.V	NS -C	Halifax	HAM	Canadair	Sabre	"Golden Hawks"
F-86 Mk.V	ON-C	Oshawa	OA	Canadair	Sabre	"Golden Hawks"
F-86 Mk.VI	ON-C	Peterborough	RP	Canadair	Sabre	
F-86 Mk V	WI	Oshko	EAAAAM	North American	Sabre	N8687D, "The Huff"
F-86 Mk V/VI	WI	Oshko	EAAAAM	North American	Sabre	N86JR
F-86A	AK	Ancho	KANGB	North American	Sabre	
F-86A	CA	Fresn	FANG	North American	Sabre	
F-86A	CT	Winds	NEAM	North American	Sabre	
F-86A	IL	Rantoul	PEGF	North American	Sabre	47-615
F-86A	MD	Silve	PEGF	North American	Sabre	
F-86A	MI	Mt Clemens	SMAM	North American	Sabre	52-4387
F-86A	MT	Great	GFANG	North American	Sabre	47-00637
F-86A	OH	Dayto	USAFM	North American	Sabre	49-1067
F-86A	TX	San A	LAFB	North American	Sabre	59-1605
F-86A	UT	Salt	SLCANG	North American	Sabre	
F-86A(P)	WA	Seatt	MoF	North American	Sabre	
F-86C	GA	Calhoun	MAM	North American	Sabre	15896
F-86D	AZ	Chand	CityPark	North American	Sabre	
F-86D	AZ	Globe	VWF1704	North American	Sabre	
F-86D	AZ	Tucso	DMAFB	North American	Sabre	16071
F-86D	CA	Sacra	McCelAFB	North American	Sabre	51-2968
F-86D	CA	West	VWF	North American	Sabre	52-3784
F-86D	CO	Auror	BANGB	North American	Sabre	
F-86D	FL	Clear	FMAM	North American	Sabre	
F-86D	FL	Panam	TAFB	North American	Sabre	52-10133
F-86D	FL	Shali	USAFAM	North American	Sabre	51-2831, FU-831
F-86D	ID	Idaho Falls	PM	North American	Sabre	53-1022

Model	State	City	Org	Manufacturer	Name	Notes
F- 86D	LA	New Orleans	FoJBMM	North American	Sabre	
F- 86D-60-NA	MI	Belleville	YAF	North American	Sabre	53-1060, N201504
F- 86D	NV	Reno	NAHS	North American	Sabre	
F- 86D	OH	Dayto	USAFM	North American	Sabre	50-477
F- 86D	OK	Oklah	45IDM	North American	Sabre	52-4043
F- 86D	OK	Oklah	45IDM	North American	Sabre	
F- 86D	OK	Tinke	TANG	North American	Sabre	
F- 86D	OK	Tulsa	TANG	North American	Sabre	
F- 86D	TN	Knoxv	CityPark	North American	Sabre	
F- 86D	TX	Austi	AGDTAG	North American	Sabre	
F- 86D	TX	FWort	SAM	North American	Sabre	
F- 86D	TX	Paris	FTAM	North American	Sabre	
F- 86D	WA	Tacoma	MAFB	North American	Sabre	
F- 86D	WI	Monroe	Park	North American	Sabre	NAtch
F- 86E	AZ	Mesa	WAFB	North American	Sabre	
F- 86E	AZ	Tucson	PAM	North American	Sabre	
F- 86E	CA	P.Hue	CIANGB	North American	Sabre	
F- 86E	CA	PHuen	CIANGB	North American	Sabre	
F- 86E	HI	Honolulu	HAFB	North American	Sabre	50-00653
F- 86E	HI	Honolulu	HANG	North American	Sabre	52-04191
F- 86E	IN	India	VFWP7119	North American	Sabre	
F- 86E	LA	Alexandria	EAB	North American	Sabre	24931, FU-931
F- 86E-15NA	NC	Golds	SJAFB	North American	Sabre	51-12972, N1028
F- 86E	NM	Alamo	HAFB	North American	Sabre	
F- 86E	OH	Newbu	WASAC	North American	Sabre	50-11123
F- 86E	TX	Addison	CFM	North American	Sabre	51-12821, N4689H, FU-821, 23293
F- 86E	WA	Spoka	FAFBHM	North American	Sabre	
F- 86E	WY	Cheye	WYANG	North American	Sabre	
F- 86F	AL	Birmingham	SMoF	North American	Sabre	
F- 86F	AZ	Mesa	CFM	North American	Sabre	
F- 86F	AZ	Phoen	LAFB	North American	Sabre	
F- 86F	CA	Chino	PoFAM	North American	Sabre	
F- 86F	CA	El Cajon	SDAMGF	North American	Sabre	
F- 86F(QF)	CA	Paso Robles	EWM	North American	Sabre	555082, N454
F- 86F	CA	Rosam	EAFB	North American	Sabre	52-5241
F- 86F	CA	Sacra	McCelAFB	North American	Sabre	51-13082
F- 86F-30NA	CO	Auror	BANGB	North American	Sabre	52-4913, AF. JASDF, Side # 609
F- 86F(RF)	CO	Auror	BANGB	North American	Sabre	
F- 86F	CO	Auror	BANGB	North American	Sabre	
F- 86F	FL	Clear	FMAM	North American	Sabre	
F- 86F	FL	Miami	WOM	North American	Sabre	
F- 86F	FL	Titusville	VAC	North American	Sabre	
F- 86F	GA	Warner Robin	MoF	North American	Sabre	53-1511
F- 86F(RF)	IL	Sugar Grove	ACM	North American	Sabre	51-13990
F- 86F	IL	Sprin	S.ArmyNG	North American	Sabre	50-27051 IL
F- 86F	IL	Sprin	SMAM	North American	Sabre	51-10822 IL
F- 86F	IN	Ft. W	FWAS	North American	Sabre	Sn 52-5139, NX86F, "No Jokes" 90 Willy 10"
F- 86F	MI	Ypsil	YAF	North American	Sabre	
F- 86F	OR	Clack	CANG	North American	Sabre	
F- 86F(QF)	OR	Clack	CANG	North American	Sabre	
F- 86F(RF)	QC-C	La Baie	ADM	Canadair	Sabre	
F- 86F-25	PA	Readi	MAAM	North American	Sabre	51-13417 N 51RS
F- 86F	WA	Seattle	MoF	North American	Sabre	51-13371, 371, FU-371
F- 86F	WA	Eastsound	FHC	North American	Sabre	49-1217, G-BZNL
F- 86H	AZ	Tucso	PAM	North American	Sabre	53-1525
F- 86H	CA	Apple Valley	Airport	North American	Sabre	53-1515
F- 86H	CA	Victorville	GAFB	North American	Sabre	
F- 86H	CA	Atwater	CAM	North American	Sabre	53-1230, Tail A
F- 86H-10NA	CA	Riverside	MFAM	North American	Sabre	53-1304
F- 86H	CA	Victorville	GAFB	North American	Sabre	53-1378A, AF
F- 86H	CO	Aurora	WOTR	North American	Sabre	
F- 86H	DE	New C	NCANG	North American	Sabre	
F- 86H	FL	Ft. Lauderdale	HP	North American	Sabre	53-1255
F- 86H	IN	Churu	CityPark	North American	Sabre	56-298, 64, 66N
F- 86H	IN	Peru	GAFB	North American	Sabre	
F- 86H	KS	Liberal	MAAM	North American	Sabre	31501
F- 86H	KS	Topek	CAM	North American	Sabre	
F- 86H	MA	Bedfo	HAFB	North American	Sabre	
F- 86H	MD	Balti	BANG	North American	Sabre	
F- 86H	MD	Ellic	VFWP7472	North American	Sabre	
F- 86H	MO	LaPla	CityPark	North American	Sabre	
F- 86H	NC	Golds	CityPark	North American	Sabre	53-1370
F- 86H	ND	Hetti	CityPark	North American	Sabre	
F- 86H	ND	James	CityPark	North American	Sabre	
F- 86H	ND	Walha	CityPark	North American	Sabre	
F- 86H	NE	Mc Co	CityPark	North American	Sabre	
F- 86H	NM	Clovi	CAFB	North American	Sabre	
F- 86H	NY	Centr	ALP915	North American	Sabre	
F- 86H	NY	Manch	ALP	North American	Sabre	
F- 86H	NY	Syrac	SMAMB	North American	Sabre	
F- 86H	OH	Cinci	CityPark	North American	Sabre	
F- 86H	OH	Dayto	USAFM	North American	Sabre	53-1352
F- 86H	PA	Beave	CityPark	North American	Sabre	
F- 86H	SC	Flore	FA&MM	North American	Sabre	
F- 86H	SC	Green	CityPark	North American	Sabre	
F- 86H	SC	McEnt	MEANGB	North American	Sabre	
F- 86H	SD	Rapid	SDA&SM	North American	Sabre	53-1375
F- 86H	VA	Hampt	LAFB	North American	Sabre	
F- 86H	WI	Argyl	CityPark	North American	Sabre	
F- 86HL-26	WI	CDoug	WNGML&M	North American	Sabre	51-3064, FU-064
F- 86H	WI	Oshko	EAAAAM	North American	Sabre	52-1993
F- 86H	WVA	Vienn	CityPark	North American	Sabre	
F- 86H(QF)	CA	Chino	PoFAM	North American	Sabre	
F- 86H-10-NH	NM	Manch	CityPark	North American	Sabre	
F- 86H-NH	NE	Ashland	SACM	North American	Sabre	53-1375
F- 86L	AL	Mobil	BMP	North American	Sabre Dog	51-2993
F- 86L	AL	Montg	MAFB	North American	Sabre Dog	
F- 86L Cockpit	AZ	Grand	PoFGCVA	North American	Sabre Dog	49-1217
F- 86L	AZ	Tucso	PAM	North American	Sabre Dog	56- 965, FU-965
F- 86L	CA	Fairf	TAFB	North American	Sabre Dog	30704, FU-704
F- 86L	CA	Fresn	FANG	North American	Sabre Dog	
F- 86L	CA	Riverside	MFAM	North American	Sabre Dog	50-0560
F- 86L	CO	CSpri	EJPSCM	North American	Sabre Dog	53-0782

F- 86L	FL	Wauchula	FMAM	North American	Sabre Dog	53-0658	
F- 86L	GA	Macon	MACF	North American	Sabre Dog		
F- 86L	GA	Savan	SMAM	North American	Sabre Dog		
F- 86L	GA	Valdo	CityPark	North American	Sabre Dog		
F- 86L	HI	Oahu	HAFB	North American	Sabre Dog		
F- 86L	HI	Honolulu	HANG	North American	Sabre Dog	52-02841	
F- 86L	IA	Iowa	CityPark	North American	Sabre Dog	53-0750	
F- 86L	ID	IFall	CityPark	North American	Sabre Dog		
F- 86L	IL	Brook	Village	North American	Sabre Dog		
F- 86L-50	KS	Wichi	K&HAP	North American	Sabre Dog	52-4256	
F- 86L	MI	Ypsil	YAF	North American	Sabre Dog		
F- 86L	MS	Hazle	VFW2567	North American	Sabre Dog		
F- 86L	MT	Butte	CityPark	North American	Sabre Dog	53-997	
F- 86L	NC	Charl	CANG	North American	Sabre Dog		
F- 86L	ND	Grand	CityPark	North American	Sabre Dog		
F- 86L	NE	Linco	LANG	North American	Sabre Dog	53-0831, Tail ANG 0-23760	
F- 86L	NJ	Lumberton	AVM	North American	Sabre Dog	FU-110	
F- 86L	NV	Battl	BMAM	North American	Sabre Dog	53-1045	
F- 86L	NY	Monro	Village	North American	Sabre Dog		
F- 86L	OH	Newbu	WASAC	North American	Sabre Dog	30959	
F- 86L	OR	Nyssa	CityPark	North American	Sabre Dog		
F- 86L	OR	Vale	CityPark	North American	Sabre Dog		
F- 86L	PA	Imper	VFWP7714	North American	Sabre Dog		
F- 86L	PA	Pitts	PANG	North American	Sabre Dog		
F- 86L	SC	McEnt	MEANGB	North American	Sabre Dog		
F- 86L	TN	Nashv	CityPark	North American	Sabre Dog		
F- 86L	TX	Abile	DLAP	North American	Sabre Dog		
F- 86L	TX	Dalla	DNAS	North American	Sabre Dog		
F- 86L	TX	Denis	VFWP2773	North American	Sabre Dog		
F- 86L	TX	FWort	NASFWJRB	North American	Sabre Dog		
F- 86L	TX	FWort	SAM	North American	Sabre Dog		
F- 86L	TX	Sherm	ALP29	North American	Sabre Dog	406Th Fl Wing of Manstan	
F- 86L	UT	Ogden	HAFBM	North American	Sabre Dog		
F- 86L	WA	Bridg	CityPark	North American	Sabre Dog		
F- 86L	WI	Apple	ALP38	North American	Sabre Dog	51-5938	
F- 86L	WVA	Milto	CityPark	North American	Sabre Dog		
F- 86L	WY	Cheye	WYANG	North American	Sabre Dog		
F- 86L (3 ea)	AL	Montg	CityPark	North American	Sabre Dog		
F- 86L-26	VA	Hampt	APM	North American	Sabre Dog	51-3064, FU-064	
F- 89 Fuse Only	TN	Memph	LS	Northrop	Scorpion		
F- 89 Fuse Only	TN	Peru	GAM	Northrop	Scorpion		
F- 89	TX	San Antonio	TAM	Northrop	Scorpion		
F- 89B	IA	Nampa	CityPark	Northrop	Scorpion	49-2457	
F- 89D	CA	Rosam	EAFB	Northrop	Scorpion	52-1959	
F- 89D	GA	Warner Robin	MoF	Northrop	Scorpion	53-2463	
F- 89D	VT	Burli	BANG	Northrop	Scorpion		
F- 89H	MN	Minne	MAGM	Northrop	Scorpion	53-2677, 373	
F- 89H	TX	Abile	DLAP	Northrop	Scorpion	54-298	
F- 89H	UT	Ogden	HAFBM	Northrop	Scorpion	54-0322	
F- 89J	AZ	Tucso	PAM	Northrop	Scorpion	53-2674	
F- 89J	CA	Atwater	CAM	Northrop	Scorpion	52-1922	
F- 89J	CA	Riverside	MFAM	Northrop	Scorpion	52-1949	
F- 89J	CO	CSpri	EJPSCM	Northrop	Scorpion	52-1941	
F- 89J	CT	Winds	NEAM	Northrop	Scorpion	52-2494	
F- 89J	FL	Shali	USAFAM	Northrop	Scorpion	53-2610	
F- 89J	ME	Bangor	MAM	Northrop	Scorpion	52-1856	
F- 89J	MT	Great Falls	GFANG	Northrop	Scorpion	53-2467	
F- 89J	MT	Helena	CoT	Northrop	Scorpion	53-2453	
F- 89J	ND	Fargo	FANG	Northrop	Scorpion	53-2465	
F- 89J	OH	Dayto	USAFM	Northrop	Scorpion	52-1911	
F- 89J	OR	Mc Minnville	EAEC	Northrop	Scorpion	53-2534	
F- 89J	SC	Flore	FA&MM	Northrop	Scorpion	53-2646	
F- 89J	TX	FWort	SAM	Northrop	Scorpion		
F- 89J	TX	Midla	CAFFM	Northrop	Scorpion	52-1868	
F- 89J	VT	Nurli	BANG	Northrop	Scorpion	52-1883	
F- 89J	WI	Oshko	EAAAAM	Northrop	Scorpion	53-3546	
F- 89J (2ea)	CA	Chino	PoFAM	Northrop	Scorpion		
F- 89J-50	VA	Hampt	APM	Northrop	Scorpion	52-2129	
F- 90(XF)	OH	Dayton	USAFM				
F- 91(XF)	OH	Dayto	USAFM	Republic	Thunderceptor	46-680	
F- 92A(XF)	OH	Dayto	USAFM	Convair		46-682	
F- 94	PA	Water	I79&RT19	Lockheed	Starfire		
F- 94A	NY	Niagara Falls	NAM	Lockheed	Starfire	49-2500	
F- 94A	OH	Dayto	USAFM	Lockheed	Starfire	49-500	
F- 94A	OH	Dayto	USAFM	Lockheed	Starfire	49-2498	
F- 94A(YF)	CA	Rosam	EAFB	Lockheed	Starfire		
F- 94B	NY	Syrac	SMAMB	Lockheed	Starfire		
F- 94C	AZ	Tucso	PAM	Lockheed	Starfire	51-5623	
F- 94C	CO	CSpri	EJPSCM	Lockheed	Starfire	50-1006	
F- 94C	CT	Winds	NEAM	Lockheed	Starfire	51-13575	
F- 94C	MN	Chish	MMoM	Lockheed	Starfire		
F- 94C	MN	Minne	MAGM	Lockheed	Starfire	51-13563	
F- 94C	NC	Fayet	VFWP670	Lockheed	Starfire		
F- 94C	ND	Fargo	FANG	Lockheed	Starfire		
F- 94C	OH	Dayto	USAFM	Lockheed	Starfire	50-980	
F- 94C	PA	Cory	VFWP264	Lockheed	Starfire		
F- 94C	VT	Burli	BANG	Lockheed	Starfire		
F-100	FL	Clear	FMAM	North American	Super Sabre		
F-100	MD	Middl	GLMAM	North American	Super Sabre		
F-100	NB	Fairb	A	North American	Super Sabre		
F-100	NM	Melrose	MBR	North American	Super Sabre		
F-100	TX	FWort	PMoT	North American	Super Sabre		
F-100	TX	Galve	LSFM	North American	Super Sabre	56-3154	
F-100 Cockpit	CT	Winds	NEAM	North American	Super Sabre		
F-100(CF)	CO	CSpri	EJPSCM	Avro	Canuck		
F-100(CF)	AB-C	Calga	AMoC	Avro	Canuck	100779	
F-100(CF)	AB-C	Edmunton	AAM	Avro	Canuck	18126	
F-100(CF)	AB-C	Nanton	NLSAM	Avro	Canuck		
F-100(CF)	NS-C	Halifax	ACAM	Avro	Canuck		
F-100(CF)	ON-C	Belle	BA	Avro	Canuck		
F-100(CF)	ON-C	Campbellford		Avro	Canuck	181106	
F-100(CF)	ON-C	Hamilton	RCAF	Avro	Canuck		
F-100(CF)	ON-C	Missi	DR	Avro	Canuck		

F-100(CF)	ON-C	MtVie	MVRCAF	Avro	Canuck	
F-100(CF)	ON-C	Toronto	WP	Avro	Canuck	
F-100(CF)	ON-C	Bagotville	CFB-3WB	Avro	Canuck	100741
F-100(CF)	PE-C	Summe	PEIHAS	Avro	Canuck	
F-100(CF)	SK-C	MJaw	WDM	Avro	Canuck	
F-100(CF) Mk.V	MB-C	Winni	WCAM	Avro	Canuck	
F-100(CF) Mk V	MB C	Winnipeg	WRACFB	Avro	Canuck	
F-100(CF) Mk V	NS -C	Halifax	HAM	Avro	Canuck	18747, #2 OTU
F-100(CF) Mk V	ON-C	CFB Borden	BHT	Avro	Canuck	18488, "RCAF"
F-100(CF) Mk.V	ON-C	CFB Borden	BHT	Avro	Canuck	100785, C
F-100(CF) Mk V	ON-C	Hamilton	CWH	Avro	Canuck	
F-100(CF)	ON-C	Burlington	WP	Avro	Canuck	
F-100(CF)	ON-C	Burlington	WP	Avro	Canuck	
F-100(CF)	ON-C	Goose Bay	5WGB	Avro	Canuck	
F-100(CF)	ON-C	Kingston	RMC	Avro	Canuck	100731
F-100(CF)	ON-C	North Bay	CFBNB	Avro	Canuck	
F-100(CF)	ON-C	North Bay	LP	Avro	Canuck	
F-100(CF) Mk IV	ON-C	Trenton	RCAFMM	Avro	Canuck	18774
F-100(CF)	Quebec-C	St Hubert	CFB	Avro	Canuck	100760, CAF 760
F-100(CF)	Quebec-C	St Jean	CFB	Avro	Canuck	104784, CAF 746
F-100(CF) Mk 38	BC-C	Langley	CMoF	Avro	Canuck	18138, RCAF18138
F-100A	CA	Rosam	EAFB	North American	Super Sabre	52-1688
F-100A	CA	Rosam	EAFB	North American	Super Sabre	52-5760
F-100A(YF)	CA	Rosam	EAFB	North American	Super Sabre	52-5755
F-100A	CO	Auror	BANGB	North American	Super Sabre	
F-100A	CT	Winds	NEAM	North American	Super Sabre	
F-100A	MI	Grand	CityPark	North American	Super Sabre	
F-100A	NM	Albuq	AANG	North American	Super Sabre	
F-100A	NM	Melro	Village	North American	Super Sabre	
F-100A	OH	Sprin	OHANG	North American	Super Sabre	
F-100A	TX	San Angelo	GAFB	North American	Super Sabre	
F-100A	TX	San A	LAFB	North American	Super Sabre	52-5759
F-100A	UT	Ogden	HAFBM	North American	Super Sabre	
F-100A	WI	Oshko	EAAAAM	North American	Super Sabre	53-1553
F-100C	AL	Montg	MAFB	North American	Super Sabre	
F-100C	AZ	Phoen	LAFB	North American	Super Sabre	
F-100C	AZ	Tucso	PAM	North American	Super Sabre	54-1823
F-100C	CA	Atwater	CAM	North American	Super Sabre	53-1709
F-100C	CA	Riverside	MFAM	North American	Super Sabre	54-1786
F-100C	FL	Shali	USAFAM	North American	Super Sabre	54-954 SS
F-100C	GA	Kenne	AFAMA	North American	Super Sabre	
F-100C	GA	Warner Robin	MoF	North American	Super Sabre	54-1851 FW 851
F-100C	IA	Sioux	SCANG	North American	Super Sabre	
F-100C	ID	Mount	MHAFB	North American	Super Sabre	
F-100C-5-NA	IL	Ranto	OCAM	North American	Super Sabre	54-1785
F-100C	IN	Peru	GAFB	North American	Super Sabre	56-3232 712Th FW
F-100C	KS	Wichita	K&HAP	North American	Super Sabre	54-1993
F-100C	OH	Dayto	USAFM	North American	Super Sabre	54-1753
F-100C	TX	Abile	DLAP	North American	Super Sabre	54-1752
F-100C	VA	Hampt	CityPark	North American	Super Sabre	
F-100C	WI	CDoug	WNGML&M	North American	Super Sabre	
F-100D	AZ	Glend	CityPark	North American	Super Sabre	
F-100D	AZ	Tucso	TANG	North American	Super Sabre	
F-100D	CA	Victorville	GAFB	North American	Super Sabre	
F-100D	CA	Chino	PoFAM	North American	Super Sabre	
F-100D	CA	Sacra	McCelAFB	North American	Super Sabre	56-3288
F-100D	CO	Puebl	PWAM	North American	Super Sabre	55-3503
F-100D	CT	Winds	BANGB	North American	Super Sabre	55-3805
F-100D	FL	Clearwater	FMAM	North American	Super Sabre	
F-100D	FL	Homes	HAFB	North American	Super Sabre	
F-100D	FL	Kissimmee	FTWM	North American	Super Sabre	
F-100D	GA	Marie	DAFB	North American	Super Sabre	
F-100D	IL	Ranto	OCAM	North American	Super Sabre	54-1784
F-100D	IN	Terre Haute	THANG	North American	Super Sabre	
F-100D	LA	New Orleans	FoJBMM	North American	Super Sabre	
F-100D	MA	Otis	OANG	North American	Super Sabre	
F-100D	MA	Westf	MAANG	North American	Super Sabre	
F-100D	MD	Silve	PEGF	North American	Super Sabre	
F-100D	ME	Westf	MAANG	North American	Super Sabre	
F-100D	MI	Mt Clemens	SMAM	North American	Super Sabre	56-3025
F-100D	MO	SLoui	MOANGSLL	North American	Super Sabre	
F-100D	NM	Alamo	HAFB	North American	Super Sabre	
F-100D	NM	Clovi	CAFB	North American	Super Sabre	
F-100D	NV	LasVe	NAFB	North American	Super Sabre	
F-100D	NY	Niaga	NFANG	North American	Super Sabre	
F-100D	OH	Colum	CDCSC	North American	Super Sabre	
F-100D	OH	Lockb	RANGB	North American	Super Sabre	55-2884 Model 224
F-100D	OH	Sprin	SMAM	North American	Super Sabre	
F-100D	OH	Swant	TANG	North American	Super Sabre	
F-100D	OK	Tulsa	TANG	North American	Super Sabre	
F-100D	SC	Myrtl	MBAFB	North American	Super Sabre	
F-100D	TX	FWort	SAM	North American	Super Sabre	
F-100D	TX	San Antonio	TANG	North American	Super Sabre	56-3000
F-100D	TX	San A	MoAMM	North American	Super Sabre	
F-100D(GF)	CO	Aurora	WOTR	North American	Super Sabre	
F-100D(GF)	TX	Wichi	SAFB	North American	Super Sabre	
F-100D-5	VA	Hampt	APM	North American	Super Sabre	54-2145, "Thunderbirds"
F-100F	AZ	Tucso	DMAFB	North American	Super Sabre	
F-100F-16	IN	Ft Wayne	Mercury	North American	Super Sabre	Sn 56-3948, N2011V, FW-948, "Victor in Valor"
F-100F	MI	Mt Clemens	SMAM	North American	Super Sabre	56-3894
F-100F	NJ	Pomon	ANG	North American	Super Sabre	
F-100F	NM	Las Cruces	LCIA	North American	Super Sabre	
F-100F	OH	Dayton	USAFM	North American	Super Sabre	
F-100F	TX	Burnet	HLS-CAF	North American	Super Sabre	
F-101	AL	Birmingham	SMoF	McDonnell	Voodoo	
F-101	FL	Callo	CityPark	McDonnell	Voodoo	
F-101	ID	Pocatello	Airport	McDonnell	Voodoo	57-0430
F-101	MI	Mt Clemens	FHCMP	McDonnell	Voodoo	57-0430
F-101	MO	SLoui	SLAM	McDonnell	Voodoo	
F-101	TX	San Antonio	TAM	McDonnell	Voodoo	
F-101	WY	RockS	CityPark	McDonnell	Voodoo	58-0312
F-101 (Black)	MN	Minne	MAGM	McDonnell	Voodoo	67
F-101(CF)	AB-C	Abbotsford	CFB	McDonnell	Voodoo	101055

F-101(CF)	AB-C	Bagotville	CFB-3WB	McDonnell	Voodoo	101027
F-101(CF)	AB-C	Cold Lake	CFB	McDonnell	Voodoo	101056
F-101(CF)	AB-C	Wetaskiwin	CFB	McDonnell	Voodoo	101038
F-101(CF)	BC-C	Lazo	CFB Comox	McDonnell	Voodoo	101030
F-101(CF)	BC-C	Lazo	CFB Comox	McDonnell	Voodoo	101057
F-101(CF)	MB-C	Winnipeg	CFB	McDonnell	Voodoo	101034
F-101(CF)	ON-C	CFB Borden	BHT	McDonnell	Voodoo	101011
F-101(CF)	ON-C	Haliburton		McDonnell	Voodoo	A683
F-101(CF)	ON-C	Levis	CFB	McDonnell	Voodoo	101015
F-101(CF)	ON-C	Lindsay	LA	McDonnell	Voodoo	101002
F-101(CF)	ON-C	Malton		McDonnell	Voodoo	18619
F-101(CF)	ON-C	Mt Hope		McDonnell	Voodoo	18506
F-101(CF)	ON-C	North Bay	CFBNB	McDonnell	Voodoo	101054
F-101(CF)	ON-C	Ottawa	OIA	McDonnell	Voodoo	101025
F-101(CF)	ON-C	Ottawa	OIA	McDonnell	Voodoo	101045
F-101(CF)	ON-C	Trenton	RCAFMM	McDonnell	Voodoo	101040
F-101(CF)	NB-C	Hillsborough	P	McDonnell	Voodoo	101028, 416 LYNX Squadron, Side # 28
F-101(CF)	NF-C	Gander	NAAM	McDonnell	Voodoo	
F-101(CF)	NF-C	Goose Bay	CFB	McDonnell	Voodoo	101003
F-101(CF)	NS-C	Bedford	CBF	McDonnell	Voodoo	101043
F-101(CF)	NS-C	Chatham	CFBC	McDonnell	Voodoo	101053, 416 LYNX Squadron
F-101(CF)	NS-C	Cornwallis	CFRSC	McDonnell	Voodoo	101006, 416 LYNX Squadron, Side # 6
F-101(CF)	PEI-C	Summerside	CFB	McDonnell	Voodoo	101037
F-101(RF)	TX	Beaum	BDZMP	McDonnell	Voodoo	
F-101A	CO	Puebl	PWAM	McDonnell	Voodoo	53-2418
F-101A	FL	Kissi	FTWAM	McDonnell	Voodoo	
F-101A	NM	Clovi	CAFB	McDonnell	Voodoo	
F-101B	AB-C	Edmonton	AAM	McDonnell	Voodoo	101021
F-101B	AB-C	Edmonton	AAM	McDonnell	Voodoo	101032
F-101B-110-MC	AB-C	Edmonton	AAM	McDonnell	Voodoo	101060, 57-433, 101-590
F-101B	AZ	Tucso	PAM	McDonnell	Voodoo	57-282
F-101B	CA	Atwater	CAM	McDonnell	Voodoo	57-0412
F-101B	CA	Fairf	TAFB	McDonnell	Voodoo	
F-101B	CA	Riverside	MFAM	McDonnell	Voodoo	59-0418
F-101B	CA	Rosam	EAFB	McDonnell	Voodoo	58-288
F-101B	CA	Sacra	McCelAFB	McDonnell	Voodoo	57-427
F-101B	CO	CSpri	EJPSCM	McDonnell	Voodoo	58-274
F-101B	CO	Aurora	WOTR	McDonnell	Voodoo	
F-101B	DE	Dover	DAFB	McDonnell	Voodoo	
F-101B	FL	Kissimmee	FTWM	McDonnell	Voodoo	60417
F-101B	FL	Panam	VMP	McDonnell	Voodoo	90478
F-101B	FL	Panam	GCCC	McDonnell	Voodoo	70438
F-101B-115-MC	FL	Titusville	VAC	McDonnell	Voodoo	59-0400
F-101B-70-MC	IL	Ranto	OCAM	McDonnell	Voodoo	56-0273
F-101B	IN	Peru	GAFM	McDonnell	Voodoo	
F-101B	KS	Topek	CAM	McDonnell	Voodoo	
F-101B	ME	Bangor	MANG	McDonnell	Voodoo	57-0377/04; CAF 101041
F-101B	MI	Mt Clemens	ALP4	McDonnell	Voodoo	57-0430
F-101B	ND	Fargo	FANG	McDonnell	Voodoo	
F-101B	ND	Grand	GFAFB	McDonnell	Voodoo	
F-101B	OH	Dayto	USAFM	McDonnell	Voodoo	58-325
F-101B	OH	Oberl	OFAA	McDonnell	Voodoo	
F-101B	OR	Portl	ORANGP	McDonnell	Voodoo	
F-101B	SD	Rapid	SDA&SM	McDonnell	Voodoo	
F-101B	TN	Chatt	CANG	McDonnell	Voodoo	
F-101B	TX	Abile	DLAP	McDonnell	Voodoo	57-287
F-101B	TX	San A	LAFB	McDonnell	Voodoo	56-241
F-101B	UT	Ogden	HAFBM	McDonnell	Voodoo	
F-101B	WA	Spoka	FAFBHM	McDonnell	Voodoo	
F-101B (2 ea)	MI	Marqu	KISAFB	McDonnell	Voodoo	
F-101B(CF)	AB-C	Calga	AMoC	McDonnell	Voodoo	
F-101B(CF)	CO	CSpri	EJPSCM	McDonnell	Voodoo	101044
F-101B(CF)	NS	Halifax	ACAM	McDonnell	Voodoo	
F-101B(CF)	NS-C	Shearwater	SAM	McDonnell	Voodoo	
F-101B(CF)	NF-C	Gander	NAAM	McDonnell	Voodoo	101065
F-101B(CF)	ON-C	Ottaw	CAM	McDonnell	Voodoo	101025
F-101B(CF)	ON-C	Trenton	RCAFMM	McDonnell	Voodoo	101046
F-101B(EB)	MN	Minne	MAGM	McDonnell	Voodoo	58-350
F-101B(NF)-40-MC	MI	Belleville	YAF	McDonnell	Voodoo	56-235
F-101B(NF)	MI	Ypsil	YAF	McDonnell	Voodoo	
F-101B(RF)	NV	Reno	MANG	McDonnell	Voodoo	
F-101B-55	VA	Hampt	APM	McDonnell	Voodoo	56-0246
F-101C	FL	Shali	USAFAM	McDonnell	Voodoo	60250
F-101C	GA	Warner Robin	MoF	McDonnell	Voodoo	41518-5656
F-101C	TX	Wichi	SAFB	McDonnell	Voodoo	
F-101C(RF)	AL	Montg	MAFB	McDonnell	Voodoo	
F-101C(RF)	AR	Littl	LRAFB	McDonnell	Voodoo	56-231
F-101C(RF)	AZ	Dougl	CityPark	McDonnell	Voodoo	
F-101C(RF)	AZ	Gila	CityPark	McDonnell	Voodoo	
F-101C(RF)	AZ	Tucso	PAM	McDonnell	Voodoo	56-214
F-101C(RF)	GA	Warner Robin	MoF	McDonnell	Voodoo	56-229
F-101C(RF)	KY	Frank	BNGC	McDonnell	Voodoo	
F-101C(RF)	MD	Silve	PEGF	McDonnell	Voodoo	
F-101C(RF)	MI	Mt Clemens	SMAM	McDonnell	Voodoo	56-048; C/N697
F-101C(RF)	MS	Bilox	KAFB	McDonnell	Voodoo	56-068
F-101C(RF)	MS	Hatti	CityPark	McDonnell	Voodoo	
F-101C(RF)	MS	Jacks	JANG	McDonnell	Voodoo	
F-101C(RF)	NY	Niaga	NFANG	McDonnell	Voodoo	
F-101C(RF)	OH	Dayto	USAFM	McDonnell	Voodoo	56-166
F-101C(RF)	SC	Sumte	SAFB	McDonnell	Voodoo	
F-101C(RF)	TX	Austi	BAFB	McDonnell	Voodoo	
F-101D	WA	Tilli	CMANGP	McDonnell	Voodoo	50-70294
F-101F	FL	Clear	FMAM	McDonnell	Voodoo	
F-101F	GA	Warner Robin	MoF	McDonnell	Voodoo	58-276
F-101F	MD	Middl	GLMAM	McDonnell	Voodoo	
F-101F	MN	Proct	CityPark	McDonnell	Voodoo	
F-101F	MT	Great	MAFB	McDonnell	Voodoo	59-0419
F-101F	NC	Charlotte	CAM	McDonnell	Voodoo	56-0243
F-101F	ND	Fargo	FANG	McDonnell	Voodoo	
F-101F	NY	Buffa	B&ECNP	McDonnell	Voodoo	80338
F-101F	NY	Buffa	City	McDonnell	Voodoo	
F-101F	NY	Niaga	NFANG	McDonnell	Voodoo	
F-101F	NY	Glenville	ESAM	McDonnell	Voodoo	59-413

132

F-101F	TX	Ellin	EANGB	McDonnell	Voodoo		
F-101F	TX	San A	LAFB	McDonnell	Voodoo	58-290	
F-101F(CF)	MB-C	Winni	WRCAF	McDonnell	Voodoo	101008	
F-101F(CF)	WA	Tacoma	MAFB	McDonnell	Voodoo	022	
F-101F(TF)	SC	Flore	FA&MM	McDonnell	Voodoo		
F-101H(RF)	AZ	Tucso	PAM	McDonnell	Voodoo	56-11	
F-101H(RF)	KY	Louis	LANG	McDonnell	Voodoo	56-001	
F-102	NY	Glenville	ESAM	Convair	Delta Dagger	61515	
F-102	WA	Spoka	FAFBHM	Convair	Delta Dagger		
F-102(YF)	LA	New Orleans	FoJBMM	Convair	Delta Dagger		
F-102A	AB-C	Stephanville	HF	Convair	Delta Dagger		
F-102A	AK	Ancho	EAFB	Convair	Delta Dagger		
F-102A	AK	Palme	MOAT&1	Convair	Delta Dagger		
F-102A	AZ	Phoen	LAFB	Convair	Delta Dagger		
F-102A	AZ	Tucso	PAM	Convair	Delta Dagger	56-1393	
F-102A	AZ	Tucso	TANG	Convair	Delta Dagger		
F-102A	CA	Atwater	CAM	Convair	Delta Dagger	56-1413	
F-102A	CA	Chino	PoFAM	Convair	Delta Dagger		
F-102A	CA	El Cajon	SDAMGF	Convair	Delta Dagger		
F-102A	CA	Fairf	TAFB	Convair	Delta Dagger		
F-102A	CA	Fresn	FANG	Convair	Delta Dagger		
F-102A	CA	Riverside	MFAM	Convair	Delta Dagger	56-1114, "Keith's Kitten"	
F-102A	CA	Sacra	McCelAFB	Convair	Delta Dagger	51-1140	
F-102A	CO	CSpri	EJPSCM	Convair	Delta Dagger	56-1109	
F-102A	CT	Winds	NEAM	Convair	Delta Dagger	56-1264	
F-102A	GA	Warner Robin	MoF	Convair	Delta Dagger	57-907	
F-102A	HI	Oahu	HAFB	Convair	Delta Dagger	54-01373	
F-102A	ID	Boise	BANG	Convair	Delta Dagger		
F-102A	MN	Minne	MAGM	Convair	Delta Dagger	50-61432	
F-102A	MT	Helena	CoT	Convair	Delta Dagger	0-6116	
F-102A	MT	Great	LP	Convair	Delta Dagger	56-1105	
F-102A	ND	Fargo	FANG	Convair	Delta Dagger		
F-102A	ND	Grand	GFAFB	Convair	Delta Dagger		
F-102A	ND	Minot	MAFB	Convair	Delta Dagger		
F-102A	NY	Syrac	SMAMB	Convair	Delta Dagger		
F-102A	NY	WHamp	SMAM	Convair	Delta Dagger		
F-102A	OH	Dayto	USAFM	Convair	Delta Dagger	56-1416	
F-102A	OR	Mc Minnville	TNSAM	Convair	Delta Dagger	56-1368	
F-102A	PA	Pitts	PANG	Convair	Delta Dagger		
F-102A	SC	McEnt	MEANGB	Convair	Delta Dagger		
F-102A	SD	Rapid	SDA&SM	Convair	Delta Dagger		
F-102A	SD	Sioux	SDANGSF	Convair	Delta Dagger		
F-102A	TX	Ellin	EANGB	Convair	Delta Dagger		
F-102A	TX	Midla	CAFFM	Convair	Delta Dagger		
F-102A	TX	Rio Grande V	TAM	Convair	Delta Dagger		
F-102A	TX	Wichi	SAFB	Convair	Delta Dagger		
F-102A	UT	Ogden	HAFBM	Convair	Delta Dagger	75833, FC-833	
F-102A	VT	Nurli	BANG	Convair	Delta Dagger		
F-102A	WA	Tacoma	McCordAFB	Convair	Delta Dagger	57-0858	
F-102A	WI	CDoug	WNGML&M	Convair	Delta Dagger		
F-102A(TF)	AL	Birmingham	SMoF	Convair	Delta Dagger		
F-102A(GF)	CO	Aurora	WOTR	Convair	Delta Dagger		
F-102A(TF)	AZ	Tucso	PAM	Convair	Delta Dagger	54-1366	
F-102A(TF)	CA	Lanca	MoFM	Convair	Delta Dagger		
F-102A(TF)	CA	Rosam	EAFB	Convair	Delta Dagger	54-1353	
F-102A(TF)-35-CO	MI	Belleville	YAF	Convair	Delta Dagger	56- 2317, "La Tina"	
F-102A(GTF)	MI	Mt Clemens	SMAM	Convair	Delta Dagger	54-1351	
F-102A(TF)	PA	Annvi	AANG	Convair	Delta Dagger		
F-102A(YF)	NC	Charlotte	CAM	Convair	Delta Dagger	53-1788	
F-102A(YF)	SC	Flore	FA&MM	Convair	Delta Dagger		
F-102A-80-CO	NY	Baldw	CityPark	Convair	Delta Dagger	61515	
F-102A-CO	NE	Ashland	SACM	Convair	Delta Dagger	54-1405	
F-102D	FL	Clear	FMAM	Convair	Delta Dagger		
F-104	AR	Little Rock	CRNGA	Lockheed	Starfighter	AUG00	
F-104	AZ	Presc	ERAU	Lockheed	Starfighter		
F-104	CA	Moffe	NASAAVC	Lockheed	Starfighter		
F-104	CO	Pueblo	PWAM	Lockheed	Starfighter		
F-104	FL	Clearwater	SI	Lockheed	Starfighter	Sn 104632, N103RB	
F-104	FL	Clearwater	SI	Lockheed	Starfighter	Sn 104850, N 104RD	
F-104	FL	Kissi	FTWAM	Lockheed	Starfighter		
F-104	MT	Dutton	AM	Lockheed	Starfighter	57-1332	
F-104	ND	Fargo	NDSU	Lockheed	Starfighter		
F-104	OK	Oklah	A&SM	Lockheed	Starfighter		
F-104	OK	Oklah	KCASM	Lockheed	Starfighter		
F-104	TX	Addison	CFM	Lockheed	Starfighter	56-0780	
F-104(CF)	AB-C	Cold Lake	CFB	Lockheed	Starfighter	12702	
F-104(CF)	AB-C	Cold Lake	CFB	Lockheed	Starfighter		
F-104(CF)	AB-C	Wetaskiwin	CFB	Lockheed	Starfighter	104763	
F-104(CF)	AB-C	Grand Center	City	Lockheed	Starfighter		
F-104(CF)	MB-C	Winnipeg	WRACFB	Lockheed	Starfighter	104753	
F-104(CF)	NS	Halifax	ACAM	Canadair	Starfighter		
F-104(CF)	ON-C	CFB Borden	BHT	Lockheed	Starfighter	104792	
F-104(CF)	ON-C	Ottaw	CAM	Lockheed	Starfighter	12700	
F-104(CF)	Quebec-C	St Jean	CFB	Lockheed	Starfighter	CAF 784	
F-104A	CA	Fairf	TAFB	Lockheed	Starfighter	56-0752	
F-104A	CO	CSpri	USAFA	Lockheed	Starfighter	55-2967	
F-104A	DC	Washi	NA&SM	Lockheed	Starfighter		
F-104A	GA	Warner Robin	MoF	Lockheed	Starfighter	56-0817	FG-817
F-104A-1-LO	IL	Ranto	OCAM	Lockheed	Starfighter	56-0732	
F-104A	LA	Alexandria	RE	Lockheed	Starfighter	56-0791	
F-104A	OH	Dayto	USAFM	Lockheed	Starfighter	56-0754	
F-104A	OH	Dayto	USAFM	Lockheed	Starfighter	56-0879	
F-104A	TX	Abile	DLAP	Lockheed	Starfighter	56-0748	
F-104A(2ea)	CA	Rosam	EAFB	Lockheed	Starfighter	56-0801	
F-104A(NF)	CA	Rosam	EAFB	Lockheed	Starfighter	56-0760	
F-104B	CA	Sacra	McCelAFB	Lockheed	Starfighter	57-1303	
F-104B	KS	Hutchinson	C	Lockheed	Starfighter	57-1301	
F-104B	SC	Flore	FA&MM	Lockheed	Starfighter		
F-104C	AZ	Phoen	LAFB	Lockheed	Starfighter	56-0892	
F-104C	AZ	Phoen	PANG	Lockheed	Starfighter	56-0891	
F-104C	CA	Victorville	GAFB	Lockheed	Starfighter	56-0934	
F-104C	CA	Van Nuys	VNAFB	Lockheed	Starfighter	56-0932	
F-104C	CO	CSpri	EJPSCM	Lockheed	Starfighter	56-0936	

Model	State	City	Location	Manufacturer	Name	Serial / Notes
F-104C	CO	Aurora	WOTR	Lockheed	Starfighter	56-0910
F-104C	CT	Winds	NEAM	Lockheed	Starfighter	56-0901
F-104C	IL	Chica	MoS&I	Lockheed	Starfighter	
F-104C	KS	Liberal	MAAM	Lockheed	Starfighter	56-0933
F-104C	MI	Kalam	KAHM	Lockheed	Starfighter	56-0898
F-104C	MS	Bilox	KAFB	Lockheed	Starfighter	56-0938
F-104C	ND	Fargo	FANG	Lockheed	Starfighter	56-0926
F-104C	NM	Alamo	HAFB	Lockheed	Starfighter	56-0886
F-104C	OH	Dayto	USAFM	Lockheed	Starfighter	56-0914
F-104C	SC	McEnt	MEANGB	Lockheed	Starfighter	57-0920, 60920
F-104C	TN	Chatt	CANG	Lockheed	Starfighter	
F-104C	TN	Knoxv	KANG	Lockheed	Starfighter	56-0890 8th FG
F-104C	TX	Wichi	SAFB	Lockheed	Starfighter	56-0912
F-104C	VA	Hampt	VA&SC	Lockheed	Starfighter	57-0916 FG-916
F-104C	WA	Seattle	MoF	Lockheed	Starfighter	56-0934, N56-934, N820NA
F-104C(TF)	FL	Shali	USAFAM	Lockheed	Starfighter	57-1331
F-104D	AZ	Tucso	PAM	Lockheed	Starfighter	57-1323
F-104D	CA	Atwater	CAM	Lockheed	Starfighter	57-1312, FG-312
F-104D	CA	Burba	VWF	Lockheed	Starfighter	57-1334
F-104D	CA	LAnge	CMoS&I	Lockheed	Starfighter	57-1333, 104545, D-MKZ
F-104D	NJ	Jackson	AP	Lockheed	Starfighter	57-1320
F-104D(CF)	ON-C	Hamilton	CWH	Lockheed	Starfighter	10-4756, Tiger Paint
F-104D(CF)	ON-C	Hamilton	CWH	Lockheed	Starfighter	104641
F-104D(CF)	ON-C	Trenton	RCAFMM	Lockheed	Starfighter	10646, Side # 646, 2 Seater
F-104D(CF)	WI	Oshko	EAAAAM	Lockheed	Starfighter	N104JR
F-104D(TF)	TX	San A	LAFB	Lockheed	Starfighter	57-1319
F-104D-10	IN	Hunti	WoF	Lockheed	Starfighter	57-1322, Total Built: F-104D=21; D-10=8
F-104G	CA	Chino	PoFAM	Lockheed	Starfighter	FX82
F-104G(TF)	CA	Paso Robles	EWM	Lockheed	Starfighter	NASA 824NA
F-104G	NJ	Lumberton	AVM	Lockheed	Starfighter	56-0933, D-8090, Side FX-81
F-105	AL	Birmingham	SMoF	Republic	Thunderchief	
F-105B-IRE	AL	Mobil	CityPark	Republic	Thunderchief	54-0102
F-105	CT	Windsor	ANG	Republic	Thunderchief	
F-105	MO	Chill	CityPark	Republic	Thunderchief	
F-105	MS	Jacks	AmLg1	Republic	Thunderchief	
F-105	NC	Kings	CityPark	Republic	Thunderchief	
F-105	NC	Wilmi	VFWP2573	Republic	Thunderchief	
F-105(CF)	ON-C	Campbellford	MMM	Avro	Arrow	181106
F-105(CF)	ON-C	Ottawa	CAM	Avro	Arrow	
F-105(CF) Mk 1	ON-C	Toronto	TAM	Avro	Arrow	
F-105	SC	Sumte	SAFB	Republic	Thunderchief	
F-105	TX	Addison	CFM	Republic	Thunderchief	
F-105	TX	San Antonio	TAM	Republic	Thunderchief	
F-105B	CA	Atwater	CAM	Republic	Thunderchief	57-837
F-105B	CA	Chino	PoFAM	Republic	Thunderchief	
F-105B	CA	Riverside	MFAM	Republic	Thunderchief	57-5803
F-105B	CA	Sacra	McCelAFB	Republic	Thunderchief	62- 4301
F-105B	CT	Winds	NEAM	Republic	Thunderchief	
F-105B	FL	Clear	FMAM	Republic	Thunderchief	
F-105B-5-RE	IL	Ranto	OCAM	Republic	Thunderchief	54-0104
F-105B	NC	Hickory	HRA	Republic	Thunderchief	54-0107
F-105B	NJ	Trent	MGANG	Republic	Thunderchief	
F-105B	NY	Garde	CoAM	Republic	Thunderchief	5783
F-105B	SC	Ander	ACA	Republic	Thunderchief	
F-105B	SD	Rapid	SDA&SM	Republic	Thunderchief	
F-105B	UT	SaltL	SLANG	Republic	Thunderchief	
F-105B	WA	Spoka	FAFBHM	Republic	Thunderchief	
F-105B	WI	CDoug	WNGML&M	Republic	Thunderchief	
F-105B(JF)	TX	San A	LAFB	Republic	Thunderchief	54-105
F-105D	AL	Montg	MAFB	Republic	Thunderchief	
F-105D	AZ	Gila	GBAFAF	Republic	Thunderchief	
F-105D	AZ	Tucso	DMAFB	Republic	Thunderchief	
F-105D	AZ	Tucso	PAM	Republic	Thunderchief	61-86
F-105D	CA	Victorville	GAFB	Republic	Thunderchief	
F-105D	CA	Fairf	TAFB	Republic	Thunderchief	
F-105D	CA	Riverside	MFAM	Republic	Thunderchief	62-4383
F-105D	CA	Rosam	EAFB	Republic	Thunderchief	61-146
F-105D	CA	Sacra	McCelAFB	Republic	Thunderchief	62-4301
F-105D	CA	San B	NAFB	Republic	Thunderchief	
F-105D	CO	CSpri	USAFA	Republic	Thunderchief	
F-105D	CT	Winds	BANGB	Republic	Thunderchief	
F-105D	DC	Washi	AAFB	Republic	Thunderchief	
F-105D	DC	Washi	BAFB	Republic	Thunderchief	
F-105D	FL	Shali	USAFAM	Republic	Thunderchief	58-771 JV
F-105D	GA	Warner Robin	MoF	Republic	Thunderchief	
F-105D	IL	Sugar Grove	ACM	Republic	Thunderchief	61-0099
F-105D	IN	Peru	GAFB	Republic	Thunderchief	61-088
F-105D	KS	Topek	CAM	Republic	Thunderchief	
F-105D	MD	Andrews	APG	Republic	Thunderchief	AF 61041
F-105D	MD	Silve	PEGF	Republic	Thunderchief	
F-105D	MS	Bilox	KAFB	Republic	Thunderchief	60-535
F-105D	NC	Fayet	PAFB	Republic	Thunderchief	
F-105D	NC	Golds	SJAFB	Republic	Thunderchief	61-056, SJ
F-105D	NM	Alamo	HAFB	Republic	Thunderchief	
F-105D	NM	Albuq	NAM	Republic	Thunderchief	
F-105D	OH	Colum	CDCSC	Republic	Thunderchief	
F-105D	OH	Dayto	USAFM	Republic	Thunderchief	60-504
F-105D	OK	Enid	VAFB	Republic	Thunderchief	
F-105D	OK	Tinke	TANG	Republic	Thunderchief	
F-105D	TN	Arnol	AAFS	Republic	Thunderchief	
F-105D	TX	Abile	DLAP	Republic	Thunderchief	59-1738
F-105D	TX	FWort	CAFB	Republic	Thunderchief	
F-105D	TX	FWort	NASFWJRB	Republic	Thunderchief	
F-105D	TX	FWort	PMoT	Republic	Thunderchief	
F-105D	TX	San A	LAFB	Republic	Thunderchief	62-4387
F-105D	TX	Wichi	SAFB	Republic	Thunderchief	
F-105D	UT	Ogden	HAFBM	Republic	Thunderchief	
F-105D	VA	Hampt	LAFB	Republic	Thunderchief	
F-105D	VA	Richm	SMAM	Republic	Thunderchief	
F-105D Simulator	NY	Garde	CoAM	Republic	Thunderchief	
F-105D(GF)	CO	Aurora	WOTR	Republic	Thunderchief	
F-105D15	VA	Hampt	APM	Republic	Thunderchief	61-73
F-105F-1-RE	IL	Ranto	OCAM	Republic	Thunderchief	63-8287, "Root Rat Pak", RK

134

F-105F	KS	Wichi	K&HAP	Republic	Thunderchief	62-4253
F-105F	TX	Dallas	FoF	Republic	Thunderchief	63-8343
F-105F	TX	FWort	SAM	Republic	Thunderchief	
F-105G Cockpit	AR	Eureka Sprg	ACM	Republic	Thunderchief	62-4422
F-105G	MD	Aberdeen	APG	Republic	Thunderchief	63-8306 to go to Eureka Sprg, AR
F-105G	CA	Victorville	GAFB	Republic	Thunderchief	
F-105G	CA	Sacramento	MHMAFB	Republic	Thunderchief	63-8278
F-105G	GA	Marie	DAFB	Republic	Thunderchief	
F-105G	GA	Warner Robin	MoF	Republic	Thunderchief	62-4438 HI
F-105G	KS	Liberal	MAAM	Republic	Thunderchief	63-8266
F-105G	LA	Alexandria	EAP	Republic	Thunderchief	63-296, MD, AD
F-105G	MD	Middl	GLMAM	Republic	Thunderchief	
F-105G	NV	LasVe	NAFB	Republic	Thunderchief	
F-105G	NY	Glenville	ESAM	Republic	Thunderchief	62-4444
F-105G	OH	Dayto	USAFM	Republic	Thunderchief	63-8320
F-105G	UT	Ogden	HAFBM	Republic	Thunderchief	"Wild Weasel"
F-105G (2 ea)	AZ	Tucso	PAM	Republic	Thunderchief	62-4427
F-105H	GA	Warner Robin	MoF	Republic	Thunderchief	63-8309
F-106	AL	Birmingham	SMoF	Convair	Delta Dart	
F-106	CT	Windsor	ANG	Convair	Delta Dart	
F-106	FL	Titusville	VAC	Convair	Delta Dart	
F-106	DE	Dover	DAFB	Convair	Delta Dart	
F-106	UT	Ogden	DAFB	Convair	Delta Dart	
F-106 Simulator	DE	Dover	DAFB	Convair	Delta Dart	
F-106A	AZ	Tucso	PAM	Convair	Delta Dart	59-3
F-106A	CA	Fresn	FANG	Convair	Delta Dart	
F-106A	CO	CSpri	EJPSCM	Convair	Delta Dart	59-0134
F-106A	DC	Washi	AAFB	Convair	Delta Dart	
F-106A	FL	Clearwater	FMAM	Convair	Delta Dart	
F-106A	FL	Jacks	JIA	Convair	Delta Dart	70230 13
F-106A	FL	Panam	TAFB	Convair	Delta Dart	59-145
F-106A	GA	Warner Robin	MoF	Convair	Delta Dart	59-123
F-106A	HI	Honolulu	HANG	Convair	Delta Dart	53366
F-106A(NF)	MI	Mt Clemens	CityPark	Convair	Delta Dart	56-451
F-106A	MI	Sawyer	SHAM	Convair	Delta Dart	59-0086
F-106A	MI	Sawyer	SHAM	Convair	Delta Dart	59-0095
F-106A	MT	Great Falls	GFANG	Convair	Delta Dart	72492
F-106A	ND	Minot	MAFB	Convair	Delta Dart	
F-106A	NY	Rome	GAFBM	Convair	Delta Dart	
F-106A	OH	Dayto	USAFM	Convair	Delta Dart	58-787
F-106A	SC	Charl	CAFB	Convair	Delta Dart	
F-106A	WA	Tacoma	MAFB	Convair	Delta Dart	56-0459
F-106A Cockpit	MI	Kalam	KAHM	Convair	Delta Dart	
F-106B	CA	Chino	YAM	Convair	Delta Dart	
F-106B	CA	Rosamond	EAFB	Convair	Delta Dart	
F-106B	NJ	Pomon	ANG	Convair	Delta Dart	
F-106B	TX	San Antonio	KAFB	Convair	Delta Dart	72533
F-106B(NF)	VA	Hampt	VA&SC	Convair	Delta Dart	N816NA, 816
F-107A	AZ	Tucso	PAM	North American	Mach 2 Jet Fighter	55- 5118, Man Sn 212-1, 1st F-107
F-107A	OH	Dayto	USAFM	North American	55- 5119	Mach 2 Jet Fighter
F-107(LF)	WA	Seattle	MoF	Let		N2170D
F-111A(EF)	NM	Clovi	CAFB	General Dynamics	Raven (ECM)	
F-111A(EF)	OH	Dayton	USAFM	General Dynamics	Raven (ECM)	
F-111	AL	Huntsville	AC	General Dynamics	Aardvark	
F-111	NM	Santa Fe	SFMA	General Dynamics	Aardvark	27FW, #408
F-111A	AL	Birmingham	SMoF	General Dynamics	Aardvark	
F-111A	CA	Rosam	EAFB	General Dynamics	Aardvark	63-9766
F-111A	IL	Ranto	OCAM	General Dynamics	Aardvark	63-9767, NA, 474th TacFW
F-111A	NV	Battl	BMAM	General Dynamics	Aardvark	66-12
F-111A	OH	Dayto	USAFM	General Dynamics	Aardvark	67-0057
F-111A(FB)	SD	Rapid	SDA&SM	General Dynamics	Aardvark	68-0248, Fighter/Bomber
F-111A	TX	Antonio	KAFB	General Dynamics	Aardvark	
F-111A	TX	Wichi	SAFB	General Dynamics	Aardvark	
F-111A(FB)	CA	Sacra	McCelAFB	General Dynamics	Aardvark	67-159, Fighter/Bomber
F-111A(NF)	CA	Rosam	EAFB	General Dynamics	Aardvark	63-9778
F-111A(RF)	ID	Mount	MHAFB	General Dynamics	Aardvark	RAAF
F-111E	AZ	Tucso	PAM	General Dynamics	Aardvark	63-33
F-111E	FL	Shali	USAFAM	General Dynamics	Aardvark	68-58 ET
F-111E	GA	Warner Robin	MoF	General Dynamics	Aardvark	68-255
F-111E	UT	Ogden	HAFBM	General Dynamics	Aardvark	"My Lucky Blonde"
F-111F	NM	Clovis	CP	General Dynamics	Aardvark	
F-111F	NM	Portales	CP	General Dynamics	Aardvark	
F-111F	OH	Dayto	USAFM	General Dynamics	Aardvark	
F-116A(CF)	ONT-C	Ottawa	CAM	Canadair		
F-117A	NV	LasVe	NAFB	Lockheed	Nighthawk	
F-117A(YF)	OH	Dayto	USAFM	Lockheed	Nighthawk	79-10781
F2F	SC	Mt Pl	PPM	Grumman	Flying Barrel	
F2H-2	CA	Miramar	FLAM	McDonnell	Banshee	
F2H-2	TX	C Christi	USS Lexi	McDonnell	Banshee	
F2H-2N	MO	SLoui	SLAM	McDonnell	Banshee	
F2H-2P	FL	Pensa	USNAM	McDonnell	Banshee	126673, MW-2, VMJ-1, Photo Recon
F2H-2P	NY	Horseheads	NWM	McDonnell	Banshee	125690, VFP-61
F2H-3	AB-C	Calga	NMoA	McDonnell	Banshee	At Naval Museum
F2H-3	NS-C	Shear	CFBS	McDonnell	Banshee	
F2H-3	ON-C	Ottaw	CAM	McDonnell	Banshee	126464
F2H-3	VA	VBeac	ONAS	McDonnell	Banshee	7693, AD 300
F2H-4(F-2D)	FL	Pensa	USNAM	McDonnell	Banshee	126419, 127663
F2G-1D (See F4U)						
F3B	NY	NYC	ISASM	McDonnell	Demon	
F3D (F-10B)	CA	Rosam	EAFB	Douglas	Skynight	125850
F3D (F-10B)	KS	Topek	CAM	Douglas	Skynight	
F3D (F-10B)	NY	NYC	ISASM	Douglas	Skynight	
F3D-2(F-10B)	AZ	Tucso	PAM	Douglas	Skynight	124629
F3D-2(F-10B)	CA	Miramar	FLAM	Douglas	Skynight	L,T VMF(AW)-531
F3D-2(F-10B)	FL	Pensa	USNAM	Douglas	Skynight	124598
F3D-2(F-10B)	RI	NKing	QAM	Douglas	Skynight	124620
F3F-2	CA	Carls	CAJM	Grumman	Flying Barrel	8F8
F3F-2	CA	San Diego	SDAM	Grumman	Flying Barrel	0964
F3F-2	FL	Pensa	USNAM	Grumman	Flying Barrel	0976, VMF-2, #16
F3F-2	NY	NYC	ISASM	Grumman	Flying Barrel	
F3F-2	TX	Galve	LSFM	Grumman	Flying Barrel	N20RW, 972
F3F-2 (2ea)	CA	Chino	PoFAM	Grumman	Flying Barrel	
F3F-3	NY	Garden City	CoAM	Grumman	Flying Barrel	

F3H	NY	NYC	ISASM	McDonnell	Demon	
F3H	FL	Clearwater	FMAM	McDonnell	Demon	
F3H-2(F-3B)	AZ	Tucso	PAM	McDonnell	Demon	145221
F.4	AL	Gunte	LGARFM	Martinsyde	Buzzard	
F4B-3(P-12E)	NC	Havelock	HTC	Boeing	Biplane	
F4B-4(P-12E)	AL	Mobile	BMP	Boeing	Biplane	9022
F4B-4(P-12E)	FL	Pensacola	PSAM	Boeing		9029, 6-F-1, Felix the Cat Sq
F4B-4(P-12E)	DC	Washi	NA&SM	Boeing		
F4D-1(F-6A)	AZ	Tucson	PAM	Douglas	Skyray	Sn 134748, Man Sn 10342
F4D-1(F-6A)	CO	Puebl	PWAM	Douglas	Skyray	1-34936
F4D-1(F-6A)	CT	Winds	NEAM	Douglas	Skyray	134836
F4D-1(F-6A)	FL	Pensa	USNAM	Douglas	Skyray	134806
F4D-1(F-6A)	MD	Lexin	PNA&EM	Douglas	Skyray	
F4D-1(F-6A)	VA	Quantico	MCAGM	Douglas	Skyray	139177
F4F	WI	Janesville	YAFS4D	Grumman	Wildcat	
F4F-2(XF)	FL	Titusville	VAC	Grumman	Wildcat	0383
F4F-3	IL	Aurora	RH	Grumman	Wildcat	
F4F-3	IL	Chica	O'Hare	Grumman	Wildcat	12320, Side # F-15
F4F-3	KS	New Century	CAF-HoAW	Grumman	Wildcat	
F4F-3	KS	Topeka	CAM	Grumman	Wildcat	12260
F4F-3(FM-2)	WA	Seattle	MoF	Grumman	Wildcat	74512
F4F-3(FM-2)	AZ	Tucson	PAM	Grumman	Wildcat	74512
F4F-3(FM-2)	WA	Olympia	OFM	Grumman	Wildcat	
F4F-3(FM-2)	FL	Pensa	USNAM	Grumman	Wildcat	3872, 72-F-7
F4F-3A(FM-2)	CA	Miramar	FLAM	Grumman	Wildcat	
F4F-3A(FM-2)	CA	San Diego	SDAM	Grumman	Wildcat	3696
F4F-3A(FM-2)	NY	Garde	CoAM	Grumman	Wildcat	5948
F4F-3A(FM-2)	TX	Breck	BAM	Grumman	Wildcat	
F4F-4(FM-2)	DC	Washi	NA&SM	Grumman	Wildcat	
F4F-4(FM-2)	VA	Quant	MCAGM	Grumman	Wildcat	12114
F4U	CA	Inglewood	PBR	Chance-Vought	Corsair	
F4U	CA	Palm Sprg	PSAM	Chance-Vought	Corsair	3890, NX62290, 301, S
F4U	DC	Washi	NM	Chance-Vought	Corsair	
F4U	FL	Titus	VACM	Chance-Vought	Corsair	
F4U	ND	Fargo	FAM	Chance-Vought	Corsair	
F4U	TX	Breck	BAF	Chance-Vought	Corsair	97302, NX 65HP, WF, VMF(N)-513
F4U	TX	Addison	CFM	Chance-Vought	Corsair	
F4U 1/3 Scale	ON-C	Wellington	G	Chance-Vought	Corsair	
F4U(F2G-1)	AZ	Mesa	CFM	Goodyear	Super Corsair	NATC 454
F4U(F2G-1D)	ND	Fargo	FAM	Goodyear	Super Corsair	N5588N, #5, Red & White
F4U(F2G-1)	OH	Newbu	WASAC	Goodyear	Super Corsair	N5577N
F4U(F2G-1)	TX	Galve	LSFM	Goodyear	Super Corsair	N5588N, 88457
F4U(F2G-1)	WA	Seattle	MoF	Goodyear	Super Corsair	88382, NATC 454, NX4324
F4U(F2G-2)	OH	Cleveland	FCAAM	Goodyear	Super Corsair	#74
F4U(FG-1D)	CO	Aurora	WOTR	Goodyear	Corsair	
F4U(FG-1D)	CT	Strat	SMA	Goodyear	Corsair	
F4U(FG-1D)	FL	Kissi	FTWAM	Goodyear	Corsair	
F4U(FG-1D)	FL	Pensa	USNAM	Goodyear	Corsair	N766JD, 92246
F4U(FG-1D)	KY	Louisville	CCA	Goodyear	Corsair	67060
F4U(FG-1D)	MI	Kalam	KAHM	Goodyear	Corsair	92509, 611
F4U(FG-1D)	MI	Mt Clemens	SMAM	Goodyear	Corsair	92085, Side # 9
F4U(FG-1D)	NY	Farmingdale	AAM	Goodyear	Corsair	115
F4U(FG-1D) Forward Fuse	OH	Akron	GWoR	Goodyear	Corsair	(Cockpit/Canopy, Wing Stubs, Cowling)
F4U(FG-1D)	OH	Batavia	TSWM	Goodyear	Corsair	
F4U(FG-1D)	OH	Newbu	WASAC	Goodyear	Corsair	
F4U(FG-1D)	OR	Mc Minnville	EAEC	Goodyear	Corsair	3356, N67HP
F4U(FG-1D)	PA	Tough	CFCM	Goodyear	Corsair	
F4U(FG-1D)	SC	Mt Pl	PPM	Chance-Vought	Corsair	
F4U(FG-1D)	TX	Lanca	CAF-DFW	Goodyear	Corsair	N9964Z
F4U(FG-1D)	TX	Midla	CAFFM	Goodyear	Corsair	
F4U(FG-1D)	VA	Quant	MCAGM	Goodyear	Corsair	13486
F4U(FG-1D	VA	Suffolk	FF	Goodyear	Corsair	82640, 4487, N46RL, VF-17
F4U(FG-1D)	WA	Belleville	AM	Goodyear	Corsair	88303, N700G
F4U(FG-1D)	WA	Olympia	OFM	Goodyear	Corsair	Side # 115
F4U(FG-1D)	WA	Seatt	MoF	Goodyear	Corsair	88382
F4U-1	MA	Stow	BCF	Chance-Vought	Corsair	
F4U-1A	CA	Chino	PoFAM	Chance-Vought	Corsair	
F4U-1D	MD	Silve	PEGF	Chance-Vought	Corsair	
F4U-1D	VA	Chantilly	UHC	Chance-Vought	Corsair	50375, 56, "Sun Setter"
F4U-4	AZ	Tucso	PAM	Chance-Vought	Corsair	Sn 97142, N22SN
F4U-4	CA	Chino	YAM	Chance-Vought	Corsair	97390, N47991, 97390
F4U-4	FL	Pensa	USNAM	Chance-Vought	Corsair	97349, WR 18, #86
F4U-4	FL	Polk	FoF	Chance-Vought	Corsair	N5215V, 5, "Angel of Okinawa"
F4U-4	ND	Wahpe	TSA	Chance-Vought	Corsair	
F4U-4	NM	STere	WEAM	Chance-Vought	Corsair	JM 53
F4U-4	VA	Quant	MCAGM	Chance Vought	Corsair	97369
F4U-4	WI	Oshko	EAAAM	Chance-Vought	Corsair	N6667, 9413
F4U-4B Rep ½ Scale	MI	Kalam	KAHM	Goodyear	Corsair	
F4U-4(XF)	CT	Winds	NEAM	Chance-Vought	Buzzard	
F4U-5	FL	Kissi	FTWAM	Chance-Vought	Corsair	
F4U-5	IL	Springfield	ACM	Chance-Vought	Corsair	124486
F4U-5N	CA	Miramar	FLAM	Chance-Vought	Corsair	
F4U-5N	IN	Valparaiso	IAM	Chance-Vought	Corsair	122179
F4U-5N	KS	Liberal	MAAM	Chance-Vought	Corsair	124447
F4U-5N	TX	Galve	LSFM	Chance-Vought	Corsair	N43RW, 121881
F4U-7	OR	Tillamook	TAM	Chance-Vought	Corsair	
F4U-7(AU-1)	AL	Mobil	BMP	Chance-Vought	Corsair	133704, LO10, VMA-212, "Marines" Rear Fuse
F5D-1(X-4)	OH	Wapak	NAA&SM	Douglas	Skylancer	142350
F6C *See P-1*						
F6C-4	VA	Quant	MCAGM	Curtiss	Hawk	A-7412
F6F-5	CA	PalmS	PSAM	Grumman	Hellcat	001006, NX4964W, #36
F6F	CA	Inglewood	PBR	Grumman	Hellcat	
F6F	CA	Point Mugu	PMMP	Grumman	Hellcat	79063
F6F	MD	Andrews	APG	Grumman	Hellcat	77722, Tail 22 White Diamond
F6F	FL	Polk City	FoF	Grumman	Hellcat	
F6F	SC	Mt Pl	PPM	Grumman	Hellcat	
F6F	TX	Midla	CAF-JK	Grumman	Hellcat	N1078Z
F6F-3	CA	Carls	CAJM	Grumman	Hellcat	41930, N30FG, 5
F6F-3	CA	San Diego	SDAM	Grumman	Hellcat	42874, 21
F6F-3	MD	Silver Hill	PEGF	Grumman	Hellcat	
F6F-3	FL	Pensa	USNAM	Grumman	Hellcat	66237, #17
F6F-3	MD	Silve	PEGF	Grumman	Hellcat	
F6F-3	VA	Quant	MCAGM	Grumman	Hellcat	41476

F6F-4	VA	Quant	MCAGM	Grumman	Hellcat	
F6F-5	CA	Chino	PoFAM	Grumman	Hellcat	93879, N4994V, 31
F6F-5	CA	Chino	YAM	Grumman	Hellcat	78645, N9265A, 78645
F6F-5	CA	Palm Sprg	PoF	Grumman	Hellcat	NX4964W, 58644, 36
F6F-5	CA	Camarillo	CAF-SCW	Grumman	Hellcat	N1078Z, 70222
F6F-5	CT	Winds	NEAM	Grumman	Hellcat	
F6F-5	FL	Pensa	USNAM	Grumman	Hellcat	94203
F6F-5	MI	Kalam	KAHM	Grumman	Hellcat	79683, 47-8960, N4PP, 4
F6F-5	NY	Garde	CoAM	Grumman	Hellcat	94263
F6F-5	RI	NKing	QAM	Grumman	Hellcat	70185
F6F-5 Replica	NY	NYC	ISASM	Grumman	Hellcat	
F6F-5N	TX	Galve	LSFM	Grumman	Hellcat	N4998V, 94204, 32
F6F-5N	TX	Midla	CAFFM	Grumman	Hellcat	
F7C-1	FL	Pensa	USNAM	Curtiss	Sea Hawk	A-7667
F7F	FL	Rialto	KA			80375
F7F	FL	Polk City	FoF			
F7F-3	CA	Palm Sprg	PSAM	Grumman	Tigercat	45-80411, NX207F, Tail BP", "King of Cats"
F7F-3 (2 ea)	FL	Pensa	USNAM	Grumman	Tigercat	N 7654C 80373
F7F-3N	AZ	Tucso	PAM	Grumman	Tigercat	80410
F7F-3N	CA	Chino	PoFAM	Grumman	Tigercat	
F7F-3P	MI	Kalam	KAHM	Grumman	Tigercat	803903
F7U-3	CA	Alameda	USSHM	Chance-Vought	Cutlass	129565
F7U-3	OH	Newbu	WASAC	Chance-Vought	Cutlass	129685
F7U-3	PA	Willo	WGNAS	Chance-Vought	Cutlass	9462
F7U-3	WA	Seattle	MoF	Chance-Vought	Cutlass	129554
F7U-3M	FL	Pensa	USNAM	Chance-Vought	Cutlass	129655
F8C/K-2	SC	Beauf	MAS	Vought	Crusader	146963, DC5, VMF(AW)-122
F8F-1 (G-58B)	CA	Palm SPrg	PSAM	Grumman	Bearcat	Sn 1262, NL700A, "Bob's Bear"
F8F-1				Grumman	Bearcat	95255, N41089, VF-6A, Tail S, Side # 204
F8F-1	TX	Breck	BAM	Grumman	Bearcat	
F8F-1D(XF)	MI	Kalam	KAHM	Grumman	Bearcat	90454, N9G
F8F-2	CA	Camarillo	CAF-SCW	Grumman	Bearcat	N7825C, Side Number 201
F8F-2	CA	Chino	PoFAM	Grumman	Bearcat	
F8F-2	FL	Pensa	USNAM	Grumman	Bearcat	121710, B, 100
F8F-2	MD	Silve	PEGF	Grumman	Bearcat	"Conquest I"
F8F-2	TX	Galve	LSFM	Grumman	Bearcat	N1030B, 121776
F8F-2	WA	Eastsound	HFM	Grumman	Bearcat	
F8U-1(F-8A)	CA	Alameda	USSHM	Vought	Crusader	143703
F8U-1	CA	Chino	PoFAM	Vought	Crusader	16
F8U-1(F-8J)	CA	El Cajon	SDAMGF	Vought	Crusader	
F8U-1	CA	SRosa	PCAM	Vought	Crusader	
F8U-1	FL	Jacks	NASCF	Vought	Crusader	14135,1 AD, 201, VF-174
F8U-1	GA	Calho	Mercer A	Vought	Crusader	
F8U-1	PA	Willo	WGNAS	Vought	Crusader	143806
F8U-1	SC	MtPleasant	PPM	Vought	Crusader	
F8U-1(XF)	WA	Seattle	MoF	Vought	Crusader	138899
F8U-1(F-8)	CO	Puebl	PWAM	Vought	Crusader	145349
F8U-1(F-8)	NV	FAllon	NASF	Vought	Crusader	
F8U-1(F-8A)	AZ	Tucso	PAM	Vought	Crusader	144427, AC, 207, VF- 32
F8U-1(F-8A)	TX	FWort	PMoT	Vought	Crusader	
F8U-1(F-8A)	VA	VBeac	ONAS	Vought	Crusader	149150, AD, VF-101
F8U-1(F-8C)	CA	SRosa	PCAM	Vought	Crusader	
F8U-1(F-8H)	KS	Liberal	MAAM	Vought	Crusader	148693
F8U-1(F-8J)	CA	San Diego	SDAM	Vought	Crusader	150297
F8U-1(F-8J)	HI	Kaneohe	KBMCAS	Vought	Crusader	146973, VMF AW235DB
F8U-1(F-8J)	MI	Kalam	KAHM	Vought	Crusader	150904
F8U-1(F-8K)	AZ	Phoenix	DVA	Vought	Crusader	
F8U-1(F-8K)	CA	Alameda	USSHM	Vought	Crusader	146931
F8U-1(F-8K)	FL	Titusville	VAC	Vought	Crusader	
F8U-1(F-8K)LTV	CT	Winds	NEAM	Vought	Crusader	
F8U-1(F-8L)	CA	Ridegrest	CLNWC	Vought	Crusader	
F8U-1(RF-8G)	CA	Rosam	EAFB	Vought	Crusader	
F8U-1(RF-8G)	DC	Dulle	DA	Vought	Crusader	
F8U-1P(F-8A)	FL	Pensa	USNAM	Vought	Crusader	144347, NP201, VF- 24
F8U-1P(F-8G(RF))	AL	Mobile	BMP	Vought	Crusader	146898
F8U-1P(F-8G(RF))	FL	Pensa	USNAM	Vought	Crusader	146898
F8U-1P(RF-8G)	CA	Miramar	FLAM	Vought	Crusader	WS, VMF-323, 14467, #21
F9-5	TX	Hawki	RRSA			
F9C-2	FL	Pensa	USNAM	Curtiss	Sparrowhawk	9056
F9F	FL	Titusville	VAC	Grumman	Panther	
F9F	KS	Topek	CAM	Grumman	Panther	
F9F	MD	Lexington	PRNAM	Grumman	Panther	144276, AD Tail
F9F	MD	Middl	GLMAM	Grumman	Panther	
F9F	MS	Petal	MWHMM	Grumman	Panther	
F9F	NY	NYC	ISASM	Grumman	Panther	
F9F	NY	Tonaw	CityPark	Grumman	Panther	
F9F	SC	Mt Pl	PPM	Grumman	Panther	
F9F	TX	FWort	PMoT	Grumman	Panther	
F9F	WI	Janes	CityPark	Grumman	Panther	
F9F	WI	Janesville	VFW 75	Grumman	Panther	
F9F-2	CA	Chino	YAM	Grumman	Panther	
F9F-2	CT	Winds	NEAM	Grumman	Panther	
F9F-2	FL	Pensa	USNAM	Grumman	Panther	123050
F9F-2	MI	Kalamazoo	KAHM	Grumman	Panther	123072
F9F-2	PA	Willo	WGNAS	Grumman	Panther	127120, V209, VF-113
F9F-2	TX	Addison	CFM	Grumman	Panther	N9525A, 123078, A 112, VF- 21, USS Kearsage
F9F-2	VA	Quant	MCAGM	Grumman	Panther	123526
F9F-2	VA	VBeac	ONAS	Grumman	Panther	123612, AD 200
F9F-5P	AL	Mobile	BMP	Grumman	Panther	126285, F21, "F21"
F9F-4 (2 ea)	AZ	Tucso	PAM	Grumman	Panther	125183
F9F-5	CA	San Diego	SDACM	Grumman	Panther	141136
F9F-5	FL	Tittusville	VACM	Grumman	Panther	
F9F-5P	CA	Alameda	USSHM	Grumman	Panther	125316
F9F-5P	CA	Chino	PoFAM	Grumman	Panther	
F9F-5P	FL	Pensa	USNAM	Grumman	Panther	94203
F9F-5P	FL	Pensa	VC	Grumman	Panther	
F9F-5P	MN	Winoma	MCA	Grumman	Panther	125952
F9F-6	FL	Pensa	USNAM	Grumman	Cougar	128109, A, 211, VF-142
F9F-6	MN	Brain	CWCRA	Grumman	Cougar	
F9F-6	TX	Rio Grande V	TAM	Grumman	Cougar	
F9F-6P	NC	Havelock	HTC	Grumman	Cougar	
F9F-7	NY	Garde	CoAM	Grumman	Cougar	124382

F9F-7	NY	Horsehead	WoE	Grumman	Cougar	53-130802
F9F-8(TAF-9J)	AZ	Tucso	PAM	Grumman	Cougar	Sn 141121
F9F-8	CO	Puebl	PWAM	Grumman	Cougar	138876
F9F-8	FL	Jacks	NASCF	Grumman	Cougar	131230, O, 401, VF- 81
F9F-8	MD	Lewington	PRNAM	Grumman	Cougar	51-44276, AD 310
F9F-8	WA	Seatt	MoF	Grumman	Cougar	131232
F9F-8(TAF-9J)	AZ	Tucso	PAM	Grumman	Cougar	368 141121
F9F-8P	CA	San Diego	SDACM	Grumman	Cougar	141702
F9F-8P	NY	Horsehead	WoE	Grumman	Cougar	144402
F9F-8P	CA	Miramar	FLAM	Grumman	Cougar	TN VMCJ-3
F9F-8T(TF-9J)	AZ	Tucso	PAM	Grumman	Cougar	Sn 147397
F9F-8T	CA	San Diego	SDACM	Grumman	Cougar	14974
F9F-8T	TX	C Christi	USS Lexi	Grumman	Cougar	
F9J(TF)	MI	Kalamazoo	KAHM	Grumman	Cougar	147283
F9F-P(RF-9J)	AZ	Tucso	PAM	Grumman	Cougar	110 144426
F11F	FL	Pensa	NASP	Grumman	Tiger	1, "Blue Angels"
F11F	FL	Pensa	PRA	Grumman	Tiger	3, "Blue Angels"
F11F	MI	Ypsil	YAF	Grumman	Tiger	
F11F	SC	Flore	FA&MM	Grumman	Tiger	
F11F-1	SC	MtPleasant	PPM	Grumman	Tiger	
F11F-1	AZ	Grand	PoFGCVA	Grumman	Tiger	141868, "Blue Angles #2"
F11F-1	AZ	Tucso	PAM	Grumman	Tiger	141824
F11F-1	KS	Topek	CAM	Grumman	Tiger	5, "Blue Angels"
F11F-1(F-11A)	MI	Kalam	KAHM	Grumman	Tiger	141872
F11F-1	NY	NYC	ISASM	Grumman	Tiger	AF 210
F11F-1	OH	Newbu	WASAC	Grumman	Tiger	141849
F11F-1F	NY	NYC	ISASM	Grumman	Tiger	
Fa 330	AZ	Tucson	PAM	Focke-Achgelis	Rotor Kite	Towed Behind U-Boats
Fa 330	MD	Silve	PEGF	Focke-Achgelis	Rotor Kite	
Fa 330A-1	OH	Dayto	USAFM	Focke-Achgelis	Sandpiper	
Fairchild 100B	AK	Ancho	AAHM	Fairchild	American Pilgrim	N709Y,"American Pilgrim"
Fairchild F-45	WY	Jackson	GWFM	Fairchild	F-45	
Fairchild F-27A	NV	Las Vegas	LBAHSM	Fairchild	Friendship	Model 27, Sn 48, N753L, "Bonanaza Airlines"
Fairey Battle 1T	ON-C	Ottaw	CAM	Fairey	Battle	
Fairey Firefly Mk.5	ON-C	Hamilton	CWH	Fairey	Firefly	C-GBD6
Fairey Firefly Mk.I	NS-C	Shear	CFBS	Fairey	Firefly	
Fairchild XAUM	NY	Garden	CoAM	Fairchild	Petrel	E278
Fairey Swordfish	NS-C	Shear	CFBS	Fairey	Swordfish	
Fairey Swordfish	ON-C	Ottaw	CAM	Fairey	Swordfish	
Fairey Swordfish Mk.II	CA	S.Mon	MoF	Fairey	Swordfish	HS 164, N2F
Fairey Swordfish Mk.IV	FL	Polk	FoF	Fairey	Swordfish	
Falck Racer	WI	Oshko	EAAAAM	Falck	Racer	
Fanjet Falcon 20	MD	Silve	PEGF	Dassault	Fanjet Falcon	"Federal Express"
Farley Vincent-Starflight	LA	Patte	WWMAM	Farley	Starflight	
Farman Sport	MD	Silve	PEGF	Farman	Sport	
FB-111A	CA	Atwater	CAM	General Dynamics	Aardvark	69-6507
FB-111A	CA	Riverside	MFAM	General Dynamics	Aardvark	68-0245, "Ready Teddy"
FB-111A	LA	Bossi	BAFB	General Dynamics	Aardvark	SAC Bomber
FB-111A	NE	Ashland	SACM	General Dynamics	Aardvark	68-0267, SAC Bomber
FB-5	CA	Chino	PoFAM	Boeing	Model 55	Model 55
FB-5	VA	Quant	MCAGM	Boeing	Model 55	
FC- 2	DC	Washi	NA&SM	Fairchild		
FC- 2	MB-C	Winni	WCAM	Fairchild		
FC- 2W-2	ON-C	Ottaw	CAM	Fairchild		NC 6621
FC- 2W2	VA	Sands	VAM	Fairchild		"Stars & Stripes"
FC- 2W-2	WI	Oshko	EAAAAM	Fairchild		NC 3569
FC-2-W2	WY	Jackson	GWFM	Fairchild		
FC-22	CA	San Carlos	HAM	Fairchild		
FC-22	IA	Ottumwa	APM	Fairchild		512, N11649
FC-24	CA	Camarillo	CAF-SCW	Fairchild		
FC-24	CA	San Carlos	HAM	Fairchild		
FC-24	CA	Santa Paula	SPAA	Fairchild		
FC-24R	FL	Miami	WOM	Fairchild		
FC-24W	WA	Seattle	MoF	Fairchild		206, N37161
FC-24	WA	Vancouver	PAM	Fairchild		
FC-24 *See C 61(UC)*				Fairchild		
FC-24-C8F	OH	Dayto	USAFM	Fairchild		For Mil Version See UC-61J
FC-27	WY	Greyb	H&PA	Fairchild		
FC-71	AB-C	Wetas	RM	Fairchild	Super 71	USAAF as C-8 or UC-96
FC-71	IA	Ottumwa	APM	Fairchild	Super 71	603, N9726
FC-71	MB-C	Winni	CC	Fairchild		USAAF as C-8 or UC-96
FC-71(C-8)	MB-C	Winni	WCAM	Fairchild	Super 71	
FC-71C	AB-C	Edmonton	AAM	Fairchild	Super 71	17
FC-82A	BC-C	Langley	CMoF	Fairchild	Packet	
FC-82A	ON-C	Ottaw	CAM	Fairchild	Packet	
FE-8	DC	Washi	NA&SM	RAF		
FE-8	MD	Silve	PEGF	RAF		
FE-8	ME	OwlsH	OHTM	RAF		
Ferret Scout Car	ON-C	Oshaw	OAM&IM	Ferret	Scout Car	
FF-1	FL	Pensa	USNAM	Grumman	Goblin	9351 5-F-1
FG-1D (See F4U)						
FH-1	DC	Washi	NA&SM	McDonnell	Phantom	
FH-1	FL	Pensa	USNAM	McDonnell	Phantom	111793
FH-1	NY	Horseheads	NWM	McDonnell	Phantom	111768, Side #5, Tail MW
FH-1099	CA	SCarl	HAM	Fairchild-Hiller	CAMEL	LargestJet Helicopter
FH-1100	CA	SCarl	HAM	Fairchild-Hiller	Light Utility 1	Commercial Helicopter
Fi-103(V-1)	CA	Chino	PoFAM	Fiesler	Flying Bomb	
Fi-103(V-1)	IN	Green	CityPark	Fiesler	Flying Bomb(Buzz)	
Fi-103(V-1)	KS	Hutch	KC&SC	Fiesler	Flying Bomb	
Fi-103(V-1) FZG-76	NS	Halifax	ACAM	Fiesler	Flying Bomb	
Fi-103(V-1)	OH	Dayton	USAFM	Fiesler	Flying Bomb	
Fi-103(V-1)	TX	San Antonio	TAM	Fiesler	Flying Bomb	
Fi-103(V-1)	UT	Ogden	HAM	Fiesler	Flying Bomb(Buzz)	
Fi-103(V-1)	VA	Suffolk	FF	Fiesler	Flying Bomb(Buzz)	
Fi-156	MD	Silve	PEGF	Fiesler	Storch	"Ms. 500"
Fi-156	NM	STere	WEAM	Fiesler	Storch	
Fi-156	OH	Dayto	USAFM	Fiesler	Storch	4389
Fi-156	TX	Midland	CAFM	Fiesler	Storch	N40FS
Fi-156A-1	VA	Suffolk	FF	Fiesler	Storch	2631.751
Fi-156	WA	Eastsound	FHC	Fiesler	Storch	4362, N43fFS
Fi-156C-2	WI	Oshko	EAAAAM	Fiesler	Storch	NX464FB
Fiat G.91 Pan	WA	Seatt	MoF	Fiat	Pan	MM6244, NC10
Fike Model A	OR	Eugen	OAM	Fike	Homebuilt	19

Fike Model C	WI	Oshko	EAAAAM	Fike	Homebuilt	13390
Fisher Kola 202	KS	Liberal	MAAM	Fisher	Kola	
Fisher F-303	FL	Lakeland	SNFAM	Fisher	Classic	
FJ-1A	CA	Chino	YAM	North American	Fury	
FJ-1	CT	Winds	NEAM	North American	Fury	
FJ-1	FL	Pensa	USNAM	North American	Fury	120351, S104
FJ-1	KY	Louisville	CCA	North American	Fury	
FJ-2	CA	Alameda	USSHM	North American	Fury	132057
FJ-2	FL	Pensa	USNAM	North American	Fury	N132023
FJ-2	NM	STere	WEAM	North American	Fury	
FJ-2	SC	Mt Pl	PPM	North American	Fury	
FJ-3	AL	Everg	MAE	North American	Fury	
FJ-3	CA	Chino	PoFAM	North American	Fury	
FJ-3	CA	Miramar	FLAM	North American	Fury	WS, VMF-323
FJ-3	NC	Hickory	HRA	North American	Fury	
FJ-3	NY	NYC	ISASM	North American	Fury	
FJ-3	SC	Beauf	MAS	North American	Fury	134841, DN9, VMF-333
FJ-3	VA	Quantico	MCAGM	North American	Fury	136119
FJ-3M	FL	Pensa	USNAM	North American	Fury	N136008
FJ-4B	GA	Cordele	GVMSP	North American	Fury	
FJ-4B	NY	Buffa	B&ECNP	North American	Fury	
FJ-4B	NY	Buffa	City	North American	Fury	
FJ-4B	PA	Willo	WGNAS	North American	Fury	143568
FJ-4B(AF-1E)	AZ	Tucso	PAM	North American	Fury	139531, FU-525
Flaglor Sky Scooter	AZ	Tucso	PAM	Flagor	Sky Scooter	1000, N6WM
Flagg	MO	Maryland Hts	HARM	Flagg	Biplane	
Fleet	NM	Kirkl	KA	Fleet		
Fleet	TX	Brown	RGVW-CAF	Fleet		N16BR
Fleet	ON-C	Collingwood	CCAF	Fleet	Canuck	48, C-FDPV
Fleet 7C	AB-C	Nanto	NLS&AM	Fleet	Fawn	
Fleet 7C	IA	Ottumwa	APM	Fleet	Fawn	
Fleet 7C	ID	Athol	NAM	Fleet	Fawn	
Fleet 7C	PA	Bethel	GAAM	Fleet	Fawn	
Fleet 7C II	ON-C	Hamilton	CWH	Fleet	Fawn	
Fleet 7C II	ON-C	Windsor	CAHS	Fleet	Fawn	
Fleet 21K	ON-C	Hamilton	CWH	Fleet		
Fleet	MB-C	Brandon	CATPM	Fleet	Fort	
Fleet 50K	ON-C	Ottaw	CAM	Fleet	Fort	
Fleet 60K	ON-C	Hamilton	CWH	Fleet	Fort	
Fleet 60K	SK-C	MJaw	WDM	Fleet	Fort	
Fleet 80K	ON-C	Ottaw	CAM	Fleet	Fort	
Fleet Biplane (2 ea)	VA	Bealt	FCA	Fleet		347
Fleet Model 1	VA	Sandston	VAM	Fleet	Finch	N605M
Fleet Model 2	AZ	Tucso	PAM	Fleet	Finch	N605M
Fleet Model 2	BC-C	Langley	CMoF	Fleet	Finch	542, RCAF4725
Fleet Model 2	CA	S.Mar	SMMoF	Fleet	Finch	
Fleet Model 2	CA	S.Mon	MoF	Fleet	Finch II	325, N1328V
Fleet Model 2	CA	San Diego	SDAM	Fleet	Finch	N648M
Fleet Model 2	NY	Garde	CoAM	Fleet	Finch	NC614M
Fleet Model 2	NY	Ghent	POMAM	Fleet	Finch	
Fleet Model 2	OH	Madis	CFR	Fleet	Finch	
Fleet Model 2	ON-C	Ottaw	CAM	Fleet	Finch	
Fleet Model 2	SK-C	MJaw	WDM	Fleet	Finch	
Fleet Model 2	TX	Brown	CAFRGVW	Fleet	Finch	
Fleet Model 16	AB-C	Wetas	RM	Fleet	Finch	
Fleet Model 16B	NY	Bayport	BA	Fleet	Finch II	
Fleet Model 16B	NY	Mayvi	DA	Fleet	Finch	
Fleet Model 16B	NY	Rhine	ORA	Fleet	Finch	
Fleet Model 16B	ON-C	Hamilton	CWH	Fleet	Finch	C-FFLA, 4738
Fleet Model 16B	ON-C	Ottaw	CAM	Fleet	Finch	4510
Fleetwings Seabird	WY	Jackson	GWFM	Fleetwings	Seabird	
Flight Simulator	BC-C	Langley	CMoF			
Fly Baby 1A	KS	Liberal	MAM		Fly Baby	
Flying Boat	CT	Winds	NEAM			
FM-2(F4F)	AZ	Tucson	PA&SM	General Motors	Wildcat	16161
FM-2(F4F)	CA	Chino	YAM	General Motors	Wildcat	85564, N4629V
FM-2(F4F)	CA	Palm Springs	PSAM	General Motors	Wildcat	F-3, N47201
FM-2(F4F)	CA	SCarl	CAF-BR	General Motors	Wildcat	N5833
FM-2(F4F)	CT	Winds	NEAM	General Motors	Wildcat	
FM-2(F4F)	FL	Pensa	USNAM	General Motors	Wildcat	16278, 7
FM-2(F4F)	FL	Polk	FoF	General Motors	Wildcat	
FM-2(F4F)	MI	Kalam	KAHM	General Motors	Wildcat	86581
FM-2(F4F)	IL	Urbana	FAM	General Motors	Wildcat	86581
FM-2(F4F)	OR	Tillamook	TAM	General Motors	Wildcat	N58918
FM-2(F4F)	PA	Tough	CFCM	General Motors	Wildcat	N315E, Side # F-13
FM-2(F4F)	TX	Addison	CFM	General Motors	Wildcat	17
FM-2(F4F)	TX	Galve	LSFM	General Motors	Wildcat	N551TC, 47160
FM-2(F4F)	TX	Midla	CAFFM	General Motors	Wildcat	N681S
FM-2(F4F)	WA	Seatt	MoF	General Motors	Wildcat	4512
FM-2(F4F)	WI	Oshko	EAAAAM	General Motors	Wildcat	86956
FO-141	CA	Riverside	MFAM	Folland	Gnat	E1076, "Green Mountain Boys"
Foose Tigercat	IL	Rantoul	OCAM			
Fokker D.VA	AZ	Mesa	CFM	Fokker	D.VIII	N111CV
Fokker D.VA	ME	Owls Head	OHTM	Fokker	D.VIII	
Fokker D.VII	AL	Birmingham	SMoF	Fokker	D.VII	Project
Fokker D.VII	AL	Gunte	LGARFM	Fokker	D.VII	
Fokker D.VII	AZ	Mesa	CFM	Fokker	D.VII	
Fokker D.VII	WA	Seattle	MoF	Fokker	D.VII	N38038
Fokker D.VII -	CA	Chino	PoFAM	Fokker	D.VII	
Fokker D.VII	DC	Washi	NA&SM	Fokker	D.VII	
Fokker D.VII	FL	Orlan	CSS	Fokker	D.VII	
Fokker D.VII	FL	Orlan	OFW	Fokker	D.VII	
Fokker D.VII	FL	Pensa	USNAM	Fokker	D.VII	1975, 18
Fokker D.VII	NY	Rhine	ORA	Fokker	D.VII	
Fokker D.VII	NY	River	RE	Fokker	D.VII	
Fokker D.VII	OH	Dayto	USAFM	Fokker	D.VII	D7625118
Fokker D.VII	ON-C	Chelt	TGWFM	Fokker	D.VII	
Fokker D.VII	ON-C	Ottaw	CAM	Fokker	D.VII	10347, 18
Fokker D.VII	PQ-C	Knowl	BCHS	Fokker	D.VII	
Fokker D.VII	TX	Kingbury	VAHF	Fokker	D.VII	Project
Fokker D.VII	TX	Slaton	TAM	Fokker	D.VII	
Fokker D.VIII	AL	Gunte	LGARFM	Fokker	D.VIII	N111CV
Fokker D.VIII	AZ	Mesa	CFM	Fokker	D.VIII	N111CV

Fokker D.VIII	WA	Seattle	MoF	Fokker	D.VIII	NX7557U
Fokker D.VIII	NY	Rhine	ORA	Fokker	D.VIII	
Fokker D.VIII	TX	Bealt	FCA	Fokker	D.VIII	
Fokker D.VIII	TX	Addison	CFM	Fokker	D.VIII	
Fokker DR.I	AB-C	Calga	AMoC	Fokker	Triplane	Dreidecker
Fokker DR.I	AL	Gunte	LGARFM	Fokker	Triplane	Dreidecker
Fokker DR.I	AZ	Mesa	CFM	Fokker	Triplane	Dreidecker
Fokker DR.I	WA	Seattle	MoF	Fokker	Triplane	535, NX2203
Fokker DR.I	CA	Chino	PoFAM	Fokker	Triplane	Dreidecker
Fokker DR.I	CA	S.Mon	MoF	Fokker	Triplane	Dreidecker
Fokker DR.I Rep	CA	San Diego	SDAM	Fokker	Triplane	Dreidecker
Fokker DR.I	CT	Winds	NEAM	Fokker	Triplane	Dreidecker
Fokker DR.I	FL	Orlan	CSS	Fokker	Triplane	Dreidecker
Fokker DR.I	FL	Orlan	OFW	Fokker	Triplane	Dreidecker
Fokker DR.I	IA	Hampton	DWWIAM	Fokker	Triplane	Dreidecker
Fokker DR.I	ID	Athol	NAM	Fokker	Triplane	Dreidecker
Fokker DR.I	ID	Cadwe	WAM	Fokker	Triplane	Dreidecker
Fokker DR.I	IL	Rantoul	OCM	Fokker	Triplane	Dreidecker
Fokker DR.I	ME	OwlsH	OHTM	Fokker	Triplane	Dreidecker
Fokker DR.I	NY	EGall	GA	Fokker	Triplane	Dreidecker
Fokker DR.I	NY	Rhine	ORA	Fokker	Triplane	Dreidecker
Fokker DR.I	OH	Dayto	USAFM	Fokker	Triplane	Dreidecker, N1387B
Fokker DR.I	OH	Leroy	PRA	Fokker	Triplane	Dreidecker
Fokker DR.I	OH	Madis	CFR	Fokker	Triplane	Dreidecker
Fokker DR.I	OK	Oklah	KCASM	Fokker	Triplane	Dreidecker
Fokker DR.I	ON-C	Chelt	TGWFM	Fokker	Triplane	Dreidecker
Fokker DR.I	OR	Eugene	OA&SM	Fokker	Triplane	Dreidecker
Fokker DR.I	OR	McMinnville	EAEC	Fokker	Triplane	Dreidecker
Fokker DR.I	PA	Bethel	GAAM	Fokker	Triplane	Dreidecker
Fokker DR.I	TX	Kingbury	VAHF	Fokker	Triplane	Dreidecker Project
Fokker DR.I	TX	Slaton	TAM	Fokker	Triplane	Dreidecker
Fokker DR.I	WA	Seatt	Restaura	Fokker	Triplane	Dreidecker, FI 102/17
Fokker DR.I	WA	Vancouver	Pam	Fokker	Triplane	Dreidecker
Fokker DR.I	WI	Oshko	EAAAAM	Fokker	Triplane	Dreidecker, Redfern, N 105RF
Fokker DR.I	WI	Oshko	EAAAAM	Fokker	Triplane	Dreidecker, Sorrell, N 4435C
Fokker E.III	AL	Gunte	LGARFM	Fokker	Eindecker	
Fokker E.III	AZ	Mesa	CFM	Fokker	Eindecker	
Fokker E.III	WA	Seattle	MoF	Fokker	Eindecker	208 226, N3363G
Fokker E.III Rep	CA	San Diego	SDAM	Fokker	Eindecker	
Fokker F.VIIA	MI	Dearb	HFM	Fokker	Trimoter	1
Fokker F.XI	MB-C	Winni	WCAM	Fokker	F.XI	
Fokker SU	MB-C	Winni	WCAM	Fokker	Super Universal	
Fokker SU Frame	AK	Fairb	APAM	Fokker	Super Universal	NC 9792
Folkerts Gullwing	WI	Oshko	EAAAAM	Folkerts	Gullwing	
Ford 4-AT	CA	MHill	Restaura	Ford	Tri-Motor	
Ford 4-AT	WY	Jackson	GWFM	Ford	Tri-Motor	
Ford 4-AT-15	MI	Dearb	HFM	Ford	Tri-Motor	NX 4542, Byrd Antarctic Expedition, "Floyd Bennett"
Ford 4-AT-B	OH	Port	IA	Ford	Tri-Motor	
Ford 4-AT-E	WI	Oshko	EAAAAM	Ford	Tri-Motor	NC 8407
Ford 5-AT	AK	Ancho	AAHM	Ford	Tri-Motor	Wreckage
Ford 5-AT	AZ	Grand	PoFGCVA	Ford	Tri-Motor	N414H, "Scenic Airways"
Ford 5-AT	DC	Washi	NA&SM	Ford	Tri-Motor	
Ford 5-AT	FL	Polk	FoF	Ford	Tri-Motor	
Ford 5-AT	MI	Kalamazoo	KAHM	Ford	Tri-Motor	
Ford 5-AT	MN	Blaine	GH	Ford	Tri-Motor	
Ford 5-AT	NV	L.Veg	MIA	Ford	Tri-Motor	
Ford 5-AT	NV	LasVe	MIAHM	Ford	Tri-Motor	
Ford 5-AT	OR	Mc Minnville	EAEC	Ford	Tri-Motor	8, N9645
Ford 5-AT(RR-5)	FL	Pensa	USNAM	Ford	Tri-Motor	46, NC7861, 9206
Ford 5-AT-B	CA	San Diego	SDAM	Ford	Tri-Motor	N9637
Ford Flivver	FL	Kissimmee	SNFAM	Ford	Flivver	
Ford Flivver	FL	India	FAHS	Ford	Flivver	
Ford Flivver	MI	Dearb	HFM	Ford	Flivver	268
Ford Flivver	WI	Oshko	EAAAAM	Ford	Flivver	268
Formula One Racer	CA	Chino	PoFAM		Racer	"Miss Cosmic Wind"
Formula One Racer	WA	Vancouver	PAM		Racer	
Fouga Magister	FL	Kissimmee	FTWAM			
Fouga Magister	FL	Miami	WOM			
Fouga Magister	TX	Ft Worth	VFM			
Found 100	BC-C	Langley	CMoF	Found	Centennail	
Found FBA-2C	ON-C	Ottaw	CAM	Found	FBA-2C	
Fournier RF-4D	WA	Seattle	MoF	Fournier	Glider	4064, N1700
Fowler-Gage Tractor	MD	Silve	PEGF	Fowler-Gage	Tractor	
FP-404	NJ	Lumberton	AVM	Fisher	Kit Biplane	
FR-1	CA	Chino	PoFAM	Ryan	Fireball	
Frasca IFR Simulator	ON-C	Sault Ste Marie	CBHC	Frasca	Simulator	
Froebe Helicopter	MB-C	Winni	WCAM	Froebe	Helicopter	
Fulton FA-3	OH	Cleveland	FCAAM	Fulton	Airphibian	
Fulton FA-3-101	MD	Silve	PEGF	Fulton	Airphibian	
Funk 1930	FL	Kissi	FTWAM	Funk		
Funk Model B	CA	Oakla	OWAM	Funk		
Funk Model B	IA	Ottumwa	APM	Funk		60, N24134
Funk Model B	KS	Wichita	KAM	Funk		
Funk Model B	NY	Rhine	ORA	Funk		
Funk Model B	OK	Fredi	AAM	Funk		
Funk Model B	WI	Oshko	EAAAAM	Funk		NC24116
Funk Model B-75	WA	Port Townsend	PTAM	Funk		196, N24170
Funk Model F-23	TX	Slaton	TAM	Funk		SM SN5, N1128Z
Fw 44	TX	Brown	RGVW-CAF	Focke-Wulf	Stieglitz	N 2497
Fw 44-J	AZ	Tucso	PAM	Focke-Wulf	Stieglitz	2827 N 133JM
Fw 190-A1	CAL	Chiriaco	GPM	Focke-Wulf		
Fw 190A-8	TX	San Antonio	TAM	Focke-Wulf		SN732070
Fw 190D-12	AZ	Mesa	CFM	Focke-Wulf		N190D, 10
Fw 190D-9	OH	Dayto	USAFM	Focke-Wulf		60- 1088
Fw 190D-13	AX	Mesa	GU	Focke-Wulf		
Fw 190F-8	MD	Silve	PEGF	Focke-Wulf		
Fw 190F-8	FL	Kissimmee	FTWRM	Focke-Wulf		SN931862, "White 1"
Fw Ta 152H	MD	Silve	PEGF	Focke-Wulf		
G-1B(YG)	CA	Chino	YAM	Kellett	Autogyro	37-381
G-1B(YG)	CT	Washi	TFC	Kellett	Autogyro	
G-21 (OA-13), (JRF)	CA	Palm Springs	PoFAM	Grumman	Goose	
G-21	DC	Washi	NA&SM	Grumman	Goose	
G-21	NY	Garde	CoAM	Grumman	Goose	1051

G-21	NY	Horsehead	NWM	Grumman	Goose	
G-21	ONT-C	Ottawa	CAM	Grumman	Goose	
G-22	MD	Silver Hill	PEGF	Grumman	Gulfhawk II	
G-44	AK	Ancho	AAHM	Grumman	Widgeon	
G-63	NY	Garde	CoAM	Grumman	Kitten	NX31808
G4M	CA	S.Mon	MoF	Mitsubishi	Betty	
G4M3	MD	Silve	PEGF	Mitsubishi	Betty	
GA-22	WI	Oshko	EAAAAM	Goodyear	Drake	N5516M
GA-36	NY	Amherst	AM			
GA-36	NY	Niagara Falls	NAM	Cunningham-Hall		
GA-400	CA	Ramona	CR	Goodyear	Gismo	4098
GA-400-R-2J	WI	Oshko	EAAAAM	Goodyear	Gismo	N69N
Gazda Helicospeeder	CA	SCarl	HAM	Gazda	Helicospeeder	
GB Penguin Trainer	WI	Oshko	EAAAAM	Gunderson/Burke	Penquin Trainer	N41047
GB-2	FL	Pensa	USNAM	Beech	Traveller	23688
GeeBee R-1	CT	Winds	NEAM	Grandville Aircraft	GeeBee Racer	711, NR2100
GeeBee R-1 Model A	CT	Winds	NEAM	Grandville Aircraft	GeeBee Racer	
GeeBee R-1 Z Replica	CA	S.Mon	MoF	Grandville Aircraft	GeeBee Racer	NR77V, #4, Model Z
GeeBee R-1 Replica	OH	Cleveland	FCAAM	Grandville Aircraft	GeeBee Racer	
GeeBee R-5 Model E	CT	Winds	NEAM	Grandville Aircraft	GeeBee Racer	
GeeBee R-6H	MEXI	CLedr	CL	Grandville Aircraft	GeeBee Racer	
GEM X-2	VA	FtEus	USATM		Little Carrier	M2500
Gemini	CA	San Diego	SDAM	McDonnell	Module	
Gemini	KS	Hutch	KC&SC	McDonnell	Space Capsule	
Gemini	KY	Louis	MoH&S	McDonnell	Trainer	
Gemini	MO	SLoui	MDPR	McDonnell	Space Capsule	
Gemini	OH	Dayton	USAFM	McDonnell	Space Capsule	
Gemini	OK	Oklah	KCASM	McDonnell	Space Capsule	
Gemini 11	CA	LAnge	CMoS&I	McDonnell	Space Capsule	
Gemini Grissom	IN	Mitch	SMSP	McDonnell	Space Capsule	
Gemini GT-3	NY	NYC	ISASM	McDonnell	Space Capsule	"Gemini"
Gemini VIII	OH	Wapak	NAA&SM	McDonnell		
Gemini XI	WA	Seatt	PSC	McDonnell		
GH-1	WA	Seattle	MoF	Howard		
GH-2	MI	Kalam	KAHM	Howard	Nightingale	32347
GH-2	MI	Ypsil	YAF	Howard	Nightingale	
GH-3	TX	C Christi	USS Lexi	Howard	Nightingale	
Gibson Twin	BC-C	Sidne	BCAM	Gibson	Twin	
GK-1	FL	Pensa	USNAM	Fairchild		7033
GK-1	OR	Tillamook	TAM	Fairchild		
Glasair	CA	Oakla	OWAM	Hamilton	Glasair	
Glasair II-FT	AL	Birmingham	SMoF	Hamilton	Glasair	
Glasair Ham-2	WI	Oshko	EAAAAM	Hamilton	Glasair	N88TH
Glasflugel BS-1	TX	Dallas	FoF	Glasflugel		
Glasflugel BS-1	NY	Elmira	NSM	Glasflugel		N
Glasflugel H-301B	NY	Elmira	NSM	Glasflugel		N260E
Glider	CA	Calis	Nance's		Glider	
Glider	CA	San F	TE		Glider	
Glider 1942	CO	Denve	JWDAS		Glider	
Gliders 6 ea	PA	Water	TGAM		Glider	
Globe GC-1B	AR	Fayetteville	AAM	Globe	Swift	
Globe GC-1B	KS	Liberal	MAAM	Globe	Swift	
Globe GC-1B	OK	Fredi	AAM	Globe	Swift	
Globe KD2G-2	WI	Oshko	EAAAAM	Globe		
Globe KD6D-2	AZ	Grand Canyon	PoFGCVA	Globe		
Go 229	MD	Silve	PEGF	Gotha		
Goddard Model A	NY	Garde	CoAM	Goddard	Rocket	
Gonzales Biplane	CA	Fairc	TAFB	Gonzales		
Gonzales Biplane	CA	Fairf	TAFB	Gonzales		
Gonzales Biplane	CA	San Carlos	HAM	Gonzales		
Goodyear 195	FL	Pensa	USNAM	Goodyear	Inflat A-Plane	Model XA029
Goodyear 195	MD	Lexin	PNA&EM	Goodyear	Inflat A-Plane	
Goodyear Blimp K Car	CT	Winds	NEAM	Goodyear	Blimp K Car	
Goodyear Blimp K Car	DC	Dulle	DA	Goodyear	Blimp K Car	
Goodyear Gondola	MD	Silver Hill	PEGF	Goodyear	Gondola	"Pilgram"
Goppingen I	NY	Elmira	NSM	Goppingen	Wolf	N31635
Goppingen III	NY	Elmira	NSM	Goppingen	Minimoa	G16923
Gossamer Albatross II	WA	Seatt	MoF	Gossamer	Albatross II	GA-11
Gossamer Condor	DC	Washi	NA&SM	Gossamery	Condor	
Gostave 21	CT	Bridg	CoveRest	Gostave	Whitehead	
Graflite	WI	Oshko	EAAAAM	Kotula-Lundy	Graflite	N780GF
Great Lakes 2T-1A	AL	Birmingham	SMoF	Great Lakes	Sport Trainer	
Great Lakes 2T-1A	CA	El Cajon	SDAMGF	Great Lakes	Sport Trainer	
Great Lakes 2T-1A	CA	S.Mar	SMMoF	Great Lakes	Sport Trainer	
Great Lakes 2T-1A	IA	Ottumwa	APM	Great Lakes	Sport Trainer	252, N11339
Great Lakes 2T-1A	NY	Rhine	ORA	Great Lakes	Sport Trainer	
Great Lakes 2T-1A	OH	Cleveland	FCAAM	Great Lakes	Sport Trainer	#8
Great Lakes 2T-1A	ON-C	Sault Ste Marie	CBHC	Great Lakes	Sport Trainer	C-APL
Great Lakes 2T-1A	PA	Bethel	GAAM	Great Lakes	Sport Trainer	N75M
Great Lakes 2T-1A	TX	Gilmer	FotP	Great Lakes	Sport Trainer	
Great Lakes 2T-1A-2	AL	Birmi	Southe	Great Lakes	Sport Trainer	
Great Lakes 2T-1AE	CT	Winds	NEAM	Great Lakes	Sport Trainer	461
Great Lakes 2T-1AE	NM	STere	WEAM	Great Lakes	Sport Trainer	
Great Lakes 2T-1AE	WI	Oshko	EAAAAM	Great Lakes	Sport Trainer	N3182
Great Lakes Special	KS	Ashla	HKAM	Great Lakes	Special	N21E
Greenwood Witch	TX	Slaton	TAM	Greenwood	Witch	N3147N
Grob 103	NM	Hobbs	NSF	Grob	Glider	
Gross Sky Ghost	NY	Elmira	NSM	Gross	Sky Ghost	G11348
Group Genesis	NY	Elmira	NSM	Genesis	I	N94GC
Groud Trainer	WI	Oshkosh	EAAAAM	Grooud	Trainer	
Gruneau 2	MB-C	Winni	WCAM	Gruneau	Glider	
Grumman AgCat	GA	Woodstock	NGWS	Grumman	AgCat	
Grumman Echo Cannister	NY	Garde	CoAM	Grumman	Echo Cannister	7
Grumman LM -13	NY	Garde	CoAM	Grumman	LM Ascent Stage	
Grumman LRV Molab	NY	Garde	CoAM	Grumman	LRV Mo Lab	
Grumman LTA-1	NY	Garde	CoAM	Grumman		
Grunau Baby IIb	BC-C	Langley	CMoF	Grunau	Baby IIb	
Grunau Baby IIb	MD	Silve	PEGF	Grunau	Baby IIb	
Gulfstream Peregrine	OK	Oklah	A&SM	Gulfstream	Peregrine	
Gulfstream Peregrine	OK	Oklah	KCASM	Gulfstream	Peregrine	
Gulfstream SC	OK	Oklah	SFG	Gulfstream	Shrike Commander	
Gun 3" M5	IN	Atterbury	CAM&MC			
Gun 3" M9 Army	IL	Sprin	S.ArmyNG		Howitzer	

Gun 5" Navy	IL	Edgew	KAALP		Howitzer	
Gun 8" M115	IN	Atterbury	CAM&MC		Howitzer	
Gun 8"	MO	SLoui	NPRC		Howitzer	
Gun 8"	OH	Hubbard	WWIIVM		Howitzer	
Gun 8" M110A2	OH	Groveport	MMM		Howitzer	
Gun 8" M110A2	TX	Pampa	FM		Howitzer	
Gun WWI Howitzer	IL	Salem			Howitzer	
Gun M1918A3	IN	Atterbury	CAM&MC		Schneider	155mm
Guns	VA	Quantico	MCAGM			
Gyrodyne 2C	NY	Garde	CoAM	Gyrodyne	Gyrodyne 2C	N6594K
GZ-22	OH	N Canton	MAM		Gondola	
H-1 Racer Rep	OR	Cottage Grove	WT	Hughes	Racer Rep	NX258Y
H-1	DC	Washi	NA&SM	Hughes	Racer	NX258Y
H-1	OR	McMinnville	EAEC	Hughes	Racer Rep	
H-1 (AH)	AL	Huntsville	AC	Bell	Huey Cobra	Bell 209
H-1 (AH)	CA	San Diego	SDAM	Bell	Huey Cobra	Bell 209
H-1 (AH)	HI	Honolulu	USAM	Bell	Huey Cobra	
H-1 (AH)	HI	Oahu	USAM	Bell	Huey Cobra	
H-1 (AH)	IA	Des Moines	ING	Bell	Huey Cobra	0-45454
H-1 (AH)	IA	Greenfield	IAM	Bell	Huey Cobra	Bell 209
H-1 (AH)	IA	Ida Grove	CMP	Bell	Huey Cobra	0-21041
H-1 (AH)	IN	Mentone	LDBM	Bell	Huey Cobra	
H-1 (AH)	KS	Topeka	MoKNG	Bell	Huey Cobra	
H-1 (AH)	KY	FKnox	PMoC&A	Bell	Huey Cobra	Bell 209
H-1 (AH)	LA	New Orleans	Belle Chasse NAS Bell		Huey Cobra	
H-1 (AH)	MD	Lexington	USNTPS	Bell	Huey Cobra	Bell 209, 0-15645, Side # 55, ARMY TPS Tail
H-1 (AH)	MI	Mt Clemens	SMAM	Bell	Huey Cobra	67-15675
H-1 (AH)	MO	SLoui	SLUPC	Bell	Huey Cobra	Bell 209
H-1 (AH)	MO	Springfield	AMMO	Bell	Huey Cobra	Bell 209
H-1 (AH)	SC	Citadel	CC	Bell	Huey Cobra	Bell 209
H-1 (AH)	SC	MtPleasant	PPM	Bell	Huey Cobra	159210
H-1 (AH)	VA	Danville	AATM	Bell	Huey Cobra	
H-1 (AH)	WA	Vancouver	PAM	Bell	Huey Cobra	77-22791, Bell 209
H-1 (AH)	WI	Madison	MTFMDCRA	Bell	Huey Cobra	Bell 209
H-1 (AH)	WI	Oshkosh	EAAAAM	Bell	Huey Cobra	Bell 209
H-1 (AH)Cockpit	PA	WChes	AHM	Bell	Huey Cobra	Bell 209
H-1A(AH)	NJ	Lumberton	AVM	Bell	Huey Cobra	
H-1A(AH)	NJ	Rio Grande	NASW	Bell	Huey Cobra	
H-1A(AH)	OH	Norwalk	FMoMH	Bell	Huey Cobra	66-00825
H-1F(AH)	AL	Huntsville	RA	Bell	Huey Cobra	
H-1F(AH)	AL	Ozark	AAM	Bell	Huey Cobra	
H-1F(AH)	AZ	Yuma	USAPG	Bell	Huey Cobra	66-15350
H-1F(AH)	CO	Burinlgton	VFW6491	Bell	Huey Cobra	67-15479
H-1F(AH)	NY	Niagara Falls	NAM	Bell	Huey Cobra	65-09834
H-1G(AH)	AL	Ozark	USAAM	Bell	Huey Cobra	66-15246 Bell 209
H-1G(AH)	GA	Hampton	AAHF	Bell	Huey Cobra	
H-1G(AH)	IL	Collinsville	AM 365	Bell	Huey Cobra	
H-1J(AH)	CA	Miramar	FLAM	Bell	Huey Cobra	
H-1P(TAH)	GA	Hampton	AAHF	Bell	Huey Cobra	
H-1S(AH)	OH	N Canton	MAM	Bell	Huey Cobra	70-16084
H-1S(AH)	AR	Fayet	AAM	Bell	Huey Cobra	70-16050
H-1S(AH)	AZ	Tucson	PAM	Bell	Huey Cobra	
H-1S(AH)	HI	Waikiki	FRAM	Bell	Huey Cobra	67-15796
H-1S(AH) 2ea	HI	Wheeler	WAFB	Bell	Huey Cobra	0-15036 & 33068
H-1S(AH)	KS	Liberal	MAAM	Bell	Huey Cobra	
H-1S(AH)	MA	Fall River	FRBC	Bell	Huey Cobra	70-16038
H-1S(AH)	NJ	Teterboro	AHoFNJ	Bell	Huey Cobra	69-16437
H-1S(AH)	RI	NKing	QAM	Bell	Huey Cobra	66-15317 Bell 209
H-1S(AH)	TX	C Cristi	USS Lexi	Bell	Huey Cobra	
H-1 (HH)	MI	Grand Rapids	GFM	Bell	Iroquois (Huey)	
H-1 (HH)	TX	Pampa	PAAF	Bell	Iroquois (Huey)	
H-1H(HH)	AK	Fairb	APAM	Bell	Iroquois (Huey)	66-934
H-1H(HH)	AZ	Tucso	PAM	Bell	Iroquois (Huey)	64-13895
H-1H(HH)	CA	Marys	FWM	Bell	Iroquois (Huey)	
H-1H(HH)	CA	Sacra	McCelAFB	Bell	Iroquois (Huey)	70-2467, "Huey Slick"
H-1H(HH)	FL	Clear	FMAM	Bell	Iroquois (Huey)	
H-1H(HH)	FL	Eglin	USAFAC	Bell	Iroquois (Huey)	
H-1H(HH)	IL	Linco	HIFM	Bell	Iroquois (Huey)	
H-1H(HH)	MD	Silve	PEGF	Bell	Iroquois (Huey)	
H-1H(HH)	OR	Tillamook	TAM	Bell	Iroquois (Huey)	
H-1H(HH)	RI	NKing	QAM	Bell	Iroquois (Huey)	64-13402
H-1H(HH)	UT	Ogden	HAFBM	Bell	Iroquois (Huey)	
H-1K(HH)	FL	Pensa	USNAM	Bell	Iroquois (Huey)	157188, 301, HAL-3
H-1L(TH)	MD	Lexington	PRNAM	Bell	Iroquois (Huey)	157842, NATC Tail
H-1L(TH)	PA	WChester	AHM	Bell	Iroquois (Huey)	
H-1L(TH)	TX	Dallas	FoF	Bell	Iroquois (Huey)	157838, N7UW
H-1 (UH)	AL	Birmingham	SMoF	Bell	Iroquois (Huey)	
H-1 (UH)	AL	Starke	BMP	Bell	Iroquois (Huey)	
H-1 (UH)	AL	Tuscalloosa	I-20/59	Bell	Iroquois (Huey)	
H-1 (UH)	CA	Los Alamitos	NAS	Bell	Iroquois (Huey)	
H-1 (UH)	CA	Paso Robles	EWM	Bell	Iroquois (Huey)	61-3859
H-1 (UH)	CA	Ridgecrest	CLNWC	Bell	Iroquois (Huey)	
H-1 (UH)	CO	Puebl	PWAM	Bell	Iroquois (Huey)	
H-1 (UH)	DE	Dover	AMCM	Bell	Iroquois (Huey)	
H-1 (UH)	FL	Shali	USAFAM	Bell	Gondola	
H-1 (UH)	FL	Tittusville	VACM	Bell	Iroquois (Huey)	
H-1 (UH)	HI	Oahu, Barbers	HMoF	Bell	Iroquois (Huey)	70-15708
H-1 (UH)	HI	Oahu	WAFB	Bell	Iroquois (Huey)	
H-1 (UH)	IA	Des Moines	ING	Bell	Iroquois (Huey)	0-38825
H-1 (UH)	IL	Sugar Grove	ACM	Bell	Iroquois (Huey)	68-16215
H-1 (UH)	IL	Sugar Grove	ACM	Bell	Iroquois (Huey)	68-16265
H-1 (UH)	IN	South Bend	MHP	Bell	Iroquois (Huey)	
H-1 (UH)	KS	Emporia	VP	Bell	Iroquois (Huey)	
H-1 (UH)	KS	Topeka	MoKNG	Bell	Iroquois (Huey)	
H-1 (UH)	KY	FKnox	FC	Bell	Iroquois (Huey)	
H-1 (UH)	MI	Monro		Bell	Iroquois (Huey)	
H-1 (UH)	MI	Sterling Hts	FHCMP	Bell	Iroquois (Huey)	15719
H-1 (UH)	MT	Helena	HA	Bell	Iroquois (Huey)	
H-1 (UH)	NJ	Rio Grande	NASW	Bell	Iroquois (Huey)	
H-1 (UH)	NV	Fallon	NASF	Bell	Iroquois (Huey)	
H-1 (UH)	OH	Groveport	MMM	Bell	Iroquois (Huey)	56-17048, Joe Sepesy
H-1 (UH)	OH	Norwalk	FMoMH	Bell	Iroquois (Huey)	66-00992
H-1 (UH)	SC	Mt Pleasant	PP	Bell	Iroquois (Huey)	

H- 1 (UH)	TN	Caryville	I-75&US25W	Bell	Iroquois (Huey)	
H- 1 (UH)	TX	Addison	CFM	Bell	Iroquois (Huey)	91E
H- 1 (UH)	TX	FWort	NASFWJRB	Bell	Iroquois (Huey)	
H- 1 (UH)	TX	FWort	VFM	Bell	Iroquois (Huey)	
H- 1 (UH)	TX	Slaton	TAM	Bell	Iroquois (Huey)	
H- 1 (UH)	WI	Madison	MTFMDCRA	Bell	Iroquois (Huey)	
H- 1 (UH)	VA	Quantico	MCAGM	Bell	Iroquois (Huey)	154760
H- 1(UH)	TX	Sweetwater	CP	Bell	Iroquois (Huey)	
H- 1A(UH)	CA	SRosa	PCAM	Bell	Iroquois (Huey)	
H- 1A(UH)	NC	Fayet	FBADM	Bell	Iroquois (Huey)	59-1711
H- 1A(UH)	NY	NYC	ISASM	Bell	Iroquois (Huey)	
H- 1B(UH)	AL	Mobile	BMP	Bell	Iroquois (Huey)	21966
H- 1B(UH)	AL	Ozark	USAAM	Bell	Iroquois (Huey)	60- 3553
H- 1B(UH)	CA	El Cajon	SDAMGF	Bell	Iroquois (Huey)	
H- 1B(UH)	CA	San Diego	SDACM	Bell	Iroquois (Huey)	60-3614
H- 1B(UH)	CT	Strat	NHM	Bell	Iroquois (Huey)	
H- 1B(UH)	CT	Winds	NEAM	Bell	Iroquois (Huey)	
H- 1B(UH)	DC	Washi	AAFB	Bell	Iroquois (Huey)	
H- 1B(UH)	GA	Hampton	AAHF	Bell	Iroquois (Huey)	
H- 1B(UH)	IA	SBluf	MAAM	Bell	Iroquois (Huey)	
H- 1B(UH)	IL	Ranto	OCAM	Bell	Iroquois (Huey)	61-0686
H- 1B(UH)	IN	Vince	IMM	Bell	Iroquois (Huey)	
H- 1B(UH)	KS	Liberal	MAAM	Bell	Iroquois (Huey)	
H- 1B(UH)	KY	FKnox	PMoC&A	Bell	Iroquois (Huey)	
H- 1B(UH)	MI	Battle Creek	BCANG	Bell	Iroquois (Huey)	
H- 1B(UH)	MO	SLoui	NPRC	Bell	Iroquois (Huey)	
H- 1B(UH)	OK	FtSil	USAFAM	Bell	Iroquois (Huey)	
H- 1B(UH)	OK	Oklah	45IDM	Bell	Iroquois (Huey)	62-4588
H- 1B(UH)	OH	N Canton	MAM	Bell	Iroquois (Huey)	
H- 1B(UH)	SC	Columbia	FJM	Bell	Iroquois (Huey)	
H- 1B(UH)	VA	Eustis	USATM	Bell	Iroquois (Huey)	61-0788
H- 1B(UH)	WA	Tacom	FL	Bell	Iroquois (Huey)	
H- 1C(UH)	NY	Horseheads	NWM	Bell	Iroquois (Huey)	
H- 1C(UH)	CA	S El Monte	ASMH	Bell	Iroquois (Huey)	
H- 1D(UH)	AL	Ozark	USAAM	Bell	Iroquois (Huey)	60-6030
H- 1D(UH)	CA	San Diego	SDAM	Bell	Iroquois (Huey)	432
H- 1D(UH)-BF	MI	Belleville	YAF	Bell	Iroquois (Huey)	66-16006, N5700
H- 1D(UH)-BF	MI	Oscoda	YAF	Bell	Iroquois (Huey)	66-16048, N13YA
H- 1D(UH)	WA	Seatt	MoF	Bell	Iroquois (Huey)	
H- 1E(UH)	WI	Brist	Museum	Bell	Iroquois (Huey)	
H- 1F(UH)	AZ	Green	TMM	Bell	Iroquois (Huey)	
H- 1F(UH)	AZ	Tucso	PAM	Bell	Iroquois (Huey)	66-1211
H- 1F(UH)	CA	Riverside	MAFB	Bell	Iroquois (Huey)	63-13143
H- 1F(UH)	MO	Knob	WAFB	Bell	Iroquois (Huey)	
H- 1F(UH)	MT	Great	MAFB	Bell	Iroquois (Huey)	65-956
H- 1F(UH)	ND	Grand	GFAFB	Bell	Iroquois (Huey)	
H- 1F(UH)	ND	Minot	MAFB	Bell	Iroquois (Huey)	
H- 1F(UH)	NM	Albuq	KAFB	Bell	Iroquois (Huey)	
H- 1F(UH)	SD	Rapid	SDA&SM	Bell	Iroquois (Huey)	66-7591
H- 1F(UH)	WY	Cheye	FEWAFB	Bell	Iroquois (Huey)	65-7959
H- 1F2(UH)	GA	Warner Robin	MoF	Bell	Iroquois (Huey)	
H- 1H(UH)	CA	S.Mon	MoF	Bell	Iroquois (Huey)	
H- 1H(UH)	CA	S.Mon	MoF	Bell	Iroquois (Huey)	0-38801
H- 1H(UH)	HI	Wheeler	WAFB	Bell	Iroquois (Huey)	0-15127
H- 1H(UH)	HI	Wheeler	WAFB	Bell	Iroquois (Huey)	27548
H- 1H(UH)	GA	Hampton	AAHF	Bell	Iroquois (Huey)	
H- 1H(UH)	IN	Fairmount	AMP313	Bell	Iroquois (Huey)	68-16504, 05/19/85
H- 1H(UH)	KS	Topek	CAM	Bell	Iroquois (Huey)	TA-897
H- 1H(UH)	ME	Augusta	MANG	Bell	Iroquois (Huey)	63-8809
H- 1H(UH)	ME	Bangor	CTM	Bell	Iroquois (Huey)	65-9915
H- 1H(UH)	ME	Bangor	MAM	Bell	Iroquois (Huey)	71-20317; 73-21661
H- 1H(UH)	NM	Angel Fire	VVNM	Bell	Iroquois (Huey)	64-13670
H- 1H(UH)	NY	Buffalo	B&ECNSSP	Bell	Iroquois (Huey)	63-12982
H- 1H(UH)	NY	Horsehead	WoE	Bell	Iroquois (Huey)	65-09589
H- 1H(UH)	NY	Horsehead	WoE	Bell	Iroquois (Huey)	66-16200
H- 1H(UH)	NY	Horsehead	WoE	Bell	Iroquois (Huey)	66-16906
H- 1H(UH)	OH	Norwalk	FMoMH	Bell	Iroquois (Huey)	67-17658
H- 1H(UH)	OR	Mc Minnville	EAEC	Bell	Iroquois (Huey)	
H- 1H(UH)	PA	Beaver Falls	AHM	Bell	Iroquois (Huey)	
H- 1H(UH)	PA	Smethport	AAAM	Bell	Iroquois (Huey)	
H- 1H(UH)	RI	NKing	QAM	Bell	Iroquois (Huey)	65-09996
H- 1H(UH)	SC	MtPleasant	PPM	Bell	Iroquois (Huey)	10132
H- 1H(UH)	TX	W Houston	Airport	Bell	Iroquois (Huey)	
H- 1H(UH)	TX	Slaton	TAM	Bell	Iroquois (Huey)	SN64-13624, 24A
H- 1(UH)	TX	San Antonio	TAM	Bell	Iroquois (Huey)	SN64-13624, 24A
H- 1H(UH)	VA	FtEus	USATM	Bell	Iroquois (Huey)	74-22376
H- 1H(UH)	WI	Kenos	KMM	Bell	Iroquois (Huey)	66-01169, "123 AVBN AMDIV"
H- 1H(UH)	WI	Kenos	KMM	Bell	Iroquois (Huey)	66-16122
H- 1H(UH)	WI	Kenos	KMM	Bell	Iroquois (Huey)	65-9534
H- 1HA(UH)	NC	Charl	CHAC	Bell	Iroquois (Huey)	
H- 1HA(UH)	NC	CPoin	CPMB	Bell	Iroquois (Huey)	
H- 1HB(UH)	NC	Charl	CHAC	Bell	Iroquois (Huey)	
H- 1HB(UH)	NC	CPoin	CPMB	Bell	Iroquois (Huey)	
H- 1M(UH)	AL	Huntsville	RA	Bell	Iroquois (Huey)	
H- 1M(UH)	AR	Littl	LRAFB	Bell	Iroquois (Huey)	
H- 1M(UH)	AZ	Tucso	PAM	Bell	Iroquois (Huey)	65-9430
H- 1M (UH)	IN	Atterbury	CAM&MC	Bell	Iroquois (Huey)	0-15084
H- 1M(UH)	FL	Pensa	VMP	Bell	Iroquois (Huey)	314 HL-3
H- 1M(UH)	GA	Hampton	AAHF	Bell	Iroquois (Huey)	
H- 1M(UH)	KS	Topek	CAM	Bell	Iroquois (Huey)	
H- 1M(UH)	MD	Silve	PEGF	Bell	Iroquois (Huey)	
H- 1M(UH)	NM	Las Cruces	WSMP	Bell	Iroquois (Huey)	
H- 1M(UH)	NY	NYC	ISASM	Bell	Iroquois (Huey)	
H- 1M(UH)	NY	Glenville	ESAM	Bell	Iroquois (Huey)	65-9435
H- 1M(UH)	MA	Fall River	FRBC	Bell	Iroquois (Huey)	66-00609
H- 1M(UH)	RI	NKing	QAM	Bell	Iroquois (Huey)	66-15083
H- 1M(UH)	SC	MtPleasant	PPM	Bell	Iroquois (Huey)	65-10132
H- 1M(UH)	TX	Amari	EFA&SM	Bell	Iroquois (Huey)	
H- 1M(UH)	VA	Hampt	VA&SC	Bell	Iroquois (Huey)	
H- 1P(UH)	FL	FtWal	HF	Bell	Iroquois (Huey)	64-15493
H- 1P(UH)	GA	Warner Robin	MoF	Bell	Iroquois (Huey)	
H- 1P(UH)	OH	Dayto	USAFM	Bell	Iroquois (Huey)	64-15476
H- 1V(UH)	FL	Tittusville	VACM	Bell	Iroquois (Huey)	

H- 1V(UH)	PA	Willow	WGNAS	Bell	Iroquois (Huey)	
H- 3C(CH)	AZ	Tucso	DMAFB	Sikorsky	Jolly Green Giant	
H- 3E(CH)	CA	Chino	YAM	Sikorsky	Jolly Green Giant	
H- 3E(CH)	CA	Rosam	EAFB	Sikorsky	Jolly Green Giant	62-12581
H- 3E(CH)	CA	Sacra	McCelAFB	Sikorsky	Jolly Green Giant	65-5690
H- 3E(CH)	GA	Warner Robin	MoF	Sikorsky	Jolly Green Giant	65-12797
H- 3E(CH)	UT	Ogden	HAFBM	Sikorsky	Jolly Green Giant	
H- 3E(CH)	OH	Dayto	USAFM	Sikorsky	Jolly Green Giant	63- 9676
H- 3F(HH)	NY	Horsehead	NWM	Sikorsky	Pelican	
H- 3F(HH)	SC	Mt Pleasant	PPM¢	Sikorsky	Pelican	149932, Side 55
H- 3F(HH)(S-61)	IL	Chica	MoS&I	Sikorsky	Pelican	
H- 3F(HH)(S-61)	FL	FtWal	HF	Sikorsky	Pelican	65-12784, AH
H- 3F(HH)(S-61)	AZ	Tucso	PAM	Sikorsky	Pelican	1476
H- 3F(HH)(S-61)	FL	Pensa	USNAM	Sikorsky	Pelican	CGNR1486
H- 3F(HH)(S-61)	FL	Clear	FMAM	Sikorsky	Pelican	
H- 3F(HH)(S-61)	PA	WChester	AHM	Sikorsky	Pelican	
H- 3F(HH)(S-61)	WI	Janesville	BHTSAC	Sikorsky	Pelican	
H- 3F(HH)(S-61)	WI	Kenosha	KMM	Sikorsky	Pelican	1485
H- 3F(HH)(S-61)	WI	Kenosha	KMM	Sikorsky	Pelican	44043
H- 3S(OH)	NY	NYC	ISASM	Bell	Souix	
H- 4A(OH)	AL	Ozark	USAAM	Ryan	Jet Ranger	62-4201
H- 5 (HH)(S-51)	AK	Palme	MOAT&I	Sikorsky	Dragonfly	
H- 5 (R)	AL	Ozark	USAAM	Sikorsky	Dragonfly	51-24352
H- 5A(OH)(S-51)	AL	Ozark	USAAM	Sikorsky	Dragonfly	62-4206
H- 5A(YH)(S-51)	OH	Dayto	USAFM	Sikorsky	Dragonfly	43-46620
H- 5G(S-51)	AZ	Tucso	PAM	Sikorsky	Dragonfly	48-548, N9845Z
H- 5G(S-51)	NM	Albuq	KAFB	Sikorsky	Dragonfly	
H- 5H(S-51)	CT	Winds	NEAM	Sikorsky	Dragonfly	
H- 6A(OH)	AL	Ozark	USAAM	Hughes	Cayuse	65-12917
H- 6A(OH)	AL	Birmingham	SMoF	Hughes	Cayuse	
H- 6A(YO)	AL	Ozark	USAAM	Hughes	Cayuse	62-4213
H- 6A(OH)	CA	Marys	FWM	Hughes	Cayuse	
H- 6A(OH)	CA	Riverside	MFAM	Hughes	Cayuse	68-17252
H- 6A(OH)	CA	S.Mon	MoF	Hughes	Cayuse	
H- 6A(OH)	CO	CO.Sp	FCBA	Hughes	Cayuse	
H- 6A(OH)	GA	Hampton	AAHF	Hughes	Cayuse	
H- 6A(OH)	KS	Liberal	MAAM	Hughes	Cayuse	
H- 6A(OH)	KS	Topeka	MoKNG	Hughes	Cayuse	
H- 6A(OH)	LA	Reser	AMHFM	Hughes	Cayuse	
H- 6A(OH)	NJ	Rio Grande	NASW	Hughes	Cayuse	
H- 6A(OH)	NY	Horseheads	NWM	Hughes	Cayuse	67-16668
H- 6A(OH)	NY	Glenville	ESAM	Hughes	Cayuse	68-17343
H- 6A(OH)	OK	Oklah	45IDM	Hughes	Cayuse	
H- 6A(OH)	PA	WChes	AHM	Hughes	Cayuse	
H- 6A(OH)	RI	NKing	QAM	Hughes	Cayuse	67-16570
H- 6A(OH)	UT	Ogden	HAFBM	Hughes	Cayuse	
H- 6A(R)	OH	Dayto	USAFM	Sikorsky		
H-6J(MH) (MN 530F)	PA	West Chester	AHM	Hughes	Little Bird	
H-12	OK	Lexington	CPT	Hiller	Raven	
H-12 (UH)	CA	SCarl	HAM	Hiller	Raven	Model 360
H-12(UH)	CO	Denve	JWDAS	Hiller	Raven	
H-12 (UH)	HI	Oahu	WAFB	Hiller	Raven	
H-12 (UH)	IN	Mentone	LDBAM	Hiller	Raven	
H-12 (UH)(U-23)	CA	Chino	PoFAM	Hiller	Raven	
H-12 (UH)(U-23)	MI	Kalam	KAHM	Hiller	Raven	51-4007
H-12 (HTE-2)	CA	SCarl	HAM	Hiller		
H-12A(HTE-1)	FL	Pensa	USNAM	Hiller	Raven HTE	41-4017, N3HK, 128647
H-12B(UH)	CA	SCarl	HAM	Hiller	Raven	Model 360
H-12C(UH)	AZ	Tucso	PAM	Hiller	Raven J	345, N7725C, Model 360
H-12C(UH)	CA	Redwo	HAM	Hiller	Raven	Model 360
H-12D(UH)(H-23)	PA	WChes	AHM	Hiller	Raven	Model 360
H-12E(UH)	OR	McMinnville	EAM	Hiller	Raven	2100, N1H
H-12E(UH)	OR	McMinnville	EAM	Hiller	Raven	2049, N5363V
H-12E(UH)(U-23)	WY	Greyb	H&PA	Hiller	Raven	
H-12E-E4(UH)NASA	CA	SCarl	HAM	Hiller	Raven	Model 360
H-12L(UH)	CA	Redwo	HAM	Hiller	Raven	
H-13	AL	Starke	CBM	Bell	Sioux	Bell 47, 0-21455
H-13	CA	Ramona	CR	Bell	Sioux	2666, N7576, Bell 47G-2A
H-13	GA	Hampton	AAHF	Bell	Sioux	Bell 47
H-13	IN	Mentone	LDBAM	Bell	Sioux	Bell 47
H-13	KS	Liberal	MAAM	Bell	Sioux	Bell 47
H-13	NJ	Rio Grande	NASW	Bell	Sioux	Bell 47
H-13	NJ	Teter	AHoFNJ	Bell	Sioux	Bell 47
H-13	SD	Rapid	SDA&SM	Bell	Sioux	
H-13	WI	Kenos	KMM	Bell	Souix	
H-13 (HTL-2)	MI	Ypsil	YAF	Bell	Air Ambulance	
H-13 (OH)	CA	SanLu	CSLO	Bell	Sioux	Bell 47
H-13 (OH)	CO	CO.Sp	FCBA	Bell	Sioux	
H-13B(OH)	AL	Ozark	USAAM	Bell	Sioux	48- 827, Bell 47
H-13E(HTL-4)	FL	Pensa	USNAM	Bell	Air Ambulance	128911
H-13E(HTL-4)	VA	Quant	MCAGM	Bell	Air Ambulance	128635
H-13E(OH)	AL	Ozark	USAAM	Bell	Sioux 51-14193	Bell 47
H-13E(OH)	KY	FKnox	PMoC&A	Bell	Sioux	Bell 47
H-13E(OH)	NM	Albuq	KAFB	Bell	Sioux	Bell 47
H-13E(OH)	OK	Oklah	45IDM	Bell	Sioux	Bell 47
H-13E(OH)	WA	Seattle	MoF	Bell	Sioux	51-14030, N795
H-13H(VH)	CA	Atwater	CAM	Bell	Sioux	Bell 47
H-13(UH)	CO	Denve	JWDAS	Bell	Sioux	
H-13J(UH)	OH	Dayto	USAFM	Bell	Sioux	57-2728,Bell 47
H-13J(VH)	MD	Silve	PEGF	Bell	Sioux	Bell 47, "Eisenhower"
H-13M(TH)	GA	Warner Robin	MoF	Bell	Sioux	142376, Bell 47
H-13M(TH)(HTL-6)	FL	Pensa	USNAM	Bell	Sioux	142377, 18, Bell 47
H-13N(TH)(HTL-7)	AZ	Tucso	PAM	Bell	Sioux	Sn 145842
H-13P(UH)	GA	Warner Robin	MoF	Bell	Sioux	143143, Bell 47
H-13S(OH)	NY	NYC	ISASM	Bell	Sioux	Bell 47
H-13T	UT	Ogden	HAFBM	Bell	Sioux	Bell 47
H-13T(TH)	AL	Ozark	USAAM	Bell	Sioux	67-17024, Bell 47
H-13T(TH)	IL	Linco	HIFM	Bell	Sioux	Bell 47
H-19 (CH)	AL	Mobile	BMP	Sikorsky	Chickasaw	554239
H-19 (CH)	CA	SanLu	CSLO	Sikorsky	Chickasaw	
H-19B(UH)	AZ	Tucso	PAM	Sikorsky	Chickasaw	52-7537, N2256G
H-19B(UH)	CA	Ramona	CR	Sikorsky	Chickasaw	57-5962, N2256G
H-19B(UH)	OH	Dayto	USAFM	Sikorsky	Chickasaw	52-7587, "Whirl-O-Way"

Model	State	City	Museum	Manufacturer	Name	Serial
H-19B(UH)-SI(S-55)	BC-C	Langley	CMoF	Sikorsky	Chickasaw	53-4414
H-19B(UH) (S-55)	MT	Helena	MHSM	Sikorsky	Chickasaw	
H-19B(UH)-ST	NE	Ashland	SACM	Sikorsky	Chickasaw	53-4426
H-19D(UH)	VA	FtEus	USATM	Sikorsky	Chickasaw	56-1550
H-19D(UH)	AL	Ozark	USAAM	Sikorsky	Chickasaw	55-5239
H-19D(UH)	CA	Ramona	CR	Sikorsky	Chickasaw	54-1409
H-19D(UH)	FL	Tittusville	VACM	Sikorsky	Chickasaw	
H-19D(HH)	GA	Warner Robin	MoF	Sikorsky	Chickasaw	55-3328
H-19D(UH)	ND	Grand	GFAFB	Sikorsky	Chickasaw	
H-19E(CH)(HRS-2)	FL	Pensa	USNAM	Sikorsky	Chickasaw	130151
H-19E(CH)(HRS-3)	FL	Pensa	USNAM	Sikorsky	Chickasaw	142432
H-19F(UH)	NM	Albuq	KAFB	Sikorsky	Chickasaw	
H-19G(HH)(H04S-1)	SC	Flore	FA&MM	Sikorsky	Chickasaw	USCG
H-20 (XH)	OH	Dayto	USAFM	McDonnell		46-689, "Lt Henery"
H-21	BC-C	Langley	CMoF	Piasecki	Workhorse	Model 44B
H-21	PA	WChester	AHM	Piasecki	Workhorse	
H-21B(UH)	CA	River	MFAM	Piasecki	Workhorse	53-4326
H-21B(CH)	AL	Mobil	BMP	Piasecki	Workhorse	515859
H-21B(CH)	CA	Fairf	TAFB	Piasecki	Workhorse	
H-21B(CH)	CA	Ramona	CR	Piasecki	Workhorse	54-4001
H-21B(CH)	CO	Puebl	PWAM	Piasecki	Workhorse	53-4347
H-21B(CH)	GA	Warner Robin	MoF	Piasecki	Workhorse	52-8685
H-21B(CH)	NM	Albuq	KAFB	Piasecki	Workhorse	
H-21B(CH)	OH	Dayto	USAFM	Piasecki	Workhorse	51-15857
H-21B(CH)	PA	Readi	MAAM	Piasecki	Workhorse	
H-21B(CH)	SC	Flore	FA&MM	Piasecki	Workhorse	
H-21B(CH)	TX	FWort	PMoT	Piasecki	Workhorse	
H-21B(CH)	UT	Ogden	HAFBM	Piasecki	Workhorse	
H-21C	WA	Seattle	MoF	Piasecki	Workhorse	53-4366, N6797, 53-4329
H-21B(CH)(PD-22)	WI	Oshko	EAAAM	Piasecki	Workhorse	N57968, 28683
H-21-B-PH(CH)	BC-C	Langley	CMoF	Piasecki	Workhorse	53-4366, N6792, Model 142
H-21-B-PH(CH)	NE	Ashland	SACM	Piasecki	Workhorse	52-8676
H-21C(CH)	AZ	Tucso	PAM	Piasecki	Workhorse	56-2159
H-21C(CH)	CA	Rosam	EAFB	Piasecki	Workhorse	52-8623
H-21C(CH)	CA	Sacra	McCelAFB	Piasecki	Workhorse	51-15886
H-21C(CH)	CO	Aurora	WOTR	Piasecki	Workhorse	
H-21C(CH)	NY	NYC	ISASM	Piasecki	Workhorse	
H-21C(CH)	VA	FtEus	USATM	Piasecki	Shawnee	56-2130
H-23 (OH)	CA	SanLu	CSLO	Hiller	Raven	
H-23 (OH)	GA	Hampton	AAHF	Hiller	Raven	
H-23 (OH)	LA	New Orleans	FoJBMM	Hiller	Raven	51-16336
H-23 (OH)	NY	NYC	ISASM	Hiller	Raven	
H-23A(OH)	AL	Ozark	USAAM	Hiller	Raven	51-3975, G
H-23A(OH)	CA	SCarl	HAM	Hiller	Raven	
H-23A(OH)	KS	Topeka	CAM	Hiller	Raven	
H-23B(OH)	CA	Ramona	CR	Hiller	Raven	729, N7299
H-23B(OH)	CA	SCarl	HAM	Hiller	Raven	
H-23B(OH)	GA	Hampton	AAHF	Hiller	Raven	
H-23B(OH)	KY	FKnox	PMoC&A	Hiller	Raven	
H-23B(OH)	TX	FWort	PMoT	Hiller	Raven	
H-23B(OH)	VA	FtEus	USATM	Hiller	Raven	51-16168
H-23C(OH)	CA	SCarl	HAM	Hiller	Raven	
H-23C(OH)	GA	Warner Robin	MoF	Hiller	Raven	56-421
H-23C(OH)	OK	Oklah	45IDM	Hiller	Raven	55-4124
H-23D(OH)	CA	SCarl	HAM	Hiller	Raven	
H-23F(OH)	AL	Ozark	USAAM	Hiller	Raven	62-12508
H-23F(OH)	CA	SCarl	HAM	Hiller	Raven	
H-23F(OH)	OK	FtSil	USAFAM	Hiller	Raven	62-3791
H-23G(OH)	CT	Winds	NEAM	Hiller	Raven	
H-23G(OH)	HI	Wheeler	WAFB	Hiller	Raven	64-15245
H-25 (UH)	MI	Kalam	KAHM	Piasecki	Army Mule	
H-25A	AL	Ozark	USAAM	Piasecki	Army Mule	51-16616
H-25A	CA	Ramona	CR	Piasecki	Retriever	51-16621
H-25A(UH)	VA	FtEus	USATM	Piasecki	Army Mule	130043
H-25C(OH)	GA	Warner Robin	MoF	Piasecki	Army Mule	
H-26 (XH)	CA	Ramona	CR	American Helicopter	Jet Jeep	
H-26 (XH)	OH	Dayto	USAFM	American Helicopter	Jet Jeep	
H-26A(XH)	AL	Ozark	USAAM	American Helicopter	Jet Jeep	50-1840
H-30(YH)	CA	Ramona	CR	Jovair	McCulloch	
H-31(YH)	CA	Ramona	CR	Doman		
H-31(YH)(LZ-5)	CA	SCarl	HAM	Doman	Carbie	
H-32(YH) See HOE						
H-32	CA	Ramona	CR	Hiller	Hornet	53-4663
H-32	CA	Ramona	CR	Hiller	Hornet	15
H-34(HSS-1)	CA	Alameda	USSHM	Sikorsky	Seahorse	140136
H-34	CA	Alameda Pt	USSHM	Sikorsky	Seahorse	
H-34	CA	Chino	PoFAM	Sikorsky	Seahorse	
H-34	FL	Kissi	FTWAM	Sikorsky	Seahorse	
H-34	GA	Calhoun	MAM	Sikorsky	Seahorse	
H-34 (CH)	AL	Ozark	USAAM	Sikorsky	Choctaw	65-7992
H-34 (CH)	CA	Chino	YAM	Sikorsky	Choctaw	
H-34 (CH)	CA	Fairf	TAFB	Sikorsky	Choctaw	
H-34 (CH)	CA	SanLu	CSLO	Sikorsky	Choctaw	
H-34 (CH)	MN	Blaine	AWAM	Sikorsky	Choctaw	14173
H-34 (CH)	NC	Camp Lejeune	CLVC	Sikorsky	Choctaw	
H-34 (CH)	SC	Flore	FA&MM	Sikorsky	Choctaw	
H-34 (HH)	NM	Albuq	KAFB	Sikorsky	Seahorse	
H-34 (UH)	NY	NYC	ISASM	Sikorsky	Seahorse	
H-34 (UH)	TX	FWort	NASFWJRB	Sikorsky	Seahorse	
H-34A	FL	Clear	FMAM	Sikorsky	Seahorse	
H-34A(CH)	AL	Ozark	USAAM	Sikorsky	Choctaw	53-4526
H-34A(CH)	WY	Greyb	H&PA	Sikorsky	Choctaw	
H-34A(VCH)	AL	Ozark	USAAM	Sikorsky	Army One	56-4320
H-34C(CH)	NC	Charlotte	CAM	Sikorsky	Choctaw	55-4496
H-34C(CH)	VA	FtEus	USATM	Sikorsky	Choctaw	64-14203
H-34C(VH)	AZ	Tucso	PAM	Sikorsky	Seahorse	57-1684
H-34C(VH)	CA	Rosam	EAFB	Sikorsky	Seahorse	57-1726
H-34D(LH)	CT	Winds	NEAM	Sikorsky	Seahorse	
H-34D(UH)	CA	Miramar	FLAM	Sikorsky	Seahorse	YP, HMM-163
H-34D(UH)	MD	Silve	PEGF	Sikorsky	Seahorse	
H-34D(UH)	PA	Willow	WGNAS	Sikorsky	Seahorse	
H-34D(UH)	PA	Readi	MAAM	Sikorsky	Seahorse	
H-34D(UH)(HUS-1)	FL	Pensa	USNAM	Sikorsky	Seahorse	X0, 657, 150227, 1

H-34E(HH)	GA	Warner Robin	MoF	Sikorsky	Seahorse	
H-34G(UH)	CA	Rosam	EAFB	Sikorsky	Seahorse	137856
H-34J	UT	Ogden	HAFBM	Sikorsky	Seahorse	
H-34J(HH)	AZ	Phoen	LAFB	Sikorsky	Seahorse	
H-34J(HH)	GA	Warner Robin	MoF	Sikorsky	Seabat	148963
H-34(SH)	SC	MtPleasant	PPM	Sikorsky	Seabat	14171
H-37 (CH)(HR2S-1)	FL	Pensa	USNAM	Sikorsky	Mojave	145864
H-37B(CH)	AL	Ozark	USAAM	Sikorsky	Mojave	55-644
H-37B(CH)	AZ	Tucso	PAM	Sikorsky	Mojave	56-1005, "Tired Dude"
H-37B(CH)	VA	FtEus	USATM	Sikorsky	Mojave	57-1651
H-41A(YH)	AL	Ozark	USAAM	Cessna	Seneca	56-4244
H-43 (HH)(HOK-1)	CA	Atwater	CAM	Kaman	Huskie	62-4513
H-43B(HH)(HOK-1)	CT	Winds	NEAM	Kaman	Huskie	289
H-43B(HH)(HOK-1)	DE	Dover	AMCM	Kaman	Huskie	4532
H-43B(HH)(HOK-1)	GA	Warner Robin	MoF	Kaman	Huskie	58-1853
H-43B(HH)(HOK-1)	NM	Albuq	KAFB	Kaman	Huskie	
H-43B(HH)(HOK-1)	TX	FWort	PMoT	Kaman	Huskie	
H-43B(HH)(HOK-1)	UT	Ogden	HAFBM	Kaman	Huskie	
H-43D(OH)(HOK-1)	AZ	Tucso	PAM	Kaman	Huskie	139974
H-43F(HH)(HOK-1)	AZ	Tucso	PAM	Kaman	Huskie	62-4531
H-43F(HH)(HOK-1)	OH	Dayto	USAFM	Kaman	Huskie	60-263
H-44 (XH)	MD	Silve	PEFG	Hiller	Commuter	
H-44(UH)	CA	SCarl	HAM	Hiller	Commuter	
H-46(HH)	CA	San Diego	SDACM	Boeing	Sea Knight	150954
H-46F	CA	Ramona	CR	Boeing	Sea Knight	980461-1101-01
H-47 (CH)	CA	SanLu	CSLO	Boeing-Vertol	Chinook	
H-47 (CH)	CO	Puebl	PWAM	Boeing-Vertol	Chinook	
H-47 (CH)	VA	Eustis	USATM	Boeing-Vertol	Chinook	59-94984
H-47A(CH)	AL	Huntsville		Boeing-Vertol	Chinook	
H-47A(CH)	AL	Ozark	USAAM	Boeing-Vertol	Chinook	60-3451 (64-13149) "Easy Money"
H-47(HK)	OK	Tulsa	TA&SC	Bell		
H-51A(XH)	AL	Ozark	USAAM	Lockheed	Rigid Rotor	61-51262
H-51A(XH)	AL	Ozark	USAAM	Lockheed	Compound	61-51263
H-52A(HH)	AZ	Tucso	PAM	Sikorsky	Seaguard USCG	62-71, N8224Q, 1390, USCG Polar Star
H-52A(HH)	CT	Winds	NEAM	Sikorsky	Seaguard USCG	1428, Polar Star
H-52A(HH)	FL	Pensa	USNAM	Sikorsky	Seaguardian	USCG Polar Star, CGNR1355
H-52A(HH)	IL	Chica	MoS&I	Sikorsky	Seaguard USCG	Polar Star
H-52A(HH)	MI	Mt Clemens	SMAM	Sikorsky	Seaguard USCG	1466, Polar Star
H-52A(HH)	NJ	Rio Grande	NASW	Sikorsky	Seaguard USCG	
H-52A(HH)	NJ	Teterboro	AHoFNJ	Sikorsky	Seaguard USCG	
H-52A(HH)	NY	NYC	ISASM	Sikorsky	Seaguard USCG	Polar Star, 1429
H-52A(HH)	PA	Readi	MAAM	Sikorsky	Seaguard USCG	Polar Star
H-52A(HH)(S-62)	PA	WChester	AHM	Sikorsky	Seaguard USCG	
H-52A(HH)(S-62)	WA	Seattle	MoF	Sikorsky	Seaguard USCG	CGNR1415
H-53A(CH)	CA	Miramar	FLAM	Sikorsky	Sea Stallion	
H-53A(CH)	FL	Pensa	USNAM	Sikorsky	Sea Stallion	151687
H-53A(CH)	HI	Kaneohe	MB	Sikorsky	Sea Stallion	
H-53A(CH)	KS	Topeka	CAM	Sikorsky	Sea Stallion	
H-53A(CH)	MD	Lexington	PRNAM	Sikorsky	Sea Stallion	151686
H-53A(UH)	PA	Willow	WGNAS	Sikorsky	Sea Stallion	
H-53A(CH)	VA	Norfolk	NASN	Sikorsky	Sea Stallion	
H-53A(CH)	VA	Quantico	MCAGM	Sikorsky	Sea Stallion	151692
H-53D(RH)	HI	Kaneohe	KBMCAS	Sikorsky	Sea Stallion	158748, 1st MAW ASE
H-53D(RH)	NJ	Lumberton	AVM	Sikorsky	Sea Stallion	158690
H-54 (CH)	MS	McLaurin	AFM	Sikorsky	Tarhe (Skycrane)	
H-54 (CH)	NC	Camp Lejeune	CLVC	Sikorsky	Tarhe (Skycrane)	
H-54 (CH)	WI	Brist	Museum	Sikorsky	Tarhe (Skycrane)	
H-54 (CH)	WI	Kenos	KMM	Sikorsky	Tarhe (Skycrane)	446, "The Bull Stops Here"
H-54 (CH)	WI	Kenos	KMM	Sikorsky	Tarhe (Skycrane)	486
H-54 (S-64)	OR	McMinnville	EAEC	Sikorsky	Tarhe (Skycrane)	
H-54A(CH)	AZ	Tucso	PAM	Sikorsky	Tarhe (Skycrane)	68-18437, 64039
H-54A(CH)	KS	Topek	CAM	Sikorsky	Tarhe (Skycrane)	
H-54A(CH)	VA	FtEus	USATM	Sikorsky	Tarhe (Skycrane)	64-14203
H-54B(CH)	AL	Birmingham	SMoF	Sikorsky	Tarhe (Skycrane)	
H-54B(CH)	CT	Winds	NEAM	Sikorsky	Tarhe (Skycrane)	
H-54B(CH)	KS	Topeka	MoKNG	Sikorsky	Tarhe (Skycrane)	
H-54B(S-64)	WY	Greyb	H&PA	Sikorsky	Tarhe (Skycrane)	
H-54D(CH)	GA	Spart	GSMA	Sikorsky	Tarhe (Skycrane)	
H-55A(TH)	AL	Ozark	USAAM	Hughes	Osage	67-16795
H-55A(TH)	AZ	Tucso	PAM	Hughes	Osage	67-18350
H-55A(TH)	AZ	Tucso	PAM	Hughes	Osage	67-18273
H-55A(TH)	AZ	Tucso	PAM	Hughes	Osage	67-18203
H-55A(TH)	AZ	Tucso	PAM	Hughes	Osage	67-18017
H-55A(TH)	AZ	Tucso	PAM	Hughes	Osage	67-118133
H-55A(TH)	CA	Ramona	CR	Hughes	Osage	291095, N125B
H-55A(TH)	CA	Ramona	CR	Hughes	Osage	N598RF
H-55A(TH)	PA	WChester	AHM	Hughes	Osage	
H-55A(TH)	OR	McMinnville	EAM	Hughes	Osage	38-0002, N79P, Huges 269A
H-55A(TH)	VA	FtEus	USATM	Hughes	Osage	67-16944
H-56A(AH)	AL	Ozark	USAAM	Lockheed	Cheyenne	66- 8830
H-57A(TH)	FL	Pensa	USNAM	Bell	Sea Ranger	157363 O4-E
H-58(OH)	HI	Oahu	WAFB	Bell	Kiowa	
H-58(OH)	KY	Lexington	AMoK	Bell	Kiowa	
H-58(OH)	LA	New Orleans	FoJBMM	Bell	Kiowa	70-15426
H-58(OH)	KS	Topeka	MoKNG	Bell	Kiowa	
H-58(OH)	MB-C	Winnipeg	WRCAFB	Bell	Kiowa	
H-58(OH)	ON-C	Kingston	CFB	Bell	Kiowa	
H-58(OH)	ON-C	Trenton	CFB	Bell	Kiowa	136408
H-58(OH)	RI	NKing	QAM	Bell	Kiowa	0-15117
H-58(OH)	TX	Denton	H10FM	Bell	Kiowa	
H-58A(OH)	HI	Wheeler	WAFB	Bell	Kiowa	0-15358
H-58A(OH)	CA	Riverside	MAFM	Bell	Kiowa	70-15258
H-58A(OH)	OK	Oklah	45IDM	Bell	Kiowa	
H-58A(OH)	OH	N Canton	MAM	Bell	Kiowa	
H-58A(OH)	TX	FWort	NASFWJRB	Bell	Kiowa	
H-58A(OH)	TX	FWort	VFM	Bell	Kiowa	
H-61A(YU)	AL	Ozark	USAAM	Boeing-Vertol	UTTAS	73-21656
H-63 (YAH)	AL	Ozark	USAAM	Bell	Model 409	74-22247, Bell 409
H-64A(AH)	AL	Huntsville	RA	Hughes	Apache	
H-64(YAH)	AL	Ozark	USAAM	Hughes	Apache	74-22249
H-65 (AH)	KY	FKnox	FC	Hughes		
HA-200A	FL	Titusville	VACM	Hispano	Cairo	
HA-200B	MD	Silve	PEGF	Hispano	Cairo	

HA-1112	AZ	Grand Canyon	PoFGCVA	Hispano	Buchon	
HA-1112	MB-C	Winni	WCAM	Hispano	Buchon	
HA-1112	MI	Kalam	KAHM	Hispano	Buchon	C4K-19
HA-1112	TX	Midla	CAFFM	Hispano	Buchon	
HA-1112	WI	Oshko	EAAAAM	Hispano	Buchon	N109BF
Halberstadt CL-IV	AL	Gunte	LGARFM	Halberstadt		
Halberstadt CL.II	OH	Dayto	USAFM	Halberstadt		
Halberstadt D.III	AL	Gunte	LGARFM	Halberstadt		
Half Track M3	AL	Starke	CBM	Armored Vehicle		
Half Track M3	LA	New Orleans	DDM	Armored Vehicle		
Half Track M16	OH	Hubbard	WWIIVM	Armored Vehicle		A-27
Hall Cherokee II	NY	Elmira	NSM	Hall	Cherokee II RM	N1658
Hall	NY	Elmira	NSM	Hall	Ibex	N63P
Hanson-Meyer Quickie	CT	Winds	NEAM	Hanson-Meyer	Quickie	
Harbinger Sailplane	ON-C	Ottaw	CAM	Harbinger	Sailplane	
Hardly Abelson	WI	Oshlosh	EAAAAM	Hardly	Abelson	
Harlow PJC-2	WI	Oshko	EAAAAM	Harlow		N3947B
Harrison Mini-Mack	AL	Birmingham	SMoF	Harrison	Mini-Mack	
Hartman 1910	NE	Minde	HWPV	Hartman		
Hawk	CO	CSpri	EJPSCM			
Hawk 2	WI	Oshko	EAAAAM	Haufe Dale	Hawk 2	N18278
Hawk Major M.2.W	WI	Oshko	EAAAAM	Miles	Hawk Major	CF-NXT
Hawker FB.1	NY	NYC	ISASM	Hawker	Sea Hawk	
Hawker FB.1	WI	Oshko	EAAAAM	Hawker	Sea Hawk	N83SH
Hawker FB.11	AB-C	Calga	NMoA	Hawker	Sea Fury	
Hawker FB.11	WA	Olympia	OFM	Hawker	Sea Fury	
Hawker FB.11	ON-C	Ottaw	CAM	Hawker	Sea Fury	
Hawker FB.11	TX	Breck	BAM	Hawker	Sea Fury	
Hawker FB.11 Fuse	TN	Memph	LS	Hawker	Sea Fury	
Hawker FB.11	WA	Olympia	OFM	Hawker	Sea Hawk	Side # 737
Hawker Hind	ON-C	Ottaw	CAM	Hawker	Hind	
Hawker Hunter	TX	Ft Worth	VFM	Hawker	Hunter	
Hawker Hunter Mk.9	ON-C	Trenton	RCAFMM	Hawker	Hunter	J-4029, Tail 30
Hawker Hunter Mk.51	WI	Oshko	EAAAAM	Hawker	Hunter	N611JR
Hawker Hunter Mk.58A	PA	Readi	MAAM	Hawker	Hunter	
Hawker Hunter Mk.58A Rep	ON-C	Hamilton	CWH	Hawker	Hunter	
Hawker	AB-C	Wetas	RM	Hawker	Hurricane	
Hawker Hurricane	FL	Polk City	FoF	Hawker	Hurricane	
Hawker Hurricane	MB-C	Brandon	CATPM	Hawker	Hurricane	
Hawker Hurricane Mk.IIB	ON-C	Hamilton	CWH	K-W Surplus, Kitchener	Hurricane	C-GCWH, P3069, YOA Replica
Hawker Hurricane	ON-C	Ottaw	CAM	Hawker	Hurricane	5584
Hawker Hurricane Rep	ON-C	Toronto	TAM	Hawker	Hurricane	
Hawker Hurricane	SK-C	MJaw	WDM	Hawker	Hurricane	
Hawker Hurricane	TX	Addison	CFM	Hawker	Hurricane	
Hawker Hurricane	TX	Hawki	RRSA	Hawker	Hurricane	5481, N678DP, Side #P2970, Tail USX
Hawker Hurricane Mk.II	CA	Santa Monica	MoF	Hawker	Hurricane	5390
Hawker Hurricane Mk.II	OH	Dayto	USAFM	Hawker	Hurricane	RCAF5667, N2549
Hawker Hurricane Mk.II	VA	Suffolk	FF	Hawker	Hurricane	Partial Static Project
Hawker Hurricane Mk.IIB	BC-C	Langley	CMoF	Hawker	Hurricane	N68RW, CCF-96
Hawker Hurricane Mk.IIB	TX	Galve	LSFM	Hawker	Hurricane	
Hawker Hurricane Mk.IIC	MD	Silve	PEGF	Hawker	Hurricane	
Hawker Hurricane Mk.X	CA	Chino	PoFAM	Hawker	Hurricane	
Hawker Hurricane Mk.XIIb	AB-C	Calga	AMoC	Hawker	Hurricane	
Hawker Hurricane Rep	AB-C	Edmonton	AAM	Hawker	Hurricane	
Hawker Tempest Mk.2	FL	Lakeland	SNF	Hawker	Tempest	
Hawker-Siddeley Kestrel	DC	Washi	NA&SM	Hawker-Siddeley	Kestral	
Haye Valmer	BC-C	Langley	CMoF	Haye	Valmer	
HD-1	CA	Chino	PoFAM	Hanriot	Scout	
HD-1	FL	Pensa	USNAM	Hanriot	Scout	A5625
HD-1	NY	Rhine	ORA	Hanriot	Scout	
HD-4 Remains	NS-C	Badde	AGBNHP	Hanriot	Hydrofoil	19
He 100	CA	Chino	PoFAM	Heinkel		
He 111/CASA 2.111	WA	Eastsound	FHC	Heinkel	Dresden	N11105
He 111/CASA 2.111	WA	Seattle	MoF	Heinkel	Dresden	G
He 111/CASA 2.111D	OH	Dayto	USAFM	Heinkel	Dresden	
He 111/CASA 2.111E	TX	Addison	CFM	Heinkel	Dresden	N99230
He 162	ON-C	Ottaw	CAM	Heinkel	Volksjager	120076
He 162	ON-C	Ottaw	CAM	Heinkel	Volksjager	120086
He 162A	MD	Silve	PEGF	Heinkel	Volksjager	
He 162A-1	CA	Chino	PoFAM	Heinkel	Volksjager	
He 219A-3	MD	Silve	PEGF	Heinkel	Uhu	
Headwind JD-HWL-7	AR	Little Rock	AEC	Headwind	Ultrlight	
Heath Feather	WI	Oshko	EAAAAM	Heath	Feather	
Heath Center Wing 115	KY	Lexington	AVoK	Heath	Center Wing 115	NR2881
Heath Parasol	CT	Winds	NEAM	Heath	Parasol	
Heath Parasol	MI	Kalamazoo	KAHM	Heath	Parasol	
Heath Parasol	NC	Hende	WNCAM	Heath	Parasol	
Heath Parasol	NY	Rhine	ORA	Heath	Parasol	
Heath Super Parasol	VA	Sands	VAM	Heath	Parasol	Sn 31919
Heath Parasol	WA	Seattle	MoF	Heath	Parasol	
Heath Parasol 5	WI	Oshko	EAAAAM	Heath	Parasol	
Heath Parasol	NE	Minde	HWPV	Heath	Parasol	
Heath Parasol Rep	NY	Mayvi	DA	Heath	Parasol	
Heath Super Parasol	FL	Lakel	SFAF	Heath	Super Parasol	N88EG
Heath Super Parasol	WI	Oshko	EAAAAM	Heath-Scimone	Super Parasol	N953M
Hegy R.C.H.I.	WI	Oshko	EAAAAM	Hegy		N9360, "El Chuparosa"
Helio 1A	MD	Silve	PEGF	Helio	Courier	
Helton Lark 95	AZ	Tucson	PAM	Helton	Lark 95	Man Sn 9512, N1512H
Henderschott	WI	Oshko	EAAAAM	Henderschott	Monoplane	
Henderson Highwing	WI	Oshko	EAAAAM	Folkerts	Henderson	8902
Henri Farman III	ME	Owls Head	OHTM	Henri Farman		
Herring-Arnot	NY	Elmira	NSM	Herring-Arnot		
Herring-Curtiss	NY	Garde	CoAM	Herring-Curtiss	Golden Glider	
Hill Hummer	WI	Oshko	EAAAAM	Hill	Hummer	N90381, "Pete"
Hiller Camel	CA	Ramona	CR	Hiller	Camel	
Hiller Flying Crane	CA	Redwo	HAM	Hiller	Flying Crane	
Hiller Flying Platform	AZ	Tucson	PAM	Hiller	Flying Platform	
Hiller Helicopter	CA	Chino	PoFAM	Hiller		
Hiller 360	CA	San Carlos	HAM	Hiller	360	
Hispano-Suiza	NY	River	TFAC	Hispano-Suiza		
Hisso Standard	MO	Maryland Hts	HARM	Hisso	Standard	
HJD-1(X)	MD	Silve	PEGF	McDonnell	Whirlaway	
HJD-1H(X)	MD	Silve	PEGF	McDonnell	Whirlaway	

HK-1	OR	McMinnville	EAEC	Hughes	Spruce Goose	NX37602
HM-14	WI	Oshko	EAAAAM	Mignet	Flying Flea	Pou du Ciel
HM-	FL	Lakeland	SNF	Midget	Flying Flea	
HM-290	BC-C	Langley	CMoF	Mignet	Pou du Ciel	
HM-360	WI	Oshko	EAAAAM	Mignet	Flying Flea	N360HM
HO-3B(YHO)	AL	Ozark	USAAM	Brantley		58-1496
HO-45	AK	Fairb	APAM	Hamilton	Metalplane	NC10002
HO-49	FL	Pensa	USNAM			1049
HO-6A(YH)	AL	Ozark	USAAM	Hughes	Cayuse	62- 4213
HO3S	VA	Quant	MCAGM	Sikorsky	Dragonfly	124344
HO3S-1(S-51)	BC-C	Langley	CMoF	Sikorsky	Dragonfly	N2842D, 124345, CF-FDF
HO3S-1(S-51)	NC	Charlotte	CAM	Sikorsky	Dragonfly	125136
HO3S-1G	AZ	Tucso	PAM	Sikorsky	Dragonfly	CG, 232, N4925E
HO4S (S-55)	FL	Pensa	USNAM	Sikorsky	Chickasaw	CGNR1258, 130151
HO4S-3	NS-C	Shear	CFBS	Sikorsky	Chickasaw	
HO4S-3	ON-C	Ottaw	CAM	Sikorsky	Chickasaw	
HO5S-1G(S-52)	CA	Ramona	CR	Sikorsky	Dragonfly	
HO5S-1G(S-52)	FL	Pensa	USNAM	Sikorsky	Dragonfly	N8003E, 125519
HO5S-1G(S-52)	PA	WChester	AHM	Sikorsky	Dragonfly	
HO5S-1G(S-52)	VA	Quantico	MCAGM	Sikorsky	Dragonfly	128610
HOE-1	CA	Hawth	WMoF	Hiller	Hornet	
HOE-1	MD	Silve	PEGF	Hiller	Hornet	
HOE-1(HJ-1)	CA	SCarl	HAM	Hiller	Hornet	
HOE-1(YH-32)	AL	Ozark	USAAM	Hiller	Hornet	55- 4965, "Sally Rand"
HOE-1(YH-32)	CA	SCarl	HAM	Hiller	Hornet	
HOE-1(YH-32)	WA	Seattle	MoF	Hiller	Hornet	55-4969
HOK-1	NC	Charlotte	CAM	Hiller	Hornet	139990
Homebuilt	AZ	Tucso	PAM		Homebuilt	
Homebuilt	NS-C	Halifax	ACAM		Scamp 1	
Horton Ho II	MD	Silve	PEGF	Horton	Flying Wing Glider	
Horton Ho III	MD	Silve	PEGF	Horton	Flying Wing Glider	
Horton Ho III-H	MD	Silve	PEGF	Horton	Flying Wing Glider	
Horton Ho IV	CA	Chino	PoFAM	Horton	Flying Wing Glider	
Horton Ho VI	MD	Silve	PEGF	Horton	Flying Wing Glider	
Hovercraft	NY	River	TFAC	Hovercraft	Hovercraft	
Howard 250	CA	Chino	PoFAM	Howard	Ero	
Howard	WA	Port Townsend	PTAM	Howard	Replica	1, N30154, "Mike"
Howard Pete	WI	Oshko	EAAAAM	Howard	Pete	N111PL, "Little Audrey"
HP-10	WI	Oshko	EAAAAM	Helisoar	Glider	N319Y
HP-8	NY	Elmira	NSM	Schreder	Airmate	N34Y
HP-10	NY	Elmira	NSM	Schreder		N4718G
HP-11A	NY	Elmira	NSM	Schreder	Airmate	N4777G
HP-16	NY	Elmira	NSM	Schreder		N45HP
HP-18	NY	Elmira	NSM	Schreder		N1YV
HP-18-LK Sailplane	WI	Oshko	EAAAAM	Bryan-Harris	Sailplane	N96326
HP-52	BC-C	Langley	CMoF	Handley-Page	Hampden	I, P, 5436, P5436
HP-52	ON-C	Trenton	RCAFMM	Handley-Page	Hampden	NA337
HRP-1	CT	Winds	NEAM	Piasecki	Rescuer	
HRP-1(X)	MD	Silve	PEGF	Piasecki	Rescuer	37969
HRP-3	IN	S Bend	JA			147608
HRS-1(S-55)	VA	Quant	MCAGM	Sikorsky	Chickasaw	127828
HRS-3(S-55)	CA	Miramar	FLAM	Sikorsky	Chickasaw	WW, MALS-16
HS-2L	ON-C	Ottaw	CAM	Curtiss		A-1876
HTK-1(K-125)	FL	Pensa	USNAM	Kaman		129313
HU- 1B	CA	Chino	YAM	Piasecki	Helicopter	147610, 147610
HU-16	AZ	Tucson	SA	Grumman	Albatross	MSN 090, N7026C
HU-16	AZ	Tucson	SA	Grumman	Albatross	131904, N7026X
HU-16	AZ	Tucson	SA	Grumman	Albatross	141271, N70258, MSN 418
HU-16	AZ	Tucson	SA	Grumman	Albatross	137933, N70275, MSN 406
HU-16	AZ	Tucson	TI	Grumman	Albatross	2132, N226GR, MSN 359
HU-16	AZ	Tucson	TI	Grumman	Albatross	N115FB, MSN 462
HU-16	AZ	Tucson	WIA	Grumman	Albatross	51-043, N7049D, MSN 119
HU-16	CT	New England	NEAM	Grumman	Albatross	*USCG 7218, MSN 310*
HU-16	FL	Ft Lauderdale	FL	Grumman	Albatross	N48318, MSN 244
HU-16	FL	Ft Lauderdale	FL	Grumman	Albatross	N113LA, MSN 219
HU-16	FL	Ft Lauderdale	FL	Grumman	Albatross	N43846, MSN 381
HU-16	FL	Ft Lauderdale	FL	Grumman	Albatross	N928J, MSN 401
HU-16	FL	Ft Lauderdale	FL	Grumman	Albatross	N42MY, MSN 464
HU-16	FL	Lantana		Grumman	Albatross	N43GL, MSN 367
HU-16	FL	Opa Locka		Grumman	Albatross	N49115, MSN 327
HU-16	FL	Opa Locka		Grumman	Albatross	141265, N7025V, MSN 412
HU-16	ID	Driggs	TAC	Grumman	Albatross	1906
HU-16	MA	Cape Cod	CGAS	Grumman	Albatross	USCG 7250, MSN 340
HU-16	MN	Blaine	ACBA	Grumman	Albatross	Owner: Patrick Harker
HU-16	NY	Brooklyn	NARF	Grumman	Albatross	
HU-16	NV	Carson City		Grumman	Albatross	51-067, N3395F, MSN 146
HU-16	NV	Carson City		Grumman	Albatross	N120FB, MSN 331
HU-16	NV	Carson City		Grumman	Albatross	N117FB, MSN 461
HU-16	NV	Carson City		Grumman	Albatross	141278, N20861, MSN 425
HU-16	VA	VA Beach	MAFB	Grumman	Albatross	USCG 7209, MSN 282
HU-16 (SA-16)	CA	Atwater	CAM	Stits	Albatross	
HU-16 (SA-16)	OK	Fredi	AAM	Stits	Albatross	
HU-16A	CA	SRosa	PCAM	Grumman	Albatross	
HU-16A	NM	Albuq	KAFB	Grumman	Albatross	USCG 1280, MSN 302
HU-16A(SA-16)	AZ	Mesa	CAFM	Grumman	Albatross	51-22, MSN 096
HU-16A(SA-16)	AZ	Tucso	PAM	Grumman	Albatross	51-22, MSN 096
HU-16B	CA	Sacra	McCelAFB	Grumman	Albatross	51-7209
HU-16B	GA	Warner Robin	MoF	Grumman	Albatross	51-7144
HU-16B	IL	Ranto	OCAM	Grumman	Albatross	51-7200
HU-16B	MD	Balti	BANG	Grumman	Albatross	
HU-16B	OH	Dayto	USAFM	Grumman	Albatross	51-5282
HU-16B	SC	Flore	FA&MM	Grumman	Albatross	51-7212, MSN 281
HU-16B	TX	FWort	PMoT	Grumman	Albatross	50-17176
HU-16B	TX	Midla	CAFFM	Grumman	Albatross	
HU-16B-GR	NE	Ashland	SACM	Grumman	Albatross	51-0006
HU-16E	AL	Mobil	BMP	Grumman	Albatross	2129
HU-16E	AZ	Phoen	LAFB	Grumman	Albatross	
HU-16E	CA	Riverside	MFAM	Grumman	Albatross	1293, "Cape Cod"
HU-16E	CT	Winds	NEAM	Grumman	Albatross	
HU-16E	FL	Pensa	USNAM	Grumman	Albatross	CGNR7236, 7236
HU-16E	NY	NYC	ISASM	Grumman	Albatross	
HU-16E	TX	Abile	DLAP	Grumman	Albatross	51-7251
Huber 101-1 Aero	WA	Seattle	MoF	Huber	Aero	001

148

Huff-Daland Duster	AL	Birmi	Southe	Huff-Daland	Duster	
Hughes Helicopter	WI	Kenos	KMM	Hughes	Helicopter	
HUK	CA	Ramona	CR	Kaman		
HUM-1	AZ	Tucson	PAM	McCulloch		133817, N4072K2
HUP-1(UH-25)	CA	Alameda	USSHM	Piasecki	Retriever	124915
HUP-1	CA	Ramona	CR	Piasecki	Retriever	124925
HUP-1	CT	Winds	NEAM	Piasecki	Retriever	7228
HUP-1	FL	Kissi	FTWAM	Piasecki	Retriever	
HUP-2(H-25A)	AZ	Tucso	PAM	Piasecki	Retriever	134434, N8SA
HUP-2	AZ	Tucso	PAM	Piasecki	Retriever	N8SA
HUP-2	CA	Chino	YAM	Piasecki	Retriever	
HUP-2	CA	Rosam	EAFB	Piasecki	Retriever	130059
HUP-2	CA	Miramar	FLAM	Piasecki	Retriever	
HUP-2	PA	WChes	AHM	Piasecki	Retriever	
HUP-2(H-25)	CT	Winds	NEAM	Piasecki	Retriever	
HUP-3	KS	Liberal	MAAM	Piasecki	Retriever	
HUP-3	MI	Kalam	KAHM	Piasecki	Retriever	146700, 51-16607
HUP-3	ON-C	Ottaw	CAM	Piasecki	Retriever	51-16623
HUP-3 PD-18	BC-C	Langley	CMoF	Piasecki	Retriever	51-16621
HUP-3(H-25A)	AZ	Tucso	PAM	Piasecki	Retriever	147595, 51-16608
HUP-3(UH-25C)	FL	Pensa	USNAM	Piasecki	Retriever	N4953S, 147607
Hutter 17	NY	Elmira	NSM	Hutter		WB153624, CF-RCD, 1934
HV2A	MD	Silve	PEGF	Herrick	Convertaplane	
Hwaker Hurricane	WY	Jackson	GWFM	Hawker	Hurricane	
Hydro-Kite Gallauder	DC	Washi	NA&SM	Gallauder	Hydro-Kite	
Hyper Light Hang Glider	AZ	Tucso	PAM	Hyper Light	Hyper Light	
I-15bis	VA	Suffolk	FF	Polikarpov		#7
I-16 Rata	VA	Suffolk	FF	Polikarpov	Rata	
I-16 Rata	WA	Eastsound	FHC	Polikarpov	Rata	
Icarus Hang Glider	AZ	Tucso	PAM	Icarus	Hang Glider	
Icarus I	MD	Silve	PEGF	Icarus		
ICBM	AL	Mobile	BMP	Redstone	Arsenal Redstone	
ICBM	OH	Dayton	USAFM	Redstone	Hard Mobile Launcher	
Ikarus Aero 3A	CA	Oakla	OWAM	Ikarus	Aero	
Ikarus Aero 3A	FL	Miami	WOM	Ikarus	Aero	
Ikenga 530Z Autogiro	MD	Silve	PEGF	Gittens	Autogiro	
Ilyushin IL-14P	CA	Santa Rosa	PCAM	Ilyushin	Model SO	1954
Ilyushin IL-2m3	AZ	Tucson	PAM	Ilyushin	Shturmovik	
Ilyushin IL-2m3	MD	Silver Hill	PEGF	Ilyushin	Shturmovik	
Ilyushin	NV	Reno	Steade	Ilyushin	Model SO	
Ingram/Foster Biplane	NM	Albuq	AA	Ingram-Foster	Biplane	
Insitu Aerosonde	WA	Seattle	MoF	Insitu	Aerosonde	
J-1	CA	San Diego	SDAM	Standard		1598, N2826D
J-1	FL	Polk	FoF	Standard		
J-1	MD	Silve	PEFG	Standard		
J-1	MD	Silve	PEGF	Standard		
J-1	ME	OwlsH	OHTM	Standard		
J-1	ND	WFarg	Bonanzav	Standard		
J-1	NY	Buffa	B&ECHM	Standard		
J-1	NY	Rhine	ORA	Standard		
J-1	OH	Dayto	USAFM	Standard		1141
J-1 Fabric Covered	OH	Dayto	USAFM	Standard		Fabric Covered
J-1	PA	Bethel	GAAM	Standard		
J-1	WI	Oshko	EAAAAM	Standard		N6948
J-2	AZ	Tucso	PAM	McCulloch	Super Gyroplane	Man Sn 019, N4309G
J-2	IA	Greenfield	IAM	Taylor	Cub	
J-2	IL	Harva	BA	Taylor	Cub	
J-2	KS	Liberal	MAAM	McCulloch	Gyro-Plane	
J-2	MD	College Park	CPAM	Taylor	Cub	NC16769
J-2	MD	Hager	HRegAirP	Taylor	Cub	
J-2	NC	Hende	WNCAM	Piper	Cub	NC16315
J-2	ND	Minot	DTAM	Piper	Cub	
J-2	NE	Minde	HWPV	Taylor	Cub	
J-2	NY	Mayvi	DA	Taylor	Cub	
J-2	NY	Niagara Falls	NAM	Taylor	Cub	NC17834
J-2	NY	Rhine	ORA	Taylor	Cub	
J-2	OK	Fredi	AAM	Taylor	Cub	
J-2	PA	Readi	MAAM	Taylor	Cub	
J-2	PA	Lock Haven	PAM	Taylor	Cub	
J-2	WA	Seatt	MoF	Wizard	Ultralight	
J-2	WI	Oshkosh	EAAAAM	Piper	Cub	
J-2A	MD	Silve	PEGF	Taylor	Cub	
J-3	AL	Birmingham	SMoF	Piper	Cub	Project
J-3	CA	San Diego	SDAM	Piper	Cub	NC333ED
J-3	CO	Aurora	WOTR	Piper	Cub	
J-3	CO	GJunc	CAF-RMW	Piper	Cub	N53503
J-3	CT	Winds	NEAM	Piper	Cub	
J-3	FL	Ameli	IAT	Piper	Cub	
J-3	FL	Kissi	FTWAM	Piper	Cub	
J-3	FL	Pensa	USNAM	Piper	Cub	8375H NC
J-3	IA	Greenfield	IAM	Piper	Cub	
J-3	ID	Zellw	BWA	Piper	Cub	
J-3	IN	Auburn	HW	Piper	Cub	
J-3	MB-C	Brand	CATPM	Piper	Cub	
J-3	MD	Silve	PEGF	Piper	Cub	
J-3	MO	Missoula	MMF	Piper	Cub	
J-3	ND	Minot	DTAM	Piper	Cub	
J-3	NM	STere	WEAM	Piper	Cub	
J-3	NY	Bayport	BA	Piper	Cub	
J-3	NY	Horsehead	WoE	Piper	Cub	N33769
J-3	NY	Mayvi	DA	Piper	Cub	
J-3	NY	Rhine	ORA	Piper	Cub	
J-3	NY	River	RE	Piper	Cub	
J-3	NC	Asheboro	PFAC	Piper	Cub	Flitfire
J-3	OH	Dayton	USAFM	Piper	Cub	
J-3	OH	Leroy	PRA	Piper	Cub	
J-3	PA	Lock Haven	PAM	Piper	Cub	
J-3	TX	Addison	CFM	Piper	Cub	N24935
J-3	TX	Gilmer	PotP	Piper	Cub	
J-3	TX	Kingbury	VAHF	Piper	Cub	Project
J-3	TX	Ladero	Airport	Piper	Cub	
J-3	UT	Heber	HVAM	Piper	Cub	
J-3	VA	Bealt	FCA	Piper	Cub	

149

Model	State	City	Code	Mfr	Type	Notes
J-3	VA	Richm	SMoV	Piper	Cub	
J-3	WA	Port Townsend	PTAM	Piper	Cub	17083, N70109
J-3	WA	Vancouver	PAM	Piper	Cub	
J-3	WA	Yakima	MMoA	Piper	Cub	
J-3	WI	Oshkosh	EAAAAM	Piper	Cub	
J-3 (3ea)	FL	Zellw	BWA	Piper	Cub	
J-3 CP-65	OK	Fredi	AAM	Piper	Cub	
J-3C	CA	Palm Sprg	PSAM	Piper	Cub	N28118
J-3C	KS	Liberal	MAAM	Piper	Cub	
J-3C	ME	OwlsH	OHTM	Piper	Cub	
J-3C	NY	Horsehead	WoE	Piper	Cub	N25769
J-3C	WA	Seattle	MoF	Piper	Cub	15641, N88023
J-3C-65	MI	Kalamazoo	KAHM	Piper	Cub	
J-3C	PA	Harri	SMoP	Piper	Cub	
J-3C-65	NC	Hende	WNCAM	Piper	Cub	N3450K
J-3C-65	OR	Mc Minnville	EAEC	Piper	Cub	G-31, N46471
J-3C-65	TX	San Antonio	TAM	Piper	Cub	SN5660, N32851
J-4A	BC-C	Langley	CMoF	Piper	Cub Coupe	
J-4A	OK	Fredi	AAM	Piper	Cub Coupe	
J-4A	WI	Oshko	EAAAAM	Piper	Cub Coupe	N30340
J-4A	AZ	Tucson	PAM	Piper	Cub Coupe	4-469, NC22783
J-4B	NY	Horsehead	WoE	Piper	Cub Coupe	4867, N26726
J-4F	KS	Liberal	MAAM	Piper	Cub Coupe	
J-4F	OK	Fredi	AAM	Piper	Cub Coupe	
J-5	GA	Woodstock	AAM	Piper	Cruiser	
J-5	GA	Woodstock	AAM	Piper	Cruiser	
J-5	GA	Woodstock	AAM	Piper	Cruiser	
J-5	NC	Hende	WNCAM	Piper	Cruiser	NC38499
J-5	OH	Madis	CFR	Piper	Cruiser	
J-5	VA	Sands	VAM	Piper	Cruiser	
J-5C(AE-1)	TX	San A	ILP&AAM	Piper	Super Cruiser	
J-6A	AZ	Tucson	PAM	Shenyang	Farmer	301
J-10-JET	CA	Redwo	HAM		Model 360	
J-29	MD	Silve	PEGF	Saab	Tunman	Swept Wing Fighter
J-35	GA	Woodstock	AAM	CuMaulaCraftMan		
J1N1-S	MD	Silve	PEGF	Nakajima	Moonlight	
J2F-6	AK	Ancho	AAHM	Grumman	Duck	
J2F-6	CA	Chino	PoFAM	Grumman	Duck	
J2F-6	CA	San Diego	SDAM	Grumman	Duck	N1273N, 33594
J2F-6	FL	Lakeland	SnF	Grumman	Duck	
J2F-6	FL	Pensa	USNAM	Grumman	Duck	33581, 149
J2F-6	FL	Polk	FoF	Grumman	Duck	
J2F-6	OR	Tillamook	TAM	Grumman	Duck	N3960C
J2F-6	WI	Oshko	EAAAAM	Grumman	Duck	36976
J2M3	CA	Chino	PoFAM	Mitsubishi	Raiden	
J4F-1(G-44A)	FL	Lakeland	SNF	Grumman	Widgeon	
J4F-1	FL	Pensa	USNAM	Grumman	Widgeon	1260, N212ST, V 212, Model G-44
J4F-2	AZ	Tucso	PAM	Grumman	Widgeon	32976, Model G-44
J4F-1	ON-C	Hamilton	CWH	Grumman	Widgeon	
J7W1	MD	Silve	PEGF	Mitsubishi	Kyushu	
J8M1	CA	Chino	PoFAM	Mitsubishi	Shusui	
JC-1	MD	Silve	PEGF		Weedhopper	
JC-1	WI	Oshko	EAAAAM	Chase-Church	Midwing	N9167
JC-24-B	WI	Oshko	EAAAAM	Weedhopper	Weedhopper	
JN-2D-1	WI	Oshko	EAAAAM	Curtiss	Jenny	N1005Z
JN-4D	AB-C	Wetas	RM	Curtiss	Jenny	
JN-4D	AL	Ozark	USAAM	Curtiss	Jenny	
JN-4D	CA	Chino	YAM	Curtiss	Jenny	N1563, D-51
JN-4D	CA	Paso Robles	EWM	Curtiss	Jenny	A-996
JN-4D	CA	S.Mon	MoF	Curtiss	Jenny	A-996
JN-4D	CA	San Diego	SDAM	Curtiss	Jenny	N5391, 3826, 38262
JN-4D	CA	San Francisco	CFAMA	Curtiss	Jenny	
JN-4D	CO	Denve	DIA	Curtiss	Jenny	SC1918, #65
JN-4D	CT	Washi	TFC	Curtiss	Jenny	
JN-4D	FL	Pensa	USNAM	Curtiss	Jenny	490, A, 995
JN-4D	FL	Polk	FoF	Curtiss	Jenny	
JN-4D	IL	Chica	MoS&I	Curtiss	Jenny	
JN-4D	KS	Topek	CAM	Curtiss	Jenny	N-101JN
JN-4D	MD	College Park	CPAM	Curtiss	Jenny	
JN-4D	MD	Silve	PEGF	Curtiss	Jenny	
JN-4D	ME	OwlsH	OHTM	Curtiss	Jenny	
JN-4D	MO	Maryland Hts	HARM	Curtiss	Jenny	
JN-4D	NE	Minde	HWPV	Curtiss	Jenny	
JN-4D	NY	Garde	CoAM	Curtiss	Jenny	1187
JN-4D	NY	Hammo	CM	Curtiss	Jenny	
JN-4D	NY	Rhine	ORA	Curtiss	Jenny	
JN-4D	NY	Niagara Falls	NAM	Curtiss	Jenny	3059
JN-4D	OH	Dayto	USAFM	Curtiss	Jenny	2805
JN-4D	OK	Tulsa	TA	Curtiss	Jenny	
JN-4D	ON-C	Ottaw	CAM	Curtiss	Jenny	39158
JN-4D	OR	Mc Minnville	EAEC	Curtiss	Jenny	
JN-4D	PA	Bethel	GAAM	Curtiss	Jenny	
JN-4D	SK-C	MJaw	WDM	Curtiss	Jenny	
JN-4D	TX	San A	LAFB	Curtiss	Jenny	
JN-4D	TX	San A	MoFM	Curtiss	Jenny	
JN-4D	TX	San A	SAMoT	Curtiss	Jenny	
JN-4D	UT	Ogden	HAFB	Curtiss	Jenny	
JN-4D	VA	Quantico	MCAGM	Curtiss	Jenny	
JN-4D	WA	Eastsound	FHC	Curtiss	Jenny	3712, N31712
JN-4D	WA	Seatt	MoF	Curtiss	Jenny	
JN-4D	WA	Stevenson	CGIC	Curtiss	Jenny	
JN-4D	WI	Oshko	EAAAAM	Curtiss	Jenny	N5357
JN-4D	WI	Oshko	EAAAAM	Curtiss	Jenny	2525
JN-6H	MN	Minne	MAGM	Curtiss	Jenny	
Johnson Adastra	NY	Elmira	NSM	Johnson	Adastra	N4921C
JRF-3(OA-13), (G-21)	FL	Pensa	USNAM	Grumman	Goose	V190, Model G-21A
JRS-1 (S-43)	AZ	Tucso	PAM	Sikorsky	Cargo Trans	4325, NC16934, 1059
JRS-1 (S-43)	MD	Silve	PEGF	Sikorsky	Cargo Trans	
Ju 52	DC	Dulle		Junkers	Aunti Ju	
Ju 52	IL	Chica	CAF-GLW	Junkers	Aunti Ju	N352JU
Ju 52/1M	MB-C	Winni	WCAM	Junkers	Aunti Ju	
Ju 52/3M	OH	Dayto	USAFM	Junkers	Aunti Ju	
Ju 87/B (7/8 Scale)	NY	Elmir	CRA	Junkers	Stuka	

Model	State	City	Code	Manufacturer	Type/Name	Serial/Reg
Ju 87B	IL	Chica	MoS&I	Junkers	Stuka	
Ju 88D/1	OH	Dayto	USAFM	Junkers	Zerstorer	430650
Ju 388L	MD	Silve	PEGF	Junkers		1945 Recon.
Junkers D.1	AL	Gunte	LGARFM	Junkers		1st All Metal Fighter
Junkers F-13	MB-C	Winni	WCAM	Junkers		
Junkers J1	ON-C	Ottaw	CAM	Junkers		586
Junkers W 34f/fi	ON-C	Ottaw	CAM	Junkers		1934
Junkin Brukner	OH	Troy	WHS	Junkin Brukner	Baby Flying Boat	
Junkers WWI	OH	Leroy	PRA	Junkers	Fighter/Bomber	
K-16 V-STOL	CT	Winds	NEAM			
K-225	CT	Winds	NEAM	Kaman		
K-225	DC	Dulle		Kaman		
K-47 CAR	FL	Pensa	USNAM		Dirigible	
K-84	WY	Jackson	GWFM	Keystone-Loening	Commuter	
K-84 Biplane	AK	Palme	MOAT&I			
KA-4	NM	Moriarty	SSM	Schleicher	2 Place Glider	
KA-6	NM	Moriarty	SSM	Schleicher	2 Place Glider	
Kaminskas RK3	CA	San Diego	SDAM	Kaminskas	Jungster VI	N8355
Kaminskas RK3	WI	Oshko	EAAAAM	Kaminskas	Jungster III	N76AQ,"Johnathan Livingston Seagull"
Kamov Ka-26	CA	Ramona	CR	Kamov	Hoodlum	7505101, N4106H
Karp Pusher	WI	Oshkosh	EAAAAM	Karp	Pusher	
Kasperwing 180-B	WA	Seattle	MoF	Kasperwing		
Kaviler	OK	Oklah	A&SM		Kaviler	
KD-1A	PA	Readi	MAAM	Kellett	Autogiro	
KD-3G	FL	Pensa	USNAM			
Ki- 43	OR	Tillamook	TAM	Nakajima	Oscar (Hayabusa)	Peregrine Falcon
Ki- 43B	TX	Ft Worth	TAF	Nakajima	Oscar (Hayabusa)	Peregrine Falcon (2ea)
Ki- 43B	WA	Eastsound	FHC	Nakajima	Oscar (Hayabusa)	750, N750
Ki- 43B	WA	Seattle	MoF	Nakajima	Oscar (Hayabusa)	
Ki- 43B	WI	Oshko	EAAAAM	Nakajima	Oscar (Hayabusa)	Peregrine Falcon
Ki- 45	MD	Silver Hill	PEGF	Kawasaki	Nick	
Ki- 46	MD	Silve	PEGF	Mitsubishi	Dinah	
Ki- 51 Replica	TX	Slaton	TAM	Mitsubishi	Ida	
Ki- 61	CA	S.Mon	MoF	Kawasaki	Tony (Hein)	Army Type 3 Hein
Ki- 61	FL	Polk	FoF	Kawasaki	Tony (Hein)	Army Type 3 Hein
Ki- 61 Rep	TX	SMarc	CTWCAF	Kawasaki	Tony (Hein)	
Ki-115	MD	Silve	PEGF	Nakajima	Tsurugi	Suicide Plane
Kiceniuk Icarus V	WI	Oshko	EAAAAM	Kiceniuk	Icarus V	
Kikka	MD	Silve	PEGF		Kikka	
Kinner Sportster	IA	Ottumwa	APM	Kinner	Sportster	
Kit Fox	CO	Aurora	WOTR	Denny Aerocraft	Speedster	
Kit Fox Model 1	FL	Lakel	SFAF	Denny Aerocraft	Speedster	N3LB
Kit Fox Model 4				Denny Aerocraft	Speedster	N177CA
Klemm 35	CA	Santa Maria	SMMoF	Klemm		
Knight Twister Imperial	WI	Oshko	EAAAAM	Payne	Twister Imperial	N5DF, "White Knight",
KR-21(C-6)	FL	Kissi	FTWAM	Fairchild	Challanger	FC Took Over Kreider-Reisner
KR-21B(C-6)	WI	Oshko	EAAAAM	Fairchild	Challanger	N954V
KR-34	FL	Kissi	FTWAM	Kreider Reiser	Challanger	
KR-34	WY	Jackson	GWFM	Fairchild	Challenger	FC Took Over Kreider-Reisner
KR-34C(C-4)	MB-C	Winnipeg	WRCAFB	Fairchild	Challanger	
KR-34C(C-4)	NS-C	Greenwood	GMAM	Fairchild	Challanger	
KR-34C(C-4)	ON-C	Sault Ste Marie	CBHC	Fairchild	Challanger	Sn 900, C-FADH
KR-34C	MD	Silve	PEGF	Fairchild	Challanger	Kreider Reiser Formerly
Kreutzer K-5	WY	Jackson	GWFM	Kreutzer	Tri-Motor Aircoach	
Krier Kraft	KS	Ashla	HKAM	Kraft	Kraft	N5400E
Kurir	NY	Horseheads	NWM	Kurir	Kurir	50-133
L- 1	TX	FWort	BCVintag	Piaggio	Royal Gull	
L- 1A(O-49)	BC-C	Langley	CMoF	Vultee	Vigilant	40-283, Stinson 74
L- 1A(O-49)	FL	Polk	FoF	Vultee	Vigilant	
L- 1A(O-49)	OH	Dayto	USAFM	Vultee	Vigilant	41-19039
L- 1A(O-49)	TX	San A	ILP&AAM	Vultee	Vigilant	
L- 2	FL	Kissi	FTWAM	Taylorcraft	Grasshopper	
L- 2	KS	New Century	CAF-HoAW	Taylorcraft	Grasshopper	N50573
L- 2	KS	New Century	CAF-HoAW	Taylorcraft	Grasshopper	N75891
L- 2	NY	Geneseo	1941AG	Taylorcraft	Grasshopper	
L- 2	NC	Hendersonville	WNCAM	Taylorcraft	Grasshopper	
L- 2	OK	Fredi	AAM	Taylorcraft	Grasshopper	
L- 2	TX	Brown	CAFRGVW	Taylorcraft	Grasshopper	
L- 2	TX	San A	ILP&AAM	Taylorcraft	Grasshopper	
L- 2	WA	Evere	CAF-EW	Taylorcraft	Grasshopper	N53768
L- 2	WA	Olympia	OFM	Taylorcraft	Grasshopper	Side # 8B
L- 2A	AL	Ozark	USAAM	Taylorcraft	Grasshopper	
L- 2A	PA	Tough	CFCM	Taylorcraft	Grasshopper	
L- 2A(D)	IA	Ottumwa	APM	Taylorcraft	Grasshopper	
L- 2B	CA	El Cajon	SDAMGF	Taylorcraft	Grasshopper	
L- 2D	OH	N Canton	MAM	Taylorcraft	Grasshopper	
L- 2M	AZ	Tucso	PAM	Taylorcraft	Grasshopper	43-26402, N59068
L- 2M	CA	Sacra	McCelAFB	Taylorcraft	Grasshopper	43- 5745, N53792
L- 2M	IL	Springfield	ACM	Taylorcraft	Grasshopper	43-26564
L- 2M	GA	Woodstock	NGWS	Taylorcraft	Grasshopper	
L- 2M	GA	Woodstock	NGWS	Taylorcraft	Grasshopper	
L- 2M	GA	Woodstock	NGWS	Taylorcraft	Grasshopper	
L- 2M	KS	Liberal	MAAM	Taylorcraft	Grasshopper	
L- 2M	OH	Dayto	USAFM	Taylorcraft	Grasshopper	43-26753
L- 3	AR	Fayet	AAM	Aeronca	Grasshopper	NC38668
L- 3B	MO	SChar	CAF-MW	Aeronca	Grasshopper	N36681
L- 3B(O-58B)	AZ	PBluf	RWCAF	Aeronca	Grasshopper	
L- 3B(O-58B)	AZ	Tucso	PAM	Aeronca	Grasshopper	43-27206, N46067
L- 3B(O-58B)	CA	Shafter	MFAM	Aeronca	Grasshopper	
L- 3B(O-58B)	CA	SRosa	PCAM	Aeronca	Grasshopper	
L- 3B(O-58B)	GA	Warner Robin	MoF	Aeronca	Grasshopper	
L- 3B(O-58B)	IA	Ottumwa	APM	Aeronca	Grasshopper	058B12783, N50334
L- 3B(O-58B)	IN	Huntington	WoF	Aeronca	Grasshopper	43-1520
L- 3B(O-58B)	KS	Liberal	MAAM	Aeronca	Grasshopper	Aeronca 65C
L- 3B(O-58B)	MI	Kalam	KAHM	Aeronca	Grasshopper	43-26772
L- 3B(O-58B)	NY	Horseheads	NWM	Aeronca	Grasshopper	
L- 3B(O-58B)	OH	Dayto	USAFM	Aeronca	Grasshopper	42-36200
L- 3B(O-58B)	OK	Fredi	AAM	Aeronca	Grasshopper	Aeronca 65C
L- 3B(O-58B)	TX	Brown	CAFRGVW	Aeronca	Grasshopper	
L- 3B(O-58B)	TX	Addison	CFM	Aeronca	Grasshopper	
L- 3B(O-58B)	TX	FWort	BCVintag	Aeronca	Defender	
L- 3B(O-58B)	TX	San A	ILP&AAM	Aeronca	Grasshopper	
L- 3B(O-58B)	WA	Port Townsend	PTAM	Aeronca	Grasshopper	058B-7742, N48145

L- 3B(O-58B)	WA	Seatt	MoF	Aeronca	Grasshopper	9223, N47427
L- 3E	IA	CBluf	CAF-GPW	Aeronca	Grasshopper	N36687
L- 4	CA	Atwater	CAM	Piper	Grasshopper	
L- 4	CA	Corno	CAF-IES	Piper	Grasshopper	
L- 4	CA	Fairf	TAFB	Piper	Grasshopper	N35786
L- 4	CO	Denve	JWDAS	Piper	Grasshopper	
L- 4	FL	Polk	FoF	Piper	Grasshopper	
L- 4	IN	Valparaiso	IAM	Piper	Grasshopper	
L- 4	KY	Lexington	AVoK	Piper	Grasshopper	NC42008
L- 4Rep	MI	Saginaw	YAF	Homebuilt	Grasshopper	
L- 4	MN	Minne	MAGM	Piper	Grasshopper	
L- 4	NC	Asheboro	PFAC	Piper	Grasshopper	
L- 4	ND	Wahpe	TSA	Piper	Grasshopper	
L- 4(O-59A)	OH	Dayton	USAFM	Piper	Grasshopper	
L- 4	OK	FtSil	USAFAM	Piper	Grasshopper	
L- 4	TX	Brown	CAFRGVW	Piper	Grasshopper	
L- 4	TX	C Christi	USS Lexi	Piper	Grasshopper	
L- 4	TX	LV	LVAM	Piper	Grasshopper	
L- 4	TX	San A	ILP&AAM	Piper	Grasshopper	
L- 4	UT	Ogden	HAM	Piper	Grasshopper	
L- 4	VA	Manassas	CAFNCS	Piper	Grasshopper	
L- 4	WA	Vancouver	PAM	Piper	Grasshopper	
L- 4A	OH	Dayto	USAFM	Piper	Grasshopper	42-36446
L- 4B	AL	Ozark	USAAM	Piper	Grasshopper	43-515
L- 4B	FL	Pensa	USNAM	Piper	Grasshopper	
L- 4B	GA	Hampton	AAHF	Piper	Grasshopper	
L- 4B	OK	Oklah	45IDM	Piper	Grasshopper	
L- 4H	MI	Kalamazoo	KAHM	Piper	Grasshopper	44-79817
L- 4J	FL	Tittusville	VACM	Piper	Grasshopper	
L- 4J	OK	Fredi	AAM	Piper	Grasshopper	
L- 4J	TX	Addison	CFM	Piper	Grasshopper	N9073C
L- 5	CA	Chino	YAM	Stinson	Sentinel	
L- 5 (SNJ)	CA	El Cajon	CAFFFM	Stinson	Sentinel	N59AF
L- 5	CA	Fairf	TAFB	Stinson	Sentinel	
L- 5	CA	Riverside	MFAM	Stinson	Sentinel	63085
L- 5	CO	Denve	JWDAS	Stinson	Sentinel	
L- 5	KS	Liberal	MAAM	Stinson	Sentinel	
L- 5	LA	New Orleans	DDM	Stinson	Sentinel	
L- 5	MD	Silve	PEGF	Stinson	Sentinel	
L- 5	NC	Charl	CHAC	Stinson	Sentinel	
L- 5	OH	Colum	CAF-OVW	Stinson	Sentinel	N5138B
L- 5	OH	Dayto	USAFM	Stinson	Sentinel	42-98667
L- 5	OK	Fredi	AAM	Stinson	Sentinel	
L- 5	PA	Pitts	CAF-KW	Stinson	Sentinel	N25818
L- 5	SD	Rapid	SDA&SM	Stinson	Sentinel	45-35046
L- 5	TX	Abile	PSCAF	Stinson	Sentinel	
L- 5	TX	Burnet	HLS-CAF	Stinson	Sentinel	
L- 5	TX	Brown	RGVW-CAF	Stinson	Sentinel	
L- 5	TX	Ft Worth	VFM	Stinson	Sentinel	
L- 5	TX	Galve	LSFM	Stinson	Sentinel	1039, N68MH
L- 5	TX	Midla	CAFFM	Stinson	Sentinel	
L- 5	TX	San A	ILP&AAM	Stinson	Sentinel	
L- 5	TX	SMarc	CTWCAF	Stinson	Sentinel	
L- 5	VA	Chesa	CAF-ODS	Stinson	Sentinel	N61100
L- 5	VA	Manassas	CAF-NCS	Stinson	Sentinel	N1156V
L- 5	VA	Suffolk	FF	Stinson	Sentinel	41-7588
L- 5A	MN	StPau	CAF-SMW	Stinson	Sentinel	N68591
L- 5B	AZ	Tucso	PAM	Stinson	Sentinel	44-16907, N4981V
L- 5E	CA	Atwater	CAM	Stinson	Sentinel	
L- 5E	CA	Chino	PoFAM	Stinson	Sentinel	
L- 5E	CA	Okdal	CAF-CCVS	Stinson	Sentinel	N5625V
L- 5E	CA	Paso Robles	EWM	Stinson	Sentinel	44-17944, N45CV
L- 5E-1VW	WI	Oshko	EAAAAM	Stinson	Sentinel	4297
L- 5E(OY-2)	OH	Columbus	CAF-OVW	Stinson	Sentinel	44-181143, N5138B (04013)
L- 5G	CA	Chino	PoFAM	Stinson	Sentinel	
L- 5Spatz-55	NS-C	Halifax	ACAM			
L- 6	AZ	Tucso	PAM	Interstate	Cadet	
L- 6	KS	Liberal	MAAM	Interstate	Cadet	
L- 6	OH	Dayto	USAFM	Interstate	Cadet	43-2680
L- 6	OH	Leroy	PRA	Interstate	Cadet	
L- 6	OK	Fredi	AAM	Interstate	Cadet	N37214
L- 6	TX	Brown	CAFRGVW	Interstate	Cadet	
L- 6	TX	Corpus Christi	CAF-TCW	Interstate	Cadet	
L- 6	TX	Denton	H10FM	Interstate	Cadet	
L- 6	TX	San A	ILP&AAM	Interstate	Cadet	
L- 6(S-1A)	AK	Palme	MOAT&I	Interstate	Cadet	1941
L- 9	CA	Chiriaco	GPM			
L- 9B	PA	Pitts	CAF-KW			N26295
L-13	AR	Fayetteville	AAM	Convair	Scorpion	
L-13	CA	Atwater	CAM	Convair	Scorpion	
L-13	MN	Minne	JJ	Convair	Scorpion	Owner: Patrick Harker
L-13	MN	Minne	JJ	Convair	Scorpion	
L-13	WA	Eastsound	HFM	Convair	Scorpion	
L-13A	CA	Chino	PoFAM	Convair	Scorpion	
L-13A	MI	Fairf	YAFNE	Convair	Scorpion	
L-13A	NJ	Fairfield	YAM	Convair	Scorpion	47-389, N65893
L-13A	NM	STere	WEAM	Convair	Scorpion	
L-13B	WA	Seatt	MoF	Convair	Scorpion	
L-15(YL)A	AL	Ozark	USAAM	Boeing	Scout	47-429
L-15(YL)A	MN	Blaine	ACBA	Boeing	Scout	Owner: Patrick Harker
L-16	AR	Fayetteville	AAM	Aeronca	Chief	
L-16	CO	Denve	JWDAS	Aeronca	Chief	
L-16	IL	Linco	HIFM	Aeronca	Chief	
L-16	NY	Geneseo	1941AG	Aeronca	Chief	
L-16	OH	Leroy	PRA	Aeronca	Chief	
L-16	OK	Fredi	AAM	Aeronca	Chief	
L-16A	AZ	Mesa	CAF-AW	Aeronca	Chief	
L-16A	CA	Paso Robles	EWM	Aeronca	Chief	47-0787, N82107
L-17	CO	Denve	JWDAS	Ryan	Navion	
L-17	GA	Calhoun	MAM	Ryan	Navion	
L-17	GA	Hampton	AAHF	Ryan	Navion	
L-17	IL	Linco	HIFM	Ryan	Navion	
L-17	KS	Liberal	MAAM	Ryan	Navion	

L-17	GA	Hampton	AAHF	Ryan	Navion	
L-17	GA	Woodstock	AAM	Ryan	Navion	
L-17	NY	Geneseo	1941AG	Ryan	Navion	
L-17	TX	Midla	CAF-Hq	Ryan	Navion	N444AC
L-17	TX	Slaton	TAM	Ryan	Navion	
L-17A	AL	Ozark	USAAM	Ryan	Navion	47-1344
L-17A	CA	Paso Robles	EWM	North American	Navion	47-1333, N91668
L-17A	OH	Dayto	USAFM	Ryan	Navion	47-1347
L-17A	OK	Oklah	45IDM	Ryan	Navion	
L-17A	TX	Denton	H10FM	Ryan	Navion	
L-17B	FL	Deland	FW-CAF	Ryan	Navion	
L-17B	IN	Crown	CPV	Ryan	Navion	
L-17B	OH	N Canton	MAM	North American	Navion	
L-17B	TX	Burnet	HLSCAF	North American	Navion	
L-19	CA	El Cajon	SDAMGF	Cessna	Bird Dog	
L-19	CO	Denve	JWDAS	Cessna	Bird Dog	
L-19	MN	Winoma	WTI	Cessna	Bird Dog	N1983AP
L-19	NJ	Rio Grande	NASW	Cessna	Bird Dog	
L-19	NY	River	RE	Cessna	Bird Dog	
L-19	OK	FtSil	USAFAM	Cessna	Bird Dog	
L-19	OK	Oklah	45IDM	Cessna	Bird Dog	56-367
L-19	ON-C	Petawawa	CFBPMM	Cessna	Bird Dog	
L-19	WA	Eastsound	HFM	Cessna	Bird Dog	
L-19(OE-1)(O-1G)	AZ	Tucson	DMAFB	Cessna	Bird Dog	
L-19(OE 1)(O-1)	FL	Pensa	USNAM	Cessna	Bird Dog	51-14981
L-19(OE-2)(O-2)	VA	Quantico	MCAGM	Cessna	Bird Dog	140090
L-19(OE-2)(O-2)	WA	Seattle	MoF	Cessna	Bird Dog	67-21363
L-19A	AL	Ozark	USAAM	Cessna	Bird Dog	50-1327
L-19A	AL	Ozark	USAAM	Cessna	Bird Dog	51- 4943
L-19A	AZ	Grand	PoFGCVA	Cessna	Bird Dog	51-12129
L-19A	GA	Hampton	AAHF	Cessna	Bird Dog	
L-19A	GA	Warner Robin	MoF	Cessna	Bird Dog	
L-19A	KY	FKnox	PMoC&A	Cessna	Bird Dog	
L-19A(O-1)	CA	SanLu	CSLO	Cessna	Bird Dog	
L-19A(O-1)	IN	India	IMoMH	Cessna	Bird Dog	
L-19A(O-1)	CA	SanLu	CSLO	Cessna	Bird Dog	53-8029
L-19A(O-1)	VA	FtEus	USATM	Cessna	Bird Dog	51-12745
L-19A(O-1A)	MD	Silve	PEGF	Cessna	Bird Dog	
L-19A(O-1E)	FL	FtWal	HF	Cessna	Bird Dog	56-4208
L-19A(O-1E)	GA	Warner Robin	MoF	Cessna	Bird Dog	51-12857
L-19A-CE	MI	Oscoda	YAM	Cessna	Bird Dog	51-12107, N3302T
L-19A	NC	Asheboro	PFAC	Cessna	Bird Dog	
L-19A(O-1G)	OH	Dayto	USAFM	Cessna	Bird Dog	51-11917
L-19D(TL)	AL	Ozark	USAAM	Cessna	Bird Dog	55- 4681
L-19D	GA	Hampton	AAHF	Cessna	Bird Dog	
L-21 (PA-18)	CA	Atwater	CAM	Piper	Super Cub	
L-21 (PA-18)	GA	Calhoun	MAM	Piper	Super Cub	
L-21A(TL)(PA-18)	AL	Ozark	USAAM	Piper	Super Cub	51-15782
L-21B(PA-18)	NY	Geneseo	1941AG	Piper	Super Cub	
L-21B(PA-18)	PA	Beave	AHM	Piper	Super Cub	
L-21B(PA-18)	PA	Readi	MAAM	Piper	Super Cub	53- 7720, N50084
L-29	FL	Miami	WOM	Aero	Delfin	
L-29	MN	Blaine	ACBA	Aero	Delfin	Owner: Dooug Weske
L-29	ND	Minot	DTAM	Aero	Delfin	
L-29	OR	Tillamook	TAM	Aero	Delfin	
L-29	WI	Amery	AMA	Aero	Delfin	
L-29C	CA	El Cajon	WW	Aero	Delfin	
L-38	MO	StCha	CAFMW			
L-39	KS	New Century	CAF-HoAW	Aerovodochody	Albatross	
L-39	MN	Blaine	Airport	Aerovodochody	Albatross	N139BH, Owner: Dooug Weske
L-39	WA	Eastsound	HFM	Aerovodochody	Albatross	
L-39A	WA	Olympia	OFM	Aerovodochody	Albatross	
L-106	WA	Seatt	MoF	Lamson	Alcor Glider	18, N924LR
L-049(C-69)	AZ	Tucso	PAM	Lockheed	Columbine	Sn 42-94549, 48-614, N90831
L-1049(EC-121D)	CA	Sacra	McCelAFB	Lockheed	Super Constellation	53-552
L-1049(EC-121K)	DC	Dulle		Lockheed	Super Constellation	USAF
L-1049(EC-121K)	IL	Ranto	OCAM	Lockheed	Super Constellation	141311, USAF
L-1049(EC-121K)	OK	Tinke	TAFB	Lockheed	Super Constellation	USAF
L-1049(EC-121T)	CO	CSpri	EJPSCM	Lockheed	Super Constellation	52-3425, USAF
L-1049(EC-121T)	KS	Topek	CAM	Lockheed	Super Constellation	52-3418
L-1049(EC-121T)	MO	Kansas City	AHM	Lockheed	Super Constellation	N6937C
L-1049(WF-2)	FL	Pensa	USNAM	Lockheed	Super Constellation	Navy
L-1649A	FL	Orlando	OSA	Lockheed	Starliner	N974R, "Jenny's Star"
L-1649A	ME	Aubur	SLP	Lockheed	Starliner	N8083H, "Jason's Star"
L-1649A	ME	Aubur	SLP	Lockheed	Starliner	N7316C, "Brian's Star"
L-450F LTVE	TX	FWort	SAM			
L.10A	CA	Oakla	OWAM	Lockheed	Electra	N3828
L.10A	CT	Winds	NEAM	Lockheed	Electra	
L.10A	MB-C	Winni	WCAM	Lockheed	Electra	
L.10A	ON-C	Ottaw	CAM	Lockheed	Electra	
L.12A	KY	Lexington	AMoK	Lockheed	Electra	1203, N12EJ
L.12A	ON-C	Ottaw	CAM	Lockheed	Electra	
L.14	CT	Winds	NEAM	Lockheed	Super Electra	
L.18(C-60)	HI	Honol	HIA	Lockheed	Lodestar	
L.18(C-60)	TX	Denton	H10FM	Lockheed	Lodestar	
L.18(C-60)	WY	Greyb	H&PA	Lockheed	Lodestar	
L.18-50	TX	Midla	CAFFM	Lockheed	Lodestar	
L-24 See U-10						
L.25J	PA	Beave	AHM	British Aircraft	Swallow	
Laird Swallow	KS	Wichi	KAM	Laird	Swallow	
Laister LP-15	NY	Elmira	NSM	Laister	Nugget	N3MH
Laister -Kauffman LK-10A	NY	Elmira	NSM	Laister		N54191
Lancair 200	WI	Oshko	EAAAAM	Lancair	Lancair 200	N384L, Neibauer
Langley Aerodrome A	MD	Silve	PEGF	Langley	Aerodrome	
Langley Aerodrome N0. 5	MD	Silve	PEGF	Langley	Aerodrome	
Langley Aerodrome	VA	Chantilly	UHC	Langley	Aerodrome	
Latter	PA	Tough	CFCM	Latter		
Lazair	FL	Lakel	SFAF	Lazair		
Lazair SS EC Ultralight	MD	Silve	PEGF	Lazair	Ultralight	
LC-DW500	CT	Winds	NEAM	Laird	Super Solution	
LC-DW500	MD	Silve	PEFG	Laird	Super Solution	
LC-DW500	MI	Dearb	HFM	Laird	Super Solution	
LC-DW500	WI	Oshko	EAAAAM	Laird	Super Solution	NR12048

LC-DW500 Fuse	MD	Silve	PEGF	Laird	Super Solution	
LCVP	LA	New Orleans	DDM	Higgins	Boat	
LCVP	DC	Washington	NM	Higgins	Boat	
Le Rhone	FL	Pensa	USNAM	Le Rhone		
Learjet 23	AZ	Tucson	PAM	Gates	Learjet	Man Sn 23-015, N88B
Learjet 23	KS	Wichita	KAM	Gates	Learjet	Sn 6
Learjet 23	MI	Kalamazoo	KAHM	Gates	Learjet	23-083
Learjet 23	VA	Richm	SMoV	Gates	Learjet	
Learjet 25	AL	Ozark	AA&TC	Gates	Learjet	
LeBel VTO	CA	Chino	PoFAM	LeBel		
LEM Grumman	NY	NYC	ISASM	Grumman	LEM	
Les Broussard 1956	MI	Hamil	ML	Les Broussard		
LF-107 Glider	WA	Seattle	MoF	Let	Lunak	N2170D
LF-2100	WA	Seatt	MoF	Learfan		001, N626BL
LF-2100	WI	Oshko	EAAAAM	Learfan		N327ML
Lilienthal Glider	CA	Chino	PoFAM	Lilienthal	Glider	
Lilienthal Glider	CA	San Diego	SDAM	Lilienthal	Glider	
Lilienthal Glider	DC	Washi	NA&SM	Lilienthal	Glider	
Lilienthal Glider	ME	Owls Head	OHTM	Lilienthal	Glider	
Lilienthal Glider	NY	Garde	CoAM	Lilienthal	Glider	
Lilienthal Glider	WA	Seatt	MoF	Lilienthal	Glider	
Linburgs Monocoupe	MO	SLoui	SLLIA	Linburgs	Monocoupe	
Lincoln Biplane	WI	Oshko	EAAAAM	Lincoln	Biplane	
Lincoln Page LP3A	IL	Paris	HAAM	Lincoln		
Lincoln PT-K	WI	Oshko	EAAAAM	Lincoln	Biplane	N275N
Lincoln Sports	NS	Halifax	ACAM	Lincoln	Sports Biplane	
Link ANT-18 Trainer	CT	Winds	NEAM	Link	Trainer	
Link Trainer	AL	Birmingham	SMoF	Link	Trainer	
Link Trainer	AB-C	Calgary	AMoC	Link	Trainer	
Link Trainer	AB-C	Nanton	NLSAM	Link	Trainer	
Link Trainer	AB-C	Wetas	RM	Link	Trainer	
Link Trainer	AR	Little Rock	AEC	Link	Trainer	
Link Trainer	AR	Walnut Ridge	WRAFSM	Link	Trainer	
Link Trainer	CA	Oakla	OWAM	Link	Trainer	
Link Trainer	CA	San Diego	SDAM	Link	Trainer	
Link Trainer	CO	Denver	DIA/UAL	Link	Trainer	
Link Trainer	DE	Dover	DAFB	Link	Trainer	
Link Trainer	FL	Tittusville	VACM	Link	Trainer	
Link Trainer	KS	Liberal	MAAM	Link	Trainer	
Link Trainer	KY	Lexington	AMoK	Link	Trainer	
Link Trainer	MI	Kalam	KAHM	Link	Trainer	
Link Trainer	MI	OScoda	YAF	Link	Trainer	
Link Trainer	MN	Duluth	CAF-LSS	Link	Trainer	
Link Trainer	MN	Minneapolis	MSPIA	Link	Trainer	
Link Trainer	NF-C	Gander	NAAM	Link	Trainer	
Link Trainer	NJ	Milli	MAAFM	Link	Trainer	
Link Trainer	NJ	Milvi	MAAFM	Link	Trainer	
Link Trainer	NM	STere	WEAM	Link	Trainer	
Link Trainer	NS	Halifax	ACAM	Link	Trainer	
Link Trainer	NY	Binghamton	LFSC	Link	Trainer	
Link Trainer	NY	Binghamton	BRA	Link	Trainer	
Link Trainer	NY	Ghent	POMAM	Link	Trainer	
Link Trainer C-3	OH	N Canton	MAM	Link	Trainer	
Link Trainer	ON-C	Hamilton	CWHM	Link	Trainer	
Link Trainer	ON-C	Sault Ste Marie	CBHC	Link	Trainer	
Link Trainer	OR	Eugen	OAM	Link	Trainer	
Link Trainer	PA	Bethel	GAAM	Link	Trainer	
Link Trainer	PA	Lock Haven	PAM	Link	Trainer	
Link Trainer	TX	Addison	CFM	Link	Trainer	
Link Trainer	VA	Quantico	MCAGM	Link	Trainer	
Link Trainer	WA	Vancouver	PAM	Link	Trainer	N192GP
Link Trainer Mk.IV	AB-C	Edmonton	AAM	Link	Trainer	
Lippisch DM-1	MD	Silve	PEGF	Lippisch		
Little Looper	CA	San Carlos	HAM	Aerobatic		"Little Looper"
Little Rocket	FL	Lakel	SFAF	Little Rocket	Racer	N345JA
Liverpuffin 11	PA	Tough	CFCM	Liverpuffin		
LK-10 Glider	CA	Chino	PoFAM	Laister-Kauffman	Glider	
LNA-40 Super	WI	Oshko	EAAAAM	Heath	Super	N16GR
LNE-1	AL	Birmingham	SMoF	Pratt-Read	Glider	31543, Sn 39, N60432
LNE-1	CA	San Martin	WoHM	Pratt-Read	Glider	31543, Sn 39, N60432
LNE-1	FL	Pensa	USNAM	Pratt-Read	Glider	N60745
LNE-1(HH-2D)	FL	Pensa	USNAM	Pratt-Read	Glider	149031
LNE-1	KY	Lexington	AMoK	Pratt-Read	Glider	PRG-01-73, N60235
LNE-1 Cockpit	MD	Ft Meade	QM	Pratt-Read	Glider	
LNE-1	NY	Elmira	NSM	Pratt-Read	Glider	31561, Sn 57, N5346G
LNE-1	ND	Fargo	BAM	Pratt-Read	Glider	31569, Sn 65, N56660
LNE-1(TG-3A)	OH	Dayto	USAFM	Pratt-Read	Glider	31523, Sn 19, N69215
LNE-1(HH-2D)	IN	Auburn	HW	Pratt-Read	Glider	
LNE-1(X)	NY	Horseheads	NWM	Pratt-Read	Glider	31506, NC4467U
LNE-1(PR-G1)	WA	Seattle	MoF	Pratt-Read	Glider	31517, Sn 13, N60353
LNS-1 Schweizer	FL	Pensa	USNAM	Schweizer	Glider	S- 4385
LNS-1 Schweizer	FL	Pensa	USNAM	Schweizer	Glider	04384, #6
Shafor Ganagobie	WI	Oshko	EAAAAM	Shafor	Ganagobie	N60G
Lockheed 402-2	NJ	Teter	AHoFNJ	Lockheed	Bushmaster	N160IL
Lockheed Hudson Mk IIIa	NF-C	Gander	NAAM	Lockheed	Hudson	
Lockheed Mk.6 (Fuse)	NS	Halifax	ACAM	Lockheed	Hudson	
Lockheed Q-5	AZ	Grand Canyon	PoFGCVA	Lockheed		
Lockheed Satellite	OH	Dayton	USAFM	Lockheed	Satellite	
Lockheed Sirius 8	DC	Washi	NA&SM	Lockheed	Sirius	
Lockheed Vega 5	MI	Dearb	HFM	Lockheed	Vega	N965Y
Lockheed Vega 5	OK	Fredi	AAM	Lockheed	Vega	
Lockheed Vega 5B	DC	Washi	NA&SM	Lockheed	Vega	
Lockheed Vega 5C	DC	Washi	NA&SM	Lockheed	Vega	"Winnie Mae"
Lockheed Vega 5C	WI	Oshko	EAAAAM	Lockheed	Vega	NC105W
Loehle 5151 Mustang	GA	Woodstock	NGWS	Loehle	Mustang Kit	
Long Eze	AZ	Tucso	PAM	Rutan	Long Eze	N82ST
Longster	MI	Kalamazoo	KAHM	Longster	Homebuilt	
Longwing Eaglerock	AL	Birmingham	SmoF	Longwing	Eaglerock	
Loving's-Love	FL	Lakeland	SNF	Loving-Wayne	Love	
Loving-Wayne WR-1 Love	WI	Oshko	EAAAAM	Loving-Wayne	Love	N351C
LP-3	CA	Chino	YAM	Lincoln	Page	156, N3830
LST	MI	Muskegon	USS S		Landing Ship Tank	
LTV4	OH	Hubbard	WWIIVM		Water Buffalo	D11

LTV4	TX	Frede	NMofPW			
Lunar Excursion Module	OK	Oklah	KCASM		Lunar Module	
Lunar Lander	KS	Hutch	KC&SC			
Lunar Orbiter	WA	Seatt	PSC			
Lunar Rover	KS	Hutch	KC&SC			
Lusac-11	OH	Dayto	USAFM	Packard LePere		SC-42133
Luscombe T-8F	KS	Liberal	MAAM	Luscombe	Observer	
Luscombe 8	MN	Winoma	WTI	Luscombe	Silvaire	NC13308
Luscombe 8A	BC-C	Sidne	BCAM	Luscombe	Silvaire	
Luscombe 8A	IL	Urban	RFIA	Luscombe	Silvaire	
Luscombe 8A	KS	Liberal	MAAM	Luscombe	Silvaire	990
Luscombe 8A	ME	Bangor	MAM	Luscombe	Silvaire	
Luscombe 8A	OH	Madis	CFR	Luscombe	Silvaire	
Luscombe 8A	OK	Fredi	AAM	Luscombe	Silvaire	
Luscombe 8A	TX	Kingbury	VAHF	Luscombe	Silvaire	
Luscombe 8A	WA	Port Townsend	PTAM	Luscombe	Silvaire	3675, N77948
Luscombe 8E	GA	Woodstock	AAM	Luscombe	Silvaire	
Luscombe 8E	NY	River	RE	Luscombe	Silvaire	
Luscombe 8F	IA	Ottumwa	APM	Luscombe	Phantom I	6735, N805B
Luscombe 8F	WI	Oshko	EAAAAM	Luscombe	Phantom I	NC1025
Luscombe 8F	OK	Fredi	AAM	Luscombe	Phantom I	
Lysander	MB-C	Brand	CATPM	Westland	Lizzie	
Lysander	MD	Silve	PEGF	Westland	Lizzie	
Lysander	TX	Lubbock	SWM	I ysander	Lizzie	
M-1	OH	Dayto	USAFM	Ryan	Messenger	68-533
M-1	PA	Bethel	GAAM	Ryan	Messenger	NX2073
M-1	WA	Seatt	MoF	Ryan	Messenger	HN-1, N46853
M-2	DC	Washi	NASM	Douglas	Mail Plane	
M.J.5 Sirocco	WI	Oshko	EAAAAM	Jurca	Sirocco	N8038E
M2-F3(HL-10)	DC	Washi	NA&SM	Northrop	Lifting Body	
M6A1	MD	Silve	PEGF	Aichi	Seiran	
MA14/LJ-5B	VA	Hampt	APM	NA-McDonnell Douglas	Spacecraft	
Mace Model III	WI	Oshkosh	EAAAAM	Mace		
Mahoney Sorceress	MD	Silve	PEGF	Mahoney	Sorceress	
Manhigh II Gondola	OH	Dayton	USAFM	Manhigh	Gondola II	
Marcoux-Bromberg Special	CT	Winds	NEAM	Marcoux-Bromberg	Special	
Marske Pioneer II	CA	Santa Martin	WoHAM	Marske	Pioneer II Glider	Year 1985, Flying Wing Glider
Marinac Flying Mercury	WI	Oshko	EAAAAM	Marinac	Flying Mercury	
Martin 162A	MD	Balti	BMoI	Martin	Martin 162A	
Martin 2-0-2A	NJ	Teter	AHoFNJ	Martin	Martinliner	14074, N93204
Martin 4-0-4	AZ	Tucson	PAM	Martin	Martinliner	14153, N462M
Martin 4-0-4	MD	Middle River	GMAM	Martin	Martinliner	
Martin 4-0-4	MO	Kansas City	AHM	Martin	Martinliner	SN 14142, N145S
Martin 4-0-4	MT	Billings		Martin	Martinliner	
Martin 4-0-4	PA	Readi	MAAM	Martin	Martinliner	"Silver Falcon"
Martin J.V. K-III	MD	Silve	PEGF	Martin	Kitten	
Maupin-Lanteri Black Dia	MD	Silve	PEGF	Maupin-Lanteri	Black Diamond	
Maurice Farman S.11	ON-C	Ottaw	CAM	Maurice	Farman	
MB-2	OH	Dayton	USAFM			
MC- 4C	AZ	Tucso	PAM	McCulloch		133817, N4072K
MC- 4C	CA	Chino	YAM	McCulloch	Helicopter	3818
MC- 12 Cricket	WI	Oshko	EAAAAM	Rombaugh	Cricket	N1377L
M.C. 200	OH	Dayto	USAFM	Macchi	Seatta	McCulloch
MC-202	DC	Washi	NA&SM	McCulloch		
McAllister Yakima Clipper	WA	Seatt	MoF	McAllister	Yalima Clipper	N10655
McCook Wind Tunnel	OH	Dayton	USAFM	McCook	Wind Tunnel	
McDowall Monoplane	ON-C	Ottaw	CAM	McDowall	Monoplane	
Me 108	CA	Chino	PoFAM	Messerschmitt	Taifun	5
Me 108	NM	Hobbs	CAF-NMW	Messerschmitt	Taifun	N2231
Me 108	NY	Geneseo	1941AG	Messerschmitt	Taifun	N2231
Me 108	WA	Seattle	MoF	Messerschmitt	Taifun	
Me 108B	TX	Midla	CAFFM	Messerschmitt	Taifun	
Me 109	CA	Inglewood	PBR	Messerschmitt	Gustav	
Me 109	FL	FtLau	WJAIS&L	Messerschmitt	Gustav	
Me 109	NY	Ghent	POMAM	Messerschmitt	Gustav	
Me 109	NY	Shirley	DLIA	Messerschmitt	Gustav	
Me 109	OR	McMinnville	EAEC	Messerschmitt	Gustav	
Me 109	TX	Midla	CAF-Hq	Messerschmitt	Gustav	N109KE
Me 109 Mock Up	KS	Topek	CAM	Messerschmitt	Gustav	
Me 109E	AZ	Mesa	CFM	Messerschmitt	Gustav	
Me 109E-3	WA	Seattle	MoF	Messerschmitt	Gustav	186, NX109J
Me 163	GA	Savan	MEHM	Messerschmitt	Komet	
Me 163	OH	Dayton	USAFM	Messerschmitt	Komet	
Me 163B	CA	Chino	PoFAM	Messerschmitt	Komet	
Me 163B	MD	Silve	PEGF	Messerschmitt	Komet	
Me 163B (2 ea)	ON-C	Ottaw	CAM	Messerschmitt	Komet	191095
Me 163B (2 ea)	ON-C	Ottaw	CAM	Messerschmitt	Komet	191916
Me 208	FL	Tittusville	VACM	Messerschmitt	Ramier	
Me 208	NY	Geneseo	1941AG	Messerschmitt	Ramier	187, Nord 1101
Me 262 A	DC	Washi	NA&SM	Messerschmitt	Stormbird	Sturmvogel
Me 262 A	WA	Everett	TMP	Messerschmitt	Stormbird 13	Sturmvogel
Me 262 A	WA	Everett	TMP	Messerschmitt	Stormbird 13	Sturmvogel
Me 262 A	WA	Everett	TMP	Messerschmitt	Stormbird 13	Sturmvogel
Me 262 A	WA	Everett	TMP	Messerschmitt	Stormbird 13	Sturmvogel
Me 262 A	WA	Everett	TMP	Messerschmitt	Stormbird 13	Sturmvogel
Me 262-1a/U3	WA	Eastsound	FHC	Messerschmitt	Stormbird 09	Sturmvogel
Me 262A	OH	Dayto	USAFM	Messerschmitt	Stormbird	Sturmvogel 121442
Me 262B-1A	PA	Willo	WGNAS	Messerschmitt	Stormbird 13	Sturmvogel
Me 410 A-3	MD	Silve	PEGF	Messerschmitt	Hornisse	
Mead C-III	SK-C	MJaw	WDM	Mead		
Mead Glider	AB-C	Wetas	RM	Mead	Glider	
Mead Primary Glider	IA	Greenfield	IAM	Mead	Glider	
Mead Primary Glider 1932	NY	Mayvi	DA	Mead	Primary Glider	
Mead Rhon Ranger	CT	Winds	NEAM	Mead	Rhon Ranger	
Melberg Biplane	NY	Mayvi	DA	Melberg	Biplane	1939
Mercury Capsule MR-2	CA	LAnge	CMoS&I	McDonnell	Mercury Capsule	
Mercury Capsule	CA	Chino	PoFAM	McDonnell	Mercury Capsule	
Mercury Capsule	CA	San Diego	SDAM	McDonnell	Mercury Capsule	
Mercury Capsule	OH	Dayton	USAFM	McDonnell	Mercury Capsule	
Mercury 7 Capsule	IL	Chicago	MoS&I	Mercury	Mercury Capsule	
Mercury 7 Capsule	KS	Hutch	KC&SC	McDonnell	Mercury Capsule	
Mercury Capsule Replica	MO	SLoui	MDPR	McDonnell	Mercury Capsule	
Mercury Capsule	NY	NYC	ISASM	McDonnell	Mercury Capsule	"Aurora 7"

Mercury Capsule Replica	NC	Charlotte	CAM	McDonnell	Mercury Capsule	
Mercury Capsule	OH	Colum	CoS&I	McDonnell	Mercury Capsule	
Mercury Capsule Rep	OK	Oklah	KCASM	McDonnell	Mercury Capsule	
Mercury 6 Capsule	TX	Houst	HMoNS	Mercury	Mercury Capsule	
Mercury Capsule Replica	WA	Seatt	MoF	McDonnell	Mercury Capsule	
Mercury Air Shoestring	CA	San Diego	SDAM	Mercury	Air Shoestring	N16V
Mercury Chick	NY	Hammo	CM	Mercury	Chick	
Mercury S-1 Racer	NY	Hammo	CM	Mercury	Racer	
Merlin Hang Glider	NY	Garde	CoAM	Merlin	Hang Glider	
Meteor 1919	CA	Oakla	MDoH	Meteor	Meteor	
Meyer Little Toot	WI	Oshko	EAAAAM	Meyers	Little Toot	N217J, "Petit Papillon",
Meyers M-1 Special	WI	Oshko	EAAAAM	Meyers	Special	N42963
Meyers OTW	FL	Pensa	USNAM	Meyers	OTW	N26482
Meyers OTW	IL	Cahokia	GSLA&SM	Meyers	OTW	
Meyers OTW	KS	Topek	CAM	Meyers	OTW	
Meyers OTW	OH	Leroy	PRA	Meyers	OTW	
Meyers OTW	OH	Madis	CFR	Meyers	OTW	
Meyers OTW	TX	Kingbury	VAHF	Meyers	OTW	
Meyers OTW	WA	Vanco	PAM	Meyers	OTW	
Meyers OTW-145	WI	Oshko	EAAAAM	Meyers	OTW	N34357
Midget Mustang	NC	Charl	CHAC	Midget	Mustang	
Midget Mustang	NC	CPoin	CPMB	Midget	Mustang	
MiG-15	AL	Birmingham	SMoF	Mikoyan-Gurevich	Midget	
MiG-15	AZ	Grand	PoFGCVA	Mikoyan-Gurevich	Midget	1301
MiG-15	AZ	Mesa	CFM	Mikoyan-Gurevich	Midget	1301
MiG-15	AZ	Phoenix	DVA	Mikoyan-Gurevich	Midget	2 Seater
MiG-15	CA	Chino	PoFAM	Mikoyan-Gurevich	Midget	1301
MiG-15	CA	Inglewood	PBR	Mikoyan-Gurevich	Midget	
MiG-15	CA	Miramar	FLAM	Mikoyan-Gurevich	Midget	
MiG-15	CA	San Diego	SDAM	Mikoyan-Gurevich	Midget	
MiG-15	CA	SRosa	PCAM	Mikoyan-Gurevich	Midget	
MiG-15	CT	Winds	NEAM	Mikoyan-Gurevich	Midget	83277
MiG-15	ID	Driggs	TAC	Mikoyan-Gurevich	Midget	358
MiG-15	KS	Topek	CAM	Mikoyan-Gurevich	Midget	B01016, N15YY
MiG-15	MD	Silve	PEGF	Mikoyan-Gurevich	Midget	
MiG-15	MI	Kalam	KAHM	Mikoyan-Gurevich	Midget	1B-01621
MiG-15	NJ	Cape May	NASWF	Mikoyan-Gurevich	Midget	N51MG
MiG-15	NV	FAllon	NASF	Mikoyan-Gurevich	Midget	
MiG-15	NV	Reno	SAFB	Mikoyan-Gurevich	Midget	
MiG-15	OH	Dayto	USAFM	Mikoyan-Gurevich	Midget	20-15357
MiG-15	TX	Amirillo	EFA&SM	Mikoyan-Gurevich	Midget	#509
MiG-15	TX	San Angelo	GAFB	Mikoyan-Gurevich	Midget	
MiG-15	UT	Heber	HVAM	Mikoyan-Gurevich	Midget	
MiG-15	VA	Quant	MCAGM	Mikoyan-Gurevich	Midget	1317
MiG-15	ONT-C	Ottawa	CAM	Mikoyan-Gurevich	Midget	1317
MiG-15	WA	Seattle	MoF	Mikoyan-Gurevich	Midget	79
MiG-15	WI	Oshko	EAAAAM	Mikoyan-Gurevich	Midget	N15MG
MiG-15 (2 Seater)	MN	Minneapolis	MAGM	Mikoyan-Gurevich	Midget	
MiG-15 (2 Seater)	NM	STere	WEAM	Mikoyan-Gurevich	Midget	640
MiG-15bis	AZ	Tucso	PAM	Mikoyan-Gurevich	Midget	Man Sn 1A-06-038, 822, VK-1 Engine
MiG-15UTI	AZ	Tucso	PAM	Mikoyan-Gurevich	Midget	38, N38BM
MiG-15UTI	OR	Mc Minnville	EAEC	Mikoyan-Gurevich	Midget	IA-242271, 38, NX271JM
MiG-15UTI/SB	TX	Addison	CFM	Mikoyan-Gurevich	Midget	
MiG-17	AL	Huntsville	AC	Mikoyan-Gurevich	Fresco	
MiG-17	AZ	Mesa	CFM	Mikoyan-Gurevich	Fresco	
MiG-17	AZ	Mesa	CAF-AWM	Mikoyan-Gurevich	Fresco	
MiG-17	CA	Chino	PoFAM	Mikoyan-Gurevich	Fresco	
MiG-17	CA	Oakland	CAF-GGW	Mikoyan-Gurevich	Fresco	
MiG-17	CA	San Diego	SDAM	Mikoyan-Gurevich	Fresco	
MiG-17	FL	Tittusvill	VACM	Mikoyan-Gurevich	Fresco	
MiG-17	KS	New Century	CAF-HoAW	Mikoyan-Gurevich	Fresco	Ic1717, N1717M
MiG-17	KS	Topek	CAM	Mikoyan-Gurevich	Fresco	611
MiG-17	MN	Blaine	ACBA	Mikoyan-Gurevich	Fresco	Owner: Douog Weske
MiG-17	NV	Fallon	NASF	Mikoyan-Gurevich	Fresco	
MiG-17	NV	Reno	SAFB	Mikoyan-Gurevich	Fresco	
MiG-17	NY	Horseheads	NWM	Mikoyan-Gurevich	Fresco	
MiG-17	OH	Dayto	USAFM	Mikoyan-Gurevich	Fresco	799
MiG-17	OH	N Canton	MAM	Mikoyan-Gurevich	Fresco	
MiG-17(Lim-5)	TN	Sevierville	TMoA	Mikoyan-Gurevich	Fresco	IC1706
MiG-17(Lim-5R)	TN	Sevierville	TMoA	Mikoyan-Gurevich	Fresco	IC1728
MiG-17	TX	Addison	CFM	Mikoyan-Gurevich	Fresco	
MiG-17	UT	Ogden	CFM	Mikoyan-Gurevich	Fresco	
MiG-17	WA	Seattle	MoF	Mikoyan-Gurevich	Fresco	1406016, IFJ-10
MiG-17A	GA	Pooler	MEAFM	Mikoyan-Gurevich	Fresco	
MiG-17A	GA	Warner Robin	MoF	Mikoyan-Gurevich	Fresco	54- 713 85
MiG-17F	AZ	Tucso	PAM	Mikoyan-Gurevich	Fresco C	1C 1905
MiG-17F	NY	Glenville	ESAM	Mikoyan-Gurevich	Fresco C	605
MiG-17F	RI	NKing	QAM	Mikoyan-Gurevich	Fresco C	1F0325
MiG-17PF	AZ	Tucso	PAM	Mikoyan-Gurevich	Fresco D	Man Sn 1A06038, 634
MiG-17PF	CA	Sacra	McCelAFB	Mikoyan-Gurevich	Fresco D	1186
MiG-19	CA	Riverside	MFAM	Mikoyan	Farmer	0301, A-5(F-9) Fantan, F-6 = China
MiG-19	CA	Riverside	MFAM	Mikoyan	Farmer	0409
MiG-19	NV	Reno	SAFB	Mikoyan	Farmer	
MiG-19S	OH	Dayto	USAFM	Mikoyan	Farmer	TB, 972, A-5(F-9) Fantan, F-6 = China
MiG-21 PFM	AZ	Tucson	PAM	Mikoyan	Fishbed	N21MF
MiG-21	AL	Birmingham	SMoF	Mikoyan	Fishbed	
MiG-21	CA	Riverside	MAFM	Mikoyan	Fishbed	1101
MiG-21	FL	Kissi	YAF	Mikoyan	Fishbed	
MiG-21	FL	Shali	USAFAM	Mikoyan	Fishbed	85 , RED
MiG-21	LA	Bossier City	BAFB	Mikoyan	Fishbed	
MiG-21	MD	Silver Hill	PEGF	Mikoyan	Fishbed	
MiG-21PF	MI	Kalam	KAHM	Mikoyan	Fishbed	4107
MiG-21F	NE	Ashland	SACM	Mikoyan	Fishbed-C	60-2105
MiG-21	NY	Horseheads	NWM	Mikoyan	Fishbed	
MiG-21	OH	Dayto	HAFBM	Mikoyan	Fishbed	
MiG-21	OH	Dayto	USAFM	Mikoyan	Fishbed	560-301, "City of Moscow"
MiG-21	OK	Wetherford	GTSM	Mikoyan	Fishbed	
MiG-21 MF	ON-C	Trenton	RCAFMM	Mikoyan	Fishbed	23 45
MiG-21	TX	Addison	CFM	Mikoyan	Fishbed	
MiG-21	UT	Ogden	HAFBM	Mikoyan	Fishbed	
MiG-21-D	VA	Quantico	MCAGM	Mikoyan	Fishbed	507
MiG-21 PF	WA	Seatt	MoF	Mikoyan	Fishbed	TT1697, 4315
MiG-21 PFM	WA	Seatt	MoF	Mikoyan	Fishbed	5411

MiG-21(F-7)	WI	Oshko	EAAAAM	Mikoyan	Fishbed	N21MG
MiG-21F	CA	Sacra	McCelAFB	Mikoyan	Fishbed	201
MiG-21PFM	NM	STere	WEAM	Mikoyan	Fishbed	
MiG-21PFM	NY	NYC	ISASM	Mikoyan	Fishbed	4105
MiG-21PFM	NY	Glenville	ESAM	Mikoyan	Fishbed	2406
MiG-21U	TN	Sevierville	TMoA	Mikoyan	Fishbed	
MiG-23	CA	Riverside	MAFM	Mikoyan	Flogger	5744
MiG-23	NV	Fallon	NASF	Mikoyan	Flogger	353
MiG-23	OH	Dayton	USAFM	Mikoyan	Flogger	
MiG-23	QC-C	La Baie	ADM	Mikoyan	Flogger	
MiG-29 Flogger D	CA	Chino	YAM	RS Systems	Target Drone	
MiG-29	OH	Dayton	USAFM	Mikoyan	Fulcrum	
MiG-29	TX	San Angelo	GAFB	Mikoyan	Fulcrum	
Miles Atwood	CA	Chino	PoFAM	Miles Atwood	Air Racer	
Miles Atwood	OH	Leroy	PRA	Miles Atwood	Air Racer	
Miller S-1 Fly Rod	KS	Liberalal	MAM	Miller	Fly Rod	
Miller Special 1949	CA	Whittier	WM	Miller	Racer	JM-101, Ol' Tiger, N74J
Miller Tern	NY	Elmira	NSM	Miller	Tern	N8591
Milliken Special	ME	OwlsH	OHTM	Milliken	Special	
Mini-Cab	WA	Vancouver	PAM			
Minimora	NY	Elmir	NSM	Minimora		56, N16923
Mitchell Wing B-10 Buzzard	AL	Birmi	Southe	Mitchell	Buzzard	Wing Ultralight
Mitchell Nimbus III	NY	Elmira	NSM	Mitchell	Nimbus III	N7864
MMC-845	CA	Rosam	EAFB			1454
Monerai S	AL	Birmi	Southe	Monerai	Powered Sailplane	
Monerai S	CT	Winds	NEAM	Monerai	Powered Sailplane	
Mong Sport	IL	Rantoul	OCAM	Mong	Sport	N1174
Mong Sport	WI	Oshko	EAAAAM	Mong	Sport	
Moni Motor Glider	CO	Aurora	WOTR	Monnett	Motor Glider	N39JG
Moni Motor Glider	FL	Lakel	SFAF	Monnett	Motor Glider	N46431
Moni Motor Glider	KS	Liberal	MAAM	Monnett	Motor Glider	
Moni Motor Glider	MD	Silve	PEGF	Monnett	Motor Glider	
Moni Motor Glider	WI	Oshko	EAAAAM	Monnett	Motor Glider	N153MX
Moni Motor Glider	WI	Oshko	EAAAAM	Monnett	Motor Glider	N82MX
Moni Motor Glider	WI	Oshko	EAAAAM	Monnett	Motor Glider	N107MX
Monnett Sonerai II	AL	Birmingham	SMoF	Monnett	Sonerai II	N11ME
Monnett Sonerai II	IN	LaPorte	DPAM	Monnett	Sonerai II	
Monnett Sonerai II	WI	Oshko	EAAAAM	Monnett	Sonerai II	N11ME
Monocoupe	PA	Readi	Restrant	Monocoupe		
Monocoupe	WY	Greyb	H&PA	Monocoupe		
Monocoupe 90A	PA	Bethel	GAAM	Monocoupe		NC11750
Monocoupe 90A	WI	Oshko	EAAAAM	Monocoupe		N11783
Monocoupe 110	CA	Oakla	OWAM	Monocoupe	Special	
Monocoupe 110	ID	Athol	NAM	Monocoupe	Special	
Monocoupe 110	MD	College Park	CPAM	Monocoupe	Special	NC 12345
Monocoupe 110	ND	Minot	DTAM	Monocoupe	Special	
Monocoupe 110	WI	Oshko	EAAAAM	Monocoupe	Special	N15E
Monocoupe 110	WI	Oshko	EAAAAM	Monocoupe	Special	NC533W
Monocoupe 113	NY	Rhine	ORA	Monocoupe		
Monocoupe 113	WI	Oshko	EAAAAM	Monocoupe		N7808
Monocoupe 90	IA	Ottumwa	APM	Monocoupe		504, NC170K
Monoprep	IA	Ottumwa	APM			6077, NC179K
Monte Copter 12	CA	Ramona	CR	Monte	Copter 12	
Montgomery Glider	CA	Hawth	WMoF	Montgomery	Evergreen Glider	
Montgomery Glider	CA	San Diego	SDAM	Montgomery	Evergreen Glider	
Montgomery Gull Glider	CA	SCarl	HAM	Stearman-Hammond	Gull Glider	
Montgomery Santa Clara	CA	SCarl	HAM	Montgomery	Glider	
Montgmery Evergreen	CA	SCarl	HAM	Montgomery	Evergreen Glider	
Mooney	FL	Dayto	ERAU	Mooney		
Mooney	MO	SLoui	SLDPA	Mooney		
Mooney M.18C	AL	Birmingham	SmoF	Mooney	Mite	
Mooney M.18C	BC-C	Langley	CMoF	Mooney	Mite	
Mooney M.18C	IA	Ottumwa	APM	Mooney	Mite	210, NC329M
Mooney M.18C	KS	Liberal	MAAM	Mooney	Mite	
Mooney M.18C	KS	Wichita	KAM	Mooney	Mite	
Mooney M.18C	OK	Fredi	AAM	Mooney	Mite	
Mooney M.18C	WA	Vancouver	PAM	Mooney	Mite	
Mooney M.20B	OK	Fredi	AAM	Mooney	Mite	
Morrisey Bravo	IA	Ottumwa	APM	Morrisey	Bravo	TRGR-1, N37HM
Mosquito H. Glider	CT	Winds	NEAM		Mosquito HG	
MPA	PA	Tough	CFCM			
MS 181	WI	Oshko	EAAAAM	Morane-Saulnier		N304JX
MS 230	BC-C	Langley	CMoF	Morane-Saulnier		
MS 230	CA	Chino	SDAM	Morane-Saulnier		
MS 230	CA	San Diego	SDAM	Morane-Saulnier		N7461
MS 230	FL	Polk	FoF	Morane-Saulnier		
MS 230	IL	Chica	MoS&I	Morane-Saulnier		
MS 500	AZ	Tucson	PAM	Morane-Saulnier	Cricquet	
MS A-1	NY	Rhine	ORA	Morane-Saulnier		
MS Alcyon 733	MI	Kalamazoo	KAHM	Morane-Saulnier		
MS BB	AL	Gunte	LGARFM	Morane-Saulnier		
MSK	NM	Moriarty	SSM	Kensure	Glider	
Muller Arrow	BC-C	Langley	CMoF	Muller	Hang Glider	
Mummert 13223	MI	Detro		Mummert	Mercury	
Mutual Aviation Blackbird	CA	El Cajon	SDAMGF	Mutual Aviation	Blackbird	
MXY7	AZ	Grand Canyon	PoFGCVA	Yokosuka	Ohka II	
MXY7	MD	Silve	PEGF	Yokosuka	Ohka II	
MXY7-K1	OH	Dayto	USAFM	Yokosuka	Ohka II	
MXY7-K1 Trainer	OH	Dayto	USAFM	Yokosuka	Ohka II	
MXY7-K2	MD	Silve	PEGF	Yokosuka	Ohka II	
N-1M	MD	Silve	PEGF	Northrop	Flying Wing	
N-62 JAMCO	WA	Seatt	MoF	JAMCO		
N-9H	FL	Pensa	USNAM	Burgess	Curtiss	N-9
N1K1	FL	Pensa	USNAM	Kawanishi	George	343-A-19
N1K2-J	FL	Pensa	USNAM	Kawanishi	George	343-A-19
N1K2-J	MD	Silve	PEGF	Kawanishi	George	
N1K2-J	OH	Dayto	USAFM	Kawanishi	George	5312
N2C-2	FL	Pensa	USNAM	Curtiss	Fledgling	A8529
N2S	NC	Hendersonville	WNCAM	Boeing-Stearman	Kaydet	
N2S-2	WA	Olympia	OFM	Boeing-Stearman	Kaydet	
N2S-2	AR	Fayet	AAM	Boeing-Stearman	Kaydet	N5862
N2S-2(PT-17)	TX	Addison	CFM	Boeing-Stearman	Kaydet	214
N2S-3				Boeing-Stearman	Kaydet	03401, Side # 401

Model	State	City	Museum	Manufacturer	Type	Notes
N2S-3	CA	San Diego	SDAM	Boeing-Stearman	Kaydet	N1301M, 5414, 39
N2S-3	CA	Shafter	MFAM	Boeing-Stearman	Kaydet	
N2S-3(B75N1)	CA	Palm Springs	PSAM	Boeing-Stearman	Kaydet	75-7990, N81235, Side 289,
N2S-3	FL	Pensa	USNAM	Boeing-Stearman	Kaydet	569, 41
N2S-3(PT-17)	IL	Glenview	VM	Boeing-Stearman	Kaydet	
N2S-3(PT-17)	IN	India	CMoI	Boeing-Stearman	Kaydet	
N2S-3(PT-17)	NY	Horseheads	NWM	Boeing-Stearman	Kaydet	07190
N2S-3	VA	Hampton	VA&SM	Boeing-Stearman	Kaydet	
N2S-3	VA	Quant	MCAGM	Boeing-Stearman	Kaydet	07481
N2S-4(PT-17)	WA	Vashon	OTA	Boeing-Stearman	Kaydet	Model 73, N68827
N2S-4(A75L3)	WY	Jackson	GWFM	Boeing Stearman	Kaydet	
N2S-4(A75N1)	CA	S.Mon	MoF	Boeing-Stearman	Kaydet	
N2S-5	CA	Palm Springs	PSAM	Boeing-Stearman	Kaydet	N5359N
N2S-5	WA	Seattle	MoF	Boeing-Stearman	Kaydet	
N2S-5	FL	Pensa	USNAM	Boeing-Stearman	Kaydet	43156
N2S-5	MD	Silve	PEGF	Boeing-Stearman	Kaydet	
N2S3(B-75N-1)	PA	Readi	MAAM	Boeing-Stearman	Kaydet	
N4S	NC	Hendersonville	WNCAM	Stearman	Kaydet	
N2T-1	FL	Pensa	USNAM	Timm	Tuter	32478, 312
N2T-1	MI	Kalam	KAHM	Timm	Tuter	32622
N2Y-1	FL	Pensa	USNAM	Consolidated	Fleet I	A8605
N3N	AZ	Tucso	PAM	Naval Aircraft Factory	Yellow Peril	N45084, 4497
N3N	CO	Denve	JWDAS	Naval Aircraft Factory	Yellow Peril	
N3N	ID	Driggs	TAC	Naval Aircraft Factory	Yellow Peril	
N3N	ID	Twin	NWWI	Naval Aircraft Factory	Yellow Peril	
N3N	MI	Kalam	KAHM	Naval Aircraft Factory	Yellow Peril	2951
N3N	NV	Carso	YF	Naval Aircraft Factory	Yellow Peril	
N3N	SC	Mt Pl	PPM	Naval Aircraft Factory	Yellow Peril	
N3N	TX	C Christi	CCMOS&H	Naval Aircraft Factory	Yellow Peril	
N3N	TX	C Christi	USS Lexi	Naval Aircraft Factory	Yellow Peril	2959, 703
N3N	TX	Houst	CAF-WHS	Naval Aircraft Factory	Yellow Peril	N44741, "The Real Thing",
N3N-3	CA	Chino	YAM	Naval Aircraft Factory	Yellow Peril	2621, N44757, 2621
N3N-3	CA	Chino	YAM	Naval Aircraft Factory	Yellow Peril	2685, N45265, 2685
N3N-3	CA	Chino	YAM	Naval Aircraft Factory	Yellow Peril	2804, N45070, 2804
N3N-3	CA	Chino	YAM	Naval Aircraft Factory	Yellow Peril	2827, N45280, 2827
N3N-3	CA	Chino	YAM	Naval Aircraft Factory	Yellow Peril	4480, N695M, 4480
N3N-3	FL	Pensa	USNAM	Naval Aircraft Factory	Yellow Peril	2693
N3N-3	FL	Pensa	USNAM	Naval Aircraft Factory	Yellow Peril	N6399T, 3046
N3N-3	MI	Ypsil	YAF	Naval Aircraft Factory	Yellow Peril	
N3N-3	MO	Maryland Hts	HARM	Naval Aircraft Factory	Yellow Peril	
N3N-3	PA	Readi	MAAM	Naval Aircraft Factory	Yellow Peril	Side # 46
N3N-3	TX	Galve	LSFM	Naval Aircraft Factory	Yellow Peril	N3NZ, 1974
N9M-B	CA	Chino	PoFAM	Northrop	Flying Wing	004, N9MB
N22S	AZ	Tucson	PAM	A/C Factories	Nomad	Man Sn F163, N6328, VH-HVZ, Searchmaster
Nangchang CJ-6A	CA	Santa Rosa	PCAM			
Nangchang C-5-6A	PA	Beaver Falls	AHM			
NASA Parasev	MD	Silve	PEGF	NASA	Paresev	
Navion	CA	Chino	PoFAM	Ryan	Navion	
Navion	GA	Calho	Mercer A	Ryan	Navion	
Navion B	MN	Blaine	Airport	Ryan	Navion	B488DS
NB-8G	MO	Maryland Hts	HARM	Nicolas-Beazley	NB-8G	
NC-9-A	FL	Pensa	USNAM		Pilgram	Gondola
NC5-Rotormatic	CA	SCarl	HAM		Rotormatic	
NE-1(J3C-65)	AR	Fayetteville	AAM	Piper	Cub	
NE-1(J3C-65)	PA	Readi	MAAM	Piper	Cub	
Nelson Dragonfly BB-1	CA	Santa Martin	WoHAM	Nelson	Dragonfly	N4ND
Nelson Dragonfly BB-1	MD	Silve	PEGF	Nelson	Dragonfly	
Nelson Dragonfly BB-1	NY	Elmira	NSM	Nelson	Dragonfly	N34921
Nelson Hummingbird	CA	SCarl	HAM	Nelson	Hummingbird	N68583
Nelson Hummingbird	NY	Elmira	NSM	Nelson	Hummingbird	N68584
Nesmith	IA	Ottumwa	APM	Nesmith	Cougar	L-1, N10162
NF-11(TT-20)	CA	Rosam	EAFB	Gloster	Meteor	
Niemi Sisu 1-A	NY	Elmira	NSM	Niemi	Susi 1-A	N255JB
Nieuport 10	NY	Rhine	ORA	Nieuport		
Nieuport 11 7/8 Scale	CA	Riverside	MAFM	Nieuport		
Nieuport 11	CA	Santa Martin	WoHAM	Nieuport		
Nieuport 11	CA	San Diego	SDAM	Nieuport	Bebe	N1486
Nieuport 11	NC	Hende	WNCAM	Nieuport	Bebe	N8217V
'Nieuport 11	OK	Oklah	KCASM	Nieuport	Bebe	
Nieuport 12	ON-C	Ottaw	CAM	Nieuport		
Nieuport 17	ON-C	Ottaw	CAM	Nieuport	Bebe	
Nieuport 17	ON-C	Ottaw	CWM	Nieuport	Bebe	
Nieuport 17	OR	Eugene	OA&SM	Nieuport	Bebe	
Nieuport 24	WA	Seattle	MoF	Nieuport		N24RL
Nieuport 24	WI	Oshko	EAAAAM	Nieuport		N65113, McGlothen
Nieuport 27	AZ	Mesa	CFM	Nieuport		N5597M, H
Nieuport 27	NY	River	RE	Nieuport		
Nieuport 27	WA	Seattle	MoF	Nieuport		N5597M, H
Nieuport 28	AL	Gunte	LGARFM	Nieuport		
Nieuport 28	AZ	Mesa	CFM	Nieuport		
Nieuport 28	CA	San Diego	SDAM	Nieuport		N28GH, 6
Nieuport 28	FL	Pensa	USNAM	Nieuport		5769, 21
Nieuport 28	IA	Hampton	DWWIAM	Nieuport		
Nieuport 28	ME	OwlsH	OHTM	Nieuport		
Nieuport 28	OH	Dayto	USAFM	Nieuport		N8539
Nieuport 28	WA	Seattle	MoF	Nieuport		14
Nieuport 28C-1	AL	Ozark	USAAM	Nieuport		
Nieuport 28C-1	MD	Silve	PEGF	Nieuport		
Nieuport 28C1	CA	Chino	PoFAM	Nieuport		
Nieuport 17 7/8 Scale	BC-C	Sidne	BCAM	Nieuport		
Nimbus II	KY	Lexington	AMoK	Schemp-Hirth	Nimbus II	N257JB
Nimbus II	WI	Oshko	EAAAAM	Schemp-Hirth	Nimbus II	N257JB
Nixon Special	CT	Winds	NEAM	Nixon	Special	
Nord 1002	FL	FtLau	WJAIS&L	Nord	Taifun	
Nord 1002	PA	Readi	MAAM	Nord	Taifun	
Nord 1101	OR	Tillamook	TAM	Nord	Noralpha	
Nord 1101	PA	Readi	MAAM	Nord	Noralpha	N1101M
Nord 3202	CO	Aurora	WOTR	Nord	Taifun	
Northrop Alhpa 4A	DC	Washi	NA&SM	Northrop	Alpha	"TWA"
Northrop Delta Fuse	ON-C	Ottaw	CAM	Northrop	Delta	
Northrop Gama	DC	Washi	NA&SM	Northrop	Gama "Polar Star"	
Northrup	IA	Greenfield	IAM	Northrop	Primary GLider	
NR-1W	ID	StMar	D.Freema	Nicholas-Beazley		

158

NR-1W	NY	Bayport	BA	Nicholas-Beazley		
NR-1W	NY	Rhine	ORA	Nicholas-Beazley		
NT-1	FL	Pensa	USNAM	New Standard		A8588
NW Porterfield	KS	Liberal	MAAM	Northwest-Porterfield		
O- 1E	MN	Blaine	AWAM			
O- 2A	AZ	Tucso	PAM	Cessna	Super Skymaster	68-6901, N37581
O- 2A	CA	Atwater	CAM	Cessna	Super Skymaster	67-21413
O- 2A	CA	El Cajon	WW	Cessna	Super Skymaster	
O- 2A	CA	Fairf	TAFB	Cessna	Super Skymaster	
O- 2A	OH	Dayton	USAFM	Cessna	Super Skymaster	62-1345
O- 2A	CO	Denve	69thB	Cessna	Super Skymaster	
O- 2A	CO	Denve	JWDAS	Cessna	Super Skymaster	
O- 2A	FL	FtWal	HF	Cessna	Super Skymaster	67-21368
O- 2A	FL	Shali	USAFAM	Cessna	Super Skymaster	86864
O- 2A	HI	Oahu	WAFB	Cessna	Super Skymaster	
O- 2A	IL	Ranto	OCAM	Cessna	Super Skymaster	67-21411
O- 2A	IN	Peru	GAFB	Cessna	Super Skymaster	68-6871
O- 2A	MD	Silve	PEGF	Cessna	Super Skymaster	
O- 2A	MI	Mt Clemens	SMAM	Cessna	Super Skymaster	67-21340
O- 2A	MN	Blaine	AWAM	Cessna	Super Skymaster	
O- 2A	NC	Asheboro	PFAC	Cessna	Super Skymaster	"Navy"
O- 2A	NC	Asheboro	PFAC	Cessna	Super Skymaster	"Air Force"
O- 2A	OH	Dayto	USAFM	Cessna	Super Skymaster	67-21331
O 2A	OH	Lockb	RANGB	Cessna	Super Skymaster	69-7630
O- 2A	OH	N Canton	MAM	Cessna	Super Skymaster	
O- 2A	RI	NKing	QAM	Cessna	Super Skymaster	68-10997
O- 2A	SC	Sumte	SAFB	Cessna	Super Skymaster	
O- 2A (337)	KS	Liberal	MAAM	Cessna	Super Skymaster	
O- 2A	SD	Rapid	SDA&SM	Cessna	Super Skymaster	
O- 2A	TX	Abile	DLAP	Cessna	Super Skymaster	67-21326
O- 2A	TX	San A	LAFB	Cessna	Super Skymaster	67-21440
O- 2A	UT	Ogden	HAFBM	Cessna	Super Skymaster	
O- 2A	WA	Everett	MoFRC	Cessna	Super Skymaster	67-21363, N18BB
O- 2A	WI	CDoug	WNGML&M	Cessna	Super Skymaster	
O- 2A (2 ea)	GA	Warner Robin	MoF	Cessna	Super Skymaster	68- 6894
O- 2A(GO)	TX	Austi	BAFB	Cessna	Super Skymaster	
O- 2B	CA	Riverside	MFAM	Cessna	Super Skymaster	67-21465
O- 2B	IN	Indianapolis	AMHF	Cessna	Super Skymaster	"Twigger Happy", 997
O- 2B	IN	Indianapolis	AMHF	Cessna	Super Skymaster	Project
O- 2B	KS	Wichi	KAM	Cessna	Super Skymaster	
O- 3A(YO)	AZ	Tucso	PAM			69-18006
O- 3A(YO)	CA	Hawth	WMoF			
O-38F	OH	Dayto	USAFM	Douglas		3-30324
O-46A	OH	Dayto	USAFM	Douglas		35-179
O-47	CA	Chino	PoFAM	North American	Observation Plane	
O-47A	MN	Minne	MAGM	North American	Observation Plane	38-295
O-47A(RO)	MD	Silve	PEGF	North American	Observation Plane	
O-47B	KS	Topek	CAM	North American	Observation Plane	
O-47B	OH	Dayto	USAFM	North American	Observation Plane	37-328, 39-112
O-52	AZ	Tucson	PAM	Curtiss	Owl	40-2746
O-52	CA	Chino	YAM	Curtiss	Owl	40- 2746, N61241
O-52	OH	Dayto	USAFM	Curtiss	Owl	40- 2763
O-52	OH	Newbu	WASAC	Curtiss	Owl	
O1-A	CO	Denver	69thB	FAC		
OA- 1A	OH	Dayto	USAFM		Loening	26- 431
OA-10A(PBY-5A)	AZ	Tucson	PAM	Consolidated	Catalina	44-34049, N322FA
OA-10A(PBY-5A)	OH	Dayto	USAFM	Consolidated	Catalina	44-33879, 46595
OA-12A(J2F-6)	OH	Dayto	USAFM	Grumman	Duck	48-563, 33587
Ohka 11 MXY7	AZ	Grand	PoFGCVA	Kugisho	Baka	I-18
Ohka 11 MXY7	CA	Chino	YAM	Kugisho	Baka	I-18 Yokosuka
Ohm Special Racer	NY	Hammo	CM	Ohm	Special Racer	
Oldfield Special BGL	WI	Oshko	EAAAAM	Oldfield	Special BGL	N11311
Olmstead Pusher	MD	Silve	PEGF	Olmstead	Pusher	
OMAC-1	WA	Seatt	MoF			
OPAS Buhl	ON-C	Sault Ste Marie	CBHC			
Ornithopter 1510	CA	San Diego	SDAM	Ornithopter		
OS2U	AL	Mobil	BMP	Vought	Kingfisher	BU0951, 60
OS2U	NC	Wilmi	USSNCBC	Vought	Kingfisher	
OS2U	VA	Suffolk	FF	Vought	Kingfisher	Storage in Virginia Beach
OS2U-3	CA	Chino	YAM	Vought-Skirosky	Kingfisher	9643, 9643
OS2U-3	FL	Pensa	USNAM	Vought-Skirosky	Kingfisher	7534, 5926
OS2U-3	MD	Silve	PEGF	Vought-Skirosky	Kingfisher	
OV- 1	GA	Dobbi	DAFB	Grumman	Mohawk	
OV- 1	MN	Blaine	AWAM	Grumman	Mohawk	61-5936
OV- 1	OR	Mc Minnville	EAEC	Grumman	Mohawk	
OV- 1B	GA	Hampton	AAHF	Grumman	Mohawk	
OV- 1B	NY	Garden City	CoAM	Grumman	Mohawk	59-2633
OV- 1	NY	Horseheads	NWM	Grumman	Mohawk	62-5856, N6744
OV- 1A(JOV)	MN	Blaine	AWAM	Grumman	Mohawk	62-5856, N6744
OV- 1B	MN	Blaine	AWAM	Grumman	Mohawk	62-5856, N6744
OV- 1B (2 ea)	AL	Ozark	USAAM	Grumman	Mohawk	59-2631
OV- 1B	TX	Amarillo	EFA&SM	Grumman	Mohawk	
OV- 1C	AZ	Tucso	PAM	Grumman	Mohawk	61-2724, "Dirty Dawg"
OV- 1C	FL	Clear	FMAM	Grumman	Mohawk	
OV- 1C(JOV)	MN	Blaine	AWAM	Grumman	Mohawk	61-2718, N-2036P
OV- 1C	NY	Horseheads	NWM	Grumman	Mohawk	62-05856
OV- 1D	AZ	FtHua	FH	Grumman	Mohawk	18930
OV- 1D	CO	Denver	69thB	Grumman	Mohawk	
OV- 1D	FL	Tittusville	VACM	Grumman	Mohawk	
OV- 1D	GA	Spart	GSMA	Grumman	Mohawk	
OV- 1D	MI	Kalam	KAHM	Grumman	Mohawk	68-16993, 993
OV- 1D	NC	Charlotte	CAM	Grumman	Mohawk	
OV- 1D	PA	Beaver Falls	AHM	Grumman	Mohawk	62-5856, N6744
OV- 1D	WI	Kenos	KMM	Grumman	Mohawk	67-18900, "Valdez II"
OV- 1D	WI	Kenos	KMM	Grumman	Mohawk	68-16992
OV- 1D	WI	Kenos	KMM	Grumman	Mohawk	
OV-2-5	OH	Dayton	USAFM			
OV- 3A(YO)	AL	Ozark	USAAM	Lockheed	Silent One	69-18000
OV-10	FL	Esther	HAP	Grumman	Bronco	
OV-10	KS	Liberal	MAAM	Grumman	Bronco	
OV-10	NC	Charlotte	CAM	Grumman	Bronco	155472
OV-10A	AZ	Tucso	DMAFB	Grumman	Bronco	
OV-10A(NH)	FL	Mary Esther	HF	Grumman	Bronco	67-14626

OV-10A	OH	Dayto	USAFM	Grumman	Bronco	68-3787	
OV-10D	AZ	Tucso	PAM	Grumman	Bronco	155499	
OV-10D	CA	Miramar	FLAM	Grumman	Bronco	UU, VMO-2	
OW-8	IA	Ottumwa	APM	Welch			
OY-1	CA	Miramar	FLAM	Convair	Sentinel		
OY-1	FL	Pensa	USNAM	Convair	Sentinel	60645	
OY-1/2	VA	Quant	MCAGM	Convair	Sentinel	120454	
P-1(F6C-1)	FL	Pensa	USNAM	Curtiss	Hawk	N6969A	
P-1(F6C-1)	MO	SLoui	SLDPA	Curtiss	Hawk		
P-1(F6C-4)	MD	Silve	PEGF	Curtiss	Hawk		
P-3A	FL	Jacks	NASJ	Lockheed	Orion	151374, LQ, 56	
P-3A	FL	Pensa	USNAM	Lockheed	Orion	152152, PJ, 1, VP-96	
P-3A	HI	Oahu	BPNAS	Lockheed	Orion	152169	
P-3A	HI	Kaneohe	KBMCAS	Lockheed	Orion		
P-3A	LA	New Orleans	Belle Chasse NAS	Lockheed	Orion		
P-3B	MI	Mt Clemens	SMAM	Lockheed	Orion	152748, VP-93	
P-3B	PA	Willow	WGNAS	Lockheed	Orion		
P-6 7/8 Scale	CA	Riverside	MAFM	Curtiss	Hawk	AC 32-240, N90DS	
P-6E(F6C)	OH	Dayto	USAFM	Curtiss	Hawk	32-261	
P-6E(F6C)	WI	Oshko	EAAAAM	Curtiss	Hawk	NX 606PE	
P-9 Pober Pixie EAA	KS	Liberal	MAAM	Pober	Pixie		
P-10 Cuby	WI	Oshko	EAAAAM	Wag-Aero	P-10 Cuby	NC23254, "Lil' Gonk"	
P-12 (F4B)	WA	Seatt	MoF	Boeing		N872H	
P-12E(F4B-4)	CA	Chino	PoFAM	Boeing			
P-12E(F4B-4)	OH	Dayto	USAFM	Boeing		31-599	
P-26A	CA	Chino	PoFAM	Boeing	Peashooter	Model 266	
P-26A	MD	Silver Hill	PEGF	Boeing	Peashooter	Model 266	
P-26A	OH	Dayto	USAFM	Boeing	Peashooter	Model 266	
P-35A	OH	Dayto	USAFM	Seversky		36-404	
P-36A	OH	Dayto	USAFM	Curtiss	Hawk	38-1	
P-38	AK	Anchorage	EAFB	Lockheed	Lightning	42-13400	
P-38	CA	Inglewood	PBR	Lockheed	Lightning		
P-38	FL	Kissi	FTWAM	Lockheed	Lightning	44-53242, N57496	
P-38	FL	Polk City	FOF	Lockheed	Lightning	42-26761	
P-38 Replica	IL	Wheeling	94 Aero Sq	Lockheed	Lightning		
P-38-L5	TX	Galve	LSFM	Lockheed	Lightning	44-53095, N9005R, 100, "Putt Putt Maru"	
P-38F-1-LO	KY	Middl	LS	Lockheed	Lightning	41-3630, N5757, 17630, "Glacier Girl"	
P-38J	MD	Chantilly	NASM	Lockheed	Lightning	42-67762	
P-38J 5/8 Rep	MI	Kalamazoo	KAHM	Lockheed	Lightning		
P-38J-20-LO	CA	Chino	PoFAM	Lockheed	Lightning	44-23314, N29Q, "Porky II"	
P-38J	UT	Ogden	HAFBM	Lockheed	Lightning	42-67638	
P-38L	AZ	Mesa	CFM	Lockheed	Lightning	44-53286, "Marge"	
P-38L	WI	Popla	RBM	Lockheed	Lightning	44-53087, N3800L, "Marge"	
P-38L-5-LO	OR	Tillamook	TAM	Lockheed	Lightning	44-27083, N38V, "Tangerine"	
P-38L-5-LO	OH	Dayto	USAFM	Lockheed	Lightning	44-53232, NX66678, FAH505	
P-38L-5-LO(F-5G)	CA	Chino	YAM	Lockheed	Lightning	44-27183, N718	
P-38L-5-LO(F-5G)	NJ	Trent	MGAFB	Lockheed	Lightning	44-53015, "Pudgy V"	
P-38L-5-LO(F-5G)	NM	STere	WEAM	Lockheed	Lightning	44-27087, N577JB, Relammpago/N345/Black	
P-38L-5-LO(F-5G)	OR	Mc Minnville	EAEC	Lockheed	Lightning	44-53186 197425-501, N503MH,	
P-38L-5-LO(F-5G)	WI	Oshko	EAAAAM	Lockheed	Lightning	44-53087, N3800L, 8342, "Marge"	
P-38M-5-LO	WA	Seattle	MoF	Lockheed	Lightning	44-53097, NL3JB, 4-JS, Displ:53097/4-JS	
P-39	AZ	Tucson	PAM	Bell	Airacobra		
P-39	FL	Polk	FoF	Bell	Airacobra		
P-39	OH	Newbu	WASAC	Bell	Airacobra		
P-39	VA	Suffolk	FF	Bell	Airacobra	Storage in Virginia Beach	
P-39N	PA	Beave	AHM	Bell	Airacobra	42-18814	
P-39N-0	CA	Chino	YAM	Bell	Airacobra	42-8740, N81575	
P-39N-5-BE	CA	Chino	PoFAM	Bell	Airacobra		
P-39Q	CA	Riverside	MFAM	Bell	Airacobra	42-20000	
P-39Q	MI	Kalam	KAHM	Bell	Airacobra	44-3908	
P-39Q-8-DC	NY	Buffa	B&ECNP	Bell	Airacobra	42-19995, "Snooks 2"	
P-39Q	NY	Niagara Falls	NAM	Bell	Airacobra	"Galloping Gertie"	
P-39Q	OH	Dayto	USAFM	Bell	Airacobra	44-3887	
P-39Q	OH	N Canton	MAM	Bell	Airacobra	42-18828	
P-39Q	TX	SMarc	CTWCAF	Bell	Airacobra	N6968	
P-39Q	VA	Hampt	VA&SC	Bell	Airacobra	220027	
P-39Q-20	CA	S.Mon	MoF	Bell	Airacobra		
P-40 Mock-Up	Hi	Wheeler	WAFB	Curtiss	Warhawk	41-18P, #155, 12 Mock-Ups	
P-40	CA	Inglewood	PBR	Curtiss	Warhawk		
P-40	KS	Tipton	NAM	Curtiss	Warhawk	Kenneth Kake	
P-40	ND	Fargo	FAM	Curtiss	Kittyhawk		
P-40	TX	Burne	CAF-OC	Curtiss	Warhawk	N1226N	
P-40	TX	Hawki	RRSA	Curtiss	Warhawk	P-40D&E in RAF/RCAF=Kittyhawk	
P-40 Replica	HI	Oahu	WAFB	Curtiss	Warhawk		
P-40C	FL	Pensa	USNAM	Curtiss	Warhawk	AK255	
P-40C	GA	Macon	MoA	Curtiss	Warhawk	AK295	
P-40C	WA	Eastsound	FHC	Curtiss	Warhawk	41-13390, N2689	
P-40E	AK	Anchorage	AAHM	Curtiss	Warhawk	AK 987	
P-40E	CA	Chino	YAM	Curtiss	Warhawk	AK827, N40245	
P-40E	CA	San Diego	SDAM	Curtiss	Warhawk	AK979, N40FT	
P-40E Rep	CO	CSpri	EJPSCM	Curtiss	Warhawk		
P-40E Mk.1	MD	Silver Hill	PEGF	Curtiss	Warhawk	AK875	
P-40E	FL	Kissi	FTWAM	Curtiss	Warhawk	41-5709	
P-40E	GA	Douglas	LF	Curtiss	Warhawk		
P-40E	GA	Griffin	CHF	Curtiss	Warhawk	41-35927 Tom Wilson	
P-40E	GA	Griffin	CHF	Curtiss	Warhawk	41-5709 Tom Wilson	
P-40E	ID	Nampa	WAM	Curtiss	Warhawk	AK933, N94466, AK863, John Paul	
P-40E	IL	Aurora	RH	Curtiss	Kittyhawk		
P-40E	IL	Batavia	RWH	Curtiss	Warhawk	AK899, N9837A, Richard W Hansen	
P-40E	IL	Herscher	HWP	Curtiss	Warhawk	AL137, N88917, Harlan W Porter	
P-40E	IL	Urban	RFIA	Curtiss	Warhawk	AK905, NX40PE	
P-40E Rep	LA	BRoug	LNWM	Curtiss	Warhawk	Tail # 191, "Joy"	
P-40E	MN-C	Carman	BD	Curtiss	Kittyhawk		
P-40E	MN	Granite Falls	RF	Curtiss	Warhawk	AK753, N4420K, Ron Fagan	
P-40E	MT	Kalispell	JS	Curtiss	Warhawk	AK752, N440PE, James E Smith	
P-40E	NM	STere	WEAM	Curtiss	Warhawk	AL152, N95JB	
P-40E	OH	Dayto	USAFM	Curtiss	Warhawk	AK987	
P-40E	ON-C	Ottaw	CAM	Curtiss	Kittyhawk	AL 135, 1076	
P-40E	TX	Midla	CAFFM	Curtiss	Kittyhawk	42-105867, N1226N	
P-40E	VA	Suffolk	FF	Curtiss	Kittyhawk	41-35918	
P-40E	VA	Suffolk	FF	Curtiss	Kittyhawk	41-35927, In Auckland New Zealand	
P-40K	AZ	Tucson	PAM	Curtiss	Warhawk	42-45984	
P-40K	OR	Mc Minnville	TASM	Curtiss	Warhawk	42-9749, FR293	

Model	State	City	Code	Manufacturer	Name	Notes
P-40K	KY	Louisville	DT	Curtiss	Warhawk	42-9733, N4436J, Dick Thurman
P-40K	GA	Griffin	CHF	Curtiss	Warhawk	42-10083 Tom Wilson
P-40K	KY	Louisville	BS	Curtiss	Warhawk	42-10266, N40K Bill Stebbins
P-40M	NY	Long Island	JC	Curtiss	Warhawk	43-5795, N1232N, Jeff Clyman
P-40N	AZ	Mesa	CFM	Curtiss	Warhawk	
P-40N	AZ	Tucson	PAM	Curtiss	Warhawk	A29-405
P-40N	CA	Chino	PoFAM	Curtiss	Warhawk	42-105192, 42-105951
P-40N	CA	Chino	PoFAM	Curtiss	Warhawk	42-106101
P-40N	CA	PalmS	PSAM	Curtiss	Warhawk	44-7084
P-40N	FL	Arcadia	HT	Curtiss	Warhawk	43-24362 Hall Thompson
P-40N	FL	Miami	WOM	Curtiss	Warhawk	
P-40N	FL	Polk City	FoF	Curtiss	Warhawk	44-47923
P-40N	GA	Douglas	TW	Curtiss	Warhawk	42-46111
P-40N	ID	Boise	JP	Curtiss	Warhawk	42-106396, N1195N, John Paul
P-40N	ID	Nampa	WAM	Curtiss	Warhawk	42-106396
P-40N	MA	Bedfo	HAFB	Curtiss	Warhawk	
P-40N	MI	Kalam	KAHM	Curtiss	Warhawk	44-7619, N222SU
P-40N	NC	Fayet	PAFB	Curtiss	Warhawk	,42-105702
P-40N	NY	Farmingdale	AAM	Curtiss	Warhawk	43-5795
P-40N	OH	N Canton	MAM	Curtiss	Warhawk	42-104818
P-40N	PA	Beave	AHM	Curtiss	Warhawk	
P-40N	TX	Addison	CFM	Curtiss	Warhawk	44-7369, 40, 40
P-40N	TX	SMarc	CTWCAF	Curtiss	Warhawk	
P-40N	UT	Ogden	HAM	Curtiss	Warhawk	42-105270
P-40N	WA	Seattle	MoF	Curtiss	Warhawk	44-7192, NL10626
P-40N(TP)	CA	Palm Sprg	PSAM	Curtiss	Warhawk	44-7284, NX999CD, "Miss Josephine"
P-40N Replica	CA	Riverside	MFAM	Curtiss	Warhawk	
P-40N-5-CU	GA	Warner Robin	MoF	Curtiss	Warhawk	42-105927
P-47 ½ Scale	AZ	Tucson	PAM	Gettings	Thunderbolt	42-8130, N555TN, Experimental
P-47	CA	Inglewood	PBR	Republic	Thunderbolt	
P-47	CA	PalmS	PSAM	Republic	Thunderbolt	45-49205 "Big Chief"
P-47	CA	Rialt	KA	Republic	Thunderbolt	45-49385, NX47D
P-47	FL	Polk City	FoF	Republic	Thunderbolt	44-32814
P-47	IL	Wheeling	94th Aero Sq	Republic	Thunderbolt	
P-47	OR	Tillamook	TAM	Republic	Thunderbolt	44-32817, N767WJ
P-47	TX	Midla	CAF-LF	Republic	Thunderbolt	N47TG
P-47D	CA	Chino	YAM	Republic	Thunderbolt	
P-47D	CA	Palm SPrg	PSAM	Republic	Thunderbolt	45-49205, NX47RP, Side # HVP, "Big Chief"
P-47D	CA	Farmingdale	AAM	Republic	Thunderbolt	44-90447, NX1345B, I-LH, 350FS,353FG
P-47D	CT	Winds	NEAM	Republic	Thunderbolt	45-49458, 54, "Norma"
P-47D	FL	Shali	USAFAM	Republic	Thunderbolt	44-89320, 26
P-47D	IL	Danville	MA	Republic	Thunderbolt	44-90471
P-47D	MI	Kalam	KAHM	Republic	Thunderbolt	45- 49181, N444SU
P-47D	NY	Farmingdale	AAM	Republic	Thunderbolt	
P-47D	OH	Dayto	USAFM	Republic	Thunderbolt	42-23278
P-47D	TN	Sevierville	TMoA	Republic	Thunderbolt	44-90438, NX647D
P-47D	TN	Sevierville	TMoA	Republic	Thunderbolt	44-90460, N9246B, Side #40, "Hun Hunter XVI"
P-47D	TX	Midla	CAFFM	Republic	Thunderbolt	
P-47D	UT	Ogden	HAM	Republic	Thunderbolt	
P-47D 3/8 Scale	WA	Bellevue	AM	Republic	Thunderbolt	
P-47D	WA	Seattle	MoF	Republic	Thunderbolt	42-8205 N14519, 88, "Big Stud"
P-47D Replica	SC	Sumte	SAFB	Republic	Thunderbolt	
P-47D-30	OH	Dayto	USAFM	Republic	Thunderbolt	45-49167
P-47D-30-NA	GA	Warner Robin	MoF	Republic	Thunderbolt	44-32691 LH-E
P-47L	OH	Newbu	WASAC	Republic	Thunderbolt	Fuse Only
P-47M	CA	Chino	YAM	Republic	Thunderbolt	42-27385, N27385
P-47N	CO	CSpri	EJPSCM	Republic	Thunderbolt	44-89425
P-47N	NY	Garde	CoAM	Republic	Thunderbolt	44-89444
P-47N	TX	Addison	CFM	Republic	Thunderbolt	44-89436, N47TB
P-47N	TX	Galveston	LSFM	Republic	Thunderbolt	42-25068, N47DG, "Little Demon"
P-47N	TX	San A	LAFB	Republic	Thunderbolt	44-89348
P-51	AL	Ozark	USAAM	North American	Mustang	44-72990
P-51	AL	Troy	TMA	North American	Mustang	
P-51	CA	Inglewood	PBR	North American	Mustang	
P-51	CA	Shafter	MFAM	North American	Mustang	N71FT, "Strega"
P-51	CA	Shafter	MFAM	North American	Mustang	"Huntress 3"
P-51	CT	Winds	NEAM	North American	Mustang	
P-51	FL	FtLau	WJAIS&L	North American	Mustang	
P-51	GA	Atlanta	ASG	North American	Mustang	
P-51	IA	CBluf	CAF-RU	North American	Mustang	N5428V
P-51	IL	Aurora	RH	North American	Mustang	
P-51	IL	Wheeling	94th Aero Sq	North American	Mustang	
P-51	IL	Sugar Grove	ACM	North American	Mustang	44-74813, N6301T, At Danville, IL (Restoration)
P-51	MN	StPau	CAF-SMW	North American	Mustang	N215CA, "Gunfighter"
P-51	MO	Branson	VMM	North American	Mustang	44-60356
P-51	NM	Albuquerque	KAFB	North American	Mustang	51-1400
P-51	NM	STere	WEAM	North American	Mustang	48-4850, "Ghost Rider"
P-51	ND	Wahpe	TSA	North American	Mustang	
P-51	OH	Cleve	100thBGR	North American	Mustang	
P-51K-NT-10	OH	Cleve	FCAAM	North American	Mustang	"Second Fiddle"
P-51	ON-C	Ottaw	CAM	North American	Mustang	9298
P-51	OR	Tillamook	TAM	North American	Mustang	
P-51	TX	Galve	LSFM	North American	Mustang	
P-51	UT	Heber	HVAM	North American	Mustang	
P-51	WA	Arlington	FHC	North American	Mustang	
P-51	WI	Madison	MWVM	North American	Mustang	
P-51 ½ Scale	IN	Auburn	HW	North American	Mustang	
P-51 Replica	GA	Savan	MEHM	North American	Mustang	
P-51(TF)	FL	Kissi	S51C	North American	Mustang	48-745, "Crazy Horse"
P-51(TF)	NM	STere	WEAM	North American	Mustang	48-4658, "Friendly Ghost"
P-51(XP)	WI	Oshko	EAAAM	North American	Mustang	41-38, NX51NA
P-51A	AZ	Grand	PoFGCVA	North American	Mustang	43- 6251, NX4235Y
P-51A	CA	Chino	PoFAM	North American	Mustang	
P-51D(CF)	WA	Seattle	MoF	North American	Mustang	NL151X, CV-J, "Ho! Hun"
P-51A	MA	Stow	BCF	North American	Mustang	
P-51A-1	CA	Chino	YAM	North American	Mustang	43- 6274, N90358, HY
P-51B	ID	Idaho Falls	PM	North American	Mustang	43-12112
P-51C	ID	Nampa	WAM	North American	Mustang	Project
P-51C	TX	Midla	CAFFM	North American	Mustang	
P-51D(F)	AL	Mobil	BMP	North American	Mustang	44-74216
P-51D	AZ	Grand Canyon	PoFGCVA	North American	Mustang	
P-51D	AZ	Mesa	CFM	North American	Mustang	
P-51D	CA	Chino	PoFAM	North American	Mustang	45-11582, N5441V, B6-Y, "Spam Cam, Glamorous Glen"

P-51D	CA	Chino	PoFAM	North American	Mustang	G4-U
P-51D-10	CA	Chino	YAM	North American	Mustang	44-74910, N74920
P-51D	CA	Fresn	FANG	North American	Mustang	
P-51D-5NA	CA	Los Angeles	CSC	North American	Mustang	44-13704, B7-H, "Ferocious Frankie"
P-51D	CA	PalmS	PSAM	North American	Mustang	44-74524, NL151HR, MY-F, "Dakota Kid II"
P-51D	CA	PalmS	PSAM	North American	Mustang	44-74908, N151BP, Side # S-E2, "Button Nose"
P-51D	CA	S.Mon	MoF	North American	Mustang	N51DP, 49, "Cotton Mouth"
P-51D-30NA	CA	S.Mon	MoF	North American	Mustang	44-74996, N5410V, 4, "Dago Red"
P-51D	CA	San Diego	SDAM	North American	Mustang	44-73683, N5551D, DGP
P-51D	CA	SRosa	PCAM	North American	Mustang	41-767, V-C5 A
P-51D	CO	Denver	CA	North American	Mustang	
P-51D	DC	Washi	NA&SM	North American	Mustang	
P-51D	DE	Dover	DAFB	North American	Mustang	569, #7, "Miss Kentucky State"
P-51D	FL	Lakeland	SNF	North American	Mustang	45-115-7, 41-3321, NL 921PHO, "Cripes A Mighty 3"
P-51D-11	FL	Shali	USAFAM	North American	Mustang	41-3571
P-51D	IL	Belvi	PW	North American	Mustang	44-63701, Owner: Bengt Kuller
P-51D-25NA	IL	Springfield	ACM	North American	Mustang	44-73287, N5445V "Worry Bird"
P-51D	IN	Hunti	WoF	North American	Mustang	44-72922, L2W, "Scat VII", Gen Olds, 434FS, 479FG
P-51D	IN	Valparaiso	IAM	North American	Mustang	45-11549
P-51D	KY	Louisville	CCA	North American	Mustang	44-73206, NL-375D, "Hurry Home Honey"
P-51D	KY	Louisville	CCA	North American	Mustang	44-11553, NL-51VF, "Shangrila"
P-51D	LA	Bossi	BAFB	North American	Mustang	"Moonbeam McSwine"
P-51D-30-NA	MI	Belleville	YAF	North American	Mustang	44-74474, N6341T,"Old Crow"
P-51D	MI	Kalam	KAHM	North American	Mustang	Winter Only
P-51D	MN	Minne	MAGM	North American	Mustang	47-5024, 489
P-51D	ND	Fargo	FAM	North American	Mustang	44-74404, Yellow, Blue & Silver, B-CH
P-51D	ND	Fargo	FANG	North American	Mustang	
P-51D	OH	Batavia	TSWM	North American	Mustang	"Cincinnati Miss"
P-51D	OH	Dayton	UASM	North American	Mustang	
P-51D	OR	Mc Minnville	EAEC	North American	Mustang	122 31302, N51DH
P-51D	PA	Pitts	PANG	North American	Mustang	
P-51D	TX	Breck	BAM	North American	Mustang	
P-51D-20-NA	TX	Addison	CFM	North American	Mustang	44-72339, N251JC, WD-C
P-51D	TX	Midla	CAFFM	North American	Mustang	
P-51D	UT	Ogden	HAFBM	North American	Mustang	41-3, OP-V, "Audrey"
P-51D	WA	Bellevue	AM	North American	Mustang	44-72364
P-51D-30NT	WA	Eastsound	HFM	North American	Mustang	44-11525, "Val-Halla" Racer
P-51D	WA	Olympia	OFM	North American	Mustang	
P-51D	WI	CDoug	WNGML&M	North American	Mustang	WIS-NG
P-51D	WVA	Charl	CANG	North American	Mustang	
P-51D	WI	Oshko	EAAAAM	North American	Mustang	
P-51D(XP)	WI	Oshko	EAAAAM	North American	Mustang	44-75007, N, "Paul I"
P-51H-5-NA	IL	Ranto	OCAM	North American	Mustang	44- 64265, MASS ANG
P-51H	TX	San A	LAFB	North American	Mustang	44-64376
P-51K	OH	Newbu	WASAC	North American	Mustang	
P-51K	SC	McEnt	MEANGB	North American	Mustang	
P-55(XP)	MI	Kalamazoo	KAHM	Curtiss	Ascender	42-78846
P-56(XP)	MD	Silve	PEGF	Northrop	Black Bullet	
P-56(XP)	WVA		Northrop	Northrop	Black Bullet	
P-59	NE	Minde	HWPV	Bell	Airacomet	
P-59(XP)	DC	Washi	NA&SM	Bell	Airacomet	
P-59A-1	CA	Riverside	MFAM	Bell	Airacomet	44-22614, Side 88
P-59A(YP)	CA	Chino	PoFAM	Bell	Airacomet	
P-59B	CA	Rosam	EAFB	Bell	Airacomet	44-22633
P-59B	OH	Dayto	USAFM	Bell	Airacomet	44-22650
P-61 Nose	MD	Ft Meade	QM	Northrop	Black Widow	
P-61B-1	PA	Readi	MAAM	Northrop	Black Widow	42-39445
P-61C	MD	Silve	PEGF	Northrop	Black Widow	
P-61C	OH	Dayto	USAFM	Northrop	Black Widow	43- 8353
P-63	FL	Lakeland	SNFAM	Bell	Kingcobra	
P-63	NJ	Atlanta	DWFFA	Bell	Kingcobra	
P-63	VA	Suffolk	FF	Bell	Kingcobra	N6763 Storage in Virginia Beach
P-63A	CA	Chino	Sq 1 Avi	Bell	Kingcobra	N 90805,Model 309
P-63A	MD	Silve	PEGF	Bell	Kingcobra	Model 309
P-63A	CA	Palm SPrg	PSAM	Bell	Kingcobra	NX163BP, 268864, "Pretty Polly"
P-63A	OH	Newbu	WASAC	Bell	Kingcobra	Model 309
P-63A	TX	Midla	CAFFM	Bell	Kingcobra	Model 309
P-63C	AZ	Mesa	GU	Bell	Kingcobra	43-11731
P-63C	CA	Chino	YAM	Bell	Kingcobra	42- 8170, N94501, Model 309
P-63E	AZ	Mesa	GU	Bell	Kingcobra	
P-63E	AZ	Tucso	PAM	Bell	Kingcobra	43-11727, N9003A, Model 309 (P-39)
P-63E	OH	Dayto	USAFM	Bell	Kingcobra	43-11728, Model 309
P-63G(RP)	TX	San A	LAFB	Bell	Kingcobra	45-57295, Model 309, Target Plane
P-75A	OH	Dayto	USAFM	Fisher	Eagle	44-44553
P-80(XP)	OH	Dayton	USAFM			
P-81(XP)	OH	Dayton	USAFM			
P1Y1-C	MD	Silve	PEGF	Kugisho	Frances (Ginga)	
P2B-1S	CA	Richm	AMS			
P2B-1S	FL	Polk	FoF			
P2V	AZ	Tucso	PAM	Lockheed	Neptune	N14448, 147957
P2V	CA	Mt View	MNAS	Lockheed	Neptune	
P2V	HI	Kaneohe	MB	Lockheed	Neptune	
P2V	NY	Brooklyn	NARF	Lockheed	Neptune	210
P2V	WY	Greyb	H&PA	Lockheed	Neptune	
P2V-1(P-2)	FL	Pensa	USNAM	Lockheed	Neptune	89082
P2V-1(P-2)	AZ	Tucson	PAM	Lockheed	Neptune	89082
P2V-1(XP)	FL	Pensa	USNAM	Lockheed	Neptune	
P2V-3	FL	Clear	FMAM	Lockheed	Neptune	Underwater in Ocean
P2V-5	CO	Puebl	PWAM	Lockheed	Neptune	128402
P2V-5	FL	Jacks	NASJ	Lockheed	Neptune	131410 LN-4
P2V-5	HI	Kaneohe	KBMCAS	Lockheed	Neptune	150279, VP-17 / VP-6
P2V-5	ME	Bruns	BNAS	Lockheed	Neptune	
P2V-7	AZ	Tucso	PAM	Lockheed	Neptune	135620
P2V-7	IN	India	IMoMH	Lockheed	Neptune	
P2V-7	NS-C	Greenwood	GMAM	Lockheed	Neptune	Side # VN101
P2V-7	OH	Newbu	WASAC	Lockheed	Neptune	140436
P2V-7	OR	Tillamook	TAM	Lockheed	Neptune	
P2V-7	PA	Beave	AHM	Lockheed	Neptune	
P2V-7	PA	Readi	MAAM	Lockheed	Neptune	144683
P2V-7(SP-2H)	FL	Pensa	USNAM	Lockheed	Neptune	141234, PG 6, VP-65
P5M(SP-5B)	FL	Pensa	USNAM	Martin	Marlin	5533, QE, 10, VP-40
P6M (Fuse/Tail)	MD	Middl	GLMAM	Martin	Marlin	
P8MU-3	MD	Silve	PEGF			

PA- 5	DC	Washi	NA&SM	Pitcairn		
PA-11	FL	Kissi	FTWAM	Piper	Cub Special	
PA-11	PA	Lock Haven	PAM	Piper	Cub Special	
PA-12	CA	Hayward	VAM	Piper	Super Cruiser	
PA-12	MD	Silve	PEGF	Piper	Super Cruiser	"City of Washington"
PA-18	MD	Silve	PEGF	Piper	Super Cub	
PA-18	MI	Dearb	HFM	Pitcairn	Autogiro	
PA-18	NE	Minde	HWPV	Pitcairn	Autogiro	
PA-18	NY	Rhine	ORA	Pitcairn	Autogiro	
PA-20	IL	Harva	BA	Piper	Pacer	
PA-20	NY	Bayport	BA	Piper	Pacer	
PA-20	WI	Oshko	EAAAAM	Piper	Pacer	N3762P
PA-22	IL	Harva	BA	Piper	Tri Pacer	
PA-22	IL	Rantoul	OCAM	Piper	Tri Pacer	N8726C
PA-22	KS	Liberal	MAAM	Piper	Tri Pacer	
PA-22	OK	Fredi	AAM	Piper	Tri-Pacer	
PA-22-125	PA	Readi	MAAM	Piper	Tri-Pacer	
PA-22-150	WI	Oshkosh	EAAAAM	Piper	Tri-Pacer	
PA-23	DC	Dulle	DA	Piper	Apache	
PA-23	KS	Liberal	MAAM	Piper	Apache	
PA-23	NE	Minde	HWPV	Piper	Apache	
PA-23	OK	Fredi	AAM	Piper	Apache	
PA-23(U-11A)(O-1)	AZ	Tucso	PAM	Piper	Aztec	149067, Model 250
PA-23-250	CA	Hayward	VAM	Piper	Aztec	
PA-23-250	OK	Fredi	AAM	Piper	Aztec	
PA-23-250	PA	Readi	MAAM	Piper	Aztec	N14281
PA-24	KS	Liberal	MAAM	Piper	Commanche	
PA-28-140	AL	Birmingham	SMoF	Piper		
PA-28-140	WI	Oshkosh	EAAAAM	Piper		
PA-29	PA	Lock Haven	PAM	Piper	Papoose	
PA-34-200	MN	Blaine	ACBA	Piper	Seneca II	Owner: Doug Weske
PA-34-200	PA	Readi	MAAM	Piper	Seneca II	N5297T
PA-38-112	PA	Readi	MAAM	Piper	Tomahawk	N382PT
PA-39	WI	Oshko	EAAAAM	Pitcairn-Larsen	Autogiro	N3908
PA-44	FL	Dayto	ERAU	Piper	Cheyenne II	
PA-44	MN	Winoma	WTI	Piper	Cheyenne II	N23MW
PA-48	CA	Rosam	EAFB	Piper	Enforcer	48-35010 2
PA-48	OH	Dayto	USAFM	Piper	Enforcer	48-83011
Pacific Airwave Kiss 89	AZ	Tucson	PAM	Pacific Airwave	Kiss	Man Sn KM92514
Packard LePere LUSAC	OH	Dayton	USAFM	Packard LePere	LUSAC	
Panavia Tornado	OH	Dayton	USAFM	Panavia	Tornado	
Paramount Cabinair	FL	Delan	OHA	Paramount	Cabinair	
Paramount Cabinaire	WY	Jackson	GWFM	Paramount	Cabinaire	
Paramotor FX-1	NY	Garden	CoAM	Paramotor	FX-1	
Parker JP-001	WI	Oshko	EAAAAM	Parker	American Special	N113JP
Parker Pusher	OK	Oklah	KCASM	Parker	Parker Pusher	
Parker Sailplane	CA	S.Mar	SMMoF	Parker	Sailplane	
Parsons Autogyro	PA	WChester	AHM	Parsons	Autogyro	
Passett Ornithopter	NY	Rhine	ORA	Passett	Ornithopter	
PB-1W	TX	Midla	CAFFM	Boeing		
PB2M-1(XP)	BC-C	P.Alb	Spoat Lk	Martin	Mars	
PB2Y-5R	FL	Pensa	USNAM	Consolidated	Coronado	57 N 69003 7099
PB4Y*1 Tail ver of B-24*	CA	Chino	PoFAM	Consolidated	Privateer	
PB4Y-2	FL	Pensa	USNAM	Consolidated	Privateer	66304 F 202
PB4Y-2	TX	Galve	LSFM	Consolidated	Privateer	59819, N3739G
PB4Y-2	WY	Greyb	H&PA	Consolidated	Privateer	
PB4Y-2G(P4Y-2G)	MI	Belleville	YAF	Consolidated	Privateer	59876, N6319D
PBM	MD	Balti	BMoI	Martin	Mariner	
PBM	TX	Hawki	RRSA	Martin	Mariner	
PBM-5A	AZ	Tucso	PAM	Martin	Mariner	N3190G 122071
PBR	AL	Mobile	BMP		River Boat	31RP7331
PBR	WI	Kenosha	KMM		River Boat	NSN 1940000BOAT, Movie "Apocalypse Now"
PBR	WI	Kenosha	KMM		River Boat	2 at this location
PBY	AZ	Mesa	CAFM	Consolidated	Catalina	
PBY	MN	St Paul	CAFMW	Consolidated	Catalina	
PBY	NC	CPoin	CPMB	Consolidated	Catalina	
PBY	NY	Brooklyn	NAAM	Consolidated	Catalina	
PBY	NF-C	Gander	NAAM	Consolidated	Catalina	
PBY	TX	Brown	CAFRGVW	Consolidated	Catalina	
PBY	TX	Rio Grande V	TAM	Consolidated	Catalina	
PBY-5	FL	Pensa	USNAM	Consolidated	Catalina	8317
PBY-5A	AK	Ancho	AAHM	Consolidated	Catalina	
PBY-5A	CA	San Diego	SDAM	Consolidated	Catalina	N5590V 48406
PBY-5A	FL	Jacks	NASJ	Consolidated	Catalina	6882 J1-P 17
PBY-5A	FL	Miami	WOM	Consolidated	Catalina	
PBY-5A	NM	Albuq	KAFB	Consolidated	Catalina	
PBY-5A	NS	Halifax	ACAM	Consolidated	Canso	
PBY-5A	ON-C	Ottaw	CAM	Consolidated	Catalina	11087
PBY-5A	NF-C	Botwood	CAM	Consolidated	Catalina	
PBY-5A	NS-C	Greenwood	GMAM	Consolidated	Catalina	
PBY-5A	OR	Tillamook	TAM	Consolidated	Catalina	N2172N
PBY-5A	TX	Brown	RGVW-CAF	Consolidated	Catalina	N68756
PBY-5A	TX	C Christi	NAS	Consolidated	Catalina	
PBY-5A	TX	Galve	LSFM	Consolidated	Catalina	N68740 407
PBY-5A	VA	Suffolk	FF	Consolidated	Catalina	48294, N9521C, VP-82
PBY-5A(OA-10A)	NM	Albuq	KAFB	Consolidated	Catalina	
PBY-6A	MN	Duluth	CAF-LSS	Consolidated	Catalina	N7179Y
PBY-6ACF	MN	Duluth	CAF-LSS	Consolidated	Catalina	N324FA
PBY-6A	MN	St Paul	CAFMW	Consolidated	Catalina	
PBY-6A	NY	Horseheads	NWM	Consolidated	Catalina	64072, N7057C, Side 62-P
PBY-6A	TX	Midla	CAFFM	Consolidated	Catalina	
PCA-1A	MD	Silve	PEGF	Pitcairn	Autogiro	
PCA-1A	PA	WChester	AHM	Pitcairn	Autogiro	
PCA-2	ON-C	Ottaw	CAM	Pitcairn	Autogiro	NC 2624
PCI-1A	CA	El Cajon	SDAMGF			
Pearson-Williams	CA	Chino	PoFAM	Pearson-Williams	W-7 Racer	"Mr Smooth"
Peacekeeper RV Bus	OH	Dayton	USAFM	Peacekeeper	RV Bus	
Pedal Plane	WI	Oshko	EAAAAM	Pedal	Pedal Plane	
Peel Z-1	CA	Santa Martin	WoHAM	Peel	Glider Boat	15-822, W
Pembroke C.51	NJ	Fairf	YAFDCWA	Hunting-Percival	Pembroke	K66B-4001, N51973
Penaud Planaphore	ME	Owls Head	OHTM	Penaud	Planaphore	
Penguin Ground Trainer	CA	Santa Martin	WoHAM	Penguin	Ground Trainer	
Pentercost E.III	AZ	Tucson	PAM	Pentercost	Hoppicopter	269

Pentercost E.III	MD	Silve	PEGF	Pentercost	Hoppicopter	
Pfalz D.III	AL	Gunte	LGARFM	Pfalz		
Pfalz D.III	AZ	Mesa	CFM	Pfalz		
Pfalz D.III	NV	Carso	YF	Pfalz		
Pfalz D.XII	WA	Seattle	MoF	Pfalz		3498, n43c
Pfalz D.XII	DC	Washi	NA&SM	Pfalz		
Pfalz D.XII	MD	Silve	PEGF	Pfalz		
PG-1 Explorer	WI	Oshko	EAAAAM	Sklier Aquq	Explorer	N6498D, "Bayou Bird"
PG-130	NY	Elmira	NSM	Perl	Penetrator	N8146H
PG-185	CA	SCarl	HAM	Nelson	Hummingbird	
PG-185	MD	Silve	PEGF	Nelson	Hummingbird	
PGM-17	AZ	Tucso	PAM	Douglas	Thor	
PGM-17A	CA	Rosamond	EAFB	Douglas	Thor	
PGM-17	OH	Dayton	USAFM	Douglas	Thor	
PGM-19	OH	Dayton	USAFM	Douglas	Jupiter	
Pheasant H-10	SK-C	MJaw	WDM	Pheasant		
Pheasant H-10	WI	Oshko	EAAAAM	Pheasant		NC151N
Phoenix 6	MD	Silve	PEGF	Phoenix		
Phoenix 6-C Hang Glider	KS	Liberal	MAAM	Phoenix		
Phoenix Streak	MD	Silve	PEGF	Phoenix	Streak	
Phoenix Vipper	MD	Silve	PEGF	Phoenix	Vipper	
PHSC Scout	NY	Rhine	ORA		Scout	
Piel-Emeraude	AL	Birmingham	SMoF	Piel	Emeraude	
Piel-Emeraude	FL	Lakeland	SNFAM	Piel	Emeraude	
Pietenpol	GA	Woodstock	NGWS	Pietenpol	Aerial	
Pietenpol B4A	AB-C	Wetas	RM	Pietenpol	Aircamper	
Pietenpol B4A	BC-C	Sidne	BCAM	Pietenpol	Aircamper	
Pietenpol B4A	CA	Santa Martin	WoHAM	Pietenpol	Aircamper	
Pietenpol B4A	CA	El Cajon	SDAMGF	Pietenpol	Aircamper	
Pietenpol B4A	CA	San Carlos	HAM	Pietenpol	Aircamper	001, N3133
Pietenpol B4A	CA	San Diego	SDAM	Pietenpol	Aircamper	N37680
Pietenpol B4A	FL	Lakeland	SNFAM	Pietenpol	Aircamper	
Pietenpol B4A	IA	Ottumwa	AAA	Pietenpol	Aircamper	N4716
Pietenpol B4A	IL	Sprin	SA	Pietenpol	Aircamper	
Pietenpol B4A	IN	LaPorte	DPAM	Pietenpol	Aircamper	
Pietenpol B4A	KS	Liberal	MAAM	Pietenpol	Aircamper	N2NK
Pietenpol B4A	MN	Minne	MAGM	Pietenpol	Aircamper	
Pietenpol B4A	MN	Fountain	FCM	Pietenpol	Aircamper	N1932A
Pietenpol B4A	ND	Minot	DTAM	Pietenpol	Aircamper	N12072
Pietenpol B4A	NY	Niagara Falls	NAM	Pliska	Aircamper	
Pietenpol B4A	NY	Rhine	ORA	Pietenpol	Aircamper	N6262
Pietenpol B4A	OK	Fredi	AAM	Pietenpol	Aircamper	
Pietenpol B4A	PA	Bethel	GAAM	Pietenpol	Aircamper	NX54N
Pietenpol B4A	PA	Readi	MAAM	Pietenpol	Aircamper	
Pietenpol B4A	VA	Sands	VAM	Pietenpol	Aircamper	Sn 410, N86404
Pietenpol B4A	WI	Fond du Lac	WAM	Pietenpol	Aircamper	N44162
Pietenpol B4A	WI	Oshko	EAAAAM	Pietenpol	Aircamper	N12937
Pietenpol B4A	WI	Oshko	EAAAAM	Pietenpol	Aircamper	N7533U
Pietenpol P-9	IA	Ottumwa	APM	Pietenpol	Sky Scout	SC1, N12942
Pietenpol P-9	TX	Kingbury	VAHF	Pietenpol	Sky Scout	
Pietenpol P-9	WI	Oshko	EAAAAM	Pietenpol	Sky Scout	N12941
Pigeon Fraser	NY	Rhine	ORA	Pigeon	Fraser	
Pilatus P-3	NC	Asheboro	PFAC	Pilatus		
Pioneer Flightstar	CT	Winds	NEAM	Pioneer	Flightstar	
Piper Commanche	IL	Elliot	CFF	Piper	Commanche	
Piper PT	WI	Oshko	EAAAAM	Piper	PT N	X4300
Piper Vegabond	MO	Maryland Hts	HARM	Piper	Vegabond	
Pitcairn AC-35	MD	Silve	PEGF	Pitcairn		
Pitcairn C-8	MD	Silve	PEGF	Pitcairn	C-8	
Pitcairn PA-5	VA	Sands	VAM	Pitcairn	Mailwing	Sn 9
Pitts P-6	WI	Oshko	EAAAAM	Pitts	Special	N58P
Pitts Racer 190	WI	Oshko	EAAAAM	Pitts	Racer 190	N8JD, "Little Monster"
Pitts S-1	AL	Birmi	Southe	Pitts	Special	
Pitts S-1	AZ	Grand Canyon	PoFGCVA	Pitts	Special	
Pitts S-1	AZ	Scott	SA	Pitts	Special	
Pitts S-1	AZ	Tucso	PAM	Pitts	Special	Man Sn 66, N2RB
Pitts S-1	WI	Oshko	EAAAAM	Pitts	Special	N58J
Pitts S-1	WI	Oshko	EAAAAM	Pitts	Special	NX528
Pitts S-1	WI	Oshko	EAAAAM	Pitts	Special	N442X
Pitts S-1-C	AZ	Tucson	PAM	Pitts	Special	DC!, N6119
Pitts S-1-C	MD	Silve	PEGF	Pitts	Special	"Little Stinker"
Pitts S-1-C	NS-C	Halifax	ACAM	Pitts	Special	
Pitts S-1-C	VA	Hampt	VA&SC	Pitts	Special	
Pitts S-1-C	WI	Oshko	EAAAAM	Pitts	Special	N66Y
Pitts S-1-S	CA	San Diego	SDAMGF	Pitts	Special	N4HS
Pitts S-1-S	MD	Silve	PEGF	Pitts	Special	"Maryann"
Pitts S-1-S	TX	Addison	CFM	Pitts	Special	N215JC
Pitts S-1-S	WI	Oshko	EAAAAM	Pitts	Special	N9J
Pitts S-2	WI	Oshko	EAAAAM	Pitts	Special	N22Q, "Big Stinker"
Pitts S-2-A	FL	KeyWe	FWIA	Pitts	Special	
Pitts S-2-B	AZ	Grand	PoFGCVA	Pitts	Special	N25CH, "Double Take"
Pitts S-2-B	OR	McMinnville	EAM	Pitts	Special	5105, N5352E
PL-4A	AL	Birmingham	SmoF	PL-4A		
Platt-LePage XR-1	MD	Silve	PEGF	Platt-LePage		
Player Sportplane	WI	Oshko	EAAAAM	Player	Sportplane	N21778
Pliska 1911	TX	Midla	PAM	Pliska	1911	
Po-2(U-2)	VA	Suffolk	FF	Polikarpov	Mule	641543, N46GU
Pober Jr. Ace	WI	Oshko	EAAAAM	Pober	Junior Ace	NX16PP
Pober P-5 Sport	WI	Oshko	EAAAAM	Poberenzy	Sport	N51G
Pober P-9 Pixie EAA	WI	Oshko	EAAAAM	Pober	Pixie	N9PH
Pober Super Ace	WI	Oshko	EAAAAM	Poberenzy	Super Ace	N113PP
Polan Special	WA	Vancouver	PAM	Polan	Racer	
PQ-14 (TD2C-1)	FL	Pensa	USNAM	Culver	Target Drone	120082
PQ-14 (TD2C-1)	MD	Silve	PEGF	Culver	Cadet	
PQ-14 (TDC-1)	AZ	Tucso	PAM	Culver	Cadet	44-21819, N1063M
PQ-14 (TDC-1)	CA	Chino	PoFAM	Culver	Cadet	
PQ-14B(TDC-1)	IA	Ottumwa	APM	Culver	Cadet	N-917, N5526ANR-D
PQ-14B(TDC-2)	OH	Dayto	USAFM	Culver	Cadet	44-68462, TDC-1, 2
PQ-14B(TDC-2)	WI	Oshko	EAAAAM	Culver	Cadet	N999ML, 68334
Pratt-Read Line-1	CT	Winds	NEAM	Pratt-Read	Line	
Primary	NY	Elmir	NSM			
Princeton Air Scooter	MD	Silve	PEGF	Princeton	Air Scooter	
Princeton Air Cycle	PA	WChester	AHM	Princeton	Air Cycle	

Provost Jet	FL	Miami	WOM	British Aerospace	Provost	
Provost Jet	WA	Seattle	MoF	British Aerospace	Provost	NX4107, XW307
Prue IIA	NY	Elmira	NSM	Prue	IIA	N86671
Prue 215	NY	Elmira	NSM	Prue	215	N86671
PS-2	FL	Pensa	USNAM	Franklin		9617
PS-2	MD	Silve	PEGF	Franklin		"Texaco Eaglet"
PS-2	NY	Elmira	NSM	Franklin		G12185
PS-2	NY	Elmira	NSM	Franklin		N4524
PS-2	NY	Elmira	NSM	Franklin		
PS-2	NY	Elmira	NSM	Franklin-Stevens		NX20646
PS-2	NY	Elmira	NSM	Franklin		
PT- 6A	CA	Riverside	MFAM	Cunningham-Hall		30-385, "Riverside"
PT- 6	CA	S. Monica	MoF	Cunningham-Hall		N1238V, Side # 8
PT- 6F	WY	Jackson	GWFM	Cunningham-Hall		
PT-1	CA	San Diego	SDAM	Consolidated	Trusty	"Husky"
PT-1	OH	Dayto	USAFM	Consolidated	Trusty	26- 233
PT-1	PA	Lock Haven	PAM	Consol;idated	Trusty	
PT-12	OH	Colum	CoS&I			
PT-13	CA	Oakla	OWAM	Boeing-Stearman	Kaydet	Model 73
PT-13	FL	Pompa	PAC	Boeing-Stearman	Kaydet	Model 73
PT-13	OK	Oklan	CAF-OW	Boeing-Stearman	Kaydet	Model 73, N51583
PT-13	OR	Mc Minnville	EAM	Boeing-Stearman	Kaydet	75-5300, n450ur
PT-13	TX	Burnet	HLS-CAF	Boeing-Stearman	Kaydet	Model 73
PT-13	TX	Odessa	CAFDS	Boeing-Stearman	Kaydet	Model 73
PT-13	WA	Eastsound	HFM	Boeing-Stearman	Kaydet	Model 73
PT-13A	WA	Seatt	MoF	Boeing-Stearman	Kaydet	75-055, n8fl
PT-13D	CA	Riverside	MAFB	Boeing-Stearman	Kaydet	Model 73, 42-16388
PT-13D(N2S-5)	MI	Kalam	KAHM	Boeing-Stearman	Kaydet	61614
PT-13D	NC	Asheboro	PFAC	Boeing-Stearman	Kaydet	Model 73,
PT-13D	OH	Dayto	USAFM	Boeing-Stearman	Kaydet	Model 73, 42-17800
PT-13D	PA	Readi	MAAM	Boeing-Stearman	Kaydet	Model 73
PT-16(YPT)(ST-A)	OH	Dayto	USAFM	Ryan		Model 73, 40-44, NC18922
PT-17	AL	Ozark	USAAM	Stearman	Kaydet	Model 73
PT-17	AZ	PBluf	RWCAF	Stearman	Kaydet	Model 73, 41-8882
PT-17	AZ	Tucso	PAM	Stearman	Kaydet	Model 73, 41-869, N58219
PT-17	AZ	Tucso	PAM	Stearman	Kaydet	Model 73
PT-17	CA	Atwater	CAM	Stearman	Kaydet	Model 73
PT-17	AZ	Grand	PoFAM	Stearman	Kaydet	
PT-17	CA	Shafter	MFAM	Stearman	Kaydet	
PT-17	DE	Dover	DAFB	Stearman	Kaydet	Model 73, # 13
PT-17	FL	Jacks	MoS&H	Stearman	Kaydet	Model 73
PT-17	FL	Kissi	FTWAM	Stearman	Kaydet	Model 73
PT-17	FL	Miami	WOM	Stearman	Kaydet	Model 73
PT-17	FL	Titusville	VACM	Stearman	Kaydet	Model 73
PT-17	GA	Pooler	M8AFHM	Stearman	Kaydet	Model 73,
PT-17	GA	Woodstock	AAM	Stearman	Kaydet	Model 73,
PT-17	GA	Woodstock	NGWS	Stearman	Kaydet	Model 73,
PT-17	GA	Woodstock	NGWS	Stearman	Kaydet	Model 73,
PT-17	IN	India	IMoMH	Stearman	Kaydet	Model 73
PT-17	IN	Valparaiso	IAM	Stearman	Kaydet	41-8311, "Delta Airlines"
PT-17	KS	Topek	CAM	Stearman	Kaydet	N-5764, Model 73
PT-17	KS	New Century	CAF-HoAW	Stearman	Kaydet	#34, N234x
PT-17	MA	Stow	BCF	Stearman	Kaydet	Model 73
PT-17	MD	College Park	CPAM	Stearman	Kaydet	Model 73
PT-17	CA	Palm SPrg	PSAM	Stearman	Kaydet	Model 73, N9955H
PT-17	MO	Missoula	MMF	Stearman	Kaydet	Model 73
PT-17	MS	Petal	MWHMM	Stearman	Kaydet	Model 73
PT-17	NC	Durham	CB	Stearman	Kaydet	N79500
PT-17	NJ	Rio Grande	NASW	Stearman	Kaydet	Model 73,
PT-17	ND	Wahpe	TSA	Stearman	Kaydet	Model 73,
PT-17	NY	Bayport	BA	Stearman	Kaydet	Model 73,
PT-17	NY	Bayport	BA	Stearman	Kaydet	Model 73,
PT-17	NY	Ghent	POMAM	Stearman	Kaydet	Model 73,
PT-17	NY	Horseheads	NWM	Stearman	Kaydet	Model 73, 07190, N64606
PT-17	OR	Tillamook	TAM	Stearman	Kaydet	Model 73, N65727
PT-17	SK-C	MJaw	WDM	Stearman	Kaydet	Model 73
PT-17	TX	Bealt	FCA	Stearman	Kaydet	Model 73
PT-17	TX	Burnet	HLSCAF	Boeing	Kaydet	Model 73, N5805V
PT-17	TX	Burnet	HLSCAF	Boeing	Kaydet	Model 73, N65355
PT-17	TX	FWort	BCVintag	Stearman	Yellow Peril	Model 73,
PT-17	TX	Ft Wort	Slanton	Stearman	Yellow Peril	Model 73,
PT-17	TX	Midla	CAFFM	Stearman	Kaydet	Model 73
PT-17	TX	SMarc	CTWCAF	Stearman	Kaydet	Model 73
PT-17	TX	San Antonio	TAM	Stearman	Kaydet	
PT-17A	UT	Ogden	HAFBM	Stearman	Provost	Model 73, 41-25284
PT-17	UT	SLake	CAF-UW	Stearman	Kaydet	Model 73, N1387V
PT-17	VA	Bealt	FCA	Stearman	Provost	Model 73
PT-17	WA	Vashon	OTA	Stearman	Kaydet	Model 73, N68462
PT-17(A75N1)	ME	OwlsH	OHTM	Boeing-Stearman	Kaydet	Model 73
PT-17(A75N1)	TX	Burnet	HLSCAF	Boeing	Kaydet	Model 73, N49943, 75-4645
PT-17(B75N1)(N2S-3)	OK	Fredi	AAM	Stearman	Kaydet	Model 73
PT-17 (See N2S)						
PT-17D	GA	Warner Robin	MoF	Stearman	Kaydet	Model 73, 42-16365, 365, C302
PT-18	CA	Palm Springs	PoFAM	Boeing Stearman	Super Kaydet	41-61042, N1391V
PT-19	AB-C	Edmonton	AAM	Fairchild	Cornell	
PT-19	AB-C	Nanton	NLSAM	Fairchild	Cornell	
PT-19	AL	Birmi	SMoF	Fairchild	Cornell	
PT-19	AZ	PBluf	RWCAF	Fairchild	Cornell	
PT-19	BC-C	Langley	CMoF	Fairchild	Cornell	
PT-19	ID	Zellw	BWA	Fairchild	Cornell	
PT-19	KS	New Century	CAF-HoAW	Fairchild	Cornell	33, N50303
PT-19	KS	New Century	CAF-HoAW	Fairchild	Cornell	44
PT-19	MB-C	Brandon	CATPM	Fairchild	Cornell	
PT-19	ND	Fargo	FAM	Fairchild	Cornell	N51437, No 21, Yellow & Blue
PT-19	NY	Bayport	BA	Fairchild	Cornell	
PT-19	OH	Newbu	WASAC	Fairchild	Cornell	
PT-19	OH	N Canton	MAM	Fairchild	Cornell	
PT-19	OK	Fredi	AAM	Fairchild	Cornell	
PT-19	TX	Brown	RGVW-CAF	Fairchild	Cornell	
PT-19	TX	Burnet	HLSCAF	Ryan	Cornell	N274351, 42-2767
PT-19	TX	Midla	CAFFM	Fairchild	Cornell	
PT-19	WA	Eastsound	HFM	Fairchild	Cornell	
PT-19	WY	Jackson	GWFM	Fairchild	Cornell	

PT-19 Cockpit	CA	Chino	PoFAM	Fairchild	Cornell	
PT-19A	AZ	Tucso	PAM	Fairchild	Cornell	41-14675, N53963
PT-19A	CA	Fairf	TAFB	Fairchild	Cornell	
PT-19A	GA	Warner Robin	MoF	Fairchild	Cornell	43-7220
PT-19A	MD	Silve	PEGF	Fairchild	Cornell	
PT-19A	MI	Ypsil	YAF	Fairchild	Cornell	
PT-19A	NY	Horseheads	NWM	Fairchild	Cornell	5203AE, N49830, #32
PT-19A	OH	Dayto	USAFM	Fairchild	Cornell	43-34023
PT-19A	PA	Toughkenamon	CFCM	Fairchild	Cornell	42-83641, N51324, Nose # 65
PT-19A	TX	Addison	CFM	Fairchild	Cornell	N58307, 44 217
PT-19A-AE	MI	Belleville	YAF	Fairchild	Cornell	43-31550, N9884
PT-19A-FA	KS	Liberal	MAAM	Fairchild	Cornell	
PT-19B	KS	New Century	CAF-HoAW	Fairchild	Cornell	AE6103, N50481
PT-19B	WA	Vancouver	PAM	Fairchild	Cornell	
PT-19B	CA	Riverside	MFAM	Fairchild	Cornell	43-5598, Side 29
PT-19B	NY	Horseheads	NWM	Fairchild	Cornell	42-47871, Side # 65
PT-19B (2ea)	PA	Readi	MAAM	Fairchild	Cornell	40-2594, N119EC, 39
PT-19B	PA	Toughkenamon	CFCM	Fairchild	Cornell	N60112, Nose # 60
PT-19B(M-62A)	WI	Oshko	EAAAAM	Fairchild	Cornell	43-7240
PT-21(NR-1)	FL	Pensa	USNAM	Ryan	Recruit	1541, 49086
PT-22	AZ	Tucso	PAM	Ryan	Recruit	41-15736, N1180C
PT-22	CA	Atwater	CAM	Ryan	Recruit	
PT-22	CA	Corno	CAF-IES	Ryan	Recruit	N48742
PT-22	CA	Palm Springs	PoFAM	Ryan	Recruit	41-15550, N441V, Side # 634
PT-22	CA	San Diego	SDAM	Ryan	Recruit	1901, N47483
PT-22	CA	Shafter	MFAM	Ryan	Recruit	
PT-22	CO	Denve	JWDAS	Ryan	Recruit	
PT-22	FL	Kissi	FTWAM	Ryan	Recruit	
PT-22	FL	Miami	WOM	Ryan	Recruit	
PT-22	GA	Warner Robin	MoF	Ryan	Recruit	41-21039, 66
PT-22	IA	Ottumwa	APM	Ryan	Recruit	1254, N50644
PT-22	KS	Liberal	MAAM	Ryan	Recruit	
PT-22	IL	Paris	HAAM	Ryan	Recruit	
PT-22	IL	Springfield	ACM	Ryan	Recruit	41-20796, 2005
PT-22	MI	Kalam	KAHM	Ryan	Recruit	41-20652
PT-22	OH	Dayto	USAFM	Ryan	Recruit	41-15721
PT-22	OH	Madis	CFR	Ryan	Recruit	
PT-22	OK	Fredi	AAM	Ryan	Recruit	
PT-22	TX	Brown	RGVW-CAF	Ryan	Recruit	N22AL
PT-22	TX	Addison	CFM	Ryan	Recruit	N46217, 4847AAF
PT-22	TX	Midla	CAFFM	Ryan	Recruit	
PT-22 (ST3KR)	AK	Fairb	APAM	Ryan	Recruit	N50880
PT-23	CA	Atwater	CAM	Fairchild	Cornell	
PT-23	KS	Liberal	MAAM	Fairchild	Cornell	
PT-23	KS	Wichita	CAF-JW	Fairchild	Cornell	N64176
PT-23HO	MI	Kalam	KAHM	Fairchild	Cornell	
PT-23	MN	Blaine	GH	Fairchild	Cornell	
PT-23	OK	Fredi	AAM	Fairchild	Cornell	
PT-23	PA	Readi	MAAM	Fairchild	Cornell	
PT-23	WI	Oshko	EAAAAM	Fairchild	Cornell	
PT-23A	WY	Jackson	GWFM	Fairchild	Cornell	
PT-23A	CT	Winds	NEAM	Fairchild	Cornell	
PT-26	AB-C	Wetas	RM	Fairchild	Cornell	
PT-26	AB-C	Nanton	NLS	Fairchild	Cornell	
PT-26	AR	PineB	CAF-RW	Fairchild	Cornell	N6072C
PT-26	AZ	Tucso	PAM	Fairchild	Cornell	Sn 10530, N127O, CF-FLY
PT-26	CA	Chino	YAM	Fairchild	Cornell	
PT-26	CA	Shafter	MFAM	Fairchild	Cornell	
PT-26	CO	Denve	JWDAS	Fairchild	Cornell	
PT-26	GA	Atlan	CAF-DW	Fairchild	Cornell	N26GA
PT-26	IN	India	CAF-IW	Fairchild	Cornell	N60535
PT-26	NM	Albuq	CAF-LW	Fairchild	Cornell	N5519N
PT-26	NY	Albion	VAG	Fairchild	Cornell	
PT-26	NY	Bayport	BA	Fairchild	Cornell	
PT-26	OH	Dayto	USAFM	Fairchild	Cornell	N2039A
PT-26	OK	Fredi	AAM	Fairchild	Cornell	
PT-26	PA	Readi	MAAM	Fairchild	Cornell	
PT-26	PA	Toughkenamon	CFCM	Fairchild	Cornell	N75463, Side # FH950
PT-26	TX	Brown	RGVW-CAF	Fairchild	Cornell	N940H
PT-26	TX	Brown	RGVW-CAF	Fairchild	Cornell	N4732G
PT-26	TX	Midla	CAFFM	Fairchild	Cornell	
PT-26	WY	Jackson	GWFM	Fairchild	Cornell	
PT-26A	BC-C	Langley	CMoF	Fairchild	Cornell	
PT-26A	ON-C	Ottaw	CAM	Fairchild	Cornell	10738
PT-26B	ON-C	Hamilton	CWH	Fairchild	Cornell	
PT-27	ON-C	Hamilton	CWH	Boeing-Stearman	RCAF Kaydet	
PT-27-BW	BC-C	Langley	CMoF	Boeing-Stearman	RCAF Kaydet	42-15683, N56773
Pterodactyl Fledgling	MD	Silve	PEGF	Manta Products	Fledgling	
Pulsar	KY	Lexington	AmoK	Pulsar	Ultralight	N156KB
PV-2 Piasecki	IN	Indianapolis	AMHF	Piasecki	Harpoon	37396, N2697C
PV-2 Piasecki	MD	Silve	PEGF	Piasecki	Helicopter	
PV-2	AZ	Tucso	PAM	Lockheed	Harpoon	N7255C, 37257
PV-2	CA	Chino	PoFAM	Lockheed	Harpoon	
PV-2	NM	Las Cruces	SA	Lockheed	Harpoon	
PV-2	OR	Tillamook	TAM	Lockheed	Harpoon	
PV-2	PA	WChes	AHM	Lockheed	Harpoon	
PV-2	SC	N Myrtle Beach M		Lockheed	Harpoon	
PV-2	TX	SAnto	CAF-YRS	Lockheed	Harpoon	N25YR
PV-2	VA	Quantico	MCAGM	Lockheed	Harpoon	34807
PV-2D	TX	C Christi	USS Lexi	Lockheed	Harpoon	
PV-2D	TX	Galve	LSFM	Lockheed	Harpoon	N6655D 37634
PV-2D	WI	Wauke	CAF/WW	Lockheed	Harpoon	N86493, "Empire Express"
Q-200	FL	Lakel	SFAF	Rutan	Quickie	N150CS
Q-3A(YQ)	AL	Ozark	USAAM			
Q-4(XQ)	CO	Monte	ALP53	Sikorsky		
Q-4(XQ)	NM	Alamo	CityPark	Sikorsky		
Quadraplane	KY	Lexington	AVoK	Sellers	Quadraplane	
QU-22B	OH	Dayton	USAFM	Beech	Beech 36	
Quick Kit Seaplane	NY	River	TFAC	Quick	Seaplane	
Quick Monplane	AL	Hunts	AS&RC	Quick	Monoplane	
Quick Silver	CA	San Diego	SDAM	Quick	Silver	Glider 1980
Quick Silver MX	AK	Fairb	APAM	Quick	Silver MX	
Quick Silver MX	TX	Rio Grande V	TAM	Quick	Silver MX	

R-3(M-B)	CT	Winds	NEAM	Keith Rider		
R-4(XR)(VS-300)Cockpit	PA	WChes	AHM	Sikorsky	Hoverfly	346514
R-4(XR)(VS-316)	MD	Silve	PEGF	Vought-Sikorsky	Hoverfly	
R-4B	AZ	Tucson	PAM	Sikorsky	Hoverfly	43-46521
R-4B	CA	Chino	YAM	Sikorsky	Hoverfly	
R-4B	CT	Winds	NEAM	Sikorsky	Hoverfly	
R-4B	OH	Dayto	USAFM	Sikorsky	Hoverfly	43-46506
R-5(XR)	MD	Silve	PEGF	Sikorsky	Dragonfly	VS-317
R-85(XR)	MD	Silve	PEGF			
R3C-2	DC	Washi	NA&SM	Curtiss		
R4B(HNS)	AZ	Tucson	PAM	Sikorsky	R4B Helicopter	Sn 43-46521
R4B(HNS)	CA	Chino	YAM	Sikorsky	R4B Helicopter	Sn 43-46534
R4B(HNS-1)	FL	Pensa	USNAM	Sikorsky		104, N75988, 39047
R4D-6(DC-3)	CA	Atwater	CAM	Douglas	Skytrooper	90407
R4D-5	NY	Horseheads	NWM	Douglas	Skytrooper	39091
R4D-6(DC-3)	PA	Readi	MAAM	Douglas	Skytrooper	26819, N68AH, GB50819, "NATS 1945"
R4D-6(DC-3)	VA	Quant	MCAGM	Douglas	Skytrooper	17278
R4D-6Q(DC-3)	AL	Birmingham	SMoF	Douglas	Skytrooper	
R4D-8(C-117)	CA	Miramar	FLAM	Douglas	Super Gooney Bird	708,MCAS, MCASIWAKUNI
R4D-8(C-117D)	AZ	Tucso	PAM	Douglas	Super Gooney Bird	50826, Skytrain, 43363, 26924
R4D-8(C-117D)	AZ	Tucso	PAM	Douglas	Super Gooney Bird	43-49663
R4D-8(C-117D)	FL	Pensa	USNAM	Douglas	Super Gooney Bird	50821, 821, Gooney Bird
R50-5	AZ	Tucso	PAM	Lockheed	Lodestar	12481, N15SA, Model 18
R50-5	CA	Riverside	MFAM	Lockheed	Lodestar	12473
RA-5C	CA	Ridgecrest	CLNWC	North American	Vigilante	
RA-5C	CA	San Diego	SDACM	North American	Vigilante	156641
RA-5C	CO	Puebl	PWAM	North American	Vigilante	
RA-5C	FL	Pensa	USNAM	North American	Vigilante	156624
RA-5C	MD	Lexin	PNA&EM	North American	Vigilante	
RA-5C	NV	Fallon	NASF	North American	Vigilante	
RA-5C	NY	NYC	ISASM	North American	Vigilante	
RA-5C(A3J-3)	AZ	Tucso	PAM	North American	Vigilante	149289
Rabbit Model A	WI	Oshko	EAAAAM	Welsh	Rabbit	N3599G
Rawdon T-1	KS	Wichita	KAM	Rawdon	T-1 Ag Plane	
Rally 3	KS	Liberal	MAAM	Rally	Ultralight	
Ranchero	FL	Lakel	SFAF	Ranchero		N4659S, "Spirit of Ft Myers"
Rand KR-1	AL	Birmingham	SMoF	Rand	Robinson	
Rand KR-1	FL	Lakel	SFAF	Rand	Robinson	N12NS
Rand KR-1	KS	Liberal	MAAM	Rand	Robinson	
Rand KR-1	OK	Fredi	AAM	Rand	Robinson	
Rand KR-1	WI	Oshko	EAAAAM	Rand	Robinson	N1436
Rand Robin KR-2	CA	Santa Maria	SMMoF	Rand Robin	KR-2	
Rand Robin KR-2	IA	SBluf	MAAM	Rand Robin	KR-2	
Rasor 21	WI	Oshko	EAAAAM	Rasor		
Raven Hang Glider	WI	Oshko	EAAAAM	Raven	Hang Glider	F28AO
Raven S-50	AK	Fairb	APAM	Raven	S-50	N24061
RB-1	AZ	Tucso	PAM	Budd	Conestoga	39307, XB-DUZ
RB-1	PA	Pitts	FI	Budd	Conestoga	
RB-1 Racer	MI	Dearb	HFM	Dayton-Wright	Racer	
RC-3	AL	Birmi	SMoF	Republic	Seabee	
RC-3	BC-C	Sidne	BCAM	Republic	Seabee	
RC-3	BC-C	Langley	CMoF	Republic	Seabee	
RC-3	Ont-C	Sault Ste Marie	CBHC	Republic	Seabee	Sn 822, C-FDKG
RC-3	CA	SCarl	HAM	Republic	Seabee	N87482
RC-3	CT	Winds	NEAM	Republic	Seabee	
RC-3	FL	KeyWe	HTC&C	Republic	Seabee	N87596
RC-3	MD	Silve	PEGF	Republic	Seabee	
RC-3	NY	Garde	CoAM	Republic	Seabee	N6461K
RC-3	PA	Readi	MAAM	Republic	Seabee	
RC-12G	AZ	Ft Huachuca	HMS	Beech	Crazyhorse	80-23372
Rearwin	WA	Vancouver	PAM	Rearwin	Sportster	
Rearwin 2000C	TX	Kingbury	VAHF	Rearwin		Project Ken-Royce
Rearwin 7000	IA	Ottumwa	APM	Rearwin	Sportster	
Rearwin 7000	KS	Liberal	MAAM	Rearwin	Sportster	NC187
Rearwin 7000	OK	Fredi	AAM	Rearwin	Sportster	
Rearwin 8135	CA	San Diego	SDAMGF	Rearwin	Cloudster	N25553
Rearwin 8135	CT	Winds	NEAM	Rearwin	Cloudster	
Rearwin 8135	KS	Liberal	MAAM	Rearwin	Cloudster	
Rearwin 8135	IA	Ottumwa	APM	Rearwin	Cloudster	832, N25555
Rearwin 8135	NY	River	TFAC	Rearwin	Cloudster	
Rearwin Skyranger 175	KS	Liberal	MAAM	Rearwin	Skyranger	
Rearwin Speedster	KS	Wichita	KAM	Rearwin	Speedster	
Redstone Booster	OH	Dayton	USAFM	Redstone	Booster	
Renegade Spirit	MI	Kalamazoo	KAHM	Murphy	Spirit	
Resures 500	WA	Seatt	MoF	Resures	Space Capsule	
Revolution Mini 500	FL	Lakeland	SNF	Revolution	Mini 500	
Rheintocher	MD	Aberd	APG	Rheintocher		
Rigid Midget	NY	Elmira	NSM	Culver	Rigid Midget	1001, N90871
Ritter Special	FL	Lakel	SFAF	Russ Ritter	Ritter Special	N1017Z
Ritz 1983	IA	Ottumwa	APM	Ritz	Pusher	
RJ-4 Ric-Jet	CA	Chino	PoFAM			
RK-86F	OH	Dayton	USAFM	North American		
RLU-1	KS	Liberal	MAAM	RLU	Breezy	
RLU-1	ND	Minot	DTAM	RLU	Breezy	
RLU-1	PA	Bethel	GAAM	RLU	Breezy	
RLU-1	OK	Fredi	AAM	RLU	Breezy	
RLU-1	WI	Oshko	EAAAAM	RLU	Breezy	N59Y
RLU-1	WI	Oshko	EAAAAM	RLU	Breezy	N555JS
RLU-1	WI	Oshko	EAAAAM	RLU	Breezy	N3915
Robinson R22	PA	West Chester	AHM	Robinson	R22	
Rockwell	NY	Garde	CoAM	Rockwell	Command Module 002	
Rockwell HiMat	DC	Washi	NA&SM	Rockwell	HiMat	
Rockwell Ranger 2000	OK	Tulsa	TA&SM	Rockwell	Ranger 2000	
RODA	OR	McMinnville	EAM	Homebuilt		
Rogallo Wing	CA	Hawth	WMoF	Rogallo	Wing	
Rogallo Wing	NC	Ralei	NCMoH	Rogallo	Wing	
Rogallo Wing	NY	Elmira	NSM	Rogallo	Wing	
RON-1(X)	MO	SLoui	NMoT	Gyrodyne	Rotorcycle	
RON-1(Y)	VA	Quant	MCAGM	Gyrodyne	Rotorcycle	4012
RON-1(YR)	FL	Pensa	USNAM	Gyrodyne	Rotorcycle	4013
Rose Parakeet A-1	IA	Ottumwa	APM	Rose	Parakeet A-1	N-13676
Rose Parakeet	PA	Bethel	GAAM	Rose	Parakeet	
Ross R-6	NY	Elmira	NSM	Ross	R-6	N34H

Ross RJ-5	NY	Elmira	NSM	Ross	RJ-5	N79T
Rotec Rally IIIB	AL	Birmi	SMoF	Rotec	Rally IIIB	
Rotec Rally IIIB	PA	Readi	MAAM	Rotec		
Rotec Rally IIIB	WA	Seatt	MoF	Rotec	Rally IIIB	
Roton	CA	Ramona	CR	Rotary Rocket Co	Roton Rocket	1
Rotor Cycle Hiller	MD	Lexin	PNA&EM	Hiller	Rotorcycle	
Rotorway Exec 152	AL	Birmingham	SMoF	Rotorway	Executive	
Rotorway Exec 152	PA	Readi	MAAM	Rotorway	Executive	
Rotorway Exec 152	WI	Oshko	EAAAAM	Rotorway	Executive	N3WN
Rotorway Exec 162	TX	Ladero	Airport	Rotorway	Executive	
Rotorway Javelin	CA	Ramona	CR	Rotorway	Javelin	
Rotorway Scorpion I	PA	WChester	EAAAAM	Rotorway	Scorpion	
Rotorway Scorpion I	WI	Oshko	EAAAAM	Rotorway	Scorpion	N6165
Rotorway Scorpion 133	AK	Fairb	APAM	Rotorway	Scorpion 133	
Rotorway Scorpion 133	CA	Ramona	CR	Rotorway	Scorpion 133	
Rotorway Scorpion II	MD	Silve	PEGF	Rotorway	Scorpion	
Rotorway Scorpion II	NJ	Teterboro	AHoF&MNJ	Rotorway	Scorpion	N96328
Rotorway Scorpion II	PA	WChester	AHM	Rotorway	Scorpion	
Rotorway Scorpion II	WA	Seatt	MoF	Rotorway	Scorpion	75rjm, n65229
Rotorway Scorpion II	WI	Oshkosh	EAAAAM	Rotorway	Scorpion	
RT-14	MD	Sllve	PEGF	Turner	Meteor	
Rumpler Taube	AZ	Mesa	CFM	Rumpler	Taube	
Rumpler Taube	WA	Seattle	MoF	Rumpler	Taube	
Rutan	FL	Tittusville	VACM	Rutan		
Rutan 354	CA	Rosam	EAFB	Rutan	Model 354	N309V
Rutan Grizzly	WI	Oshko	EAAAAM	Rutan	Grizzly	N80RA, "Griz"
Rutan Quickie	AB-C	Calga	AMoC	Rutan	Quickie	
Rutan Quickie	BC-C	Langley	CMoF	Rutan	Quickie	
Rutan Quickie	AZ	Tucso	PAM	Rutan	Quickie	N 80EB
Rutan Quickie	CT	Winds	NEAM	Rutan	Quickie	
Rutan Quickie	FL	Lakel	SFAF	Rutan	Quickie	N303Q
Rutan Quickie	IA	Des M	ISHD	Rutan	Quickie	
Rutan Quickie	MD	Silve	PEGF	Rutan	Quickie	
Rutan Quickie	OR	Tillamook	TAM	Rutan	Quickie	
Rutan Quickie	NF-C	Gander	NAAM	Rutan	Quickie	
Rutan Quickie	WA	Seatt	MoF	Rutan	Quickie	1, n77q
Rutan Quickie	WA	Vancouver	PAM	Rutan	Quickie	
Rutan Quickie	WI	Oshko	EAAAAM	Rutan-Herron	Quickie	N2WX
Rutan Quickie (2ea)	BC-C	Langley	CMoF	Rutan	Quickie	
Rutan Quickie II	AZ	Grand Canyon	PoFGCVA	Rutan	Quickie	
Rutan Quickie II	CA	S.Mon	MoF	Rutan	Quickie II	N635AB
Rutan Quickie II	MB-C	Winni	WCAM	Rutan	Quickie	USAAF as C-8 or UC-96
Rutan Quickie Q1	CA	Santa Martin	WoHAM	Rutan	Quickie	
Rutan Vari-eze	AL	Birmingham	SMoF	Rutan	Vari-eze	
Rutan Vari-eze	AK	Fairb	APAM	Rutan	Vari-eze	N37840
Rutan Vari-eze	CA	Chino	PoFAM	Rutan	Vari-eze	
Rutan Vari-eze	CT	Winds	NEAM	Rutan	Vari-eze	
Rutan Vari-eze	FL	Lakel	SFAF	Rutan	Vari-eze	
Rutan Vari-eze	KS	Liberal	MAAM	Rutan	Vari-eze	
Rutan Vari-eze	MD	Silve	PEGF	Rutan	Vari-eze	
Rutan Vari-eze	ND	Minot	DTAM	Rutan	Vari-eze	
Rutan Vari-eze	OK	Fredi	AAM	Rutan	Vari-eze	
Rutan Vari-eze	PA	Readi	MAAM	Rutan	Vari-eze	
Rutan Vari-eze	VA	Hampt	VA&SC	Rutan	Vari-eze	
Rutan Vari-eze	WI	Oshko	EAAAAM	Rutan	Vari-eze	N7EZ
Rutan Varigiggen	AL	Birmingham	SMoF	Rutan	Varigiggen	
Rutan Varigiggen	CA	S.Mon	MoF	Rutan	Varigiggen	
Rutan Varigiggen	FL	Lakel	SFAF	Rutan	Varigiggen	
Rutan Varigiggen	WA	Seatt	MoF	Rutan	Varigiggen	115, n27ms
Rutan Variviggen 50-160	WI	Oshko	EAAAAM	Rutan	Varigiggen	N27VV
Rutan Voyager	CA	S.Mon	MoF	Rutan	Voyager	
Rutan Voyager	DC	Washi	NA&SM	Rutan	Voyager	
RV-4 Homebuilt Monoplane	CA	San Diego	SDAMGF	Homebuilt	Monoplane	N32KM
RV-6 Homebuilt	FL	Zellw	BWA	Homebuilt	Monoplane	
RV-6 Homebuilt	WI	Fond du Lac	WAM	Homebuilt	Monoplane	
Ryan D-16	AZ	Tucso	PAM	Ryan	Twin Navion	N5128K
Ryan D-16	KS	Liberal	MAAM	Ryan	Twin Navion	
Ryan D-16	OK	Fredi	AAM	Ryan	Twin Navion	
Ryan M-1	CA	San Diego	SDAM	Ryan		
Ryan Navion A	OK	Fredi	AAM	Ryan	Navion	
Ryan NYP	CA	San Diego	SDAMGF	Ryan	NYP, NX-211	"Spirit of St. Louis"
Ryan NYP	DC	Washi	NA&SM	Ryan	NYP, NX-211	"Spirit of St. Louis"
Ryan NYP	IL	Rantoul	OCAM	Ryan	NYP, NX-211	"Spirit of St. Louis"
Ryan NYP	MI	Dearb	HFM	Ryan	NYP, NX-211	"Spirit of St. Louis"
Ryan NYP	MN	Bloom	SPMIA	Ryan	NYP, NX-211	"Spirit of St. Louis"
Ryan NYP	MN	Minne	MSPIA	Ryan	NYP, NX-211	"Spirit of St. Louis"
Ryan NYP	MO	SLoui	MHM	Ryan	NYP, NX-211	"Spirit of St. Louis"
Ryan NYP	NY	Garde	CoAM	Rutan	NYP, NX-211	"Spirit of St Louis" B-1 Brougham
Ryan NYP	NY	Rhine	ORA	Ryan	NYP, NX-211	"Spirit of St. Louis"
Ryan NYP	OK	Weatherford	GTSM	Ryan	NYP, NX-211	"Spirit of St. Louis"
Ryan NYP	WI	Oshko	EAAAAM	Ryan	NYP, NX-211	"Spirit of St. Louis"
Ryan SCW-145	WI	Oshko	EAAAAM	Ryan		NC17372
Ryan SCW-147	CA	San Diego	SDAM	Ryan		
Ryan STA	CA	Hayward	VAM	Ryan	Special	N14954
Ryan STA	CA	San Diego	SDAM	Ryan	Special	NC17361
Ryan STA	IA	Ottumwa	APPM	Ryan	Special	198, N18902
Ryan STA	WA	Vancouver	PAM	Ryan	Special	
Ryan ST3-W	OH	Leroy	PRA	Ryan		
S- 2	CA	Hemet	HAAB	Grumman	Tracker	70
S- 2	FL	Kissi	FTWAM	Grumman	Tracker	
S- 2	HI	Kaneohe	KBMCAS	Grumman	Tracker	147870, #22
S- 2(CP-121)	MB-C	Winnipeg	WRCAFB	Grumman	Tracker	
S- 2(CP-121)	NS	Halifax	SAM	Grumman	Tracker	Side # 157
S- 2(S2F-1)	AZ	Tucso	PAM	Grumman	Tracker	136468
S- 2(S2F-1)	CA	S.Mon	MoF	Grumman	Tracker	
S- 2(CS)	ON-C	Toronto	TAMD	Grumman	Tracker	
S- 2A	FL	Jacks	NASCF	Grumman	Tracker	148730, AU, 32 ,VS-27
S- 2A	MI	Mt Clemens	SMAM	Grumman	Tracker	144721
S- 2A	OK	Fredi	AAM	Grumman	Tracker	
S- 2A	ON-C	Sault Ste Marie	CBHC	Grumman	Tracker	577
S- 2A(S2F-1)	KS	Topek	CAM	Grumman	Tracker	486
S- 2A(TS)	NY	NYC	ISASM	Grumman	Tracker	
S- 2B(E-1B)(WF-2)	AZ	Tucso	PAM	Grumman	Tracker	Sn 147227, "Willie Fudd"

S- 2B(E-1B)	CT	Winds	NEAM	Grumman	Tracker	147217
S- 2B(E-1B)	NY	NYC	ISASM	Grumman	Tracker	
S- 2B(E-1B)(WF-2)	FL	Pensa	USNAM	Grumman	Tracker	48146, AE 711, VAW-121
S- 2B(US-2B)	CA	Alameda	USSHM	Grumman	Tracker	136691
S- 2D(US)(E-1B)	CA	Paso Robles	EWM	Grumman	Tracker	44-17944, N45CV
S- 2E	NY	NYC	ISASM	Grumman	Tracker	
S- 2E(S2F)	MD	Lexin	PNA&EM	Grumman	Tracker	
S- 2E(S2F)	NY	Garde	CoAM	Grumman	Tracker	151664
S- 2E(S2F)	PE-C	Summe	PEIHAS	Grumman	Tracker	Model 131
S- 2E(S2F)	TX	Addison	CFM	Grumman	Tracker	
S- 2E(S2F) Fuse	TN	Memph	LS	Grumman	Tracker	
S- 2E(S2F)	MD	Lexin	PNA&EM	Grumman	Tracker	
S- 2E(S2F-1)	FL	Pensa	USNAM	Grumman	Tracker	151647, AW-334, 27, VS-73
S- 2E(S2F-1)	KS	Liberal	MAAM	Grumman	Tracker	
S- 2E(S2F-1)	OK	Fredi	AAM	Grumman	Tracker	
S- 2E(TS)	NY	NYC	ISASM	Grumman	Tracker	
S- 2F(CS2F)	FL	Titusville	VAC	Grumman	Tracker	
S- 2F(CS2F-3)	MB-C	Winnipeg	CFB	Grumman	Tracker	12155
S- 2F(CS2F-3)	NS-C	Shear	CFBS	Grumman	Tracker	
S- 2F(CS2F)	OH	N Canton	MAM	Grumman	Tracker	
S- 2F(CS2F)	ON-C	CFB Borden	BHT	Grumman	Tracker	1506
S- 2F(CS2F-3)	PEI-C	Summerside	CFB	Grumman	Tracker	12131
S- 2F(US-2A)	AZ	Tucso	PAM	Grumman	Tracker	N8225E, 147552, "Stoof"
S- 2F1T	AZ	Mesa	MAC	Grumman	Tracker	Firefighter
S- 2R	AZ	Mesa	MAC	Grumman	Tracker	Firefighter
S- 3A	CA	San Diego	NINAS	Lockheed	Viking	Tail NH, Side VS29, 700
S- 3B	CA	San Diego	SDACM	Lockheed	Viking	159766
S- 3A	FL	Jacks	NASCF	Lockheed	Viking	157993, AA, 700, VS-30
S- 4B	NY	Rhine	ORA	Thomas-Morse	Scout	
S- 4B	VA	Quant	MCAGM	Thomas-Morse	Scout	NR66Y
S- 4B(T-4M)	FL	Polk	FoF	Thomas-Morse	Scout	
S- 4C	CA	San Diego	SDAM	Thomas-Morse	Tommy	
S- 4C	CT	Washi	TFC	Thomas-Morse	Tommy	
S- 4C	FL	Pensa	USNAM	Thomas-Morse	Tommy	A5858
S- 4C	NY	Garde	CoAM	Thomas-Morse	Tommy	38934
S- 4C	OH	Dayto	USAFM	Thomas-Morse	Tommy	SC-38944
S-39	CT	Winds	NEAM			
S-43	AK	Ancho	AAHM	Sikorsky		
S-43	AZ	Tucson	PAM	Sikorsky	Baby Clipper	1059, NC16934
S-51(H-5)	AB-C	Calga	AMoC	Sikorsky	Dragonfly	
S-51(H-5)	CT	Winds	NEAM	Sikorsky	Dragonfly	
S-51(H-5)	ON-C	Hamilton	CWH	Sikorsky	Dragonfly	9601
S-51(H-5)	ON-C	Ottaw	CAM	Sikorsky	Dragonfly	9601
S-51(R-5)	PA	WChes	AHM	Sikorsky	Dragonfly	
S-55	AB-C	Calga	AMoC	Sikorsky	Chickasaw	
S-55	BC-C	Langley	CMoF	Sikorsky	Chickasaw	53-4414
S-55	FL	Sandf	VAT	Sikorsky	Chickasaw	
S-55	TX	FtBli	TCRM	Sikorsky	Chickasaw	
S-56	NY	Garde	CoAM	Sikorsky		NC349N
S-58D	NY	NYC	ISASM	Sikorsky	Seabat	
S-58(SH-34G)	PA	Willo	WGNAS	Sikorsky	Seabat	
S-60	CT	Winds	NEAM	Sikorsky		
S-61	MN	Winoma	WTI	Sikorsky	Houston	46008, "Disposal"
S-62A	NJ	Teter	AHoFNJ	Sikorsky		
S-64E	CT	Winds	NEAM	Sikorsky	Skycrane	
S.P. 3	AK	Fairb	APAM	Pereira	Osprey II	N345JD
SA- 2A	WI	Oshko	EAAAAM	Stits	SA-2A	N5K
SA- 3A	WI	Oshko	EAAAAM	Stits	Playboy	N8KK
SA- 8	WI	Oshko	EAAAAM	Stits	Skeeto	N6048C
SA- 11A	WI	Oshko	EAAAAM	Stits	Playmate	N9681Z
SA-100	AL	Birmingham	SMoF	Stolp	Starduster	
SA-100	CA	S.Mon	MoF	Stolp	Starduster	
SA-102-5	KS	Liberal	MAAM		Cavalier	
SA-102-5	OK	Fredi	AAM		Cavalier	
SA-300	MI	Belleville	YAF	Stolp	Starduster Too	SN 001, N693DH
SA-300	ND	Minot	DTAM	Stolp	Starduster Too	
SA-300	NV	Carso	YF	Stolp	Starduster Too	
SA-300	WA	Vanco	PAM	Stolps	Starduster Too	
SA-300	WI	Oshko	EAAAAM	Stolp	Starduster Too	N32CH
SA-500L Starlet	WI	Oshko	EAAAAM	Stolp	Starlet	N2300
SA-700	WI	Oshkosh	EAAAAM	Hayes-Greffenius-Green	Acroduster-1	
Santa Clara Glider	CA	San Carlos	HAM	Santa Clara	Glider 1905	
Saturn V Boat Tail	NY	Coron	NYHoS	Saturn	Flying Boat	
Saunders ST-27	MB-C	Winni	WCAM	Saunders	Commuter	
Saunders ST-28	MB-C	Winni	WCAM	Saunders	Commuter	
Saunders ST-28 Simulator	ON-C	Sault Ste Marie	CBHM	Saunders	Commuter	Sn 009, G-GCML,
SB2C-1A (A-25)	OH	Dayton	USAFM	Curtiss	Helldiver	
SB2C-3 Replica	NY	NYC	ISASM	Curtiss	Helldiver	
SB2C-5	MD	Chantilly	UHC	Curtiss	Helldiver	83479, 212
SB2C-5	MN	Eden Prairie	WotN	Curtiss	Helldiver	
SB2C-5	TX	Midla	CAFFM	Curtiss	Helldiver	
SBD	CA	Alameda Pt	USSHM	Douglas	Dauntless	
SBD	CA	El Cajon	SDAMGF	Douglas	Dauntless	
SBD	CA	Inglewood	PBR	Douglas	Dauntless	
SBD(3/4 Scale)	CA	S.Mon	MoF	Douglas	Dauntless	
SBD	GA	Atlan	CAF-DW	Douglas	Dauntless	N54532
SBD	IL	Chicago	MA	Douglas	Dauntless	10575
SBD-3	MI	Kalam	KAHM	Douglas	Dauntless	06624
SBD-3	SC	MtPleasant	PPM	Douglas	Dauntless	36173, Side # 2
SBD	TX	Breck	BAM	Douglas	Dauntless	
SBD	CA	San Diego	SDACM	Douglas	Dauntless	1612
SBD(A-24B)	CT	Winds	NEAM	Douglas	Dauntless	
SBD-3	AL	Mobile	BMP	Douglas	Dauntless	06583
SBD-3	FL	Pensa	USNAM	Douglas	Dauntless	6508
SBD-3	FL	Pensa	USNAM	Douglas	Dauntless	132MSB7, 6583
SBD-3	OR	Tillamook	TAM	Douglas	Dauntless	N5254
SBD-3	TX	C Christi	USS Lexi	Douglas	Dauntless	6508
SBD-4	AZ	Tucson	PAM	Douglas	Dauntless	Sn 10508
SBD-4	CA	Chino	YAM	Douglas	Dauntless	10518, N4864J, 10518
SBD-4	FL	Pensa	USNAM	Douglas	Dauntless	6583, 25
SBD-5	CA	Chino	PoFAM	Douglas	Dauntless	
SBD-5	CA	San Diego	SDAM	Douglas	Dauntless	N4522
SBD-5	CA	Palm Sprg	PSAM	Douglas	Dauntless	36176, B-25

169

Model	State	City	Code	Manufacturer	Type	Notes
SBD-5	VA	Quant	MCAGM	Douglas	Dauntless	42-54582
SBD-5(A-24B)	TX	Galve	LSFM	Douglas	Dauntless	N93RW
SBD-6	DC	Washi	NA&SM	Douglas	Dauntless	
SBS 2- 8	WI	Oshko	EAAAAM	Schweizer	Glider	N10VV
Sceptre	WA	Yakima	MmoA	Sceptre	Pusher	Twin Tail Monoplane
Scheibe Bergfalke II	BC-C	Langley	CMoF	Scheibe-Bergfalke		
Scheibe L-Spatz 55	NY	Elmira	NSM	Scheibe		N1346B
Schleiche ASW-12	VA	Hampt	VA&SC	Schleiche	Glider	N491V
Schleicher Ka-64	NY	Elmira	NSM	Schleicher	Ka-64	N139N
Schmidt Helicopter	AZ	Grand Canyon	PoFGCVA	Schmidt	Helicopter	
Schmitt Commuter	AZ	Grand	PoFGCVA	Schmitt	Helicopter	N17RS
Schulgleiter SG. 38	MD	Silve	PEGF	Schulgleiter		
Schupal & Nylander	CA	Chino	PoFAM	Schupal-Nylander	Wing	
Schweizer Secondary Glider	IA	Greenfield	IAM	Schweizer	Glider	
Schweizer 1-23	NY	Niagara Falls	NAM	Schweizer	Glider	
Schweizer 1-26	NM	Hobbs	NSF	Schweizer	Glider	
Schweizer 2-22	MB-C	Winni	WCAM	Schweizer	Glider	
Schweizer 2-33	NM	Hobbs	NSF	Schweizer	Glider	
SE-5A	AL	Gunte	LGARFM	RAF	Farnborough	
SE-5A	AL	Ozark	USAAM	RAF	Farnborough	
SE-5A Rep	AR	Fayet	AAM	RAF	Farnborough	
SE-5A	AZ	Mesa	CFM	RAF	Farnborough	
SE-5A	WA	Seattle	MoF	RAF	Farnborough	
SE-5A	BC-C	Langley	CMoF	RAF	Farnborough	002, CF-QGL
SE-5A	FL	Lakel	SFAF	RAF	Farnborough	RAF
SE-5A	FL	Orlan	CSS	RAF	Farnborough	
SE-5A	FL	Orlan	OFW	RAF	Farnborough	
SE-5A	ID	Athol	NAM	RAF	Farnborough	
SE-5A	ME	Owls Head	OHTM	RAF	Farnborough	
SE-5A	NC	Hendersonville	WNCAM	RAF	Farnborough	
SE-5A 4/5 scale	NY	Bayport	BA	RAF	Farnborough	
SE-5A	NY	NYC	ISASM	RAF	Farnborough	
SE-5A	OH	Dayto	USAFM	RAF	Farnborough	22-325
SE-5A	OH	Leroy	PRA	RAF	Farnborough	
SE-5A	ON-C	Chelt	TGWFM	RAF	Farnborough	
SE-5A	TX	Kingbury	VAHF	RAF	Farnborough	
SE-5A 7/8 Scale	ON-C	Chelt	TGWFM	RAF	Farnborough	
Sea-Bee	FL	Key West	CRTC			N87596
Sea Prince	ON-C	Toronto	TAM		Sea Prince	
Seahawker	WA	Vanco	PAM		Biplane	
Security Airster	CA	Santa Martin	WoHAM	Security	Airster	Year 1939
Sellers Quadroplane	KY	Louis	MoH&S	Sellers	Quadroplane	
SG-1A	NM	Moriarty	SSM	Scanlon	Boom Glider	
SGP 1-1	NY	Elmira	NSM	Schweizer	Primary	N50SZ
SGU 1-7	NY	Elmira	NSM	Schweizer		NR23036
SGU 1-19	NY	Elmira	NSM	Schweizer	Glider	14, N91806
SGU 1-19	NY	Elmira	NSM	Schweizer	Glider	CF-ZBE
SG 1-19	NY	Elmira	NSM	Schweizer	Glider	
SGU 1-19	NY	Mayvi	DA	Schweizer	Glider	
SGU 1-23D	NY	Elmira	NSM	Schweizer	Glider	N91899
SGS 1-23HM	NY	Elmira	NSM	Schweizer	Glider	N94298
SGS 1-24	NY	Elmira	NSM	Schweizer	Brigadoon	N91888
SGS 1-26	NY	Elmir	NSM	Schweizer	Glider	1, N91889
SGS 1-26E	NY	Elmir	NSM	Schweizer	Glider	N36122
SGS 1-26B	CA	Calis	CG	Schweizer	Glider	
SGS 1-29	NY	Elmir	NSM	Schweizer	Glider	
SGS 1-35	NY	Elmir	NSM	Schweizer	Glider	N17900
SGS 2-8	NY	Elmir	NSM	Schweizer	Glider	N10VV
SGS 2-12	NY	Elmir	NSM	Schweizer	Glider	N61279
SGS 2-22EK	MD	Silve	PEGF	Schweizer	Glider	
SGS 2-32	CA	Calis	CG	Schweizer	Glider	N8600R
SGS 2-32	NY	Elmir	NSM	Schweizer	Glider	N2767Z
SGS 2-33	CA	Calis	CG	Schweizer	Glider	
SH- 2F(HH-2D)	PA	WChester	AHM	Kaman	Sea Sprite	
SH- 2F	CA	San Diego	NINAS	Kaman	Sea Sprite	Nose 33
SH- 2F	CA	San Diego	SDACM	Kaman	Sea Sprite	150157
SH- 2F	VA	Norfo	NNAS	Kaman	Sea Sprite	149029, HT 33, HSL-30
SH- 2G	MD	Lexington	PRNAM	Kaman	Sea Sprite	161642,
SH- 3(HH-52)	AL	Mobile	BMP	Sikorsky	Sea King	1378
SH- 3	CA	S.Mon	MoF	Sikorsky	Sea King	
SH- 3	CA	San Diego	SDACM	Sikorsky	Sea King	149711
SH- 3	CA	San Diego	NINAS	Sikorsky	Sea King	Tail HC11, Side 727
SH- 3	CA	Simi Valley	PRL	Sikorsky	Sea King	150611
SH- 3(UH)	HI	Oahu, Barbers	HMoF	Sikorsky	Sea King	148043
SH- 3	NB	Omaha	FP	Sikorsky	Sea King	
SH- 3	NY	Brooklyn	NARF	Sikorsky	Sea King	
SH- 3B	FL	Jacks	NASJ	Sikorsky	Sea King	9696, AR 401
SH- 3D(H-3)	FL	Pensa	USNAM	Sikorsky	Sea King	150613, 148990, 156484
SH- 3H	RI	NKing	QAM	Sikorsky	Sea King	149738
SH-34	OH	Newbu	WASAC	Sikorsky	Sea Horse	
SH-34J	CO	Puebl	PWAM	Sikorsky	Sea Horse	17217
SH-60B	CA	San Diego	NINAS	Sikorsky		Tail T2, Side HSL 45
SHK-1	AZ	Tucson	PAM	Schemmp-Hirth		13, N77320
Sherpa C203A	MT	Misso	AFDSC	Sherpa		
Shober Willie II	KS	Liberal	MAAM	Shober	Willie II	
Shober Willie II	OK	Fredi	AAM	Shober	Willie II	
Short S-29	NY	Rhine	ORA	Short		
Short Skyvan	IL	Cahok	PCUSL	Short	Skyvan	
Short Solent Mark 3	CA	Oakla	OWAM	Short	Solent	
Shultz G-6	CA	Chino	YAM	Schultz	Glider	
Siemens-Schuckert D.III	NY	Rhine	ORA	Siemens-Schuckert		
Siemens-Schuckert D.IV	AL	Gunte	LGARFM	Siemens-Schuckert		
Siemens-Schuckert D.IV Rep	AZ	Grand	PoFGCVA	Siemens-Schuckert	Fliegertruppe D IV	N1094G
Siersma SRC-B7	MI	Kalamazoo	KAHM	Siersma		
Sikorsky	AR	Pocahontas	PMA	Sikorsky		3251
Sikorsky	NE	Minde	HWPV	Sikorsky		1944
Silver Dart	NS-C	Halifax	ACAM	A.E.A.	Silver Dart	Replica
Silver Dart	NY	Hammonds	CM	A.E.A.	Silver Dart	
Silver Dart	ON-C	Ottaw	CAM	A.E.A.	Silver Dart	
Silver Dart	ON-C	Sault Ste Marie	CBHC	A.E.A.	Silver Dart	
Simulator 2B13	FL	Titusville	VAC	Navy	Multi Engine	
Skycat	NC	Charl	CHAC		Skycat	

Skycat	NC	CPoin	CPMB		Skycat	
Skylab Command Module	FL	Pensa	USNAM	Skylab	Command Module	116
SL-4	WY	Greyb	H&PA			
Slingsby Kirby Gull	NY	Elmira	NSM	Slingsby	Kirby Gull	N41829
Slingsby T-3	NY	Elmira	NSM	Slingsby	Grasshopper	
Smith DSA	FL	Zellw	BWA	Smith	Miniplane	
Smith DSA	IA	Ottumwa	APM	Smith	Miniplane	ES-1, N44ES
Smith DSA	IN	Auburn	HW	Smith	Miniplane	
Smith DSA	OH	Madis	CFR	Smith	Miniplane	
Smith DSA	ON-C	Collingwood	CCAF	Smith	Miniplane	
Smith DSA	WI	Green	GBPHoF	Smith	Miniplane	N358L
Smith DSA-1	WI	Oshko	EAAAAM	Smith	Miniplane	N90P
Smith Eroplane	IN	FWayn	GFWAM	Smith	Pusher	
Smith H1	OK	Fredi	AAM	Smith	Termite	
Smyth Playmate	FL	Lakel	SFAF	Smyth	Playmate	N77JA
Smyth Sidewinder	FL	Lakel	SFAF	Smyth	Sidewinder	N28Z
Smyth Sidewinder	WI	Oshko	EAAAAM	Smyth	Sidewinder	N55P
SNC-1	FL	Pensa	USNAM	Curtiss		5194
Soko Galeb	IL	Springfield	ACM	Soko	Galeb	23172
Solar Riser	WI	Oshko	EAAAAM	UFM	Solar Riser	
Solbrig Biplane	IA	Des M	ISHD	Solbrig	Biplane	
Solitaire Motor-Glider	WI	Oshko	EAAAAM	Rutan	Solitaire	N142SD
Sollar Challenger	VA	Richm	SMoV		Sollar Challenger	
Sopwith 1- Strutter	AL	Gunte	LGARFM	Sopwith	Strutter	
Sopwith 1- Strutter	FL	Polk	FoF	Sopwith	Strutter	
Sopwith Camel	AL	Gunte	LGARFM	Sopwith	Camel	
Sopwith Camel F.1	AR	Little Rock	AEC	Sopwith	Camel	
Sopwith Camel	AZ	Mesa	CFM	Sopwith	Camel	
Sopwith Camel	BC-C	Langley	CMoF	Sopwith	Camel	
Sopwith Camel	CA	SCarl	HAM	Sopwith	Camel	
Sopwith Camel	ID	Athol	NAM	Sopwith	Camel	
Sopwith Camel	MI	Kalamazoo	KAHM	Sopwith	Camel	
Sopwith Camel	NY	Rhine	ORA	Sopwith	Camel	
Sopwith Camel	OH	Dayto	USAFM	Sopwith	Camel	F6034
Sopwith Camel	TX	Addison	CFM	Sopwith	Camel	
Sopwith Camel 2F.1	ON-C	Ottaw	CAM	Sopwith	Camel	N8156
Sopwith Camel F.1	WA	Seattle	MoF	Sopwith	Camel	NX6330
Sopwith Camel F.1	FL	Pensa	USNAM	Sopwith	Camel	A5658
Sopwith Camel F.1	PA	Beave	AHM	Sopwith	Camel	
Sopwith Dolphin	NY	Rhine	ORA	Sopwith	Dolphin	
Sopwith Pup	AL	Gunte	LGARFM	Sopwith	Pup	
Sopwith Pup	AZ	Mesa	CFM	Sopwith	Pup	
Sopwith Pup	BC-C	Langley	CMoF	Sopwith	Pup	
Sopwith Pup	CA	El Cajon	SDAMGF	Sopwith	Pup	
Sopwith Pup	FL	Polk	FoF	Sopwith	Pup	
Sopwith Pup	IA	Hampton	DWWIAM	Sopwith	Pup	
Sopwith Pup	ME	OwlsH	OHTM	Sopwith	Pup	
Sopwith Pup	ON-C	DonMi	OSC	Sopwith	Pup	
Sopwith Pup	ON-C	Hamilton	CWH	Sopwith	Pup	
Sopwith Pup	ON-C	Ottaw	CAM	Sopwith	Pup	
Sopwith Pup	ON-C	Toronto	OSC	Sopwith	Pup	
Sopwith Pup	TX	Dalla	FoF	Sopwith	Pup	SN:NCH1, N914W
Sopwith Pup	WA	Seattle	MoF	Sopwith	Pup	A 635, NX6018
Sopwith Pup	WI	Madison	MWVM	Sopwith	Pup	
Sopwith Snipe	AZ	Mesa	CFM	Sopwith	Snipe	
Sopwith Snipe	DC	Washi	NA&SM	Sopwith	Snipe	
Sopwith Snipe	MD	Silve	PEGF	Sopwith	Snipe	
Sopwith Snipe	ON-C	Ottaw	CAM	Sopwith	Snipe	
Sopwith Snipe F.1	WA	Seattle	MoF	Sopwith	Snipe	NX67650
Sopwith Triplane	AL	Gunte	LGARFM	Sopwith	Triplane	
Sopwith Triplane	AZ	Mesa	CFM	Sopwith	Triplane	
Sopwith Triplane	WA	Seattle	MoF	Sopwith	Triplane	N318057
Sopwith Triplane	FL	Polk	FoF	Sopwith	Triplane	
Sopwith Triplane	ON-C	Ottaw	CAM	Sopwith	Triplane	N5492
Sorrell Bathtub	WA	Seatt	MoF	Sorrell	Bathtub	1, N5087K
SP-2E	CT	Winds	NEAM	Lockheed	Neptune	
SP-2E	NY	NYC	ISASM	Lockheed	Neptune	
SP-2H	PA	Readi	MAAM	Lockheed	Neptune	145915, N45309, VP 67
Space Capsule	NY	NYC	ISASM		GT-3	"Unsinkable Molly Brown"
Space Shuttle	AL	Huntsville	SC		Shuttle	
Space Shuttle	DC	Dulle	DA		Space Shuttle	"Enterprise"
Space Shuttle 1/3	CA	Moffe	NASAAVC			
Space Shuttle Cargo Bay	CA	LAnge	CMoS&I			
Spacecraft	AL	Hunts	AS&RC			
Spacecraft	CA	San F	TE			
Spacecraft	FL	Cocoa	USAFSM			
Spacecraft	FL	Merri	KSC			
Spacecraft	FL	Orlan	JYM&P			
Spacecraft	MO	SLoui	MP			
Spacecraft (5 ea)	MA	Bosto	MoSP			
Spad IV	VA	Quant	MCAGM	Spad		
Spad VII	AL	Gunte	LGARFM	Spad		
Spad VII	CA	Santa Martin	WoHAM	Spad		
Spad VII	FL	Polk	FoF	Spad		
Spad VII	MI	Kalamazoo	KAHM	Spad	AS	
Spad VII	OH	Dayto	USAFM	Spad	AS	94099
Spad VII	ON-C	Ottaw	CAM	Spad		
Spad VII	VA	Sands	VAM	Spad		Sn 9913
Spad VII	WI	Oshko	EAAAAM	Spad		N9104A
Spad VII.c.1	CA	San Diego	SDAM	Spad		5334, S 3
Spad XIII	AL	Gunte	LGARFM	Spad		
Spad XIII	AZ	Mesa	CFM	Spad		
Spad XIII	AZ	Tucso	PAM	Spad		
Spad XIII	CA	Inglewood	PBR	Spad		
Spad XIII	DC	Washi	NA&SM	Spad		"Smith IV"
Spad XIIIc.1	ME	OwlsH	OHTM	Spad		
Spad XIII	NY	Rhine	ORA	Spad		
Spad XIII	OH	Dayto	USAFM	Spad		
Spad XIII	OR	Tillamook	TAM	Spad		
Spad XIII	WA	Seattle	MoF	Spad		NX3883F
Spartan C-3	NY	Rhine	ORA	Spartan	Executive	
Spartan C2-60	WY	Jackson	GWFM	Spartan	Executive	
Spartan Executive 7W	WI	Oshko	EAAAAM	Spartan	Executive	N13993, "Mrs. Mennon"

171

Name	State	City	Museum	Manufacturer	Model	Notes
Speedbird	IN	Auburn	HW	Speedbird	Air Car	
Spencer Air Car	AK	Ancho	AAHM	Spencer	Air Car	
Spencer Air Car S-14	WI	Oshko	EAAAAM	Spencer	Air Car	N14NX
Spinks Akromaster	WI	Oshko	EAAAAM	Spinks	Akromaster	N31SA
Spitfire	CA	Camarillo	CAF-SCW	Supermarine	Spitfire	FR MK XIVe
Spitfire	LA	New Orleans	DDM	Supermarine	Spitfire	
Spitfire	VA	Suffolk	FF	Supermarine	Spitfire	MS730, N730MSJ
Spitfire		Lazo	CAFM	Supermarine	Spitfire	MS730, N730MSJ
Spitfire Mk.VIIIc LF	TX	Addison	CFM	Supermarine	Spitfire	N719MT, YB-J
Spitfire Mk.IA	IL	Chica	MoS&I	Supermarine	Spitfire	
Spitfire Mk.II	TX	Breck	BAM	Supermarine	Spitfire	DB
Spitfire Mk.II B	ON-C	Ottaw	CAM	Supermarine	Spitfire	
Spitfire Mk.V	CA	Inglewood	PBR	Supermarine	Spitfire	
Spitfire Mk.VII	DC	Washi	NA&SM	Supermarine	Spitfire	
Spitfire Mk.VIII	IL	Urbana	FAM	Supermarine	Spitfire	
Spitfire Mk.VII	ON-C	Ottawa	CWM	Supermarine	Spitfire	
Spitfire Mk.VIII	OR	Tillamook	TAM	Supermarine	Spitfire	TE 356, N58JE
Spitfire Mk.IX Replica	ON-C	N Kitchener	SE	Supermarine	Spitfire	Replica
Spitfire Mk.IX	TX	Midla	CAFFM	Supermarine	Spitfire	
Spitfire Mk.IX	WA	Seattle	MoF	Supermarine	Spitfire	MK923, MJ772, N8R
Spitfire Mk.IX	WA	Seattle	MoF	Supermarine	Spitfire	C8AF-1X-1886, N521R
Spitfire Mk.IX	AB-C	Lazo	CAFM	Supermarine	Spitfire	
Spitfire Mk.IX L.F.	ON-C	Ottaw	CAM	Supermarine	Spitfire	
Spitfire Mk.IXe	WI	Oshko	EAAAAM	Supermarine	Spitfire	N62EA
Spitfire Mk.IXe	CA	Chino	PoFAM	Supermarine	Spitfire	
Spitfire Mk.XI	OH	Dayto	USAFM	Supermarine	Spitfire	PA908
Spitfire Mk.XIV	CA	Palm Sprg	PSAM	Supermarine	Spitfire	65-648206, NX114BP, WZ-P
Spitfire Mk.XIV	TX	Galve	LSFM	Supermarine	Spitfire	TZ138, N5505A
Spitfire Mk.XVI	CA	San Diego	SDAM	Supermarine	Spitfire	WK-W
Spitfire Mk.XVI	ON-C	Hamilton	CWHM	Supermarine	Spitfire	
Spitfire Mk.XVI	ON-C	Ottaw	CAM	Supermarine	Spitfire	
Spitfire Mk.XVI	OR	McMinnville	EAM	Supermarine	Spitfire	TE 356, NX356EV
Spitfire Parts	SK-C	MJaw	WDM	Supermarine	Spitfire	
Sport Fury	AL	Birmingham	SmoF		Sport Fury	
SR-71A See Also A-12				Loockheed	Blackbird	
SR-71	LA	Bossier City	BAFB	Lockheed	Blackbird	61-7967
SR-71	CA	Palmd	PAFB	Lockheed	Blackbird	61-7973
SR-71	DC	Dulle	NASM	Lockheed	Blackbird	61-7972
SR-71A	AZ	Tucso	PAM	Lockheed	Blackbird	61-7951
SR-71A	CA	Atwater	CAM	Lockheed	Blackbird	61-7960
SR-71A	CA	Marys	BAFB	Lockheed	Blackbird	61-7963
SR-71A	CA	Riverside	MFAM	Lockheed	Blackbird	61-7975
SR-71A	OR	McMinnville	EAEC	Lockheed	Blackbird	61-7971
SR-71A	CA	Rosam	EAFB	Lockheed	Blackbird	67-7980
SR-71A	CA	Rosam	AFFTCM	Lockheed	Blackbird	61-7955
SR-71A	FL	Shali	USAFAM	Lockheed	Blackbird	61-7959
SR-71A	GA	Warner Robin	MoA	Lockheed	Blackbird	61-7958,"Ichi Ban", 958
SR-71A	KS	Hutch	KC&SC	Lockheed	Blackbird	61-7961
SR-71A	OH	Dayto	USAFM	Lockheed	Blackbird	61-7976
SR-71A	TX	San A	LAFB	Lockheed	Blackbird	61-7979
SR-71A	VA	Sandstrom	VAM	Lockheed	Blackbird	61-7968
SR-71A	WA	Seattle	MoF	Lockheed	Blackbird	61-7977
SR-71A-LO	NE	Ashland	SACM	Lockheed	Blackbird	61-7964
SR-71B	MI	Kalamazoo	AZ	Lockheed	Blackbird	61-7956
SR-71C	UT	Ogden	HAFBM	Lockheed	Blackbird	61-7981
ST-34KR	PA	Tough	CFCM	Ryan		
Stahltaube	CA	Santa Martin	WoHAM	Stahltaube		
Staib LB-5	KS	Liberal	MAAM	Staib	Tiny	
Stampe SV4	NY	Rhine	ORA	Stampe		
Stan Hall Cherokee II	CA	Santa Martin	WoHAM	Stan Hall	Sherokee II	Glider
Stan Hall Safari	CA	Santa Martin	WoHAM	Stan Hall	Safari	Powered Glider
Stanley Nomad	MD	Silve	PEGF	Stanley	Nomad	
Stargazer Gondola	OH	Dayton	USAFM		Stargazer	
Starr Bumble Bee	AZ	Tucson	PAM	Starr	Bumble Bee	N83WS, Worlds Smallest Aircraft
Stearman	AB-C	Wetas	RM	Stearman		
Stearman	CA	Hayward	VAM	Stearman		
Stearman	CO	Pueblo	PWAM	Stearman		
Stearman (8ea)	FL	Zellw	BWA	Stearman		
Stearman	LA	Patte	WWMAM	Stearman		"Delta Airlines"
Stearman	ON-C	Trenton	CAHS	Stearman		
Stearman	MO	Maryland Hts	HARM	Stearman		
Stearman	NY	Bayport	BA	Stearman		
Stearman	TX	Ft Worth	VFM	Stearman		
Stearman	UT	Heber	HVAM	Stearman	Kaydet	
Stearman	VA	Suffolk	FF	Stearman	75-2743	
Stearman	WA	Vancoouver	PAM	Stearman		
Stearman 4-CM-1	CA	Hayward	VAM	Stearman	Bull	
Stearman 4-D	CA	Chino	YAM	Stearman	Bull	4026, N11224
Stearman 4-D	KS	Wichita	KAM	Stearman		
Stearman 4-E	NV	Carso	YF	Stearman	Bull	
Stearman 4-EM	ON-C	Ottaw	CAM	Stearman	Bull	
Stearman A-75 (8 ea)	VA	Bealt	FCA	Stearman		
Stearman C-2B	AK	Ancho	AAHM	Stearman		N5415
Stearman C-3B	WA	Seatt	MoF	Stearman		166, N7550
Stearman EC 75	OR	McMinnville	EAEC	Stearman		
Stearman Fr 24	FL	Arcia	AA Clark	Stearman		
Stearman 73 NS-1	KS	Wichita	KAM	Stearman		
Stearman Super	WI	Oshko	EAAAAM	Boeing	Super Stearman	N5051V
Stearman-Hammond Y	MD	Silve	PEGF	Stearman-Hammond		
Stearman-Hammond YS-1	CA	SCarl	HAM	Stearman-Hammond		
Steco 1911	MN	St Paul	MA&SM	Steco	Aerohydro-Plane	
Steen Skybolt	KS	Liberal	MAAM	Steen	Skybolt	
Steen Skybolt	NV	Carso	YF	Steen	Skybolt	
Steen Skybolt	WI	Fond du Lac	WAM	Steen	Skybolt	
Stephens Akro	WA	Seatt	MoF	Stephens	Akro	434, N78JN
Stinson 105	ON-C	Collingwood	CCAF	Stinson	Voyager	7055, Parts: 7102, 7246
Stinson 105	SK-C	MJaw	WDM	Stinson	Voyager	
Stinson 108	AB-C	Edmonton	AAM	Stinson	Voyager	
Stinson 108	AK	Ancho	AAHM	Stinson	Voyager	
Stinson 108	GA	Woodstock	NGWS	Stinson	Voyager	
Stinson 108	OH	Madis	CFR	Stinson	Voyager	
Stinson 108-3	OK	Fredi	AAM	Stinson	Voyager	
Stinson 7-B	NV	Carso	YF	Stinson		

Stinson 7M-7A	WY	Jackson	GWFM	Stinson		
Stinson A Trimotor	AK	Ancho	AAHM	Stinson	Tri-Motor	NC15165, 15, "Pennsylvania Central"
Stinson A Trimotor	MN	Blaine	GH	Stinson	Trimotor	
Stinson Junior	IA	Ottumwa	APM	Stinson	Junior	8074, NC-12165
Stinson SA-10A	AL	Birmingham	SMoF	Stinson	Voyager	
Stinson SA-10A	AK	Palme	MOAT&I	Stinson	Voyager	
Stinson SA-10A	CA	Santa Martin	WoHAM	Stuart	Voyager	
Stinson SA-10A	IA	Ottumwa	APM	Stinson	Voyager	7655, N27710
Stinson SA-10A	MB-C	Brand	CATPM	Stinson	Voyager	
Stinson SA-10A	MI	Oscoda	YAF	Stinson	Voyager	7883, N32235
Stinson SA-10A	NJ	Teter	AHoFNJ	Stinson	Voyager	
Stinson SA-10A	OK	Fredi	AAM	Stinson	Voyager	
Stinson SA-10A	OK	Oklah	KCASM	Stinson	Voyager	
Stinson SA-10A	WA	Tacoma	MAFB	Stinson	Voyager	43-43847
Stinson SA-10A(L- 9)	KS	Liberal	MAAM	Stinson	Voyager	
Stinson SM-1	CA	San Carlos	HAM	Stinson	Detroiter	
Stinson SM-1	CT	Winds	NEAM	Stinson	Detroiter	
Stinson SM-1	MI	Dearb	HFM	Stinson	Detroiter	
Stinson SM-1	NE	Minde	HWPV	Stinson	Detroiter	
Stinson SM-1B	WY	Jackson	GWFM	Stinson	Detroiter	
Stinson SM-6000B	OR	McMinnville	EAEC	Stinson	Detroiter	"Flagship Texas"
Stinson SM-8A Jr.	FL	Titusville	VACM	Stinson	SMS-8A Junior	
Stinson SM-8A	WA	Port Townsend	PTAM	Stinson	Detroiter	4009, NC418M
Stinson SM-8A	WA	Port Townsend	PTAM	Stinson	Detroiter	4098, NC930W
Stinson SM-8A Jr.	WI	Oshko	EAAAAM	Stinson	SMS-8A Junior	NC408Y, "Spirit of EAA"
Stinson SM-8A Jr.	WI	Oshko	EAAAAM	Stinson	SMS-8A Junior	N1026
Stinson SR	CA	S.Mar	SMMoF	Stinson	Reliant	
Stinson SR V-77	IN	Auburn	HW	Stinson	Reliant	
Stinson SR	NC	Morga	CWCAF	Stinson	Reliant	
Stinson SR	ON-C	Ottaw	CAM	Stinson	Reliant	
Stinson SR	PA	Latro	WCM	Stinson	Reliant	
Stinson SR Float Plane	WA	Seatt	MoF	Stinson	Reliant	8732, N13477
Stinson SR(AT19)V-77	KS	Liberal	MAAM	Stinson	Reliant	
Stinson SR-5 Replica	AL	Birmingham	SMoF	Stinson	Junior	
Stinson SR-5A	ND	Minot	DTAM	Stinson	Junior	
Stinson SR-5E	OR	Eugen	OAM	Stinson	Junior	
Stinson SR-5JR	AK	Fairb	APAM	Stinson	Junior	N13482, "Spirit of Barter Island"
Stinson SR-5	AR	Fayet	AAM	Stinson	Junior	NC12143
Stinson SR-8	MB-C	Winni	WCAM	Stinson	Reliant	
Stinson SR-9FM	AB-C	Edmonton	AAM	Stinson	Reliant	5732
Stinson SR-9	ON-C	Sault Ste Marie	CBHC	Stinson	Reliant	Sn 5702, CF-BGN
Stinson SR-9 CM	AK	Ancho	AAHM	Stinson	Reliant	
Stinson SR-9 CM	WI	Oshkosh	EAAAAM	Stinson	Reliant	
Stinson SR-10F	DC	Washi	USPM	Stinson	Reliant	NC2311, "Human Pick-Up"
Stinson SR-10F	MD	Silve	PEGF	Stinson	Reliant	
Stinson SR-10G	VA	Sandston	VAM	Stinson	Reliant	Sn 5903
Stits DS-1	WI	Oshko	EAAAAM	Stits		N4453H, "Baby Bird"
Stits SA-3A	ON-C	Ottaw	CAM	Stits		
Stolp Starduster II	R1	NKing	QAM	Stolp	Starduster II	N100LF
Stolp V Star	WI	Oshko	EAAAAM	Stolp	V Star	N9LS
Stout Skycar	MD	Silve	PEGF	Stout	Skycar	
Struchen Helicopter	BC-C	Langley	CMoF	Strechen	Helicopter	
Stuart M-5	WA	Tilli	CMANGP	Stuart		
Student Prince	WA	Vancouver	PAM	Acft Bldg Corp	Student Prince	"Ladt Summer"
Sud Aviation SE 210	AZ	Tucso	PAM	Sud Aviation	Caravelle	N1001U
Sud Ouese SO1221 S	CA	Ramona	CR	Sud Aviation	Caravelle	
Sun Standard Hang Glider	MI	Kalamazoo	KAHM	Sun Aircraft	Hang Glider	
Sundancer I Racer	CA	San Diego	SDAMGF	Sundancer	Racer	N1AE
Super Lancer Hang Glider	FL	Lakeland	SNF	Lancer	Hang Glider	
Supermarine F.1	NY	NYC	ISASM	Supermarine	Scimitar	
Supermarine S6B	CA	Chino	PoFAM	Supermarine		
Supermarine Stranraer	BC-C	Langley	CMoF	Supermarine	Stranraer	
Surca-Tempete Homebuilt	FL	Lakel	SFAF	Surca-Tempete	Homebuilt	
SV-4C	BC-C	Langley	CMoF	Stampe		
SV-5D	OH	Dayton	USAFM	Martin	PRIME	Lifting Body
SV-5J	CO	CSpri	USAFA	Martin	PRIME	Lifting Body
SVA-9	CT	Washi	TFC	Ansaldo		
Swallow	KS	Wichita	KAM	Swallow		
Swallow	WA	Seattle	MoF	Swallow		968, N6070
Swallow Model 1924	WI	Oshko	EAAAAM	Swallow	Three Seater	N4028
Swallow 1926	NE	Minde	HWPV	Swallow		
Swallow A	AZ	Tucso	PAM	Swallow		
Swallow C	KS	Wichita	KAM	Swallow		
Swallow TP	CA	Chino	YAM	Swallow		
Swallow TP	CA	San Diego	SDAM	Swallow		N8761
T- 1	FL	Miami	WOM	Folland	Gnat	
T- 1	IN	Ft Wayne	Mercury	Folland	Gnat	
T- 1	KS	Liberal	MAAM	Folland	Gnat	
T- 2	AR	Fayetteville	AAM	North American	Buckeye	
T- 2	CA	Chino	PoFAM	North American	Buckeye	
T- 2	DC	Washi	NA&SM	North American	Buckeye	
T- 2	IN	India	IMoMH	North American	Buckeye	
T- 2	OH	Newbu	WASAC	North American	Buckeye	
T- 2	TX		TAM	North American	Buckeye	47, 5
T- 2A	NC	Charlotte	CAM	North American	Buckeye	148239
T- 2B	ID	Driggs	TAC	North American	Buckeye	Sn 155226, Side # 300S, Tail B
T- 2C	AZ	Tucson	PAM	North American	Buckeye	157050
T- 2C	CA	San Diego	SDACM	North American	Buckeye	156697
T- 2C	FL	Pensacola	NMoNA	North American	Buckeye	157058
T- 3	CA	San Carlos	HAM	Boeing		
T-11	IN	India	IMoMH			
T-11	LA	New Orleans	FJB			
T-18	BC-C	Langley	CMoF	Thorp	Tiger	
T-18	IA	SBluf	MAAM	Thorp	Tiger	
T-18	KS	Liberal	MAAM	Thorp	Tiger	
T-18	OK	Fredi	AAM	Thorp	Tiger	
T-18	WA	Seatt	MoF	Thorp	Tiger	1093, N1093
T-18	WI	Oshko	EAAAAM	Thorp	Tiger	N455DT, "Victoria 76"
T-28	CO	Denve	JWDAS	North American	Trojan	
T-28	DC	Washi	NHND	North American	Trojan	
T-28	DC	Washington	ANAS	North American	Trojan	
T-28	FL	Milto	CityPark	North American	Trojan	
T-28	FL	Tittusville	VACM	North American	Trojan	

T-28	IA	Ankeny	CAFHSS	North American	Trojan	N70743
T-28	ID	Driggs	TAC	North American	Trojan	Cowl # 249, Tail NATC
T-28	IL	Rockf	CRA	North American	Trojan	
T-28	IN	India	IMoMH	North American	Trojan	
T-28	KS	New Century	CAF-HoAW	North American	Trojan	
T-28	LA	Reser	AMHFM	North American	Trojan	
T-28	MI	Ypsil	YAF	North American	Trojan	
T-28	MS	Bilox	KAFB	North American	Trojan	13747
T-28 Cockpit	NC	Charlotte	CAM	North American	Trojan	
T-28	NM	STere	WEAM	North American	Trojan	
T-28	NV	Carso	YF	North American	Trojan	
T-28	ON-C	Hamilton	CWH	North American	Trojan	
T-28	PA	Beaver Falls	AHM	North American	Trojan	
T-28	TX	Big Springs	H25	North American	Trojan	
T-28	TX	C Christi	NAS	North American	Trojan	
T-28	TX	FWort	PMoT	North American	Trojan	
T-28	TX	San Angelo	GAFB	North American	Trojan	91679
T-28	TX	Ladero	Airport	North American	Trojan	
T-28	UT	Heber	HVAM	North American	Trojan	0-37799
T-28	WI	Beloi	BA	North American	Trojan	
T-28	WI	Boscobel	BA	North American	Trojan	
T-28A	AL	Ozark	USAAM	North American	Trojan	51-3612
T-28A	GA	Warner Robin	MoF	North American	Trojan	51-3612, "Rocly Yates"
T-28A-NI	MI	Belleville	YAF	North American	Trojan	50-234, N234NA
T-28A	MI	Kalam	KAHM	North American	Trojan	51-7700
T-28A	OH	Dayto	USAFM	North American	Trojan	49-1494
T-28A	OH	Newbu	WASAC	North American	Trojan	4021800
T-28A	OK	Enid	VAFB	North American	Trojan	
T-28A	OK	Fredi	AAM	North American	Trojan	
T-28A	TX	D Rio	LAFB	North American	Trojan	
T-28A	TX	San A	RAFB	North American	Trojan	
T-28A(GT)	TX	San A	LAFB	North American	Trojan	49-1611
T-28B	CA	Palm Springs	PSAM	North American	Trojan	140041, NX28BP
T-28B	CA	Paso Robles	EWM	North American	Trojan	138303
T-28B	CA	Rosam	EAFB	North American	Trojan	137702
T-28B	CA	S.Mon	MoF	North American	Trojan	
T-28B	CA	Sacra	McCelAFB	North American	Trojan	138327
T-28B	FL	Pensa	USNAM	North American	Trojan	136326, 2W, 341, VT-3
T-28B	IN	Valparaiso	IAM	North American	Trojan	140018
T-28B	KS	Topek	CAM	North American	Trojan	137759, N-759T
T-28B	NC	Asheboro	CHAC	North American	Trojan	
T-28B	NC	Charl	CHAC	North American	Trojan	
T-28B	OH	Dayto	USAFM	North American	Trojan	140048
T-28B	OR	Mc Minnville	EAEC	North American	Trojan	13 8334, N394W
T-28B	TN	Sevierville	TMoA	North American	Trojan	138129, N32257, "Showtime"
T-28B	TX	C Christi	USS Lexi	North American	Trojan	
T-28B	UT	Ogden	HAFBM	North American	Trojan	
T-28C	AL	Everg	MA	North American	Trojan	
T-28C	AL	Everg	MAE	North American	Trojan	
T-28C	AZ	Tucso	PAM	North American	Trojan	140481
T-28C	CA	El Cajon	WW	North American	Trojan	
T-28C	CA	SRosa	PCAM	North American	Trojan	7696, 2G, 133, VT-2
T-28C	CO	Puebl	PWAM	North American	Trojan	140064
T-28C	CT	Winds	NEAM	North American	Trojan	
T-28C	MA	Fall	USSMM	North American	Trojan	
T-28C	MI	Belleville	YAF	North American	Trojan	140531, N944SD, "Tough Old Bird"
T-28C	NJ	Rio Grande	NASW	North American	Trojan	
T-28C	TX	Galveston	LSM	North American	Trojan	
T-28C	VA	Quantico	MCAGM	North American	Trojan	140557
T-28D	PA	Readi	MAAM	North American	Trojan	
T-28D(AT-28D-5)	VA	Suffolk	FF	North American	Trojan	1634
T-28D(AT)	FL	FtWal	HF	North American	Trojan	
T-28S	OH	N Canton	MAM	North American	Trojan	51-3565, N85227
T-29	VT	Burlington	NANG	Convair	Flying Classroom	
T-29 (C-131)	GA	Calho	Mercer A	Convair	Flying Classroom	
T-29A(C-131)	NE	Ashland	SACM	Convair	Flying Classroom	50-0190
T-29A(C-131A)	AZ	Tucso	PAM	Convair	Flying Classroom	49-1918
T-29A(C-131A)	GA	Warner Robin	MoF	Convair	Flying Classroom	49-1938
T-29A(C-131A)	TX	Wichi	SAFB	Convair	Flying Classroom	
T-29A(GT)(C-131)	TX	Wichi	SAFB	Convair	Flying Classroom	
T-29B(VT)	AZ	Tucso	PAM	Convair	Flying Classroom	51-7906
T-29B(VT)	TX	San A	LAFB	Convair	Flying Classroom	51-5172
T-29C(C-131)	CA	Sacra	SWAM	Convair	Flying Classroom	
T-29C(C-131)	TX	Abile	DLAP	Convair	Flying Classroom	52-1175
T-29C(C-131)	UT	Ogden	HAFBM	Convair	Flying Classroom	
T-33	AR	Fayetteville	AAM	Lockheed	Shooting Star	
T-33	CA	Torrance	Airport	Lockheed	Shooting Star	
T-33	GA	Griffin	SCA	Lockheed	Shooting Star	
T-33	GA	Marietta	NASA	Lockheed	Shooting Star	
T-33	IA	SBluf	MAAM	Lockheed	Shooting Star	
T-33	IN	Hobar	DickBoyd	Lockheed	Shooting Star	
T-33	LA	Bossi	BAFB	Lockheed	Shooting Star	
T-33	MI	Jackson	EAAC	Lockheed	Shooting Star	
T-33	MN	Alexandria	Airport	Lockheed	Shooting Star	
T-33	MT	Helena	CoT	Canadair	Shooting Star	
T-33 Cockpit	NC	Charlotte	CAM	Lockheed	Shooting Star	
T-33	NC	Hickory	HRA	Lockheed	Shooting Star	52-9529
T-33	ND	Minot	DTAM	Lockheed	Shooting Star	
T-33	NJ	Rio Grande	NASW	Lockheed	Shooting Star	
T-33	ON-C	Grand Bend	PAFM	Lockheed	Shooting Star	
T-33	NM	STere	WEAM	Lockheed	Shooting Star	
T-33	TX	Big Springs	H25	Lockheed	Shooting Star	
T-33	TX	Ft Worth	SAM	Lockheed	Shooting Star	
T-33	WA	Seatt	MoF	Lockheed	Shooting Star	
T-33	WI	Janesville	BHTSAC	Lockheed	Shooting Star	
T-33	WI	Stoughton	VFW	Loockheed	Shooting Star	
T-33 Cockpit Trainer	CA	S.Mon	MoF	Lockheed	Shooting Star	
T-33 Mk 3	TN	Sevierville	TMoA	Lockheed	Shooting Star	X-R CAF 21566
T-33 Mk 3	WI	Oshko	EAAAAM	Lockheed	Shooting Star	N72JR
T-33A	AK	Ancho	EAFB	Lockheed	Shooting Star	
T-33A	AK	Ancho	KANGB	Lockheed	Shooting Star	
T-33A	AL	Atmor	CityPark	Lockheed	Shooting Star	
T-33A	AL	Birmingham	SMoF	Lockheed	Shooting Star	

T-33A	AL	Flora	CityPark	Lockheed	Shooting Star	
T-33A	AL	Mobil	CityPark	Lockheed	Shooting Star	
T-33A	AL	Monro	CityPark	Lockheed	Shooting Star	
T-33A	AL	Tusca	CityPark	Lockheed	Shooting Star	
T-33A	AR	Grave	VWF	Lockheed	Shooting Star	
T-33A	AR	Helen	VWF	Lockheed	Shooting Star	
T-33A	AR	Littl	LRAFB	Lockheed	Shooting Star	51-9080
T-33A	AZ	Gila	GBAFAF	Lockheed	Shooting Star	
T-33A	AZ	Grand	PoFGCVA	Lockheed	Shooting Star	71-5262
T-33A	AZ	Mesa	WAFB	Lockheed	Shooting Star	
T-33A	AZ	Phoenix	DVA	Lockheed	Shooting Star	
T-33A	AZ	Tucso	PAM	Lockheed	Shooting Star	53-6145
T-33A	CA	Atwater	CAM	Lockheed	Shooting Star	58-0629
T-33A	CA	Chino	YAM	Lockheed	Shooting Star	
T-33A	CA	Shafter	MFAM	Lockheed	Shooting Star	
T-33A	CA	Fresn	FANG	Lockheed	Shooting Star	
T-33A	CA	Los G	VWF	Lockheed	Shooting Star	
T-33A	CA	Mader	VWF	Lockheed	Shooting Star	
T-33A	CA	Oakland	CAF-GGW	Lockheed	Shooting Star	16581, NX91242Z
T-33A	CA	Paso Robles	EWM	Lockheed	Shooting Star	52-9769
T-33A	CA	Richm	AMS	Lockheed	Shooting Star	
T-33A	CA	Riverside	MFAM	Lockheed	Shooting Star	58-0513
T-33A	CA	S.Mon	MoF	Lockheed	Silver Star	69330, Side # FT-330
T-33A	CA	Sacra	McCelAFB	Lockheed	T-Bird	53-5205
T-33A	CA	Torrence	FAAF	Lockheed	T-Bird	52-9239
T-33A	CO	CSpri	EJPSCM	Lockheed	Shooting Star	57-0713
T-33A	CO	Aurora	WOTR	Lockheed	Shooting Star	
T-33A	CO	Flage	VWF	Lockheed	Shooting Star	
T-33A	CT	Winds	NEAM	Lockheed	Shooting Star	
T-33A	DE	Dover	AL P-2	Lockheed	Shooting Star	
T-33A	DE	Dover	DAFB	Lockheed	Shooting Star	TR-497
T-33A	FL	Clear	FMAM	Lockheed	Shooting Star	
T-33A	FL	De Fu	CityPark	Lockheed	Shooting Star	
T-33A	FL	Jacks	JIA	Lockheed	Shooting Star	35325, 27
T-33A	FL	Lakel	SFAF	Lockheed	Shooting Star	58-697
T-33A	FL	Shali	USAFAM	Lockheed	Shooting Star	53-5947
T-33A	GA	Calhoun	MAM	Lockheed	Shooting Star	29574, TR-574
T-33A	GA	Corde		Lockheed	Shooting Star	
T-33A	GA	Dougl	CityPark	Lockheed	Shooting Star	
T-33A	GA	Griff	CityPark	Lockheed	Shooting Star	
T-33A	GA	Thoma	CityPark	Lockheed	Shooting Star	
T-33A	GA	Warner Robin	MoF	Lockheed	Shooting Star	52-9633
T-33A	GA	Wayne	ALP120	Lockheed	Shooting Star	
T-33A	GA	Willa	CityPark	Lockheed	Shooting Star	
T-33A	HI	Oahu	HAFB	Lockheed	Shooting Star	
T-33A	IA	Burli	CityPark	Lockheed	Shooting Star	
T-33A	IA	Cedar Rapids	Vet Memorial	Lockheed	Shooting Star	53-5916
T-33A	IA	Oelwe	ALP19	Lockheed	Shooting Star	
T-33A	IA	Sheld	CityPark	Lockheed	Shooting Star	
T-33A	IA	Sigou	CityPark	Lockheed	Shooting Star	
T-33A	ID	Burle	CityPark	Lockheed	Shooting Star	
T-33A	ID	Lewis	CityPark	Lockheed	Shooting Star	
T-33A	ID	Malad	CityPark	Lockheed	Shooting Star	
T-33A	ID	Twin	CityPark	Lockheed	Shooting Star	
T-33A	IL	Sugar Grove	ACM	Lockheed	Shooting Star	58-0632
T-33A	IL	Bloom	PAM	Lockheed	Shooting Star	35979
T-33A	IL	Cahok	PCUSL	Lockheed	Shooting Star	
T-33A	IL	Centr	CityPark	Lockheed	Shooting Star	
T-33A	IL	Highl	CityPark	Lockheed	Shooting Star	
T-33A	IL	Linco	HIFM	Lockheed	Shooting Star	
T-33A	IL	Pinck	CityPark	Lockheed	Shooting Star	
T-33A	IL	Quicy	CityPark	Lockheed	Shooting Star	
T-33A-1-LO(F-80)	IL	Ranto	OCAM	Lockheed	Shooting Star	55-9797
T-33A	IL	Versa	CityPark	Lockheed	Shooting Star	
T-33A	IN	Covin	VFWP2395	Lockheed	Shooting Star	50-29326
T-33A	IN	Elkhart	NIAM	Lockheed	Shooting Star	70688, TCD17
T-33A	IN	Hunti	CityPark	Lockheed	Shooting Star	
T-33A	IN	Peru	GAFB	Lockheed	Shooting Star	52-9563
T-33A	KS	Indep	VFWP1186	Lockheed	Shooting Star	
T-33A	KS	Topek	CAM	Lockheed	Shooting Star	0-29632
T-33A-5-LO	KS	Wichi	K&HAP	Lockheed	Shooting Star	53-5998
T-33A	LA	Houma	CityPark	Lockheed	Shooting Star	
T-33A	LA	Mansf	VFWP4586	Lockheed	Shooting Star	
T-33A	LA	New Orleans	FoJBMM	Lockheed	Shooting Star	
T-33A	LA	Rusto	LTUD305	Lockheed	Shooting Star	
T-33A	LA	Sprin	CityPark	Lockheed	Shooting Star	
T-33A	MA	Bourne	HQMMR	Lockheed	Shooting Star	14335
T-33A	MA	Otis	OANG	Lockheed	Shooting Star	
T-33A	MA	Stow	BCF	Lockheed	Shooting Star	
T-33A	MD	Cumbe	CityPark	Lockheed	Shooting Star	
T-33A	MD	Middl	GLMAM	Lockheed	Shooting Star	
T-33A	MD	Pocom	ALP93	Lockheed	Shooting Star	52-9650, TR-650
T-33A	MD	Rockv	CityPark	Lockheed	Shooting Star	
T-33A	MD	Silve	PEGF	Lockheed	Shooting Star	
T-33A	MI	Breck	ALP295	Lockheed	Shooting Star	
T-33A	MI	Calum	CAFS	Lockheed	Shooting Star	
T-33A	MI	Grayl	ALP106	Lockheed	Shooting Star	
T-33A	MI	Hart	City Fog	Lockheed	Shooting Star	35073, 8436, T33-600-2282
T-33A	MI	Iron	CityPark	Lockheed	Shooting Star	
T-33A	MI	Roseb	ALP383	Lockheed	Shooting Star	
T-33A	MI	Sebew	CityPark	Lockheed	Shooting Star	
T-33A	MI	Mt Clemens	SMAM	Lockheed	Shooting Star	53-6099
T-33A	MI	Ypsil	YAF	Lockheed	Shooting Star	
T-33A	MN	Alber	CityPark	Lockheed	Shooting Star	
T-33A	MN	Buffa	CityPark	Lockheed	Shooting Star	
T-33A	MN	Hecto	CityPark	Lockheed	Shooting Star	
T-33A	MN	Minne	CityPark	Lockheed	Shooting Star	
T-33A	MN	Minne	MAGM	Lockheed	Shooting Star	52-9806
T-33A	MN	Winoma	WTI	Lockheed	Shooting Star	N86905
T-33A	MN	Under	VFW874	Lockheed	Shooting Star	
T-33A	MO	Carut	CityPark	Lockheed	Shooting Star	
T-33A	MO	Mount	CityPark	Lockheed	Shooting Star	
T-33A	MO	Richm	ALP237	Lockheed	Shooting Star	

T-33A	MO	SLoui	ALP179	Lockheed	Shooting Star	
T-33A	MO	SLoui	NMoT	Lockheed	Shooting Star	52-9446
T-33A	MO	StCha	CityPark	Lockheed	Shooting Star	
T-33A	MS	Bilox	KAFB	Lockheed	Shooting Star	58-0567
T-33A	MS	Colum	CityPark	Lockheed	Shooting Star	
T-33A	MT	Glasg	CityPark	Lockheed	Shooting Star	52-9564
T-33A	MT	Great Falls	CityPark	Lockheed	Shooting Star	
T-33A	MT	Great Falls	GFANG	Lockheed	Shooting Star	
T-33A	MT	Great Falls	MAFB	Lockheed	Shooting Star	52-9672
T-33A	MT	Great Falls	MAFB	Lockheed	Shooting Star	57-0574
T-33A	NC	Charl	CHAC	Lockheed	Shooting Star	
T-33A	NC	CPoin	CPMB	Lockheed	Shooting Star	
T-33A	ND	Dicke	CityPark	Lockheed	Shooting Star	
T-33A	ND	Hatto	CityPark	Lockheed	Shooting Star	
T-33A	ND	Minot	MAFB	Lockheed	Shooting Star	
T-33A	ND	Vela	CityPark	Lockheed	Shooting Star	
T-33A	NE	Beatr	CityPark	Lockheed	Shooting Star	51-8880
T-33A	NE	Fairb	CityPark	Lockheed	Shooting Star	
T-33A	NE	Frank	CityPark	Lockheed	Shooting Star	
T-33A	NE	Linco	LANG	Lockheed	Shooting Star	52-9264, Tail ANG 29264
T-33A	NM	Clovi	CAFB	Lockheed	Shooting Star	
T-33A	NM	Truth	CAFB	Lockheed	Shooting Star	
T-33A	NY	Albion	VAG	Lockheed	Shooting Star	
T-33A	NY	NYC	ISASM	Lockheed	Shooting Star	
T-33A	NS-C	Greenwood	GMAM	Lockheed	Silver Star	
T-33A	OH	Brook	CityPark	Lockheed	Shooting Star	
T-33A	OH	Dayto	USAFM	Lockheed	Shooting Star	53-5974
T-33A(NT)	OH	Dayto	USAFM	Lockheed	Shooting Star	51-4120
T-33A	OH	Lockb	RANGB	Lockheed	Shooting Star	58-586, Model 580
T-33A	OH	Marie	CityPark	Lockheed	Shooting Star	
T-33A	OH	Newar	NAFM	Lockheed	Shooting Star	
T-33A	OH	Newbu	WASAC	Lockheed	Shooting Star	
T-33A	OH	Wadsw	CityPark	Lockheed	Shooting Star	
T-33A	OK	Coman	CityPark	Lockheed	Shooting Star	
T-33A	ON-NF	Goose Bay	TH	Canadair	Silver Star	
T-33A	OK	Elk C	CityPark	Lockheed	Shooting Star	
T-33A	OK	Enid	VAFB	Lockheed	Shooting Star	
T-33A	OK	Musko	City	Lockheed	Shooting Star	
T-33A	OK	Oklah	45IDM	Lockheed	Shooting Star	58-0505
T-33A	OK	Oklah	A&SM	Lockheed	Shooting Star	
T-33A	OK	Oklah	KCASM	Lockheed	Shooting Star	
T-33A	OK	Tinke	TANG	Lockheed	Shooting Star	
T-33A	OR	Woodb	CityPark	Lockheed	Shooting Star	
T-33A	PA	New K	CityPark	Lockheed	Shooting Star	
T-33A	PA	NHunt	VFWP781	Lockheed	Shooting Star	
T-33A	PA	Phila	FI	Lockheed	Shooting Star	
T-33A	SC	Charl	CAFB	Lockheed	Shooting Star	
T-33A	SC	Flore	FA&MM	Lockheed	Shooting Star	
T-33A	SC	Harts	CityPark	Lockheed	Shooting Star	
T-33A	SC	Huron	VFWP1776	Lockheed	Shooting Star	
T-33A	SC	Lake	CityPark	Lockheed	Shooting Star	
T-33A	SC	McEnt	MEANGB	Lockheed	Shooting Star	
T-33A	SD	Rapid	SDA&SM	Lockheed	Shooting Star	57-0590
T-33A	SD	Sioux	SDANGSF	Lockheed	Shooting Star	
T-33A	TN	Johnson City	R/CF	Lockheed	Shooting Star	
T-33A	TN	Crossville	CCHS	Lockheed	Shooting Star	51-6756, "Miss Netie"
T-33A	TN	Dayto	CityPark	Lockheed	Shooting Star	
T-33A	TN	Johns	CityPark	Lockheed	Shooting Star	
T-33A	TN	Sevierville	TMoA	Lockheed	Shooting Star	53-6069
T-33A	TN	Pulas	CityPark	Lockheed	Shooting Star	
T-33A	TX	Abile	DLAP	Lockheed	Shooting Star	51-4300
T-33A	TX	D Rio	CityPark	Lockheed	Shooting Star	36124
T-33A	TX	D Rio	LAFB	Lockheed	Shooting Star	
T-33A	TX	Addison	CFM	Lockheed	Shooting Star	8069
T-33A	TX	Addison	CFM	Lockheed	Shooting Star	56-1747,
T-33A	TX	Eagle	ALP211	Lockheed	Shooting Star	
T-33A	TX	Ellin	EANGB	Lockheed	Shooting Star	
T-33A	TX	FWort	PMoT	Lockheed	Shooting Star	
T-33A	TX	FWort	SAM	Lockheed	Shooting Star	
T-33A	TX	Lubbock	LSS	Lockheed	Shooting Star	2920, ATC
T-33A	TX	Odessa	CAFDS	Lockheed	Shooting Star	
T-33A	TX	Plainview	HCA	Lockheed	Shooting Star	16753, TR-753
T-33A	TX	San A	RAFB	Lockheed	Shooting Star	
T-33A	TX	Slaton	TAM	Lockheed	Shooting Star	52-519
T-33A	TX	Sweet	CityPark	Lockheed	Shooting Star	
T-33A	TX	Sweetwater	CP	Lockheed	Shooting Star	
T-33A	TX	Texar	CityPark	Lockheed	Shooting Star	
T-33A	TX	Wichi	SAFB	Lockheed	Shooting Star	
T-33A	UT	Murra	CityPark	Lockheed	Shooting Star	
T-33A	UT	Ogden	HAFBM	Lockheed	Shooting Star	
T-33A	VA	Hampt	APM	Lockheed	Shooting Star	51-9086
T-33A-1	VA	Hampt	APM	Lockheed	Shooting Star	52-9734
T-33A	VT	Burli	BANG	Lockheed	Shooting Star	
T-33A	WA	Othel	CityPark	Lockheed	Shooting Star	
T-33A	WA	Spoka	CityPark	Lockheed	Shooting Star	
T-33A	WA	Spoka	FAFBHM	Lockheed	Shooting Star	
T-33A	WI	Brill	CityPark	Lockheed	Shooting Star	
T-33A	WI	Fall	VFWP2219	Lockheed	Shooting Star	
T-33A	WI	Madis	VFWP8483	Lockheed	Shooting Star	
T-33A	WI	Milwa	MANG	Lockheed	Shooting Star	TR476
T-33A	WI	Prentice	Vetrans Park	Lockheed	Shooting Star	0-18814
T-33A	WI	Oshko	EAAAAM	Lockheed	Shooting Star	51-8627
T-33A	WI	Oshko	EAAAAM	Lockheed	Shooting Star	53-5250
T-33A	WY	Cheye	WYANG	Lockheed	Shooting Star	
T-33A	WY	New R	ALP80	Lockheed	Shooting Star	
T-33A	WY	Reeds	ALP199	Lockheed	Shooting Star	
T-33A	WY	Sherw	ALP496	Lockheed	Shooting Star	
T-33A	WY	Stoug	VFWP328	Lockheed	Shooting Star	
T-33A (2 ea)	AL	Selma	CityPark	Lockheed	Shooting Star	
T-33A (3ea)	CA	Chino	PoFAM	Lockheed	Shooting Star	
T-33A Last Built	WA	Tacoma	MAFB	Lockheed	Shooting Star	58-2106
T-33A(3ea)	CA	Rosam	EAFB	Lockheed	Shooting Star	58-669
T-33A(QT)	TX	Wichi	SAFB	Lockheed	Shooting Star	

Model	Loc	City	Org	Manufacturer	Name	Serial/Registration
T-33A-1-LO	MI	Belleville	YAF	Lockheed	Shooting Star	51-8786, N6570
T-33A-1-LO	MI	Belleville	YAF	Lockheed	Shooting Star	51-17445, N133CK, "Kalitta Bounty Hunter"
T-33A-1-LO	MI	Oscoda	YAF	Lockheed	Shooting Star	52-9843, N58417
T-33A-1-LO	WA	Tacom	G Spieth	Lockheed	Shooting Star	52-9646
T-33A-5-LO	MI	Oscoda	YAF	Lockheed	Shooting Star	53-5948
T-33A-5-LO	MI	Belleville	YAF	Lockheed	Shooting Star	53-5484, N1541
T-33A-5-LO	NE	Ashland	SACM	Lockheed	Silver Star	61-7964
T-33A-5-LO	OR	Mc Minnville	EAEC	Lockheed	Shooting Star	53-5943
T-33A-5-LO	WI	Kenos	KMM	Lockheed	Shooting Star	0-29141
T-33AN	TN	Sevierville	TMoA	Canadair	Silver Star	T33-566, N307FS
T-33B	CO	Puebl	PWAM	Lockheed	Shooting Star	137936
T-33B	CT	Winds	NEAM	Lockheed	Shooting Star	53-5646
T-33B	IN	India	IMoMH	Lockheed	Shooting Star	
T-33B	NC	Charl	CHAC	Lockheed	Shooting Star	
T-33B	NC	CPoin	CPMB	Lockheed	Shooting Star	
T-33B	NV	Battl	BMAM	Lockheed	Shooting Star	1338064
T-33B(TV-2)	AZ	Tucso	PAM	Lockheed	Shooting Star	53-2704, 136810
T-33B(TV-2)	CA	Chino	PoFAM	Lockheed	Seastar (T-33)	
T-33B(TV-2)	CT	Winds	NEAM	Lockheed	Seastar (T-33)	138048
T-33B(TV-2)	KS	Wichita	KAM	Lockheed	Seastar (T-33)	
T-33B(TV-2)	MI	Kalam	KAHM	Lockheed	Shooting Star	53-5696, 138090
T-33B(TV-2)	NY	NYC	ISASM	Lockheed	Seastar (T-33)	
T-33(CT)	AB-C	Calga	NMoA	Lockheed	Silver Star	
T-33(CT)	AB-C	Cold Lake	CFB	Lockheed	Silver Star	133181
T-33(CT)	AB-C	Edson	CFB	Lockheed	Silver Star	21506, 21097
T-33(CT)	AB-C	Leduc	CFB	Lockheed	Silver Star	21518
T-33(CT)	AB-C	Lethbridge	CFB	Lockheed	Silver Star	21578
T-33(CT)	AB-C	Nanton	NLSAM	Lockheed	Silver Star	21500
T-33(CT)	AB-C	St Albert	CFB	Lockheed	Silver Star	Xx271
T-33(CT)	MB-C	Gimli	CFB	Lockheed	Silver Star	21239
T-33(CT)	NF-C	Goose Bay	CFB	Lockheed	Silver Star	
T-33(CT)	NS-C	Greenwood	GMAM	Canadair	Silver Star	133434, 434 Bluenose Squadron
T-33(CT)	NS-C	Halifax	ACAM	Canadair	Silver Star	
T-33(CT)	ON-C	Barrie	CFB	Lockheed	Silver Star	21100, Red Knight Colours
T-33(CT)	ON-C	CFB Borden	BHT	Lockheed	Silver Star	21079
T-33(CT)	ON-C	Campbellford	MMM	Lockheed	Silver Star	133303
T-33(CT)	ON-C	Cornwall	RCAFA	Lockheed	Silver Star	21347
T-33(CT)	ON-C	Cornwall	RCAFA	Lockheed	Silver Star	133423
T-33(CT)	ON-C	Dundas	CFB	Lockheed	Silver Star	21123
T-33(CT)	ON-C	Ft Erie	NP	Lockheed	Silver Star	21373, Red Knight Colours
T-33(CT)	ON-C	Hamilton	HAA	Lockheed	Silver Star	
T-33(CT)	ON-C	Picton	CFB	Lockheed	Silver Star	133238
T-33(CT) Mk III	ON-C	Trenton	RCAFMM	Lockheed	Silver Star	21435, Red Knight Colours
T-33(CT)	SK-C	Moose Jaw	CFB	Lockheed	Silver Star	21297
T-33(CT)	SK-C	Saskatoon	CFB	Lockheed	Silver Star	21630, Red Knight Colours
T-33A(CT)	AB-C	Wetas	RM	Lockheed	Silver Star	
T-33(CT)	MB -C	Brandon	BA	Canadair	Silver Star	21130
T-33(CT)	MB-C	Portage	S	Canadair	Silver Star	21277
T-33(CT)	MB -C	Winnipeg	WRCAFB	Canadair	Silver Star	133186
T-33(CT)	MB -C	Winnipeg	WRCAFB	Canadair	Silver Star	21232, Golden Hawks
T-33(CT)	MB-C	Dudas	HAA	Canadair	Silver Star	
T-33A(CT)	MB-C	Winni	WCAM	Lockheed	Silver Star	133401
T-33A(CT)	NS-C	Cornwallis	CFBS	Lockheed	Silver Star	
T-33A(CT)	NS-C	Shear	CFBS	Lockheed	Silver Star	
T-33A(CT)	ON-C	Hamilton	CWH	Canadair	Silver Star 3	21275, PP275
T-33A(CT)	ON-C	Ottaw	CAM	Canadair	Silver Star 3	21574
T-33A(CT)	SK-C	MJaw	WDM	Lockheed	Silver Star	21001
T-33AN(CT)	AB-C	Edmonton	AAM	Lockheed	Silver Star	21001
T-33AN(CT)	BC-C	Langley	CMoF	Lockheed	Silver Star 3	33-4787, rcaf21487
T-34	AZ	Scott	SA	Beechcraft	Mentor	
T-34	CO	Denve	JWDAS	Beechcraft	Mentor	
T-34	CA	Palm Sprg	PSAM	Beechcraft	Mentor	BG-33, N8662E
T-34	ON-C	Hamilton	CWH	Beechcraft	Mentor	
T-34	TX	Galve	LSFM	Beechcraft	Mentor	53- 4135, N134
T-34	VA	Suffolk	FF	Beechcraft	Mentor	55-0221, VT-6, Tail GP, #117
T-34(YT)	CA	Atwater	CAM	Beechcraft	Mentor	50-0735
T-34A	CA	El Cajon	WW	Beechcraft	Mentor	
T-34A	IL	Springfield	ACM	Beechcraft	Mentor	675
T-34A	MI	Kalamazoo	KAHM	Beechcraft	Mentor	140768
T-34A	MN	Blaine	AWAM	Beechcraft	Mentor	
T-34A	OH	Dayto	USAFM	Beechcraft	Mentor	53-3310
T-34A	TX	San A	LAFB	Beechcraft	Mentor	55-206
T-34B	AR	Fayetteville	AAM	Beechcraft	Mentor	
T-34B	CA	S.Mon	MoF	Beechcraft	Mentor	
T-34B	FL	Pensa	USNAM	Beechcraft	Mentor	144040, F-4033, 41, VT-1
T-34B	GA	Atlan	SW	Beechcraft	Mentor	SW4130, 30
T-34B	IN	Valparaiso	IAM	Beechcraft	Mentor	BG-411
T-34B	OK	Altus	AAFB	Beechcraft	Mentor	
T-34B	TX	Abile	DLAP	Beechcraft	Mentor	140810
T-34B	TX	C Christi	USS Lexi	Beechcraft	Mentor	
T-34B	TX	D Rio	LAFB	Beechcraft	Mentor	
T-34B	TX	San A	RAFB	Beechcraft	Mentor	
T-34C	FL	Whitt	WNAS	Beechcraft	Mentor	
T-37	CA	Chino	YAM	Cessna	Tweedie Bird	
T-37	FL	Clear	FMAM	Cessna	Tweedie Bird	
T-37	FL	Tittusville	VACM	Cessna	Tweedie Bird	
T-37	KS	Liberal	MAAM	Cessna	Tweedie Bird	
T-37	KS	Wichita	KAM	Cessna	Tweedie Bird	67-21469
T-37	OK	Tulsa	TA&SC	Cessna	Tweedie Bird	
T-37	TX	Big Springs	H25	Cessna	Tweedie Bird	
T-37	TX	Burnet	HLS-CAF	Cessna	Tweedie Bird	
T-37	TX	Waco	WRA	Cessna	Tweedie Bird	
T-37	UT	Ogden	HAFBM	Cessna	Tweedie Bird	
T-37A	TX	D Rio	LAFB	Cessna	Tweedie Bird	
T-37B	AL	Birmingham	SMoF	Cessna	Tweedie Bird	
T-37B	AZ	Tucso	PAM	Cessna	Tweedie Bird	57-2267
T-37B	CA	Riverside	MAFM	Cessna	Tweedie Bird	57-2316
T-37B	FL	Clearwater	FMAM	Cessna	Tweedie Bird	
T-37B	GA	Warner Robin	MoF	Cessna	Tweedie Bird	57-2261
T-37B	MI	Battl	BCANG	Cessna	Tweedie Bird	
T-37B	MS	Colum	CAFB	Cessna	Tweedie Bird	
T-37B	OH	Dayto	USAFM	Cessna	Tweedie Bird	
T-37B	TX	Abile	PSCAF	Cessna	Tweedie Bird	54-2734

T-37B	TX	San A	RAFB	Cessna	Tweedie Bird	
T-38	CA	Carls	CAJM	Northrop	Talon	
T-38	CA	LAnge	CMoS&I	Northrop	Talon	
T-38	IL	Bloom	PAM	Northrop	Talon	50-549
T-38	IN	Edinburg	VFW 233	Northrop	Talon	00558
T-38	KS	Liberal	MAAM	Northrop	Talon	00583
T-38	MN	Dulut	CityPark	Northrop	Talon	
T-38	NM	Gallup	GMA	Northrop	Talon	10829
T-38	NY	Moria	AL	Northrop	Talon	
T-38	OK	Weatherford	GTSM	Northrop	Talon	
T-38A(YT)	SD	Rapid	SDA&SM	Northrop	Talon	58-1192
T-38	TX	Big Springs	H25	Northrop	Talon	
T-38	TX	Burnet	HLS-CAF	Northrop	Talon	
T-38	TX	C Christi	USS Lexi	Northrop	Talon	
T-38	TX	D Rio	LAFB	Northrop	Talon	
T-38A	AL	Montg	MAFB	Northrop	Talon	
T-38A	AZ	Tucso	PAM	Northrop	Talon	61-854
T-38A	CA	Appley Valley	LCfER	Northrop	Talon	60-0591
T-38A	CA	Chino	YAM	Northrop	Talon	
T-38A	CA	Riverside	MFAM	Northrop	Talon	60-0593
T-38A	CA	Rosam	EAFB	Northrop	Talon	61-810
T-38A	CA	Sacra	McCelAFB	Northrop	Talon	60- 551
T-38A	CO	CSpri	USAFA	Northrop	Talon	
T-38A	KS	Hutch	KC&SC	Northrop	Talon	
T-38A	MS	Colum	CAFB	Northrop	Talon	
T-38A	NM	Santa Teresa	WEAM	Northrop	Talon	64-13267
T-38A(AT)	OH	Dayto	USAFM	Northrop	Talon	
T-38A	OR	Mc Minnville	EAEC	Northrop	Talon	63-8224
T-38A	TX	Abile	DLAP	Northrop	Talon	60-0592
T-38A	TX	Wichi	SAFB	Northrop	Talon	
T-38A(QT)	AZ	Mesa	WAFB	Northrop	Talon	
T-38B	KY	Lexington	AMoK	Northrop	Talon	64-13292
T-39A	CA	Riverside	MFAM	North American	Sabreliner	62-4465
T-39	MO	SLoui	SLUPC	North American	Sabreliner	
T-39	MT	Helena	CoT	North American	Sabreliner	
T-39 Parts	TX	Ladero	Airport	North American	Sabreliner	
T-39	UT	Ogden	HAFBM	North American	Sabreliner	
T-39A	CA	Fairf	TAFB	North American	Sabreliner	
T-39A	GA	Warner Robin	MoF	North American	Sabreliner	62-4461A
T-39A	OH	Dayto	USAFM	North American	Sabreliner	62-4478
T-39A	TX	Abile	DLAP	North American	Sabreliner	61-634
T-39A	WI	Milwa	MANG	North American	Sabreliner	
T-39A(CT)	AZ	Tucso	PAM	North American	Sabreliner	62-4449
T-39A(CT)	CA	Rosam	EAFB	North American	Sabreliner	60-3505
T-39A(CT)	CA	Sacra	McCelAFB	North American	Sabreliner	61-660
T-39A(CT)	CA	San B	NAFB	North American	Sabreliner	
T-39A(CT)	IL	Sugar Grove	ACM	North American	Sabreliner	60-3503
T-39A(CT)	IL	Belle	SAFB	North American	Sabreliner	
T-39A(CT)	IL	Cahokia	PCUSL	North American	Sabreliner	03504
T-39A-1-NO(CT)	IL	Ranto	OCAM	North American	Sabreliner	62-4494
T-39A-NA	NE	Ashland	SACM	North American	Sabreliner	62- 4487
T-39D	AL	Birmingham	SMoF	North American	Sabreliner	
T-39D	MD	Lexington	PRNAM	North American	Sabreliner	150987, USNTPS Tail
T-40	WI	Oshko	EAAAAM	Turner	TEDDE	N191T, "Ophelia Bumps"
T-41	FL	Clearwater	FMAM	Cessna	Mescalero	
T-41	IN	Peru	GAFB	Cessna	Mescalero	
T-41A	OH	Dayto	USAFM	Cessna	Mescalero	
T-41B	GA	Hampton	AAHF	Cessna	Mescalero	
T-41B	NC	Asheboro	PFAC	Cessna	Mescalero	
T-46A	CA	Rosam	EAFB	Fairchild/Republic	Demonstrator	
T-46(NGT)	NY	Garde	CoAM	Fairchild/Republic	Demonstrator	N73RA
T-20	AB-C	Nanton	NLSAM	Cessna	Crane 1	Bamboo Bomber
T-50	AB-C	Calga	AMoC	Cessna	Crane 1	Bamboo Bomber
T-50	AB-C	Wetas	RM	Cessna	Crane 1	Bamboo Bomber
T-50	AK	Ancho	AAHM	Cessna	Crane 1	Bamboo Bomber
T-50	CA	Shafter	MFAM	Cessna	Crane 1	Bamboo Bomber
T-50	CA	Chino	YAM	Cessna	Crane 1	Bamboo Bomber, N46617, 5193
T-50	FL	Pensa	USNAM	Cessna	Crane 1	Bamboo Bomber, N63426, 5515
T-50	IL	Harva	BA	Cessna	Crane 1	Bamboo Bomber
T-50(UC-78)	IN	Auburn	HW	Cessna	Crane 1	Bamboo Bomber
T-50D	KS	Liberal	MAAM	Cessna	Crane 1	Bamboo Bomber
T-50(UC-78)	KS	Wichita	CAF-JW	Cessna	Crane 1	Bamboo Bomber
T-50	MB-C	Brandon	CATPM	Cessna	Crane 1	Bamboo Bomber
T-50	MB-C	Winni	WCAM	Cessna	Crane 1	Bamboo Bomber
T-50	OH	Newbu	WASAC	Cessna	Crane 1	Bamboo Bomber, NC60145
T-50	OK	Fredi	AAM	Cessna	Crane 1	Bamboo Bomber
T-50	OH	Newbu	WASAC	Cessna	Crane 1	Bamboo Bomber, NC60145
T-50	OH	Trotwood	WSS	Cessna	Crane 1	Bamboo Bomber, N1238N
T-50	ON-C	Campbellford	MMM	Cessna	Crane 1	Bamboo Bomber
T-50	ON-C	Ottaw	CAM	Cessna	Crane 1	Bamboo Bomber
T-50	SK-C	MJaw	WDM	Cessna	Crane 1	Bamboo Bomber
T-50	TX	Galve	LSFM	Cessna	Crane 1	Bamboo Bomber, N51469, 6614
T-50	TX	Midla	CAF-Hq	Cessna	Crane 1	Bamboo Bomber, N1238N
T2C	TX	C Christi	USS Lexi			
T2V(T-1A)	AZ	Tucso	PAM	Lockheed	Seastar	144200
T8P-1	AB-C	Calga	AMoC	Barkley	Grow	Storage
Tacit Blue	OH	Dayto	USAFM	Northrop	Whale	"Tatic Blue",
Task Silhouette	WA	Seatt	MoF	Task	Silhouette	TR601, N84TR
Taylor Aerocar	WI	Oshko	EAAAAM	Taylor	Aerocar	N4994P
Taylor Aerocar	WY	Jackson	GWFM	Taylor	Aerocar	
Taylor Monoplane	BC-C	Langley	CMoF			
Taylor Monoplane	MI	Kalamazoo	KAHM	Taylor	Monoplane	
Taylor Monoplane	WI	Fond du Lac	WAM	Taylor	Monoplane	
Taylor Monoplane HB	WI	Oshko	EAAAAM	Taylor		N5406E
Taylor Titsch	CA	Santa Martin	WoHAM	Taylor	Titsch	Homebuilt, Year 1980
Taylor Young	FL	Kissi	FTWAM	Taylor	Young	
Taylor Young A	IA	Ottumwa	APM	Taylor	Young	
Taylor Young Model A	PA	Readi	MAAM	Taylor Young	Model A	
Taylorcraft	MN	Winoma	WTI	Taylorcraft		N438RM
Taylorcraft	ND	Minot	DTAM	Taylorcraft		
Taylorcraft	WA	Vancouver	PAM	Taylorcraft		
Taylorcraft A	OH	Allia	FBA	Taylorcraft		
Taylorcraft A	WA	Seattle	MoF	Taylorcraft	Classic CG	398, NC19893

Type	Loc	City	Org	Manufacturer	Name	Notes
Taylorcraft BC	WI	Oshko	EAAAAM	Taylorcraft		N21292
Taylorcraft BC-12	AR	Fayetteville	AAM	Taylorcraft		
Taylorcraft BC-12	IA	Greenfield	IAM	Taylorcraft		
Taylorcraft BC-12	WA	Seatt	MoF	Taylorcraft		8171, N95871
Taylorcraft BC-12D	NY	River	RE	Taylorcraft		
Taylorcraft BC-12D	NC	Hendersonville	WNCAM	Taylorcraft		
Taylorcraft BC-12D	PA	Bethel	GAAM	Taylorcraft		
Taylorcraft BC-65	MD	College Park	CPAM	Taylorcraft		
Taylorcraft BC-65	NY	Rhine	ORA	Taylorcraft		
Taylorcraft BC-65	OC-C	Ottawa	CAM	Taylorcraft		
Taylorcraft Model 20	ON-C	Sault Ste Marie	CBHC	Taylorcraft	Auster	CF-FTC
Taylorcraft Mk.VII	AB-C	Calga	AMoC	Taylorcraft	Auster	
Taylorcraft TG-6	AZ	Tucson	PAM	Taylorcraft	TG-6	Sn 42-58662, N59134
TBF	CA	S.Mon	MoF	Grumman	Avenger	
TBF	LA	New Orleans	DDM	Grumman	Avenger	
TBF	ND	Fargo	FAM	Grumman	Avenger	# 89, CO
TBF	TX	C Christi	USS Lexi	Grumman	Avenger	
TBF-1	CA	Chino	YAM	Grumman	Avenger	5997, 5997
TBF-1	MD	Silve	PEGF	Grumman	Avenger	
TBF-1C	MA	Westfield	Harland Avezzie	Grumman	Avenger	05954, N5954A
TBM	AB-C	Wetas	RM	Grumman	Avenger	
TBM	AL	Troy	TMA	Grumman	Avenger	
TBM	CA	Chino	D Tallichet	Grumman	Avenger	53229, N7236C, Parts
TBM	CA	Inglewood	PBR	Grumman	Avenger	
TBM	FL	Deland	DNASM	Grumman	Avenger	
TBM	FL	FtLau	WJAIS&L	Grumman	Avenger	
TBM	ID	Twin	NWWI	Grumman	Avenger	
TBM	MB-C	N Brunswick	NBM	Grumman	Avenger	14, C-GLEK
TBM	NM	STere	WEAM	Grumman	Avenger	
TBM	NJ	Rio	NASW	Grumman	Avenger	
TBM	NS-C	Halifax	ACAM	Grumman	Avenger	
TBM	NS-C	Shear	CFBS	Grumman	Avenger	
TBM	NY	E Garden City	CoA	Grumman	Avenger	
TBM	NY	Farmingdale	AAM	Grumman	Avenger	2, 401SL
TBM	OH	Newbu	WASAC	Grumman	Avenger	
TBM	TX	Frede	NMofPW	Grumman	Avenger	
TBM-3	OH	Batavia	TSWM	Grumman	Avenger	69-375
TBM-3	CA	Alameda	UUSHM	Grumman	Avenger	86123, N6831C, E2, "The Admiral"
TBM-3	CA	Oakla	OWAM	Grumman	Avenger	91264, 69374, NX7835C
TBM-3	CA	Chino	PoF	Grumman	Avenger	53503, N53503, #309, ATA
TBM-3	CO	GJunc	CAF-RMW	Grumman	Avenger	53489, N6580D, #25
TBM-3	FL	Ocala	Corky Meyer	Grumman	Avenger	91598, N9548Z
TBM-3	FL	Miami	WOM	Grumman	Avenger	
TBM-3	MN	Minne	JJ	Grumman	Avenger	
TBM-3	KS	Liberal	MAAM	Grumman	Avenger	R8 123
TBM-3	MN	Minne	JJ	Grumman	Avenger	
TBM-3	MO	St Louis	Wes Strickler	Grumman	Avenger	85715, N65VC
TBM-3	ND	Wahpenton	TSA	Grumman	Avenger	53829, NL293E
TBM-3	NM	Santa Fe	WoH	Grumman	Avenger	
TBM-3	NS-C	Halifax	HAM	Grumman	Avenger	
TBM-3	OK	Fredi	AAM	Grumman	Avenger	
TBM-3	TX	College Station	GBLM	Grumman	Avenger	
TBM-3	TX	C Christi	NAS	Grumman	Avenger	
TBM-3	TX	Hawki	RRSA	Grumman	Avenger	
TBM-3	TX	Midla	CAFFM	Grumman	Avenger	53353, N5264V, 53/WS
TBM-3	VA	Quant	MCAGM	Grumman	Avenger	85890
TBM-3	WA	Olmypia	OFM	Grumman	Avenger	69325, N325GT, Side # T-88
TBM-3C	ON-C	Hamilton	Allan Rubin	Grumman	Avenger	53638, CF-KCL,
TBM-3E	AZ	Tucso	PAM	Grumman	Avenger	N9593C, 69472
TBM-3E	CA	Chino	Carl Scholl	Grumman	Avenger	53828, N28FB
TBM-3E	CA	Palm Springs	PoFAM	Grumman	Avenger	53785, NL7075C, JR456, RP
TBM-3E	CA	Paso Robles	J Arrango	Grumman	Avenger	85983, N28SF
TBM-3E	CA	Miramar	FLAM	Grumman	Avenger	VMTB-242
TBM-3E	CO	Basalt	Wayne Rudd	Grumman	Avenger	85632, N81865
TBM-3E	FL	Jacks	NASCF	Grumman	Avenger	91664, SM
TBM-3E	FL	Pensa	USNAM	Grumman	Avenger	N 6822C, 53593
TBM-3E	ID	Sugar City	Danny Summers	Grumman	Avenger	85938, N776C, 308, Sank Jap Cruiser
TBM-3E	IL	Wilmette	Gary Applebaum	Grumman	Avenger	53454, NL7030C
TBM-3E	IN	Goshen	Stave Hay	Grumman	Avenger	91521, N4171A, #25
TBM-3E	MA	Stow	BCF	Grumman	Avenger	91733, N9590Z
TBM-3E	MD	Fredericks	CAFS&S	Grumman	Avenger	
TBM-3E	MI	Northville	Dave Tinker	Grumman	Avenger	85882, N9584Z, "Ida Red"
TBM-3E	MO	Columbia	Wes Strickler	Grumman	Avenger	91714, N9429Z
TBM-3E	NC	Asheboro	PFAC	Grumman	Avenger	91388, N9564Z
TBM-3E	NB-C	Boiestown	CNBWM	Grumman	Avenger	85733, #14, C-GLEK, N6824C
TBM-3	NB-C	Fredricton	Forest Protection	Grumman	Avenger	85460, C-GFPS, #3
TBM-3E	NB-C	Fredricton	Forest Protection	Grumman	Avenger	53787, C-GFPT, #10
TBM-3E	NB-C	Fredricton	Forest Protection	Grumman	Avenger	86180, C-GFPL, #12
TBM-3S	NB-C	Fredricton	Forrest Protection	Grumman	Avenger	53200, C-GLEL, #13
TBM-3E	NB-C	Fredricton	Forest Protection	Grumman	Avenger	91426, C-FMUE, #18
TBM-3E	NB-C	Fredricton	Forest Protection	Grumman	Avenger	53857, CGFPM, #21
TBM-3E	NB-C	Fredricton	Forest Protection	Grumman	Avenger	86020, C-GFPL, #22
TBM-3	NB-C	Fredricton	Forest Protection	Grumman	Avenger	53610, C-FIMR, #23
TBM-3E	NB-C	Fredricton	Forest Protection	Grumman	Avenger	69323, C-GLEJ, #24
TBM-3E	NY	Garde	CoAM	Grumman	Avenger	91586
TBM-3E	NY	Horseheads	NWM	Grumman	Avenger	91752, #64, 401SL
TBM-3E	NY	New York	ISASM	Grumman	Avenger	85886, N9586Z, 401, "The Cockpit"
TBM-3E	OR	Beaaverton	PANW	Grumman	Avenger	
TBM-3E	OR	McMinnville	EAEC	Grumman	Avenger	91726, N5260V, #32
TBM-3E	OR	Tillamook	TAM	Grumman	Avenger	53575, 91726, N6447C
TBM-3E	PA	Philadelphia	Tom Duffy	Grumman	Avenger	53522, NL188TD, #88
TBM-3E	RI	NKing	QAM	Grumman	Avenger	53914
TBM-3E	SC	Mt Pleasant	PPM	Grumman	Avenger	
TBM-3E	TN	Sevierville	TMoA	Grumman	Avenger	91453, N4170A, VMT232
TBM-3E	TX	Big Springs	Connie Edwards	Grumman	Avenger	53119, N33BM
TBM-3E	TX	C Christi	USS Lexi	Grumman	Avenger	
TBM-3E	TX	Addison	CFM	Grumman	Avenger	86280, N86280, # 54, ATA
TBM-3E	TX	Galve	LSFM	Grumman	Avenger	N700RW, 69329
TBM-3E	TX	Spring	Bill Hill	Grumman	Avenger	85794, N8001C
TBM-3E	VA	Manassas	Chris Johnson	Grumman	Avenger	91453, N4170A, #15
TBM-3E	VA	Suffolk	FF	Grumman	Avenger	53454, VS-22/801
TBM-3R	MN	Blaine	Wally Fisk	Grumman	Avenger	86123, N93818, #17
TBM-3S	MO	St Louis	Wes Strickler	Grumman	Avenger	53139, N6VC

TBM-3S	TX	Austin	Byron Neely	Grumman	Avenger	85597, N7040Z
TBM-3S	WA	Arlington	Jeff Thomas	Grumman	Avenger	53420, N420GP
TBM-3U	AR	Hazen	Gary Scarda	Grumman	Avenger	53835, N3967A
TBM-3S	BC-C	Dawson Creek	Ag Air Inc	Grumman	Avenger	91171, C-FBQT
TBM-3U	IL	Joliet	Tom Buck	Grumman	Avenger	53768, N683G, #63
TBM-3W	NC	Morganton	Hank Avery	Grumman	Avenger	85650, N452HA
Teal Ruby Satellite	OH	Dayton	USAFM	Teal	Ruby	
Teasdale	NY	Elmira	NSM			
Temple Aero Sportsman	TX	Dallas	FoFM	Temple Aero Corp	Sportsma	C-987N, "Texas Temple"
Terrapin	NY	Garde	CoAM	Republic	Terrapin Rocket	
TG-1A	MD	Silve	PEGF	Frankfort	Cinema B	
TG-1A	NM	Moriarty	SSM	Frankfort	Cinema B	
TG-1A	WY	Jackson	GWFM	Frankfort	Cinema B	
TG-1A-FR	BC-C	Langley	CMoF	Frankfort	Cinema B	42-52, CF-MDZ Cinema
TG-2(LNS-1)	CA	Riverside	MFAM	Great Lakes	Martin TG-2	N54301
TG-2(LNS-1)	MI	Kalam	KAHM	Great Lakes	Martin TG-2	04383
TG-2(LNS-1)	NY	Horseheads	NWM	Great Lakes	Martin TG-2	
TG-3A	AZ	Tucso	PAM	Schweizer	Glider	Man Sn 15, N69064
TG-3A	AZ	Tucso	PAM	Schweizer	Glider	Man Sn 32, N63905
TG-3A	BC-C	Langley	CMoF	Schweizer	Glider	42-529, N33637
TG-3A	CA	Atwater	CAM	Schweizer	Glider	
TG-3A	CA	Chino	YAM	Schweizer	Glider	
TG-3A	CO	Denve	JWDAS	Schweizer	Glider	
TG-3A	NY	Elmir	NSM	Schweizer	Glider	43, N61279
TG-3A(LNE-1)	NY	Ghent	POMAM	Schweizer	Glider	
TG-3A(LNE-1)	OH	Dayto	USAFM	Schweizer	Glider	
TG-3A	TX	Midla	CAF-Hq	Schweizer	Glider	N87603
TG-4A	AL	Birmingham	SMoF	Laister-Kauffman	Glider	
TG-4A	CO	Denve	JWDAS	Laister-Kauffman	Glider	
TG-4A	GA	Warner Robin	MoF	Laister-Kauffman	Glider	42-43740, N43LK
TG-4A	MI	Kalam	KAHM	Laister-Kauffman	Glider	92
TG-4A	NM	Moriarty	SSM	Laister-Kauffman	Glider	
TG-4A	OH	Dayto	USAFM	Laister-Kauffman	Glider	
TGM-13	CO	Flage	VWF			
Thaden Transporter	CA	SCarl	HAM	Thaden	Transporter	
Thomas Pidgeon	CA	Chino	YAM	Thomas	Pidgeon	1
Thomas Pusher	NY	Rhine	ORA	Thomas	Pusher	
Tilbury Flash	IL	Bloom	McLCHS	Tilbury	Flash	NR12931
Tocan Ultrlight	AB-C	Edmonton	AAM	Tocan	Ultrlight	
Trains 6	OH	Dayto	CP			
Trains 60	MO	SLoui	NMoT			
Transporter-Erector	ND	Grand	GFAFB			
Travel Air	CA	Calistoga	CG	Travel Air		
Travel Air	IL	Urban	RFIA	Travel Air		
Travel Air 1000	CA	Lanca	BA	Travel Air	Mystery	
Travel Air 1000	IL	Chica	MoS&I	Travel Air	Mystery	
Travel Air 1000	TN	Tulla	SMF	Travel Air	Mystery	
Travel Air 2000	KS	Wichita	KAM	Travel Air	Mystery	
Travel Air 2000	ON-C	Ottaw	CAM	Travel Air		
Travel Air 2000	PA	Bethel	GAAM	Travel Air		
Travel Air 2000	VA	Sands	VAM	Travel Air	Mystery	Sn 721 CAM Travel Air
Travel Air 2000	WA	Port Townsend	PTAM	Travel Air		645, NC6147
Travel Air 2000	WI	Oshko	EAAAAM	Travel Air		N241
Travel Air 3000	ND	Minot	DTAM	Travel Air		
Travel Air 4000	AR	Fayet	AAM	Travel Air	Mystery Ship	
Travel Air 4000	CA	Hayward	VAM	Travel Air		
Travel Air 4000(D4D)	KY	Lexington	AMoK	Travel Air		N434N
Travel Air 4000	MO	Maryland Hts	HARM	Travel Air		
Travel Air 4000	NY	Ghent	POMAM	Travel Air		
Travel Air 4000	NY	River	TFAC	Travel Air		
Travel Air 4000	TN	Tulla	SMF	Travel Air		
Travel Air 4000	WA	Port Townsend	PTAM	Travel Air		850, NC9049
Travel Air 4000	WA	Vancouver	PAM	Travel Air		
Travel Air 4000E	ON-C	Hamilton	CWH	Travel Air		
Travel Air 4000E	WI	Oshko	EAAAAM	Travel Air		NC 648H
Travel Air 6000-A	WY	Jackson	GWFM	Travel Air		
Travel Air 6000A	TN	Tulla	SMF	Travel Air		
Travel Air 6000B	AK	Ancho	AAHM	Travel Air		
Travel Air 6000B	GA	Atlanta	DATHM	Curtiss-Wright	Sedan 6B	6B-2040, ATC 352, Reg 447W
Troyer VX	PA	Readi	MAAM	Troyer	Troyer VX	
TS-1	FL	Pensa	USNAM			A 6446
TS-11	CA	Chino	PoFAM	Polish	Iskra	
TS-11	MI	Belleville	YAF	Polish	Iskra	1H1019, N101TS
TS-11	TX	Addison	CFM	Polish	Iskra	
Tu-2	FL	Polk	FoF	Tupolev	Bat	
Tu-2	NM	STere	WEAM	Tupolev	Bat	
TU-6	TX	Ft Worth	SAM	Charic		
U-2	CA	Moffe	NASAAVC			
U-2	MD	Silve	PEGF	Mitchell		
U-2	NY	Elmira	NSM	Mitchell	Superwing	N103WT
U-2 Flying Wing	AB-C	Calga	AMoC	Mitchell	Flying Wing	
U-2A	OH	Dayto	USAFM			56-6722
U-2C	AZ	Tucso	DMAFB	Lockheed	Gray Ghost	
U-2C	DC	Washi	NA&SM	Lockheed	Gray Ghost	
U-2C	GA	Warner Robin	MoF	Lockheed	Dragon Lady	56- 6682
U-2C	TX	D Rio	LAFB	Lockheed	Gray Ghost	
U-2C-LO	NE	Ashland	SACM	Lockheed	Gray Ghost	56- 6701, "Dragon Lady"
U-2CT	CA	Rosam	EAFB	Lockheed	Gray Ghost	56- 6953
U-2D	CA	Rosam	EAFB			
U-2R	CA	Marys	BAFB			
U-3A	AL	Ozark	USAAM	Cessna	Blue Canoe	57- 5863
U-3A	CA	Atwater	CAM	Cessna	Blue Canoe	57-5849
U-3A	CA	Fairf	TAFB	Cessna	Blue Canoe	
U-3A	CO	Denve	JWDAS	Cessna	Blue Canoe	
U-3A	CO	Aurora	WOTR	Cessna	Blue Canoe	
U-3A	IN	Peru	GAFB	Cessna	Blue Canoe	57- 5922
U-3A	MI	Mt Clemens	SMAM	Cessna	Blue Canoe	58-2111
U-3A	OH	Dayto	USAFM	Cessna	Blue Canoe	58-2124
U-3A	SD	Rapid	SDA&SM	Cessna	Blue Canoe	57-5872
U-3A	UT	Ogden	HAFBM	Cessna	Blue Canoe	
U-3A(L-27A)	AZ	Tucso	PAM	Cessna	Blue Canoe	58- 2107
U-3B9D	GA	Warner Robin	MoF	Cessna	Blue Canoe	60- 6052
U-4A	AL	Ozark	USAAM	Aero	Commander	55- 4640

U-4B	GA	Warner Robin	MoF	Aero	Commander	63- 7948, N37948
U-4B	OH	Dayton	USAFM	Aero	Commander	
U-505 German	IL	Chica	MoS&I		Submarine	
U-8	CO	Denve	JWDAS	Beech	Queen-Air	
U-8	KS	Wichita	KAM	Beech	Queen-Air	
U-8	GA	Hampton	AAHF	Beech	Queen-Air	
U-9A(YU)	AL	Ozark	USAAM	Aero Eng.	Commander	52- 6219
U-9A	CA	Riverside	MFAM	Aero	Commander	52-6218
U-9A	WI	Kenos	KMM	Aero	Commander	
U-10	CO	Denve	JWDAS	Helio	Courier	
U-10(YU)(YL-24)	AL	Ozark	USAAM	Helio	Courier	52-2540
U-10A	FL	FtWal	HF	Helio	Courier	62- 3606, AH
U-10D	GA	Warner Robin	MoF	Helio	Super Courier	63-13096, N87743
U-10D	OH	Dayto	USAFM	Helio	Super Courier	
U-21	CO	Denve	JWDAS	Beech	Ute	
U-21(YU)	AL	Ozark	USAAM	Beech	Ute	63-12902
U-21G	GA	Hampton	AAHF	Beech	Ute	
UFM Easy Riser	WI	Oshko	EAAAM	UFM	Easy Riser	
Ultra-Light	CA	Chino	PoFAM			
Ultimate 100	ON-C	Toronto	TAM	Ultimate	100	
Unident Atec	MN	Winoma	WTI	Unident	Aztec	
Unruh	WI	Oshko	EAAAM	Unruh	Unruh	N1473V, "Pretty Prairie Special III"
UTVA-66	FL	Titusville	VAC	YUGO	Trainer	
UAV	MD	Lexington	PRNAM	Israeli Aircraft Industry	Pioneer	101
UV-18	CO	Denver	69thB		Twin Turboprop	
V-1 * See Fi-103* Flying Bomb						
V-1	FL	Shali	USAFAM	Vultee	Voland	
V-1	ON-C	Ottaw	CAM	Vultee	Voland	
V-1	UT	Ogden	HAM	Vultee	Voland	
V1-A	VA	Sands	VAM	Vultee	Voland	Sn 25
V-1(Fi-103)	VA	Suffolk	FF	Vultee	Voland	
V-1(XV)	AL	Ozark	USAAM	McDonnell	Convertiplane	53- 4016
V-2	KS	Hutch	KC&SC	Peene Munde	Rocket	
V-2	MD	Aberd	APG	Peene Munde	Rocket	
V-2	NM	Las Cruces	WSMP	Peene Munde	Rocket	
V-2	NJ	Rio Grande	NASW	Peene Munde	Rocket	
V-2	OK	Oklah	KCASM	Peene Munde	Rocket	
V-2	OH	Dayton	USAFM	Peene Munde	Rocket	
V-6A(XV)	AL	Ozark	USAAM	Hawker-Siddley	Kestrel	64-19264
V-6A(XV)	OH	Dayto	USAFM	Hawker-Siddley	Kestrel	NASA 521
V-6A(XV)	VA	Hampton	HAP	Hawker-Siddley	Kestrel	64-18266, NASA 520
V-22 Osprey II	AZ	Tucso	PAM	Pereira	Osprey	105, N17EH, A
V-22 Osprey II	ON-C	Toronto	TAM	Pereira	Osprey	
V-22 Osprey II	PA	West Chester	AHM	Bell-Boeing	Osprey	
V-22 Osprey II	WI	Oshko	EAAAM	Pereira	Osprey	N346JS
V-101B	AR	Roger				
V-173	MD	Silve	PEGF	Vought	Flying Pancake	
Valkyrie Hang Glider	MD	Silve	PEGF	Valkyrie	Hang Glider	
Van Dellen LH-2	IA	Ottumwa	APM	Van Dellen		
Vansgrunsven RV-3	FL	Lakel	SFAF	Vansgrunsven	Homebuilt	N920SR
Vansgrunsven RV-3	WI	Oshkosh	EAAAM	Vansgrunsven	Homebuilt	
Vansgrunsven RV-4	WI	Oshkosh	EAAAM	Vansgrunsven	Homebuilt	
Vector 27	WI	Oshko	EAAAM	Vector		
Velie Model 70	CA	LAnge	CMoS&I	Velie	Monocoupe	
Veligdans Monerai	NY	Garde	CoAM	Veligdans	Monerai Glider	N525S
Venture 200	WI	Oshko	EAAAM	Questair		N62V
Ventuier Airship	NY	Geneseo	1941AG	Ventuier	Airship	
Vertol 44	BC-C	Langley	CMoF*T	Vertol		
Vertol 44B	CA	Ramona	CR	Vertol	Holly One	
Verville Sport Trainer	MD	Silve	PEGF	Verille	Sport	
Vickers Vedette V	MB-C	Winni	WCAM	Vickers	Vedette	
Vickers Viking Mk.IV Rep	AB-C	Edmonton	AAM	Vickers	Viking Mk.IV	
Vickers Viscount 744	AZ	Tucso	PAM	Vickers	Viscount 744	Sn 40, N22SN
Vickers Viscount	MB-C	Winni	WCAM	Vickers	Viscount 757	
Vickers Viscount	ON-C	Ottaw	CAM	Vickers	Viscount	
Vickers Viscount	PA	Readi	MAAM	Vickers	Viscount	
Viking Dragonfly	KS	Liberal	MAAM	Viking	Dragonfly	
Viking Dragonfly	OK	Fredi	AAM	Viking	Dragonfly	
Viking Kittyhawk	CT	Winds	NEAM	Viking	Kittyhawk	
VJ-21	CA	Santa Martin	WoHAM	Volmer-Jensen	Powered Glider	
VJ-23	IA	Ottumwa	APM	Volmer-Jensen		
VJ-24	FL	Lakel	SFAF	Lazair	Ultralight	
Voisin Model 8	DC	Washi	NA&SM	Voisin	Model 8	
Voisin Model 8	MD	Silve	PEGF	Voisin	Model 8	
Voisin Model 8	NY	NYC	ISASM	Voisin	Model 8	
Voisin Model 8	NY	Rhine	ORA	Voisin	Model 8	
Volmer Jensen	CA	S.Mar	SMMoF	Volmer-Jensen	Hang Glider	
VP-1	AZ	Tucso	PAM	Evans	Volksplane	N 47188
VP-1	FL	Kissimmee	SNFAM	Evans	Volksplane	
VP-1	IA	Ottumwa	APM	Evans	Volksplane	
VP-1	ND	Minot	DTAM	Evans	Volksplane	
VPS Hu-Go Craft	WI	Oshko	EAAAM	Hugo	VPS Hu-Go Craft	N29H
VS-300A	DC	Washi	NA&SM	Sikorsky		
VS-300A	MI	Dearborn	HFM	Sikorsky	Helicopter	
VS-300A Cockpit	PA	WChester	AHM	Sikorsky		
VS-316(R-4B)	ON-C	Ottaw	CAM	Sikorsky	Hoverfly	43-46565
VS-44A	CT	Windsor Locks	NEAM	Sikorsky	Excambian	
VZ-2A Vertol	MD	Silve	PEGF	Boeing	Vertol	
VZ-3RY	AL	Ozark	USAAM	Ryan	Vertiplane	56- 6941
VZ-4-DA Doak	VA	FtEus	USATM	Doak		56-9642
VZ-8P	PA	WChes	AHM	Piasecki	Airgeep	
VZ-8P	PA	Willo	WGNAS	Piasecki	Airgeep	
VZ-8P-2	VA	FtEus	USATM	Piasecki	Airgeep	58-5511
VZ-9V	MD	Silve	PEGF	Avro-Canada	Avrocar	
VZ-ZAP	AL	Ozark	USAAM			
VZ1 Hiller 1031	CA	SCarl	HAM	Hiller	Flying Platform	
VZ1 Hiller 1031	MD	Silve	PEGF	Hiller	Flying Platform	
Waco	AK	Palme	MOAT&I	Waco		
Waco	AZ	Scott	SA	Waco		
Waco	CA	Calistoga	CG	Waco		
Waco	IL	Urban	RFIA	Waco		
Waco	ND	Minot	DTAM	Waco		
Waco	NY	Rhine	ORA	Waco		

Waco	TX	Houston	1940ATM	Waco		
Waco Model F	MO	Maryland Hts	HARM	Waco	Model F	
Waco 4	OH	Troy	WHS	Waco		
Waco 9	ID	Athol	NAM	Waco		
Waco 9	MD	Silve	PEGF	Waco		
Waco 9	NY	Rhine	ORA	Waco		
Waco 10	CA	San Carlos	HAM	Waco		
Waco 10	CA	Santa Martin	WoHAM	Waco		
Waco 10	FL	Ameli	IAT	Waco		
Waco 125	MN	Bloom	SPMIA	Waco		
Waco 128	MN	Minne	MSPIA	Waco		NC 4576, "Northwest Airways"
Waco AQC-6	BC-C	Langley	CMoF	Waco		4646, CF-CCW
Waco Arisocraft "W"	OH	Troy	WHS	Waco	Arisocraft	
Waco ATO	PA	Reading	WAM&ALC	Waco		Sn A118
Waco Cabin UIC	MD	Silve	PEGF	Waco	Cabin	
Waco CTO	OH	Troy	WHS	Waco		
Waco CTO	WI	Oshko	EAAAAM	Waco		NC75527
Waco CUC-1	WY	Jackson	GWFM	Waco	Custom Cabin	
Waco EQC-6	AB-C	Calga	AMoC	Waco	Custom	
Waco Glider	MD	Silve	PEGF	Waco	Glider	
Waco Glider	OH	Troy	WHS	Waco	Glider	
Waco GXE	CA	S.Mon	MoF	Waco	Model 10	
Waco GXE	ND	Minnot	DTAM	Waco	Model 10	
Waco INF	BC-C	Langley	CMoF	Waco		3324, N6005Y, CF-CJR
Waco INF	MI	Kalam	KAHM	Waco	INF	NC644V
Waco RNF	AZ	Tucson	PAM	Waco	RNF	Man Sn 3392, NC11206
Waco RNF	WI	Oshkosh	EAAAAM	Waco	RNF	
Waco UBF-2	ME	OwlsH	OHTM	Waco		
Waco UEC	CA	S.Mon	MoF	Waco	Cabin	C Cabin
Waco UIC	AB-C	Edmonton	AAM	Waco		
Waco UPF-7	AB-C	Wetas	RM	Waco		
Waco UPF-7	AZ	Tucso	PAM	Waco		N30135
Waco UPF-7	FL	KeyWe	FWIA	Waco		
Waco UPF-7	MN	Blaine	ACBA	Waco		Owner: Patrick Harker
Waco UPF-7	ND	Minot	DTAM	Waco		
Waco UPF-7	OH	Troy	WHS	Waco		
Waco UPF-7	VA	Bealt	FCA	Waco		
Waco UPF-7	WA	Vashon	OTA	Waco		Sn 5540, NC30143
Waco UPF-7	WA	Vashon	OTA	Waco		Sn 5871, NC39738
Waco YKS	AK	Ancho	AAHM	Waco		
Waco YKS	AL	Birmi	Southe	Waco		
Waco YKS	SK-C	MJaw	WDM	Waco		
Waco YKS-6	WA	Vashon	OTA	Waco	Trainer	NC16241
Waco YKS-6	ID	Athol	NAM	Waco		
Waco YKS-6	MB-C	Winni	WCAM	Waco		
Waco YKS-7	CA	San Diego	SDAM	Waco		N48980
Waco YKS-7	WI	Oshkosh	EAAAAM	Waco		
Waco YMF	OH	Troy	WHS	Waco		
Waco YPF-7	NC	Durham	CB	WACO	YPF-7	5644
Waco YOC	AL	Birmi	Southe	Waco		
Waco YOC	VA	Sands	VAM	Waco		Sn 4279
Waco ZKS-6	AZ	Tucso	PAM	Waco		N16523
Wag-Aero CUBy	WI	Oshko	EAAAAM	Brugioni	CUBy	N1933J
Wallis Model 3	MI	Belleville	YAM	Wallis	Redwing Black Bird	N65022
Warwick W-4	WI	Oshko	EAAAAM	Warwick		N4777W, "Hot Canary"
Wasol Racer	WA	Vancouver	PAM	Wasol	Formula 1 Racer	Reno
Waspair Tomcat Tourer	WI	Oshko	EAAAAM	Waspair	Tomcat Tourer	"Feeline Fokker IV"
Waterman Aeromobile	MD	Silve	PEGF	Waterman	Aeromobile	
Waterman Whatsit	MD	Silve	PEGF	Waterman	Whatsit	
Watkins Skylark	KS	Wichita	KAM	Watkins	Skylark	
WD-A	WI	Oshko	EAAAAM	Estupinan Hovey	Wing Ding	N6272
WE-1	WI	Oshko	EAAAAM	Evans	Volksplane	N6414
Weddell-Williams	LA	Patte	WWMAM	Weddell-Williams	Racer	44
Weddell-Williams	OH	Cleve	FCAAM	Weddell-Williams	Special	Model 44
Wee Bee	CA	San Diego	SDAM	Wee Bee		
Weedhopper	NE	Minde	HWPV	Gypsy	Weedhopper	
Weedhopper	TX	Rio Grande V	TAM	Gypsy	Weedhopper	
Weeks Solution	FL	Polk	FoF	Weeks	Solution	
Weeks Special	FL	Polk	FoF	Weeks	Special	
Westland Lysander Rep	AB-C	Edmonton	AAM	Westland	Lysander	
Westland Mk.III	BC-C	Langley	CMoF	Westland	Lysander	1194, RCAF2349
Westland Mk.III	ON-C	Hamilton	CWH	Westland	Lysander	2361
Westland Mk.III	ON-C	Ottaw	CAM	Westland	Lysander	
Westland WASP	CA	Ramona	CR	Westland	Lysander	
Wirlwind	NY	Horsehead	WoE			
Whirlwind	NY	River	TFAC			
Whitaker Centerwing	WI	Oshko	EAAAAM	Whitaker	Centerwing	N121LW
White 1912 Monoplane	TX	McAll	MIA	White	Monoplane	
Wiley Post Biplane	OK	Oklah	KCASM	Wiley	Post Biplane	
Wills Wing XC	ON-C	Ottaw	CAM	Wills	Wing XC	
Windecker Eagle I	MD	Silve	PEGF	Windecker	Eagle	
Windstead Special	PA	Bethel	GAAM	Windstead	Special	2297
Wiseman-Cooke	DC	Washi	USPM	Wiseman-Cooke		
Wiseman-Cooke	MD	Silve	PEGF	Wiseman-Cooke		
Wisman-Prescott	KS	Wichita	KAM	Wittman	Pusher	
Wisman-Prescott	WI	Oshko	WRA	Wittman	Pusher	
Wittman W	WI	Oshko	EAAAAM	Wittman	Midwing	N4486E, "Bonzo"
Wittman Buster	DC	Washi	NA&SM	Wittman	Buster	
Wittman DFA	WI	Oshko	EAAAAM	Wittman		N1292, "Little Bonzo"
Wittman W-8C	NC	Hendersonville	WNCAM	Wittman	Tailwind	
Wittman W-8C	WI	Oshko	WRA	Wittman	Tailwind	N5747N
Woodstock Glider	WI	Fond du Lac	WAM	Woodstock	Glider	
Woody Pusher	CO	Aurora	WOTR	Woody	Pusher	
Woody Pusher	FL	Lakel	SFAF	Woody	Pusher	N100FQ
Woolaroc Airplane	OK	Bartl	WM	Woolaroc		NX- 869
Wright 1903	NE	Minde	HWPV	Wright Brothers		
Wright Brothers B	CA	SCarl	HAM	Wright Brothers		
Wright Brothers B	MD	College Park	CPAM	Wright Brothers		
Wright Brothers B	OH	Dayto	USAFM	Wright Brothers		
Wright Brothers B	PA	Phila	FI	Wright Brothers		
Wright Brothers B	VA	Suffolk	FF	Wright Brothers		
Wright EX Vin Fiz	CA	Oakla	OWAM	Wright Brothers	Vin Fiz	
Wright EX Vin Fiz	CA	San Diego	SDAM	Wright Brothers	Vin Fiz	

Wright Ex Vin Fiz	DC	Washi	NA&SM	Wright Brothers	Vin Fiz	
Wright EX Vin Fiz	MA	Stow	BCF	Wright Brothers	Vin Fiz	
Wright EX Vin Fiz	ME	OwlsH	OHTM	Wright Brothers	Vin Fiz	
Wright Flyer	AR	Little Rock	AEC	Wright Brothers	Kitty Hawk Flyer	
Wright Flyer	AZ	Tucso	PAM	Wright Brothers	Kitty Hawk Flyer	
Wright Flyer	CA	San Diego	SDAM	Wright Brothers	Kitty Hawk Flyer	
Wright Flyer	CA	Santa Martin	WoHAM	Wright Brothers	Kitty Hawk Flyer	
Wright Flyer	DC	Washi	NA&SM	Wright Brothers	Kitty Hawk Flyer	
Wright Flyer	FL	Dayto	ERAU	Wright Brothers	Kitty Hawk Flyer	
Wright Flyer	FL	Polk	FoF	Wright Brothers	Kitty Hawk Flyer	
Wright Flyer	IL	Rantoul	OCM	Wright Brothers	Kitty Hawk Flyer	
Wright Flyer	IN	Hagerstown	WWBP	Wright Brothers	Kitty Hawk Flyer	
Wright Flyer	MI	Kalamazoo	KAHM	Wright Brothers	Kitty Hawk Flyer	
Wright Flyer	NC	Mante	WBNM	Wright Brothers	Kitty Hawk Flyer	
Wright Flyer	NC	Ralei	NCMoH	Wright Brothers	Kitty Hawk Flyer	
Wright Flyer	NY	Rhine	ORA	Wright Brothers	Kitty Hawk Flyer	
Wright Flyer	OH	Dayto	CP	Wright Brothers	Kitty Hawk Flyer	
Wright Flyer	OH	Dayto	USAFM	Wright Brothers	Kitty Hawk Flyer	
Wright Flyer	OH	Miamisburg	WBF	Wright Brothers	Kitty Hawk Flyer	Flyable Replica
Wright Flyer	OK	Wetherford	GTSM	Wright Brothers	Kitty Hawk Flyer	
Wright Flyer	OR	McMinnville	EAM	Wright Brothers	Kitty Hawk Flyer	
Wright Flyer	WA	Hampton	VA&SM	Wright Brothers	Kitty Hawk Flyer	
Wright Flyer	WA	Vancouver	PAM	Wright Brothers	Kitty Hawk Flyer	
Wright Flyer	WI	Oshko	EAAAAM	Wright Brothers	Kitty Hawk Flyer	
Wright Glider	CA	LAnge	CMoS&I	Wright Brothers	Wright Glider	
Wright Glider	NC	Charl	CHAC	Wright Brothers	Wright Glider	
Wright Glider	NC	Mante	WBNM	Wright Brothers	Wright Glider	
Wright Glider	NY	Elmira	NSM	Wright Brothers	Wright Glider	1902, 5
Wright Glider	NY	Elmira	NSM	Wright Brothers	Wright Glider	1911
Wright Glider	NY	Rhine	ORA	Wright Brothers	Wright Glider	
Wright Glider	VA	Richm	SMoV	Wright Brothers	Wright Glider	
Wright Glider 1900	VA	Sands	VAM	Wright Brothers	Glider	
Wright Glider 1901	VA	Sands	VAM	Wright Brothers	Glider	
Wright Glider 1902	VA	Sands	VAM	Wright Brothers	Glider	
Wright Glider	WA	Seatt	MoF	Wright Brothers	Wright Glider	
Wright Model G Aeroboat	OH	Wapak	NAA&SM	Wright	Aeroboat	
WSA-1	WA	Vancouver	PAM			
X- 1	CA	Chino	PoFAM	Bell	Research	
X- 1	CA	Inglewood	PBR	Bell	Research	
X- 1	DC	Washi	NA&SM	Bell	Research	"Glamorous Glennis"
X- 1B	OH	Dayto	USAFM	Bell	Research	
X- 1E	OH	Dayton	USAFM		Princeton	46-63
X- 2	CA	Chino	PoFAM			
X- 2	PA	Willo	WGNAS			
X- 3	OH	Dayto	USAFM	Douglas	Stiletto	
X- 4	CA	Rosamond	EAFB	Northrop	Skylancer	
X- 4	CO	CSpri	USAFA	Northrop	Skylancer	
X- 4	OH	Dayto	USAFM	Northrop	Skylancer	
X- 4	WVA		Northrop	Northrop	Skylancer	
X- 5	OH	Dayto	USAFM	Bell	Swept Wing	
X- 7	CA	Chino	PoFAM	Lockheed		
X- 7	OH	Dayton	USAFM	Lockheed		
X- 10	OH	Dayton	USAFM	North American		
X- 13	CA	San Diego	SDAM	Ryan	Vertijet	41619
X- 13	OH	Dayto	USAFM	Ryan	Vertijet	
X- 15A-1	DC	Washi	NA&SM	North American	Research	
X- 15A-2	AZ	Tucso	PAM	North American		56- 6671
X- 15A-2	OH	Dayto	USAFM	North American		
X- 17	OH	Dayton	USAFM	Lockheed		
X- 21	CA	Rosam	EAFB			55- 408
X- 21	OH	Dayton	USAFM	Bell		
X- 22	NY	Niagara Falls	NAM	Bell		151521
X- 24A(SV-5J)	OH	Dayto	USAFM	Martin	Marietta	
X- 24B	OH	Dayto	USAFM	Martin	Marietta	
X- 25A	CA	Boron	SAM	Benson	Gyrocopter	
X- 25A	CA	Hawthorne	WMoF	Benson	Gyrocopter	
X- 25A	CA	Ramona	CR	Benson	Gyrocopter	VWK-1
X- 25A	GA	Warner Robin	MoF	Benson	Gyrocopter	N 61CN
X- 25A	OH	Dayton	USAFM	Benson	Gyrocopter	
X- 25B	CA	Sacra	SWAM			
X- 26B	AL	Ozark	USAAM	Lockheed	Quiet One	67-15345
X- 28	KS	Liberal	MAAM	Sopery	Air Skimmer	
X- 28	MI	Kalam	KAHM	Pereira	Air Skimmer	
X- 28A	MI	Ypsil	YAF	Sopery	Air Skimmer	
X- 29	DC	Washi	NA&SM	Grumman		
X- 29A	OH	Dayto	USAFM	Grumman		
X- 32	OH	Dayton	USAFM	Boeing	Fighter	
X-112	WI	Oshko	EAAAAM	Lippisch	Aerofoil Boat	N 5961V
XB-25B	CA	Rosam	EAFB	Bensen	Gyro-Chute	
XC-99	OH	Dayton	USAFM	Convair		
XC-124A	OH	Dayton	USAFM			Tilt Wing 1964
XF-81	OH	Dayton	USAFM	Consolidated	Vultee	44-91000
XF-81	OH	Dayton	USAFM	Consolidated	Vultee	44-91001
XF15C-1	CT	Winds	NEAM	Curtiss-Wright	Stingaree	
XF15C-1	RI	NKing	QAM	Curtiss-Wright	Stingaree	01215
XF2Y-1	MD	Balti	OMA	Convair	Sea Dart	
XF2Y-1	MD	Silve	PEGF	Convair	Sea Dart	
XF2Y-1	PA	Willo	WGNAS	Convair	Sea Dart	135764
XF2Y-1	WA	Seatt	MoF	Convair	Sea Dart	135765
XF2Y-1(SF)	FL	Lakel	SFAF	Convair	Sea Dart	135765
XF2Y-1(YF)	CA	San Diego	SDAM	Convair	Sea Dart	135763
XFV-1	FL	Lakel	SFAF	Lockheed	Salmon	138657
XFV-1	FL	Pensa	USNAM	Lockheed	VTO	
XFY-1	MD	Silve	PEGF	Convair		
XJL-1	AZ	Tucso	PAM	Columbia	Columbia	31400 N 54205
XO-60	MD	Silve	PEGF	Kellett	Autogiro	
XR-8	MD	Silve	PEGF	Kellett	Autogiro	
XRG-65	PA	WChes	AHM	Glaticopter	Helicopter	
XROE	CA	SCarl	HAM			
XROE	MD	Lexington	PRNAM	Goodyear	Inflatoplane	
XROE-1	AL	Ozark	USAAM			4004
XRON-1	NY	Elmira	B&ECN&SP	Gyrodyne	Rotorcycle	
XRON-1	NY	Garde	CoAM	Gyrodyne	Rotorcycle	4014

Name	State	City	Museum				
XV-1	MD	Silve	PEGF		Conovertiplane		
Yak 3	CA	Camarillo	CAF-SCW	Yakovlev		VK-105PF-2	
Yak 3	ID	Nampa	WAM	Yakovlev			
Yak 3	VA	Manassas	CAFNCS	Yakovlev			
Yak 3UA	CA	Santa Monica	MoF	Yakovlev		NX854DP	
Yak 9	WA	Seattle	MoF	Yakovlev			
Yak 11	CA	Chino	PoFAM	Yakovlev	Moose		
Yak 18	CA	Chino	PoFAM	Yakovlev	Max		
Yak 18	MD	Silve	PEGF	Yakovlev	Max		
Yak 18	VA	Suffolk	FF	Yakovlev		1160314	
Yak 50	OR	Mc Minnville	EAEC	Yakovlev		832604	
Yak 52	CA	S.Mon	MoF	Yakovlev			
Yak 52	CA	Santa Rosa	PCAM	Yakovlev			
Yak 52	FL	Miami	WOM	Yakovlev			
Yak 55	VA	Suffolk	FF	Yakovlev			
YF-12A(YF)	OH	Dayto	USAFM	Lockheed		60- 6935	Model A-11
YF-22	OH	Dayto	USAFM				
YIM-99B	WA	Brews	CityPark				
YCGM-121B	OH	Dayton	USAFM	Boeing	Brave 200		"Seek Spinner"
YO3A	CA	SanCarlos	HAM	Lockheed	Quiet Star		
Yokosuka P1Y1c	MD	Silver Hill	PEGF	Yokosuka	Frances		
Youngsters Simulator	KY	Lexington	AmoK	Youngsters	Simulator		
YPT-9B	CA	Chino	YAM			6004 N 795H	
YS-11A-600	TX	Ladero	Airport	Nihon		N-173RV	
Zenair Zenith	MO	Maryland Hts	HARM	Zenair	Zenith		
Zenair Zenith	ON-C	Toronto	TAM	Zenair	Zenith		
Zephyr Zal	CT	Winds	NEAM	Zephyr	Zal		
Zimmerman	MD	Silve	PEGF	Zimmerman	Flying Platform		
Zlin 526M	CA	Santa Rosa	PCAM	Zlin			
Zoegling Glider Rep	NM	Moriarty	SSM	Zoegling	Glider		
Zoegling Glider	SK-C	MJaw	WDM	Zoegling	Glider		
ZPG Rudder	FL	Pensa	USNAM	ZRG	Rudder	141561	
Zugvogel III-B	AZ	Tucso	PAM	Zugvogel		N 111MG	

Armored Vehicles

Personnel Carrier:

Name	State	City	Museum			
Fort T-16	OH	Norwalk	FmoMH		Armored Personel	
Mark VII Ferrett	OH	Norwalk	FmoMH	British	Armored Car	
M75 APC	AL	Mobil	BMP		Armored Personel	16196782
M84 APC	NY	Buffa	B&ECNP		Armored Personel	

Tanks:

Name	State	City	Museum			
Tank	IL	Sprin	S.ArmyNG			
Tank	IN	Van Buren	VFW			
Tank	IN	Warsaw	City Square			
Tank	NB	Beaver City	City Park			GPS: N40(08.102), W99(50.025)
Tank	TX	Harli	MMA			
Tanks	IA	Des Moines	ING			6 Different Tanks
Tank M-1A	WI	Kenosha	KMM	Abrams		In Movie "Curage Under Fire"
Tank M-3	NJ	Dover	PAAM			
Tank M-3	TX	Frede	NMofPW			
Tank M-4	AL	Mobile	BMP	Stuart	Sherman Light	D51011
Tank M-4	AL	Starke	CBM	Stuart	Sherman Light	
Tank M-4	CA	Chino	PoF	Stuart	Sherman Light	
Tank M-4	IN	Scottsburg	INGC	Stuart	Sherman Light	
Tank M-4	LA	Many	VFW	Stuart	Sherman Light	
Tank M-4	ON-C	Oshaw	OAM&IM	Stuart	Sherman Light	
Tank M-4	WI	Appleton	VFW	Stuart	Sherman Light	
Tank M-4	WI	Kenos	KMM	Stuart	Sherman Light	D706
Tank M-4	WI	Kenos	KMM	Stuart	Sherman Light	70676A, Training Turret
Tank M-4A1	IL	Wheat	Cantigny	Stuart	Sherman Light	
Tank M-4A1	IN	Atterbury	CAM&MC	Stuart	Sherman Light	2-2084
Tank M-4A1	IN	Atterbury	CAM&MC	Stuart	Sherman Light	1-2451
Tank M-4A1E8	OH	Hubbard	WWIIVM	Stuart	Sherman Light	
Tank M-4A3(75)VVSS	IN	Sunman	AM	Stuart	Sherman Light	
Tank M-4A3	LA	New Orleans	DDM	Stuart	Sherman Light	
Tank M-4A3	CA	S El Monte	ASMH	Stuart	Sherman Light	
Tank M-4A3	OH	Hubbard	WWIIVM	Stuart	Sherman Light	
Tank M-4A3	SC	Citadel	CC	Stuart	Sherman Light	
Tank M-4A3	TX	FtBli	TCRM	Stuart	Sherman Light	
Tank M-4A3E8	IL	Wheaton	FDM	Stuart	Sherman Light	
Tank M-4A3E8	CA	S El Monte	ASMH	Stuart	Sherman Light	
Tank M-5	IL	Wheaton	FDM	Stuart	Sherman Light	C105826
Tank M-5A	WI	Kenos	KMM	Stuart	Sherman Light	M5058147
Tank M-5A1	OH	Carroll	HAS	Stuart	Sherman Light	
Tank M-7B1	OH	Hubbard	WWIIVM	Stuart	105 mm	
Tank M-7	WI	Kenos	KMM	Stuart	105 mm	
Tank M-8	PA	Tough	CFCM	Barlett	Hovercraft	
Tank M-18C	MD	Silve	PEGF	Mooney	Mite	
Tank M-19	OH	Hubbard	WWIIVM		Duster	
Tank M-24	ON-C	Oshaw	OAM&IM			
Tank M-26	AL	Mobile	BMP		Pershing	E10609
Tank M-31	NJ	Dover	PAAM			
Tank M-37	WI	Kenos	KMM	Stuart	105 mm	
Tank M-38	WI	Kenos	KMM	Stuart	105 mm	
Tank M-38A1	WI	Kenos	KMM	Stuart		
Tank M-41	IL	Wheaton	FDM	Walker	Walker Bulldog	254
Tank M-41	IN	Atterbury	CAM&MC	Stuart	Walker Bulldog	38-1-1, 138
Tank M-41	IN	Atterbury	CAM&MC	Stuart	Walker Bulldog	
Tank M-41	IN	Atterbury	CAM&MC	Stuart	Walker Bulldog	
Tank M-41	NY	Buffa	B&ECNP	Walker	Walker Bulldog	
Tank M-41	WA	Tilli	CMANGP	Walker	Walker Bulldog	
Tank M-41	WI	Kenosha	KMM	Walker	Walker Bulldog	#26
Tank M-42A1	AL	Mobile	BMP	General Motors	Duster	112L729
Tank M-42 Twin	IN	Atterbury	CAM&MC	General Motors	Duster	
Tank M-42 Twin	NY	NYC	ISASM	General Motors	Duster	
Tank M-42 Twin	OH	Groveport	MMM	General Motors	Duster	40 mm
Tank M-42 Twin	OH	Norwalk	FMoMH	General Motors	Duster	40 mm
Tank M-42 Twin	PA	Smethport	AAAM	General Motors	Duster	40 mm
Tank M-42 Twin	WI	Kenosha	KMM	General Motors	Duster	40 mm
Tank M-46	IL	Wheat	Cantigny	Chrysler	Patton	J26E4

Tanks:

Tank M-46	WI	Kenos	KMM	Chrysler	Patton	
Tank M-47	CA	S El Monte	ASMH	Chrysler	Patton	
Tank M-47	IL	Wheat	FDM	Chrysler	Patton	2313
Tank M-47	IN	Atterbury	CAM&MC	Chrysler	Patton	A00193, 753710338
Tank M-47	IN	Atterbury	CAM&MC	Chrysler	Patton	38-11, 138, K7389955 Ser 4
Tank M-47	OH	Groveport	MMM	Chrysler	Patton	331
Tank M-47	WI	Kenos	KMM	Chrysler	Patton	Korean
Tank M-48	CA	S El Monte	ASMH	Chrysler	Patton	
Tank M-48	IL	Wheat	FDM	Chrysler	Patton	2650
Tank M-48	NC	C Lejuene	CL	Chrysler	Patton	
Tank M-48A1	AL	Mobil	BMP	Chrysler	Patton	8369684
Tank M-48A1	CA	S El Monte	ASMH	Chrysler	Patton	
Tank M-48A1	PA	Smethport	AAAM	Chrysler	Patton	
Tank M50	IN	Atterbury	CAM&MC		OWTOS	Six 106mm's
Tank M-51	NJ	Dover	PAAM	Douglas		
Tank M-60	AL	Starke	CBM	Chrysler	Patton	
Tank M-60	AL	Tuscalloosa	I-20/59	Chrysler	Patton	
Tank M-60	AR	Littl	LRAFB	Chrysler	Patton	
Tank M-60	CA	Imperial	PM	Chrysler	Patton	
Tank M-60	CA	Paso Robles	EWM	Chrysler	Patton	
Tank M-60	D.C.	Washington	USS&AH	Chrysler	Patton	
Tank M-60	IL	Wheaton	FDM	Chrysler	Patton	280
Tank M-60	IN	Atterbury	CAM&MC	Chrysler	Patton	1201 (7953748) 105mm
Tank M-60	IN	South Bend	MHP	Chrysler	Patton	
Tank M-60	KS	Emporia	VP	Chrysler	Patton	
Tank M-60	KY	Middleboro	LS	Chrysler	Patton	
Tank M-60	NY	NYC	ISASM	Chrysler	Patton	
Tank M-60	NC	C Lejuene	CL	Chrysler	Patton	
Tank M-60	OH	Norwalk	FMoMH	Chrysler	Patton	
Tank M-60	WI	Appleton	FMoMH	Chrysler	Patton	
Tank M-60A1	AL	Mobile	BMP	Chrysler	Patton	8208
Tank M-60A1	CA	S El Monte	ASMH	Chrysler	Patton	
Tank M-60A-1	MI	Sterling Hts	FHCMP	Chrysler	Patton	
Tank M-60A-3	TN	Caryville	I-75 & US25W	Chrysler	Patton	
Tank M-60	WI	Kenos	KMM	Chrysler	Patton	
Tank M551	CA	S El Monte	ASMH		Sheridan	
Tank M551	IL	Wheaton	FDM		Sheridan	725
Tank M551A	NC	Charlotte	CAM		Sheridan	1447 Airborne
Tank MK3	TX	Frede	NMofPW			
Tank T-55	AL	Mobile	BMP			1184 USATTU
Tank T-26E4	IL	Wheat	FDM		Pershing	
Tanks	WA	Tacom	FL			
Tanks	VA	Quantico	MCAGM			

Missiles

Missile	AZ	Green	TMM		Missile	
Missile	CA	Point	PMMP		Missile	
Missile	FL	Cocoa	USAFSM		Missile	
Missile	GA	Cochr	CityPark		Missile	
Missile	WA	Tacom	FL		Missile	
Missile Silo	AZ	Green Valley	TMM		Titan II	571-7
Missile Silo	SD	Rapid	SDA&SM		Minuteman	
A6M	MO	StCha	CAF-MW	Maxson	Bullpup	
ADM-20C	AZ	Tucso	PAM	McDonnell	Quail	
ADM-20C	CA	Sacra	SWAM	McDonnell	Quail	
ADM-20C	OH	Dayton	USAFM	McDonnell	Quail	
ADM-20C	SD	Rapid City	SDA&SM	McDonnell	Quail	
AGM-12	AZ	Tucso	PAM	Maxson	Bullpup	D79
AGM-12C	NY	Garde	CoAM	Maxson	Bullpup	
AGM-22A	NJ	Dover	PAAM			
AGM-28(GAM-77)	NY	Horsehead	WoE	North American	Hound Dog	60-2173
AGM-28A(GAM-77)	AZ	Tucso	PAM	North American	Hound Dog	59-2866
AGM-28A(GAM-77)	AZ	Tucso	PAM	North American	Hound Dog	60-2092
AGM-28A(GAM-77)	CA	Sacra	SWAM	North American	Hound Dog	
AGM-28A(GAM-77)	IL	Rantoul	OCAM	North American	Hound Dog	20796
AGM-28A(GAM-77)	OK	Oklah	CityPark	North American	Hound Dog	
AGM-28A(GAM-77)	TX	Abilene	DLAP	North American	Hound Dog	
AGM-28A(GAM-77)	WY	Buffa	S&SHome	North American	Hound Dog	
AGM-28A(GAM-77)	WY	River	ALP121	North American	Hound Dog	
AGM-28B(GAM-77)	ME	Blain	ALP118	North American	Hound Dog	
AGM-28B(GAM-77)	OH	Dayto	USAFM	North American	Hound Dog	
AGM-28C(GAM-77)	CA	Atwater	CAM	North American	Hound Dog	
AGM-65	UT	Ogden	HAM	Hughes	Maverick	
AGM-86(ALCM)	NY	Rome	GAFBM	Boeing		
AGM-86B(ALCM)	OH	Dayton	USAFM	Boeing	ALCM	
AGM-86B(ALCM)	UT	Ogden	HAM	Boeing	ALCM	
AGM-86B(ALCM)	WA	Seattle	MoF	Boeing	ALCM	
AGM-129	CA	El Cajon	SDAMGF		Missile	
AGM-129	OH	Dayton	USAFM		Missile	
AGM-136	OH	Dayton	USAFM	Tatic	Rainbow	
AIM-4	AZ	Tucso	PAM	Hughes	Falcon	AF3660021263
AIM-4	UT	Ogden	HAM	Hughes	Falcon	
AIM-4	VA	Hampton	HAP	Hughes	Falcon	
AIM-4D	GA	Warner Robin	MoF	Hughes	Falcon	
AIM-4E	GA	Warner Robin	MoF	Hughes	Falcon	
AIM-4F	GA	Warner Robin	MoF	Hughes	Falcon	
AIM-4G	GA	Warner Robin	MoF	Hughes	Falcon	
AIM/RIM-7	NY	Horsehead	WoE		Sparrow	
AIM-7	UT	Ogden	HAM	Hughes	Sparrow	
AIM-9B	UT	Ogden	HAM	Hughes	Sidewinder	
AIM-9J	CA	Ridgecrest	CLNWC	Ford	Sidewinder	
AIM-9J	GA	Warner Robin	MoF	Ford	Sidewinder	
AIM-26A	GA	Warner Robin	MoF		Super Falcon	
AIR-2A	GA	Warner Robin	MoF	McDonnell/Douglas	Genie	
AIR-2A	UT	Ogden	HAM	McDonnell/Douglas	Genie	
AIR-21	AZ	Tucson	PAM	Douglas	Genie	Sn TE-04813
AQM-34	AZ	Tucso	PAM	Teledyne-Ryan	Compass Dawn	69-6108
AQM-34	CA	Rosamond	EAFB	Ryan	Firebee	
AQM-34	CA	San Diego	SDAM	Ryan	Firebee	
AQM-34L	AZ	Tucso	PAM	Teledyne-Ryan	Compass Bin	69-432
AQM-34L	OH	Dayton	USAFM	Teledyne-Ryan	Compass Bin	

AQM-34L	TX	San Antonio	VMP	Teledyne-Ryan	Compass Bin	
AQM-34L	UT	Ogden	HAFBM	Teledyne-Ryan	Compass Bin	Firebee
AQM-34N	OH	Dayton	USAFM	Teledyne-Ryan	Compass Bin	
AQM-34V	GA	Warner Robin	MoF	Teledyne-Ryan	Compass Bin	74-2147
AQM-37A	CA	Chino	YAM	Maxson	Drone	
AQM-37A	FL	Pensa	USNAM	Maxson	Drone	
AQM-37A	NY	Garde	CoAM	Maxson	Drone	
AQM-91A	OH	Dayton	USAFM	Ryan	Drone	
AQM-91A	SC	FLore	FA&MM	Ryan	Drone	
Atlas	CA	El Cajon	SDAMGF		Atlas Missile	
BQM-34	OH	Dayton	USAFM	Ryan	Firebee Drone	
BQM-34A	CA	Rosamond	EAFB	Ryan	Firebee Drone	
BQM-34A	FL	Panam	TAFB	Ryan	Firebee Drone	
BQM-34A	FL	Shali	USAFAM	Ryan	Firebee Drone	
BQM-34F	CA	San Diego	SDAM	Ryan	Firebee Drone	
BQM-34F	FL	Panam	TAFB	Ryan	Firebee Drone	
BQM-34F	FL	Shali	USAFAM	Ryan	Firebee Drone	
BQM-34F	GA	Warner Robin	MoF	Ryan	Firebee Drone	71-1812
BQM-34F	OH	Dayton	USAFM	Ryan	Firebee Drone	
BQM-34S	CA	San Diego	SDAM	Ryan	Firebee Drone	
BQM-126A	CA	Chino	YAM	Beechcraft	Target Drone	
BGM 109A	OH	Dayton	USAFM	General Dynamics	Cruise Missle	
BGM 109G	AZ	Tucson	PAM	General Dynamics	Cruise Missle	Sn 12436C0001
BGM 109G	UT	Ogden	HAM	General Dynamics	Cruise Missle	Sn 12436C0001
BOLT-117	UT	Ogden	HAM		Laser Missile	Laser Guided
CBU Mk 20	UT	Ogden	HAM		Rockeye II	Cluster Bomb
CGM-13	FL	Panam	TAFB		Mace Missile	
CGM-13B	FL	Wildw	ALP-18		Mace Missile	
CGM-13B	GA	Warner Robin	AFASSOC		Mace Missile	
CGM-13B	OH	Dayton	USAFM		Mace Missile	
CIM-10A	CO	CSpri	EJPSCM	Boeing	Bomarc	59-2051
CIM-10A	GA	Warner Robin	MoF	Boeing	Bomarc 59-1953	
CIM-10A	OH	Dayton	USAFM	Boeing	Bomarc	
CIM-10A	UT	Ogden	HAM	Boeing	Bomarc	
CIM-10B	UT	Ogden	HAM	Boeing	Bomarc Missile	
CIM-10B	VA	Hampt	APM	Boeing	Bomarc Missile	
Convair Atlas	OH	Dayton	USAFM	Convair	Atlas Missile	
Corporal M2	KS	Topeka	CAM	Firestone Tire-JPL	Missile	From Ft Riley, KS
Corporal M2	VA	Hampton	HAP	Firestone Tire-JPL	Missile	
Corporal M2	WI	Kenos	KMM	Firestone Tire-JPL	Missile	
D-21	AZ	Tucso	PAM	Lockheed	Mini Blackbird	Drone, 3, Carried By Blackbird
D-21	CA	Palmd	PAFB	Lockheed	Mini Blackbird	Drone
D-21	CA	Rosamond	EAFB	Lockheed	Mini Blackbird	Drone
D-21	GA	Warner Robin	MoF	Lockheed	Mini Blackbird	Drone
D-21	OH	Dayton	USAFM	Lockheed	Mini Blackbird	Drone
D-21B	WA	Seatt	MoF	Lockheed	Mini Blackbird	90-0510Drone
Drone Missile	WI	Kenos	KMM		Drone Missile	
Eberhart Target Glider	MD	Silve	PEGF	Eberhart	Drone	
H-50A(OH)	SC	MtPleasant	PPM	Gyrodyne	Drone	
H-50C(OH)	CT	Winds	NEAM	Gyrodyne	Drone	
H-50C(OH)	GA	Warner Robin	MoF	Gyrodyne	Drone	
H-50C(OH)	MD	Lexington	PRNAM	Gyrodyne	Drone	DS-1679
H-50C(QH)	NC	Charlotte	CAM	Gyrodyne	Drone	1355
H-50C(QH)	PA	WChester	AHM	Gyrodyne	Drone	
KAQ-1	CA	Atwater	CAM	Kawasaki	Drone	
GAM-54	AZ	Grand Canyon	PoFGCVA	Northrop	Crossbow	
GAM-63	CA	Atwater	CAM	McDonnell	Quail	
GAM-63	OK	Midwe	ALP170			
GAM-63(X)	OH	Dayton	USAFM	Bell	Rascal	
GAM-67(X)	CA	Banni	VWF			
GAM-67(X)	WA	Bridg	CityPark			
GAM-72	AL	Montg	GAFB	McDonnell	Quail	
GAM-72	CA	Oakland	WAM	McDonnell	Quail	
GAM-77	CA	Fairf	TAFB		Hound Dog Missile	
GAM-77	FL	Shali	USAFAM		Hound Dog Missile	
GBU-8	UT	Ogden	HAM		Optical Bomb	
GBU-12	UT	Ogden	HAM		Paveway II	
GBBU-24A/B	UT	Ogden	HAM		Paveway III	
Grumman Rigel	NY	Garde	CoAM	Grumman	Rigel Missile	
Hawk Missile	WI	Kenos	KMM		Hawk Missile	
HGM-25A	OH	Dayton	USAFM		Titan I	Missile
IM-99	FL	Shali	USAFAM	Boeing	Bomarc Missile	
JB-1	CA	Hawth	WMoF	Northrop	Bat Bomb	
JB-2	AL	Wasilla	MoAT&I	Republic	Loon Missile	
JB-2	CT	Winds	NEAM	Republic	Loon Missile	
JB-2	IL	Milford	LC	Republic	Loon Missile	
JB-2	NY	Garde	CoAM	Republic	Loon Missile	Buzz Bomb
KD2G-2	FL	Pensa	USNAM	Globe	Target Drone	1268
KD6G-2	AZ	Tucso	PAM	Globe	TargetDrone	633
KD6G-2	CA	Chino	YAM	Globe	Target Drone	
KDB-1	CA	Chino	YAM	Beech	Target Missile Drone	
KDB-1	FL	Pensa	USNAM			
Kettering Bug Torpedo	OH	Dayton	USAFM	Kettering	Bug Torpedo	
Lacrosse Missile	WI	Kenos	KMM		Lacrosse Missile	
LGM-25C(N-10)	AZ	Tucso	PAM	Martin Marietta	Titan II Missile	60- 8817, 9510003, "Small Paul's Pocket Rocket"
LGM-25C(N-10)	NY	Coron	NYHoS	Martin Marietta	Titan II Missile	Gemini
LGM	UT	Ogden	HAM	Boeing	Minuteman	
LGM-30	CA	Riverside	MAFM	Boeing	Minuteman II	
LGM-30	OH	Dayton	USAFM	Boeing	Minuteman II	
LGM-30A	OH	Dayton	USAFM	Boeing	Minuteman I	
LGM-30A	UT	Ogden	HAM	Boeing	Minuteman I	
LGM-30G	OH	Dayton	USAFM	Boeing	Minuteman III	
LTV	NC	Hickory	HRA			
LTV	OH	Dayton	USAFM		AST Missile	
Mark 6	UT	Ogden	HAM		Nuclear Bomb	
Mark 7	UT	Ogden	HAM		Nuclear Bomb	
Martin Marietta MX	OH	Dayton	USAFM	Martin	Peacekeeper Missile	
MGM-1	GA	Hawki	CityPark			
MGM-13A	FL	Shali	USAFAM	Martin	Mace	
MGM-13B	AR	Pocah	VWF	Martin	Mace	
MGM-13B	GA	Calhoun	MAM	Martin	Mace	62863
MGM-13B	GA	Warner Robin	I-75 E45	Martin	Mace	
MGM-13B	GA	Warner Robin	MoF	Martin	Mace	58-1465

MGM-13B	PA	Mildr	ALP452	Martin	Mace	
MGM-109	AZ	Tucson	PAM	General Dynamics	Cruise Missile	
MQM-107	FL	Panam	TAFB		Drone	
MQM-107	OH	Dayton	USAFM		Drone	
MQM-57	AZ	Tucso	PAM	Northrop	Drone	
MQM-74	CA	Chino	PoFAM	Northrop	Chukar II Drone	
Minuteman I	IL	Ranto	OCAM		Minuteman Missile	
Minuteman II	AZ	Tucso	PAM		Minuteman Missile	
Minuteman II	ND	Grand	GFAFB		Minuteman Missile	
Minuteman II	OH	Dayton	USAFM		Missile Trainer	
Minuteman Missile	SD	Rapid	SDA&SM		Minuteman	
Nike Missile	WI	Kenos	KMM		Nike Missile	
Nike-Ajax Missile	SD	Rapid	SDA&SM		Nike-Ajax	
NIM Missile	CO	CSpri	EJPSCM	Western Electric	Nike Ajax	
NIM Missile	MD	Handc	VFW	Western Electric	Nike Ajax	
NIM Missile	VA	Hampt	APM	Western Electric	Nike Ajax	
NIM-14 Missile	CO	CSpri	EJPSCM	Western Electric	Nike Hercules	
NIM-14 M-6	NY	Garden	CoAM	Douglas	Nike Hercules	
NIM-14 Missile	VA	Hampt	APM	Western Electric	Nike Hercules	
NIM-14 Missile	WA	FtLew	Ft.Lewis	Western Electric	Nike Hercules	
QH-50C	GA	Warner Robin	MoF	Gyrodyne	Dash Drone	DS-1045
QH-50C	NY	Garde	CoAM	Gyrodyne	Dash Drone	1235
QH-50C	WA	Seatt	MoF	Gyrodync	Dash Drone	
QH-50C/DSN-3	AZ	Tucso	PAM	Gyrodyne	Dash Drone	DS-1045
OQ-1	CA	San Diego	SDAM	Radioplane	Drone	
OQ-2	BC-C	Langley	CMoF	Radioplane	Drone	
OQ-2A	MI	Kalamazoo	KAHM	Radioplane	Drone	
OQ-2A	OH	Dayton	USAFM	Radioplane	Drone	
OQ-2A	UT	Ogden	HAM	Radioplane	Drone	
OQ-2A	WI	Oshko	EAAAAM	Radioplane	Drone	
OQ-3	AZ	Tucso	PAM	Radioplane	Drone	
OQ-A	WI	Oshko	EAAAAM	Globe	Drone	26, "Wimpy"
OQ-14	OH	Dayton	USAFM		Drone	
OQ-19(MQM-33)	AZ	Tucso	PAM	Northrop	Drone	KD2R-5
OQ-19(MQM-33)	CA	Hawthorne	WMoF	Northrop	Drone	KD2R-5
OQ-19(MQM-33)	KS	Liberal	MAAM	Northrop	Drone	
OQ-19D	WI	Oshko	EAAAAM	Northrop	Drone	
Pershing II	VA	Hampton	VA&SM		Pershing II	
Posedon Missile	DC	Washi	NM		Posedon	
Rocket Honest John	WI	Kenos	KMM		Honest John Rocket	
Rockets	AL	Hunts	AS&RC			
Rockets	FL	Cocoa	USAFSM			
Rockets	FL	Merri	KSC			
Rockets	MD	Green	NASAGVC			
Rockets	MI	Jacks	MSCJCC			
Rockets	NM	Las Cruces	WSMP			
Rockets	NM	Roswe	RM&AC			
Rocket Launcher M139C	IN	Atterbury	CAM&MC		Honest John	762mm, 22 Miles
Rocket Launcher XM33	IN	Atterbury	CAM&MC		Honest John	762mm, 22 Miles
RQ-1A	OH	Dayton	USAFM	General Atomics	Predator	
RQ-3A	OH	Dayton	USAFM	Lockheed Martin-Boeing	Dark Star	
RQ-3A	OH	Dayton	USAFM	Northrop Grumman	Global Hawk	
RP-5A Drone	AZ	Grand	PoFAM	Radioplane	Drone	
RP-5A Drone	CA	Hawthorne	WMoF	Radioplane	Drone	
RP-76B Drone	AZ	Grand Canyon	PoFGCVA	Radioplane	Drone	
RP-76B Drone	CA	Hawthorne	WMoF	Radioplane	Drone	
Ryan G Drone	CA	El Cajon	SDAMGF	Ryan	Firebee Drone	
Ryan G Drone	SC	FLore	FA&MM	Ryan	Firebee Drone	
SA-3 GOA	NV	Las Vegas	NAFB		Missile Transporter	
SA-8	NV	Las Vegas	NAFB		Launch Vehicle	
SAM S-2A	OH	Dayton	USAFM	Soviet	Missile	
SAM S-2A	TX	Paris	FTAM	Soviet		
SAM AT Replica	NY	Garde	CoAM	Sperry		
SAM M1 Replica	NY	Garde	CoAM	Sperry		
SAM-N-7(SM-2)	NY	Garden	CoAM	Sperry	Terrier	Missile
SAM-N-8	NC	Surf City	TIM	Bendiz/McDonnell	Talos	# 114
SAM-N-8	SC	MtPleasant	PPM	Bendiz/McDonnell	Talos	
SICM	OH	Dayton	USAFM	Boeing	Midgetman Missile	
SM-62	OH	Dayton	USAFM	Northrop	Snark	
SM-62(XSM)	UT	Ogden	HAM	Northrop	Snark	
SM-65	OH	Dayton	USAFM	Northrop	Atlas	
SM-68(B-68)	AZ	Tucso	PAM	Martin Marietta	Titan I Missile	4515
SM-68(B-68)	FL	Kissi	HJFPPH	Martin Marietta	Titan I Missile	Lox/Kerosene Fuel
SM-68(B-68)	GA	Corde	I-75 E32	Martin Marietta	Titan I Missile	
SM-68	OH	Dayton	USAFM	Northrop	Titan II Missile	N2O4/Aerozine Fuel
SM-68(B-68)	NE	Kimba	CityPark	Martin Marietta	Titan I Missile	
SM-68(B-68)	SC	FLore	FA&MM	Martin Marietta	Titan I Missile	
SM-78(PGM-19)	VA	Hampt	APM	Chrysler	Jupiter Missile	58-5282
T-72	NV	Las Vegas	NAFB		Missile Launcher	
Talos Rocket	SC	Topsail Beach	TIM			
Target Drone	NM	STere	WEAM			
Target Drone	NY	Hammo	CM			
Tartar	KS	Topeka	CAM		Missile	Navy
TDD-1	FL	Pensa	USNAM	Radioplane	Target Drone	43-2, A
TDD-2(PQ-14A)	FL	Pensa	USNAM	Radioplane	Target Drone	120082
TDD-2(PQ-14A)	MD	Silver Hill	PEGF	Radioplane	Target Drone	
TDR-1	FL	Pensa	USNAM			33529
TDU-25B	CA	Chino	YAM	Hayes Int'l	Tow Target Drone	
Texas Space Lines	TX	Rio Grande V	TAM	Texas Space Lines	Test Rocket	
Titan II Missile	CA	Paso Robles	EWM		Upper Stage	Titan I
Titan I Missile	SD	Rapid	SDA&SM		Titan I	
TM-61	AZ	Grand Canyon	PoFGCVA	Martin	Matador	
TM-61A	GA	Warner Robin	MoF	Martin	Matador	52-1891
TM-61A	OH	Dayton	USAFM	Martin	Matador	
TM-61C	SC	FLore	FA&MM	Martin	Matador	
Tomahawk II	PA	Phila	FI			
Tomahawk Missile	CA	Ridgecrest	CLNWC	Convair	Tomahawk Missile	
Tomahawk Missile	CA	San Diego	SDAM	Convair	Tomahawk Missile	
Torpedo Mk.14	MI	Sterling Hts	FHCMP	US Navy	Torpedo	
Trinity	UT	Ogden	HAM		Atommic Bomb	
YQM-94A RPV	OH	Dayton	USAFM	Boeing	Compass Cope B	
YQM-98A Drone	AZ	Tucso	PAM			72-1872

Naval Ships

CSS Neuse	NC	Kinston	CSS N&GCM	Confederate Navy	Ironclad Gunboat	"Ram" 1862, 1 of 3 survor out of 22
German Seehund	DC	Washi	NM	German WWII	Submarine	
HMCS Haida	ONT	Hamilton	OP	Vickers Armstrong	Destroyer	Tribal Class, # G63
Japanese Kaiten II	NJ	Hackensack	SMA-NJNM	Japanese WWII	Submarine	
LCVP	LA	New Orleans	DDM	Higgins	Landing Craft	
LCVP	OH	Groveport	MMM	Higgins	Landing Craft	PA 36-7
PBR Mk l	SC	Mt Pleasant	PP		Patrol Boat River	Mark l
PBR	WI	Pleasant Prairie	BMP			
PT-309	TX	Fredericksburg	NmotPW	Higgins	Patrol Boat	
PT-617	MA	Fall	USSMM	Higgins	Patrol Boat	
PTF-17	NY	Buffalo	BECNSP		Patrol Boat Fast	Built 1968
Russian Juliett 484	RI	Providence	RSM	Gorky Shipyard	Juliett	K-77
SS American Victory	FL	Tampa	AVMM&MS		Liberty Ship	
SS Keewatin	MI	Douglas	KMM		Passenger Steamer	
SS Queen Mary	CA	Long	QM&SG		Ocean Liner	
USCG Taney	MD	Baltimore	BMM		Cutter	
USD-4	GA	Agust	FG			
USD-5	GA	Agust	FG			
USF Constitution	MA	Boston			Frigate	
USF Constellation	MD	Baltimore	BIH		Frigate Sister Ship	
USS Airzona	HI	Honol	AM		Battleship	BB- 39
USS Alabama	AL	Mobil	BMP		Battleship	BB- 60
USS Becuna	PA	Philadelphia	ISM			
USS Blueback	OR	Portland	OmoS&I		Submarine	SS-581
USS Bowfin	HI	Honol	AM		Submarine	SS-287
USS Cassin Young	MA	Boston	USSC		Destroyer	DD-793, DestroyerDD-793
USS Chesapeake	MD	Baltimore	BMM		Lightship	
USS Clamagore	SC	Mt Pl	PPM		Submarine	SS-343
USS Cobia	WI	Manit	WMM		Submarine	SS-245
USS Cod	OH	Cleveland	SUSSC		Submarine	SS-224
USS Croaker	NY	Buffa	B&ECN&SP		Submarine	SSK-246
USS Drum	AL	Mobil	BMP		Submarine	SS-228
USS Edson	NY	NYC	ISASM		Destroyer	DD-946
USS Fall River	MA	Fall River	BC		Cruiser	
USS Forrestal	MD	West River	USSFNM		Aircraft Carrier	# "59"
USS Growler	NY	NYC	ISASM		Submarine	SS-215
USS Guadalcanal	NY	NYC	ISASM		Helicopter Carrier	LPH- 7
USS Hazard	NB	Omaha	FP		Mine Sweeper	AM-240
USS Helena Parts	OH	Newcomerstown NNM				CL50
USS Hornet	CA	Alameda	USSH		Aircraft Carrier	
USS Ingham	SC	Mt Pl	PPM		Coast Guard Cutter	35
USS Intelligent Whale	NJ	Sea Grit	NJNGMM		Submarine	
USS Intrepid	NY	NYC	ISASM		Aircraft Carrier	CVA-11
USS Jeremiah O'Brian	CA	SFransico	SF		Liberty Ship	
USS JP Kennedy	MA	Fall	USSMM		Destroyer	DD-850
USS John Brown	MD	Baltimore	PLS		Liberty Ship	
USS Kidd	LA	BRoug	LNWM		Destroyer	DD-661
USS LSM-45	NB	Omaha	FP		Landing Ship	
USS Laffey	SC	Mt Pl	PPM		Destroyer	DD-724
USS Lane Victory	CA	San Diego			Liberty Ship	
USS Lexington	TX	C Christi	USS Lexi		Aircraft Carrier	CV- 16
USS Lionfish	MA	Fall	USSMM		Submarine	SS-298
USS Ling	NJ	Hackensack	SMA-NJNM		Submarine	SS-297
USS Little Rock	NY	Buffa	B&ECNP		Cruiser	CLG-4
USS Maiale SSB	DC	Washi	NM		Submarine	
USS Marlin	NB	Omaha	FP		Submarine	SST-2, T-2
USS Massachusetts	MA	Fall	USSMM		Battleship	BB- 59
USS Misouri	HI	Honolua	AM		Battleship	BB- 63
USS New Jersey	NJ	Camden	PSNS		Battleship	BB- 62
USS North Carolina	NC	Wilmi	USSNCBC		Battleship	BB- 55
USS Olympia	PA	Philadelphia	ISM		Cruiser	
USS Orleck	TX	Orange	STWM		Destroyer	DD-886
USS Pamanito	CA	San Franciso	USSC		Submarine	
USS Pinato Tower	TX	Frede	NMotPW		Submarine	SS-387
USS Radford Parts	OH	Newcomerstown NNM			Battleship	DD-446
USS Requin	PA	Pittsburg	CSC		Submarine	SS-481
USS Roncador Tower	CA	San Francisco	MPA		Submarine	SS-301
USS Salem	MA	Quincy	USN&SM		Battleship	CA-139, Flagship, Graf Spee Movie
USS Saratoga	RI	Providence	USSSM		Aircraft Carrier	CV-60
USS Savannah	VA	Newpo				
USS Silversides	MI	Muske	USS SILV		Submarine	SS-236
USS Slater	NY	Albany	USS S		Destroyer	DE-766
USS Sullivans	NY	Buffa	B&ECNP		Destroyer	DD-537
USS Texas	TX	LaPor	USS Texa		Battleship	BB- 35
USS Towers	NB	Omaha	FP		Captains Gig	DDG-9
USS Torsk	MD	Baltimore	BMM		Submarine	
USS Turner Joy	WA	Breme	PSNS		Destroyer	DD-951
USS Turtle	DC	Washi	NM		Submarine	
USS Wisconsin	VA	Norfolk	TBW		Battleship	BB- 64
USS Yorktown	SC	Mt Pleasant	PPM		Aircraft Carrier	CV- 10

Engine Displays:

OX-5	FL	Kissi	FTWAM
OX-5	PA	Harri	SMoP

FACILITY INFORMATION FORM

Please fill out the following questions and return to:
Guide to Aircraft Museums
Michael A. Blaugher
124 East Foster Parkway
Ft. Wayne, IN 46806-1730
email: airmuseums@aol.com

Facility Name:
Address of Aircraft:
Mailing Address:
Phone Number:
Web Site Address:
Email address:
Days & Hours Open:
What Holidays Closed:
Price of Admission:
Do You Have the Following :
  If so, also list Phone Number:
Gift Shop:
Theater:
Cafe:
Restoration Facility:
  If so, can public view activity:

 Please List All Aircraft By the Following:

Manufacture, Designation, Model, Serial #, N #, Personal Name
North American, P-51, D, 44-3321, NL921, "Cripes A Mighty"

Tail Letters,   Side Numbers,   Squadron Markings
P- HO,   1,   328FS, 352FG,

List the aircraft current status as follows:
Static Indoor Display **(D)**, Storage **(S)**, Restoration Project **(P)**
Static Outdoor Display **(O)**, Flyable **(F)**, On Loan To **(L)**